PEARSON CUSTOM BUSINESS RESOURCES

Saint Leo University
GBA 334
Balakrishnan / Render

ISBN 10: 1-269-23601-6
ISBN 13: 978-1-269-23601-0

Folder for QM (version 4)
C:\Program Files (x86)\POMQMV4
Back UP → C:\---\POMQMV4\BACKUP

Folder for Excel QM V4
C:\Program Files (x86)\ExcelQMV4
Back UP - C:\--\ExcelQMV4\BACKUP

EDITORIAL ADVISORY BOARD

Table of Contents

I

Introduction to Quantitative Analysis

From Chapter 1 of *Quantitative Analysis for Management,* 11/e. Barry Render. Ralph M. Stair, Jr. Michael E. Hanna. Copyright © 2012 by Pearson Education. All rights reserved.

1 Introduction

People have been using mathematical tools to help solve problems for thousands of years; however, the formal study and application of quantitative techniques to practical decision making is largely a product of the twentieth century. The techniques we study in this text have been applied successfully to an increasingly wide variety of complex problems in business, government, health care, education, and many other areas. Many such successful uses are discussed throughout this text.

It isn't enough, though, just to know the mathematics of how a particular quantitative technique works; you must also be familiar with the limitations, assumptions, and specific applicability of the technique. The successful use of quantitative techniques usually results in a solution that is timely, accurate, flexible, economical, reliable, and easy to understand and use.

In this chapter, there are QA (Quantitative Analysis) in Action boxes that provide success stories on the applications of management science. They show how organizations have used quantitative techniques to make better decisions, operate more efficiently, and generate more profits. Taco Bell has reported saving over $150 million with better forecasting of demand and better scheduling of employees. NBC television increased advertising revenue by over $200 million between 1996 and 2000 by using a model to help develop sales plans for advertisers. Continental Airlines saves over $40 million per year by using mathematical models to quickly recover from disruptions caused by weather delays and other factors.

To see other examples of how companies use quantitative analysis or operations research methods to operate better and more efficiently, go to the website www.scienceofbetter.org. The success stories presented there are categorized by industry, functional area, and benefit. These success stories illustrate how operations research is truly the "science of better."

2 What Is Quantitative Analysis?

Quantitative analysis uses a scientific approach to decision making.

Quantitative analysis is the scientific approach to managerial decision making. Whim, emotions, and guesswork are not part of the quantitative analysis approach. The approach starts with data. Like raw material for a factory, these data are manipulated or processed into information that is valuable to people making decisions. This processing and manipulating of raw data into meaningful information is the heart of quantitative analysis. Computers have been instrumental in the increasing use of quantitative analysis.

In solving a problem, managers must consider both qualitative and quantitative factors. For example, we might consider several different investment alternatives, including certificates of deposit at a bank, investments in the stock market, and an investment in real estate. We can use quantitative analysis to determine how much our investment will be worth in the future when deposited at a bank at a given interest rate for a certain number of years. Quantitative analysis can also be used in computing financial ratios from the balance sheets for several companies whose stock we are considering. Some real estate companies have developed computer programs that use quantitative analysis to analyze cash flows and rates of return for investment property.

Both qualitative and quantitative factors must be considered.

In addition to quantitative analysis, *qualitative* factors should also be considered. The weather, state and federal legislation, new technological breakthroughs, the outcome of an election, and so on may all be factors that are difficult to quantify.

Because of the importance of qualitative factors, the role of quantitative analysis in the decision-making process can vary. When there is a lack of qualitative factors and when the problem, model, and input data remain the same, the results of quantitative analysis can *automate* the decision-making process. For example, some companies use quantitative inventory models to determine automatically *when* to order additional new materials. In most cases, however, quantitative analysis will be an *aid* to the decision-making process. The results of quantitative analysis will be combined with other (qualitative) information in making decisions.

Quantitative analysis has been in existence since the beginning of recorded history, but it was Frederick W. Taylor who in the early 1900s pioneered the principles of the scientific approach to management. During World War II, many new scientific and quantitative techniques were developed to assist the military. These new developments were so successful that after World War II many companies started using similar techniques in managerial decision making and planning. Today, many organizations employ a staff of operations research or management science personnel or consultants to apply the principles of scientific management to problems and opportunities. In this text, we use the terms **management science**, *operations research*, and *quantitative analysis* interchangeably.

The origin of many of the techniques discussed in this text can be traced to individuals and organizations that have applied the principles of scientific management first developed by Taylor.

3 The Quantitative Analysis Approach

Defining the problem can be the most important step.

Concentrate on only a few problems.

FIGURE 1

The Quantitative Analysis Approach

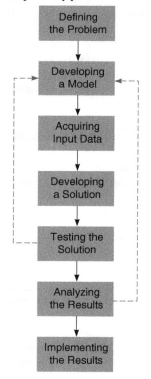

The quantitative analysis approach consists of defining a problem, developing a model, acquiring input data, developing a solution, testing the solution, analyzing the results, and implementing the results (see Figure 1). One step does not have to be finished completely before the next is started; in most cases one or more of these steps will be modified to some extent before the final results are implemented. This would cause all of the subsequent steps to be changed. In some cases, testing the solution might reveal that the model or the input data are not correct. This would mean that all steps that follow defining the problem would need to be modified.

Defining the Problem

The first step in the quantitative approach is to develop a clear, concise statement of the **problem**. This statement will give direction and meaning to the following steps.

In many cases, defining the problem is the most important and the most difficult step. It is essential to go beyond the symptoms of the problem and identify the true causes. One problem may be related to other problems; solving one problem without regard to other related problems can make the entire situation worse. Thus, it is important to analyze how the solution to one problem affects other problems or the situation in general.

It is likely that an organization will have several problems. However, a quantitative analysis group usually cannot deal with all of an organization's problems at one time. Thus, it is usually necessary to concentrate on only a few problems. For most companies, this means selecting those problems whose solutions will result in the greatest increase in profits or reduction in costs to the company. The importance of selecting the right problems to solve cannot be overemphasized. Experience has shown that bad problem definition is a major reason for failure of management science or operations research groups to serve their organizations well.

When the problem is difficult to quantify, it may be necessary to develop *specific, measurable* objectives. A problem might be inadequate health care delivery in a hospital. The objectives might be to increase the number of beds, reduce the average number of days a patient spends in the hospital, increase the physician-to-patient ratio, and so on. When objectives are used, however, the real problem should be kept in mind. It is important to avoid obtaining specific and measurable objectives that may not solve the real problem.

Developing a Model

Once we select the problem to be analyzed, the next step is to develop a **model**. Simply stated, a model is a representation (usually mathematical) of a situation.

Even though you might not have been aware of it, you have been using models most of your life. You may have developed models about people's behavior. Your model might be that friendship is based on reciprocity, an exchange of favors. If you need a favor such as a small loan, your model would suggest that you ask a good friend.

The types of models include physical, scale, schematic, and mathematical models.

Of course, there are many other types of models. Architects sometimes make a *physical model* of a building that they will construct. Engineers develop *scale models* of chemical plants,

IN ACTION   Operations Research and Oil Spills

Operations researchers and decision scientists have been investigating oil spill response and alleviation strategies since long before the BP oil spill disaster of 2010 in the Gulf of Mexico. A four-phase classification system has emerged for disaster response research: mitigation, preparedness, response, and recovery. *Mitigation* means reducing the probability that a disaster will occur and implementing robust, forward-thinking strategies to reduce the effects of a disaster that does occur. *Preparedness* is any and all organization efforts that happen *a priori* to a disaster. *Response* is the location, allocation, and overall coordination of resources and procedures during the disaster that are aimed at preserving life and property. *Recovery* is the set of actions taken to minimize the long-term impacts of a particular disaster after the immediate situation has stabilized.

Many quantitative tools have helped in areas of risk analysis, insurance, logistical preparation and supply management, evacuation planning, and development of communication systems. Recent research has shown that while many strides and discoveries have been made, much research is still needed. Certainly each of the four disaster response areas could benefit from additional research, but recovery seems to be of particular concern and perhaps the most promising for future research.

Source: Based on N. Altay and W. Green. "OR/MS Research in Disaster Operations Management," *European Journal of Operational Research* 175, 1 (2006): 475–493.

---

called pilot plants. A *schematic model* is a picture, drawing, or chart of reality. Automobiles, lawn mowers, gears, fans, typewriters, and numerous other devices have schematic models (drawings and pictures) that reveal how these devices work. What sets quantitative analysis apart from other techniques is that the models that are used are mathematical. A **mathematical model** is a set of mathematical relationships. In most cases, these relationships are expressed in equations and inequalities, as they are in a spreadsheet model that computes sums, averages, or standard deviations.

Although there is considerable flexibility in the development of models, most of the models presented in this text contain one or more variables and parameters. A **variable**, as the name implies, is a measurable quantity that may vary or is subject to change. Variables can be *controllable* or *uncontrollable*. A controllable variable is also called a *decision variable*. An example would be how many inventory items to order. A **parameter** is a measurable quantity that is inherent in the problem. The cost of placing an order for more inventory items is an example of a parameter. In most cases, variables are unknown quantities, while parameters are known quantities. All models should be developed carefully. They should be solvable, realistic, and easy to understand and modify, and the required **input data** should be obtainable. The model developer has to be careful to include the appropriate amount of detail to be solvable yet realistic.

Acquiring Input Data

Garbage in, garbage out means that improper data will result in misleading results.

Once we have developed a model, we must obtain the data that are used in the model (*input data*). Obtaining accurate data for the model is essential; even if the model is a perfect representation of reality, improper data will result in misleading results. This situation is called *garbage in, garbage out*. For a larger problem, collecting accurate data can be one of the most difficult steps in performing quantitative analysis.

There are a number of sources that can be used in collecting data. In some cases, company reports and documents can be used to obtain the necessary data. Another source is interviews with employees or other persons related to the firm. These individuals can sometimes provide excellent information, and their experience and judgment can be invaluable. A production supervisor, for example, might be able to tell you with a great degree of accuracy the amount of time it takes to produce a particular product. Sampling and direct measurement provide other sources of data for the model. You may need to know how many pounds of raw material are used in producing a new photochemical product. This information can be obtained by going to the plant and actually measuring with scales the amount of raw material that is being used. In other cases, statistical sampling procedures can be used to obtain data.

Developing a Solution

Developing a solution involves manipulating the model to arrive at the best (optimal) solution to the problem. In some cases, this requires that an equation be solved for the best decision. In other cases, you can use a *trial and error* method, trying various approaches and picking the one that results in the best decision. For some problems, you may wish to try all possible values for the variables in the model to arrive at the best decision. This is called *complete enumeration*. This text also shows you how to solve very difficult and complex problems by repeating a few simple steps until you find the best solution. A series of steps or procedures that are repeated is called an **algorithm**, named after Algorismus, an Arabic mathematician of the ninth century.

The input data and model determine the accuracy of the solution.

The accuracy of a solution depends on the accuracy of the input data and the model. If the input data are accurate to only two significant digits, then the results can be accurate to only two significant digits. For example, the results of dividing 2.6 by 1.4 should be 1.9, not 1.857142857.

Testing the Solution

Before a solution can be analyzed and implemented, it needs to be tested completely. Because the solution depends on the input data and the model, both require testing.

Testing the data and model is done before the results are analyzed.

Testing the input data and the model includes determining the accuracy and completeness of the data used by the model. Inaccurate data will lead to an inaccurate solution. There are several ways to test input data. One method of testing the data is to collect additional data from a different source. If the original data were collected using interviews, perhaps some additional data can be collected by direct measurement or sampling. These additional data can then be compared with the original data, and statistical tests can be employed to determine whether there are differences between the original data and the additional data. If there are significant differences, more effort is required to obtain accurate input data. If the data are accurate but the results are inconsistent with the problem, the model may not be appropriate. The model can be checked to make sure that it is logical and represents the real situation.

Although most of the quantitative techniques discussed in this book have been computerized, you will probably be required to solve a number of problems by hand. To help detect both logical and computational mistakes, you should check the results to make sure that they are consistent with the structure of the problem. For example, (1.96)(301.7) is close to (2)(300), which is equal to 600. If your computations are significantly different from 600, you know you have made a mistake.

Analyzing the Results and Sensitivity Analysis

Analyzing the results starts with determining the implications of the solution. In most cases, a solution to a problem will result in some kind of action or change in the way an organization is operating. The implications of these actions or changes must be determined and analyzed before the results are implemented.

Sensitivity analysis determines how the solutions will change with a different model or input data.

Because a model is only an approximation of reality, the sensitivity of the solution to changes in the model and input data is a very important part of analyzing the results. This type of analysis is called **sensitivity analysis** or *postoptimality analysis*. It determines how much the solution will change if there were changes in the model or the input data. When the solution is sensitive to changes in the input data and the model specification, additional testing should be performed to make sure that the model and input data are accurate and valid. If the model or data are wrong, the solution could be wrong, resulting in financial losses or reduced profits.

The importance of sensitivity analysis cannot be overemphasized. Because input data may not always be accurate or model assumptions may not be completely appropriate, sensitivity analysis can become an important part of the quantitative analysis approach.

Implementing the Results

The final step is to *implement* the results. This is the process of incorporating the solution into the company. This can be much more difficult than you would imagine. Even if the solution is optimal and will result in millions of dollars in additional profits, if managers resist the new solution, all of the efforts of the analysis are of no value. Experience has shown that a large

MODELING IN THE REAL WORLD

Railroad Uses Optimization Models to Save Millions

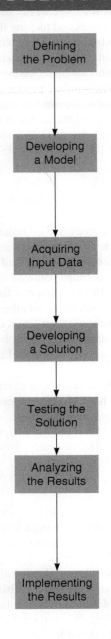

Defining the Problem

Developing a Model

Acquiring Input Data

Developing a Solution

Testing the Solution

Analyzing the Results

Implementing the Results

Defining the Problem

CSX Transportation, Inc., has 35,000 employees and annual revenue of $11 billion. It provides rail freight services to 23 states east of the Mississippi River, as well as parts of Canada. CSX receives orders for rail delivery service and must send empty railcars to customer locations. Moving these empty railcars results in hundreds of thousands of empty-car miles every day. If allocations of railcars to customers is not done properly, problems arise from excess costs, wear and tear on the system, and congestion on the tracks and at rail yards.

Developing a Model

In order to provide a more efficient scheduling system, CSX spent 2 years and $5 million developing its Dynamic Car-Planning (DCP) system. This model will minimize costs, including car travel distance, car handling costs at the rail yards, car travel time, and costs for being early or late. It does this while at the same time filling all orders, making sure the right type of car is assigned to the job, and getting the car to the destination in the allowable time.

Acquiring Input Data

In developing the model, the company used historical data for testing. In running the model, the DCP uses three external sources to obtain information on the customer car orders, the available cars of the type needed, and the transit-time standards. In addition to these, two internal input sources provide information on customer priorities and preferences and on cost parameters.

Developing a Solution

This model takes about 1 minute to load but only 10 seconds to solve. Because supply and demand are constantly changing, the model is run about every 15 minutes. This allows final decisions to be delayed until absolutely necessary.

Testing the Solution

The model was validated and verified using existing data. The solutions found using the DCP were found to be very good compared to assignments made without DCP.

Analyzing the Results

Since the implementation of DCP in 1997, more than $51 million has been saved annually. Due to the improved efficiency, it is estimated that CSX avoided spending another $1.4 billion to purchase an additional 18,000 railcars that would have been needed without DCP. Other benefits include reduced congestion in the rail yards and reduced congestion on the tracks, which are major concerns. This greater efficiency means that more freight can ship by rail rather than by truck, resulting in significant public benefits. These benefits include reduced pollution and greenhouse gases, improved highway safety, and reduced road maintenance costs.

Implementing the Results

Both senior-level management who championed DCP as well as key car-distribution experts who supported the new approach were instrumental in gaining acceptance of the new system and overcoming problems during the implementation. The job description of the car distributors was changed from car allocators to cost technicians. They are responsible for seeing that accurate cost information is entered into DCP, and they also manage any exceptions that must be made. They were given extensive training on how DCP works so they could understand and better accept the new system. Due to the success of DCP, other railroads have implemented similar systems and achieved similar benefits. CSX continues to enhance DCP to make DCP even more customer friendly and to improve car-order forecasts.

Source: Based on M. F. Gorman, et al. "CSX Railway Uses OR to Cash in on Optimized Equipment Distribution," *Interfaces* 40, 1 (January–February 2010): 5–16.

number of quantitative analysis teams have failed in their efforts because they have failed to implement a good, workable solution properly.

After the solution has been implemented, it should be closely monitored. Over time, there may be numerous changes that call for modifications of the original solution. A changing economy, fluctuating demand, and model enhancements requested by managers and decision makers are only a few examples of changes that might require the analysis to be modified.

The Quantitative Analysis Approach and Modeling in the Real World

The quantitative analysis approach is used extensively in the real world. These steps, first seen in Figure 1 and described in this section, are the building blocks of any successful use of quantitative analysis. As seen in our first *Modeling in the Real World* box, the steps of the quantitative analysis approach can be used to help a large company such as CSX plan for critical scheduling needs now and for decades into the future. Throughout this text, you will see how the steps of the quantitative analysis approach are used to help countries and companies of all sizes save millions of dollars, plan for the future, increase revenues, and provide higher-quality products and services. The *Modeling in the Real World* box will demonstrate to you the power and importance of quantitative analysis in solving real problems for real organizations. Using the steps of quantitative analysis, however, does not guarantee success. These steps must be applied carefully.

4 How to Develop a Quantitative Analysis Model

Developing a model is an important part of the quantitative analysis approach. Let's see how we can use the following mathematical model, which represents profit:

$$\text{Profit} = \text{Revenue} - \text{Expenses}$$

Expenses include fixed and variable costs.

In many cases, we can express revenues as price per unit multiplied times the number of units sold. Expenses can often be determined by summing fixed costs and variable cost. Variable cost is often expressed as variable cost per unit multiplied times the number of units. Thus, we can also express profit in the following mathematical model:

$$\text{Profit} = \text{Revenue} - (\text{Fixed cost} + \text{Variable cost})$$
$$\text{Profit} = (\text{Selling price per unit})(\text{Number of units sold})$$
$$- [\text{Fixed cost} + (\text{Variable cost per unit})(\text{Number of units sold})]$$
$$\text{Profit} = sX - [f + vX]$$
$$\text{Profit} = sX - f - vX \tag{1}$$

where

$$s = \text{selling price per unit}$$
$$f = \text{fixed cost}$$
$$v = \text{variable cost per unit}$$
$$X = \text{number of units sold}$$

The parameters in this model are f, v, and s, as these are inputs that are inherent in the model. The number of units sold (X) is the decision variable of interest.

EXAMPLE: PRITCHETT'S PRECIOUS TIME PIECES We will use the Bill Pritchett clock repair shop example to demonstrate the use of mathematical models. Bill's company, Pritchett's Precious Time Pieces, buys, sells, and repairs old clocks and clock parts. Bill sells rebuilt springs for a price per unit of $10. The fixed cost of the equipment to build the springs is $1,000. The variable cost per unit is $5 for spring material. In this example,

$$s = 10$$
$$f = 1,000$$
$$v = 5$$

The number of springs sold is X, and our profit model becomes

$$\text{Profit} = \$10X - \$1,000 - \$5X$$

If sales are 0, Bill will realize a $1,000 loss. If sales are 1,000 units, he will realize a profit of $4,000 ($4,000 = ($10)(1,000) − $1,000 − ($5)(1,000)). See if you can determine the profit for other values of units sold.

The BEP results in $0 profits.

In addition to the profit models shown here, decision makers are often interested in the **break-even point** (BEP). The BEP is the number of units sold that will result in $0 profits. We set profits equal to $0 and solve for X, the number of units at the break-even point:

$$0 = sX - f - vX$$

This can be written as

$$0 = (s - v)X - f$$

Solving for X, we have

$$f = (s - v)X$$

$$X = \frac{f}{s - v}$$

This quantity (X) that results in a profit of zero is the BEP, and we now have this model for the BEP:

$$\text{BEP} = \frac{Fixed\ cost}{(Selling\ price\ per\ unit) - (Variable\ cost\ per\ unit)}$$

$$\text{BEP} = \frac{f}{s - v} \tag{2}$$

For the Pritchett's Precious Time Pieces example, the BEP can be computed as follows:

$$\text{BEP} = \$1,000/(\$10 - \$5) = 200 \text{ units, or springs, at the break-even point}$$

The Advantages of Mathematical Modeling

There are a number of advantages of using mathematical models:

1. Models can accurately represent reality. If properly formulated, a model can be extremely accurate. A valid model is one that is accurate and correctly represents the problem or system under investigation. The profit model in the example is accurate and valid for many business problems.
2. Models can help a decision maker formulate problems. In the profit model, for example, a decision maker can determine the important factors or contributors to revenues and expenses, such as sales, returns, selling expenses, production costs, transportation costs, and so on.
3. Models can give us insight and information. For example, using the profit model from the preceding section, we can see what impact changes in revenues and expenses will have on profits. As discussed in the previous section, studying the impact of changes in a model, such as a profit model, is called sensitivity analysis.
4. Models can save time and money in decision making and problem solving. It usually takes less time, effort, and expense to analyze a model. We can use a profit model to analyze the impact of a new marketing campaign on profits, revenues, and expenses. In most cases, using models is faster and less expensive than actually trying a new marketing campaign in a real business setting and observing the results.
5. A model may be the only way to solve some large or complex problems in a timely fashion. A large company, for example, may produce literally thousands of sizes of nuts, bolts, and fasteners. The company may want to make the highest profits possible given its manufacturing constraints. A mathematical model may be the only way to determine the highest profits the company can achieve under these circumstances.
6. A model can be used to communicate problems and solutions to others. A decision analyst can share his or her work with other decision analysts. Solutions to a mathematical model can be given to managers and executives to help them make final decisions.

Mathematical Models Categorized by Risk

Some mathematical models, like the profit and break-even models previously discussed, do not involve risk or chance. We assume that we know all values used in the model with complete certainty. These are called **deterministic models**. A company, for example, might want to

Deterministic means with complete certainty.

minimize manufacturing costs while maintaining a certain quality level. If we know all these values with certainty, the model is deterministic.

Other models involve risk or chance. For example, the market for a new product might be "good" with a chance of 60% (a probability of 0.6) or "not good" with a chance of 40% (a probability of 0.4). Models that involve chance or risk, often measured as a probability value, are called **probabilistic models**. In this text, we will investigate both deterministic and probabilistic models.

5   The Role of Computers and Spreadsheet Models in the Quantitative Analysis Approach

Developing a solution, testing the solution, and analyzing the results are important steps in the quantitative analysis approach. Because we will be using mathematical models, these steps require mathematical calculations. Fortunately, we can use the computer to make these steps easier. Two programs that allow you to solve many of the problems found in this chapter are provided at the Companion Website for this text:

1. **POM-QM for Windows** is an easy-to-use decision support system that was developed for use with production/operations management (POM) and quantitative methods or quantitative management (QM) courses. POM for Windows and QM for Windows were originally separate software packages for each type of course. These are now combined into one program called POM-QM for Windows. As seen in Program 1, it is possible to display all the modules, only the POM modules, or only the QM modules. The images shown in this text will typically display only the QM modules. Hence, in this text, reference will usually be made to QM for Windows.

2. **Excel QM**, which can also be used to solve many of the problems discussed in this text, works automatically within Excel spreadsheets. Excel QM makes using a spreadsheet even easier by providing custom menus and solution procedures that guide you through every step. In Excel 2007, the main menu is found in the Add-Ins tab, as shown in Program 2. To solve the break-even problem discussed in Section 4, we illustrate Excel QM features in Programs 3A and 3B.

PROGRAM 1

The QM for Windows Main Menu of Quantitative Models

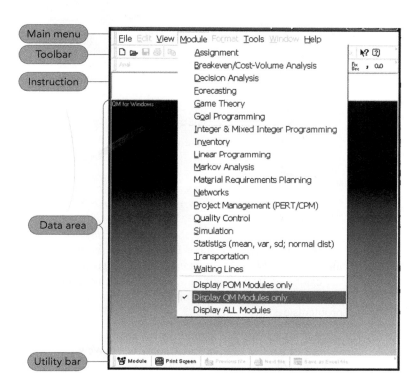

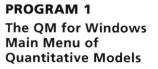

PROGRAM 2

Excel QM Main Menu of Quantitative Models in Excel 2010

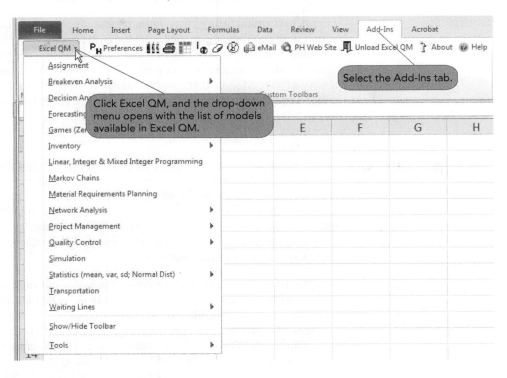

PROGRAM 3A

Selecting Breakeven Analysis in Excel QM

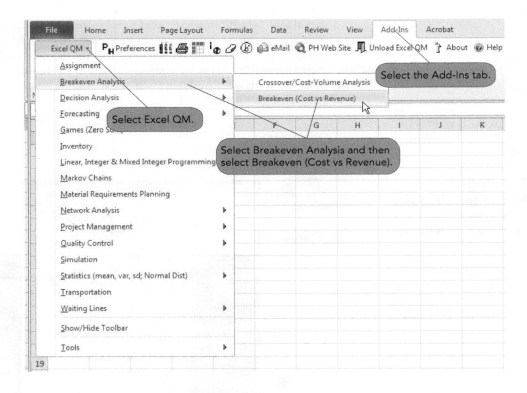

Add-in programs make Excel, which is already a wonderful tool for modeling, even more powerful in solving quantitative analysis problems. Excel QM and the Excel files used in the examples throughout this text are also included on the Companion Website for this text. There are two other powerful Excel built-in features that make solving quantitative analysis problems easier:

1. **Solver.** Solver is an optimization technique that can maximize or minimize a quantity given a set of limitations or constraints. We will be using Solver throughout the text to solve optimization problems.

PROGRAM 3B

Breakeven Analysis in Excel QM

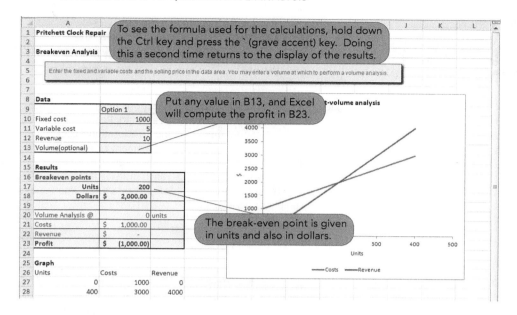

2. **Goal Seek.** This feature of Excel allows you to specify a goal or target (Set Cell) and what variable (Changing Cell) that you want Excel to change in order to achieve a desired goal. Bill Pritchett, for example, would like to determine how many springs must be sold to make a profit of $175. Program 4 shows how Goal Seek can be used to make the necessary calculations.

PROGRAM 4

Using Goal Seek in the Break-Even Problem to Achieve a Specified Profit

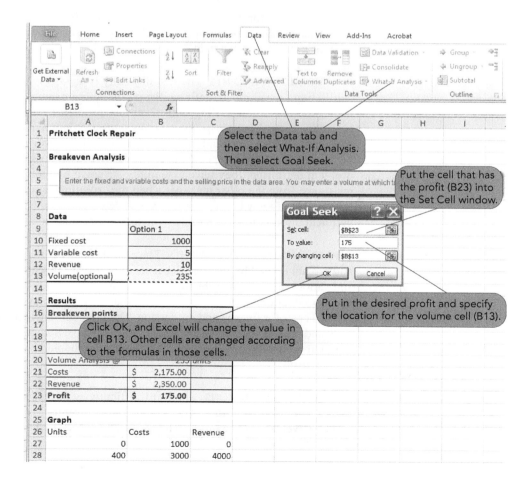

IN ACTION — Major League Operations Research at the Department of Agriculture

In 1997, the Pittsburgh Pirates signed Ross Ohlendorf because of his 95-mph sinking fastball. Little did they know that Ross possessed operations research skills also worthy of national merit. Ross Ohlendorf had graduated from Princeton University with a 3.8 GPA in operations research and financial engineering.

Indeed, after the 2009 baseball season, when Ross applied for an 8-week unpaid internship with the U.S. Department of Agriculture, he didn't need to mention his full-time employer because the Secretary of the Department of Agriculture at the time, Tom Vilsack, was born and raised in Pittsburgh and was an avid Pittsburgh Pirates fan. Ross spent 2 months of the ensuing off-season utilizing his educational background in operations research, helping the Department of Agriculture track disease migration in livestock, a subject Ross has a vested interest in as his family runs a cattle ranch in Texas. Moreover, when ABC News asked Ross about his off-season unpaid internship experience, he replied, "This one's been, I'd say, the most exciting off-season I've had."

6   Possible Problems in the Quantitative Analysis Approach

We have presented the quantitative analysis approach as a logical, systematic means of tackling decision-making problems. Even when these steps are followed carefully, there are many difficulties that can hurt the chances of implementing solutions to real-world problems. We now take a look at what can happen during each of the steps.

Defining the Problem

One view of decision makers is that they sit at a desk all day long, waiting until a problem arises, and then stand up and attack the problem until it is solved. Once it is solved, they sit down, relax, and wait for the next big problem. In the worlds of business, government, and education, problems are, unfortunately, not easily identified. There are four potential roadblocks that quantitative analysts face in defining a problem. We use an application, inventory analysis, throughout this section as an example.

All viewpoints should be considered before formally defining the problem.

CONFLICTING VIEWPOINTS   The first difficulty is that quantitative analysts must often consider conflicting viewpoints in defining the problem. For example, there are at least two views that managers take when dealing with inventory problems. Financial managers usually feel that inventory is too high, as inventory represents cash not available for other investments. Sales managers, on the other hand, often feel that inventory is too low, as high levels of inventory may be needed to fill an unexpected order. If analysts assume either one of these statements as the problem definition, they have essentially accepted one manager's perception and can expect resistance from the other manager when the "solution" emerges. So it's important to consider both points of view before stating the problem. Good mathematical models should include all pertinent information. Both of these factors are included in inventory models.

IMPACT ON OTHER DEPARTMENTS   The next difficulty is that problems do not exist in isolation and are not owned by just one department of a firm. Inventory is closely tied with cash flows and various production problems. A change in ordering policy can seriously hurt cash flows and upset production schedules to the point that savings on inventory are more than offset by increased costs for finance and production. The problem statement should thus be as broad as possible and include input from all departments that have a stake in the solution. When a solution is found, the benefits to all areas of the organization should be identified and communicated to the people involved.

BEGINNING ASSUMPTIONS   The third difficulty is that people have a tendency to state problems in terms of solutions. The statement that inventory is too low implies a solution that inventory levels should be raised. The quantitative analyst who starts off with this assumption will probably indeed find that inventory should be raised. From an implementation standpoint, a "good" solution to the *right* problem is much better than an "optimal" solution to the *wrong* problem. If a problem has been defined in terms of a desired solution, the quantitative analyst should ask questions about why this solution is desired. By probing further, the true problem will surface and can be defined properly.

An optimal solution to the wrong problem leaves the real problem unsolved.

SOLUTION OUTDATED Even with the best of problem statements, however, there is a fourth danger. The problem can change as the model is being developed. In our rapidly changing business environment, it is not unusual for problems to appear or disappear virtually overnight. The analyst who presents a solution to a problem that no longer exists can't expect credit for providing timely help. However, one of the benefits of mathematical models is that once the original model has been developed, it can be used over and over again whenever similar problems arise. This allows a solution to be found very easily in a timely manner.

Developing a Model

FITTING THE TEXTBOOK MODELS One problem in developing quantitative models is that a manager's perception of a problem won't always match the textbook approach. Most inventory models involve minimizing the total of holding and ordering costs. Some managers view these costs as unimportant; instead, they see the problem in terms of cash flow, turnover, and levels of customer satisfaction. Results of a model based on holding and ordering costs are probably not acceptable to such managers. This is why the analyst must completely understand the model and not simply use the computer as a "black box" where data are input and results are given with no understanding of the process. The analyst who understands the process can explain to the manager how the model does consider these other factors when estimating the different types of inventory costs. If other factors are important as well, the analyst can consider these and use sensitivity analysis and good judgment to modify the computer solution before it is implemented.

UNDERSTANDING THE MODEL A second major concern involves the trade-off between the complexity of the model and ease of understanding. Managers simply will not use the results of a model they do not understand. Complex problems, though, require complex models. One trade-off is to simplify assumptions in order to make the model easier to understand. The model loses some of its reality but gains some acceptance by management.

One simplifying assumption in inventory modeling is that demand is known and constant. This means that probability distributions are not needed and it allows us to build simple, easy-to-understand models. Demand, however, is rarely known and constant, so the model we build lacks some reality. Introducing probability distributions provides more realism but may put comprehension beyond all but the most mathematically sophisticated managers. One approach is for the quantitative analyst to start with the simple model and make sure that it is completely understood. Later, more complex models can be introduced slowly as managers gain more confidence in using the new approach. Explaining the impact of the more sophisticated models (e.g., carrying extra inventory called safety stock) without going into complete mathematical details is sometimes helpful. Managers can understand and identify with this concept, even if the specific mathematics used to find the appropriate quantity of safety stock is not totally understood.

Acquiring Input Data

Gathering the data to be used in the quantitative approach to problem solving is often not a simple task. One-fifth of all firms in a recent study had difficulty with data access.

Obtaining accurate input data can be very difficult.

USING ACCOUNTING DATA One problem is that most data generated in a firm come from basic accounting reports. The accounting department collects its inventory data, for example, in terms of cash flows and turnover. But quantitative analysts tackling an inventory problem need to collect data on holding costs and ordering costs. If they ask for such data, they may be shocked to find that the data were simply never collected for those specified costs.

Professor Gene Woolsey tells a story of a young quantitative analyst sent down to accounting to get "the inventory holding cost per item per day for part 23456/AZ." The accountant asked the young man if he wanted the first-in, first-out figure, the last-in, first-out figure, the lower of cost or market figure, or the "how-we-do-it" figure. The young man replied that the inventory model required only one number. The accountant at the next desk said, "Hell, Joe, give the kid a number." The kid was given a number and departed.

VALIDITY OF DATA A lack of "good, clean data" means that whatever data are available must often be distilled and manipulated (we call it "fudging") before being used in a model. Unfortunately, the validity of the results of a model is no better than the validity of the data that go into the model. You cannot blame a manager for resisting a model's "scientific" results when he or she knows that questionable data were used as input. This highlights the importance of the analyst understanding other business functions so that good data can be found and evaluated by the analyst. It also emphasizes the importance of sensitivity analysis, which is used to determine the impact of minor changes in input data. Some solutions are very robust and would not change at all for certain changes in the input data.

Developing a Solution

Hard-to-understand mathematics and one answer can be a problem in developing a solution.

HARD-TO-UNDERSTAND MATHEMATICS The first concern in developing solutions is that although the mathematical models we use may be complex and powerful, they may not be completely understood. Fancy solutions to problems may have faulty logic or data. The aura of mathematics often causes managers to remain silent when they should be critical. The well-known operations researcher C. W. Churchman cautions that "because mathematics has been so revered a discipline in recent years, it tends to lull the unsuspecting into believing that he who thinks elaborately thinks well."[1]

ONLY ONE ANSWER IS LIMITING The second problem is that quantitative models usually give just one answer to a problem. Most managers would like to have a *range* of options and not be put in a take-it-or-leave-it position. A more appropriate strategy is for an analyst to present a range of options, indicating the effect that each solution has on the objective function. This gives managers a choice as well as information on how much it will cost to deviate from the optimal solution. It also allows problems to be viewed from a broader perspective, since nonquantitative factors can be considered.

Testing the Solution

The results of quantitative analysis often take the form of predictions of how things will work in the future if certain changes are made now. To get a preview of how well solutions will really work, managers are often asked how good the solution looks to them. The problem is that complex models tend to give solutions that are not intuitively obvious. Such solutions tend to be rejected by managers. The quantitative analyst now has the chance to work through the model and the assumptions with the manager in an effort to convince the manager of the validity of the results. In the process of convincing the manager, the analyst will have to review every assumption that went into the model. If there are errors, they may be revealed during this review. In addition, the manager will be casting a critical eye on everything that went into the model, and if he or she can be convinced that the model is valid, there is a good chance that the solution results are also valid.

Assumptions should be reviewed.

Analyzing the Results

Once a solution has been tested, the results must be analyzed in terms of how they will affect the total organization. You should be aware that even small changes in organizations are often difficult to bring about. If the results indicate large changes in organization policy, the quantitative analyst can expect resistance. In analyzing the results, the analyst should ascertain who must change and by how much, if the people who must change will be better or worse off, and who has the power to direct the change.

---

[1]C. W. Churchman. "Relativity Models in the Social Sciences," *Interfaces* 4, 1 (November 1973).

IN ACTION — PLATO Helps 2004 Olympic Games in Athens

The 2004 Olympic Games were held in Athens, Greece, over a period of 16 days. More than 2,000 athletes competed in 300 events in 28 sports. The events were held in 36 different venues (stadia, competition centers, etc.), and 3.6 million tickets were sold to people who would view these events. In addition, 2,500 members of international committees and 22,000 journalists and broadcasters attended these games. Home viewers spent more than 34 billion hours watching these sporting events. The 2004 Olympic Games was the biggest sporting event in the history of the world up to that point.

In addition to the sporting venues, other noncompetitive venues, such as the airport and Olympic village, had to be considered. A successful Olympics requires tremendous planning for the transportation system that will handle the millions of spectators. Three years of work and planning were needed for the 16 days of the Olympics.

The Athens Olympic Games Organizing Committee (ATHOC) had to plan, design, and coordinate systems that would be delivered by outside contractors. ATHOC personnel would later be responsible for managing the efforts of volunteers and paid staff during the operations of the games. To make the Athens Olympics run efficiently and effectively, the Process Logistics Advanced Technical Optimization (PLATO) project was begun. Innovative techniques from management science, systems engineering, and information technology were used to change the planning, design, and operations of venues.

The objectives of PLATO were to (1) facilitate effective organizational transformation, (2) help plan and manage resources in a cost-effective manner, and (3) document lessons learned so future Olympic committees could benefit. The PLATO project developed business-process models for the various venues, developed simulation models that enable the generation of what-if scenarios, developed software to aid in the creation and management of these models, and developed process steps for training ATHOC personnel in using these models. Generic solutions were developed so that this knowledge and approach could be made available to other users.

PLATO was credited with reducing the cost of the 2004 Olympics by over $69 million. Perhaps even more important is the fact that the Athens games were universally deemed an unqualified success. The resulting increase in tourism is expected to result in economic benefit to Greece for many years in the future.

Source: Based on D. A. Beis, et al. "PLATO Helps Athens Win Gold: Olympic Games Knowledge Modeling for Organizational Change and Resource Management," *Interfaces* 36, 1 (January–February 2006): 26–42.

7 Implementation—Not Just the Final Step

We have just presented some of the many problems that can affect the ultimate acceptance of the quantitative analysis approach and use of its models. It should be clear now that implementation isn't just another step that takes place after the modeling process is over. Each one of these steps greatly affects the chances of implementing the results of a quantitative study.

Lack of Commitment and Resistance to Change

Even though many business decisions can be made intuitively, based on hunches and experience, there are more and more situations in which quantitative models can assist. Some managers, however, fear that the use of a formal analysis process will reduce their decision-making power. Others fear that it may expose some previous intuitive decisions as inadequate. Still others just feel uncomfortable about having to reverse their thinking patterns with formal decision making. These managers often argue against the use of quantitative methods.

Many action-oriented managers do not like the lengthy formal decision-making process and prefer to get things done quickly. They prefer "quick and dirty" techniques that can yield immediate results. Once managers see some quick results that have a substantial payoff, the stage is set for convincing them that quantitative analysis is a beneficial tool.

Management support and user involvement are important.

We have known for some time that management support and user involvement are critical to the successful implementation of quantitative analysis projects. A Swedish study found that only 40% of projects suggested by quantitative analysts were ever implemented. But 70% of the quantitative projects initiated by users, and fully 98% of projects suggested by top managers, *were* implemented.

Lack of Commitment by Quantitative Analysts

Just as managers' attitudes are to blame for some implementation problems, analysts' attitudes are to blame for others. When the quantitative analyst is not an integral part of the department facing the problem, he or she sometimes tends to treat the modeling activity as an end in itself.

That is, the analyst accepts the problem as stated by the manager and builds a model to solve only that problem. When the results are computed, he or she hands them back to the manager and considers the job done. The analyst who does not care whether these results help make the final decision is not concerned with implementation.

Successful implementation requires that the analyst not *tell* the users what to do, but work with them and take their feelings into account. An article in *Operations Research* describes an inventory control system that calculated reorder points and order quantities. But instead of insisting that computer-calculated quantities be ordered, a manual override feature was installed. This allowed users to disregard the calculated figures and substitute their own. The override was used quite often when the system was first installed. Gradually, however, as users came to realize that the calculated figures were right more often than not, they allowed the system's figures to stand. Eventually, the override feature was used only in special circumstances. This is a good example of how good relationships can aid in model implementation.

Summary

Quantitative analysis is a scientific approach to decision making. The quantitative analysis approach includes defining the problem, developing a model, acquiring input data, developing a solution, testing the solution, analyzing the results, and implementing the results. In using the quantitative approach, however, there can be potential problems, including conflicting viewpoints, the impact of quantitative analysis models on other departments, beginning assumptions, outdated solutions, fitting textbook models, understanding the model, acquiring good input data, hard-to-understand mathematics, obtaining only one answer, testing the solution, and analyzing the results. In using the quantitative analysis approach, implementation is not the final step. There can be a lack of commitment to the approach and resistance to change.

Glossary

Algorithm A set of logical and mathematical operations performed in a specific sequence.

Break-Even Point The quantity of sales that results in zero profit.

Deterministic Model A model in which all values used in the model are known with complete certainty.

Input Data Data that are used in a model in arriving at the final solution.

Mathematical Model A model that uses mathematical equations and statements to represent the relationships within the model.

Model A representation of reality or of a real-life situation.

Parameter A measurable input quantity that is inherent in a problem.

Probabilistic Model A model in which all values used in the model are not known with certainty but rather involve some chance or risk, often measured as a probability value.

Problem A statement, which should come from a manager, that indicates a problem to be solved or an objective or a goal to be reached.

Quantitative Analysis or **Management Science** A scientific approach that uses quantitative techniques as a tool in decision making.

Sensitivity Analysis A process that involves determining how sensitive a solution is to changes in the formulation of a problem.

Stochastic Model Another name for a probabilistic model.

Variable A measurable quantity that is subject to change.

Key Equations

(1) $\text{Profit} = sX - f - vX$

where

s = selling price per unit
f = fixed cost
v = variable cost per unit
X = number of units sold

An equation to determine profit as a function of the selling price per unit, fixed costs, variable costs, and number of units sold.

(2) $\text{BEP} = \dfrac{f}{s - v}$

An equation to determine the break-even point (BEP) in units as a function of the selling price per unit (s), fixed costs (f), and variable costs (v).

Self-Test

- Before taking the self-test, refer to the learning objectives at the beginning of the chapter, the notes in the margins, and the glossary at the end of the chapter.
- Use the key at the end of the chapter to correct your answers.
- Restudy pages that correspond to any questions that you answered incorrectly or material you feel uncertain about.

1. In analyzing a problem, you should normally study
   a. the qualitative aspects.
   b. the quantitative aspects.
   c. both a and b.
   d. neither a nor b.
2. Quantitative analysis is
   a. a logical approach to decision making.
   b. a rational approach to decision making.
   c. a scientific approach to decision making.
   d. all of the above.
3. Frederick Winslow Taylor
   a. was a military researcher during World War II.
   b. pioneered the principles of scientific management.
   c. developed the use of the algorithm for QA.
   d. all of the above.
4. An input (such as variable cost per unit or fixed cost) for a model is an example of
   a. a decision variable.
   b. a parameter.
   c. an algorithm.
   d. a stochastic variable.
5. The point at which the total revenue equals total cost (meaning zero profit) is called the
   a. zero-profit solution.
   b. optimal-profit solution.
   c. break-even point.
   d. fixed-cost solution.
6. Quantitative analysis is typically associated with the use of
   a. schematic models.
   b. physical models.
   c. mathematical models.
   d. scale models.
7. Sensitivity analysis is most often associated with which step of the quantitative analysis approach?
   a. defining the problem
   b. acquiring input data
   c. implementing the results
   d. analyzing the results
8. A deterministic model is one in which
   a. there is some uncertainty about the parameters used in the model.
   b. there is a measurable outcome.
   c. all parameters used in the model are known with complete certainty.
   d. there is no available computer software.
9. The term *algorithm*
   a. is named after Algorismus.
   b. is named after a ninth-century Arabic mathematician.
   c. describes a series of steps or procedures to be repeated.
   d. all of the above.
10. An analysis to determine how much a solution would change if there were changes in the model or the input data is called
    a. sensitivity or postoptimality analysis.
    b. schematic or iconic analysis.
    c. futurama conditioning.
    d. both b and c.
11. Decision variables are
    a. controllable.
    b. uncontrollable.
    c. parameters.
    d. constant numerical values associated with any complex problem.
12. _____ is the scientific approach to managerial decision making.
13. _____ is the first step in quantitative analysis.
14. A _____ is a picture, drawing, or chart of reality.
15. A series of steps that are repeated until a solution is found is called a(n) _____.

Discussion Questions and Problems

Discussion Questions

1 What is the difference between quantitative and qualitative analysis? Give several examples.
2 Define *quantitative analysis*. What are some of the organizations that support the use of the scientific approach?
3 What is the quantitative analysis process? Give several examples of this process.
4 Briefly trace the history of quantitative analysis. What happened to the development of quantitative analysis during World War II?
5 Give some examples of various types of models. What is a mathematical model? Develop two examples of mathematical models.
6 List some sources of input data.
7 What is implementation, and why is it important?

8   Describe the use of sensitivity analysis and postoptimality analysis in analyzing the results.

9   Managers are quick to claim that quantitative analysts talk to them in a jargon that does not sound like English. List four terms that might not be understood by a manager. Then explain in nontechnical terms what each term means.

10   Why do you think many quantitative analysts don't like to participate in the implementation process? What could be done to change this attitude?

11   Should people who will be using the results of a new quantitative model become involved in the technical aspects of the problem-solving procedure?

12   C. W. Churchman once said that "mathematics … tends to lull the unsuspecting into believing that he who thinks elaborately thinks well." Do you think that the best QA models are the ones that are most elaborate and complex mathematically? Why?

13   What is the break-even point? What parameters are necessary to find it?

Problems

14   Gina Fox has started her own company, Foxy Shirts, which manufactures imprinted shirts for special occasions. Since she has just begun this operation, she rents the equipment from a local printing shop when necessary. The cost of using the equipment is $350. The materials used in one shirt cost $8, and Gina can sell these for $15 each.
  (a) If Gina sells 20 shirts, what will her total revenue be? What will her total variable cost be?
  (b) How many shirts must Gina sell to break even? What is the total revenue for this?

15   Ray Bond sells handcrafted yard decorations at county fairs. The variable cost to make these is $20 each, and he sells them for $50. The cost to rent a booth at the fair is $150. How many of these must Ray sell to break even?

16   Ray Bond, from Problem 15, is trying to find a new supplier that will reduce his variable cost of production to $15 per unit. If he was able to succeed in reducing this cost, what would the break-even point be?

17   Katherine D'Ann is planning to finance her college education by selling programs at the football games for State University. There is a fixed cost of $400 for printing these programs, and the variable cost is $3. There is also a $1,000 fee that is paid to the university for the right to sell these programs. If Katherine was able to sell programs for $5 each, how many would she have to sell in order to break even?

18   Katherine D'Ann, from Problem 17, has become concerned that sales may fall, as the team is on a terrible losing streak, and attendance has fallen off. In fact, Katherine believes that she will sell only 500 programs for the next game. If it was possible to raise the selling price of the program and still sell 500, what would the price have to be for Katherine to break even by selling 500?

19   Farris Billiard Supply sells all types of billiard equipment, and is considering manufacturing their own brand of pool cues. Mysti Farris, the production manager, is currently investigating the production of a standard house pool cue that should be very popular. Upon analyzing the costs, Mysti determines that the materials and labor cost for each cue is $25, and the fixed cost that must be covered is $2,400 per week. With a selling price of $40 each, how many pool cues must be sold to break even? What would the total revenue be at this break-even point?

20   Mysti Farris (see Problem 19) is considering raising the selling price of each cue to $50 instead of $40. If this is done while the costs remain the same, what would the new break-even point be? What would the total revenue be at this break-even point?

21   Mysti Farris (see Problem 19) believes that there is a high probability that 120 pool cues can be sold if the selling price is appropriately set. What selling price would cause the break-even point to be 120?

22   Golden Age Retirement Planners specializes in providing financial advice for people planning for a comfortable retirement. The company offers seminars on the important topic of retirement planning. For a typical seminar, the room rental at a hotel is $1,000, and the cost of advertising and other incidentals is about $10,000 per seminar. The cost of the materials and special gifts for each attendee is $60 per person attending the seminar. The company charges $250 per person to attend the seminar as this seems to be competitive with other companies in the same business. How many people must attend each seminar for Golden Age to break even?

23   A couple of entrepreneurial business students at State University decided to put their education into practice by developing a tutoring company for business students. While private tutoring was offered, it was determined that group tutoring before tests in the large statistics classes would be most beneficial. The students rented a room close to campus for $300 for 3 hours. They developed handouts based on past tests, and these handouts (including color graphs) cost $5 each. The tutor was paid $25 per hour, for a total of $75 for each tutoring session.
  (a) If students are charged $20 to attend the session, how many students must enroll for the company to break even?
  (b) A somewhat smaller room is available for $200 for 3 hours. The company is considering this possibility. How would this affect the break-even point?

Note: ☺ means the problem may be solved with QM for Windows; ✖ means the problem may be solved with Excel QM; and ✖ means the problem may be solved with QM for Windows and/or Excel QM.

Case Study

Food and Beverages at Southwestern University Football Games

Southwestern University (SWU), a large state college in Stephenville, Texas, 30 miles southwest of the Dallas/Fort Worth metroplex, enrolls close to 20,000 students. The school is the dominant force in the small city, with more students during fall and spring than permanent residents.

A longtime football powerhouse, SWU is a member of the Big Eleven conference and is usually in the top 20 in college football rankings. To bolster its chances of reaching the elusive and long-desired number-one ranking, in 2010 SWU hired the legendary Bo Pitterno as its head coach. Although the number-one ranking remained out of reach, attendance at the five Saturday home games each year increased. Prior to Pitterno's arrival, attendance generally averaged 25,000–29,000. Season ticket sales bumped up by 10,000 just with the announcement of the new coach's arrival. Stephenville and SWU were ready to move to the big time!

With the growth in attendance came more fame, the need for a bigger stadium, and more complaints about seating, parking, long lines, and concession stand prices. Southwestern University's president, Dr. Marty Starr, was concerned not only about the cost of expanding the existing stadium versus building a new stadium but also about the ancillary activities. He wanted to be sure that these various support activities generated revenue adequate to pay for themselves. Consequently, he wanted the parking lots, game programs, and food service to all be handled as profit centers. At a recent meeting discussing the new stadium, Starr told the stadium manager, Hank Maddux, to develop a break-even chart and related data for each of the centers. He instructed Maddux to have the food service area break-even report ready for the next meeting. After discussion with other facility managers and his subordinates, Maddux developed the following table showing the suggested selling prices, and his estimate of variable costs, and the percent revenue by item. It also provides an estimate of the percentage of the total revenues that would be expected for each of the items based on historical sales data.

Maddux's fixed costs are interesting. He estimated that the prorated portion of the stadium cost would be as follows: salaries for food services at $100,000 ($20,000 for each of the five home games); 2,400 square feet of stadium space at $2 per square foot per game; and six people per booth in each of the

ITEM	SELLING PRICE/UNIT	VARIABLE COST/UNIT	PERCENT REVENUE
Soft drink	$1.50	$0.75	25%
Coffee	2.00	0.50	25%
Hot dogs	2.00	0.80	20%
Hamburgers	2.50	1.00	20%
Misc. snacks	1.00	0.40	10%

six booths for 5 hours at $7 an hour. These fixed costs will be proportionately allocated to each of the products based on the percentages provided in the table. For example, the revenue from soft drinks would be expected to cover 25% of the total fixed costs.

Maddux wants to be sure that he has a number of things for President Starr: (1) the total fixed cost that must be covered at each of the games; (2) the portion of the fixed cost allocated to each of the items; (3) what his unit sales would be at break-even for each item—that is, what sales of soft drinks, coffee, hot dogs, and hamburgers are necessary to cover the portion of the fixed cost allocated to each of these items; (4) what the dollar sales for each of these would be at these break-even points; and (5) realistic sales estimates per attendee for attendance of 60,000 and 35,000. (In other words, he wants to know how many dollars each attendee is spending on food at his projected break-even sales at present and if attendance grows to 60,000.) He felt this last piece of information would be helpful to understand how realistic the assumptions of his model are, and this information could be compared with similar figures from previous seasons.

Discussion Question

1. Prepare a brief report with the items noted so it is ready for Dr. Starr at the next meeting.

Adapted from J. Heizer and B. Render. *Operations Management*, 6th ed. Upper Saddle River, NJ: Prentice Hall, 2000, pp. 274–275.

Bibliography

Ackoff, R. L. *Scientific Method: Optimizing Applied Research Decisions.* New York: John Wiley & Sons, Inc., 1962.

Beam, Carrie. "ASP, the Art and Science of Practice: How I Started an OR/MS Consulting Practice with a Laptop, a Phone, and a PhD," *Interfaces* 34 (July–August 2004): 265–271.

Board, John, Charles Sutcliffe, and William T. Ziemba. "Applying Operations Research Techniques to Financial Markets," *Interfaces* 33 (March–April 2003): 12–24.

Churchman, C. W. "Relativity Models in the Social Sciences," *Interfaces* 4, 1 (November 1973).

Churchman, C. W. *The Systems Approach.* New York: Delacort Press, 1968.

Dutta, Goutam. "Lessons for Success in OR/MS Practice Gained from Experiences in Indian and U.S. Steel Plants," *Interfaces* 30, 5 (September–October 2000): 23–30.

Eom, Sean B., and Eyong B. Kim. "A Survey of Decision Support System Applications (1995–2001)," *Journal of the Operational Research Society* 57, 11 (2006): 1264–1278.

Horowitz, Ira. "Aggregating Expert Ratings Using Preference-Neutral Weights: The Case of the College Football Polls," *Interfaces* 34 (July–August 2004): 314–320.

Keskinocak, Pinar, and Sridhar Tayur. "Quantitative Analysis for Internet-Enabled Supply Chains," *Interfaces* 31, 2 (March–April 2001): 70–89.

Laval, Claude, Marc Feyhl, and Steve Kakouros. "Hewlett-Packard Combined OR and Expert Knowledge to Design Its Supply Chains," *Interfaces* 35 (May–June 2005): 238–247.

Pidd, Michael. "Just Modeling Through: A Rough Guide to Modeling," *Interfaces* 29, 2 (March–April 1999): 118–132.

Saaty, T. L. "Reflections and Projections on Creativity in Operations Research and Management Science: A Pressing Need for a Shifting Paradigm," *Operations Research* 46, 1 (1998): 9–16.

Salveson, Melvin. "The Institute of Management Science: A Prehistory and Commentary," *Interfaces* 27, 3 (May–June 1997): 74–85.

Wright, P. Daniel, Matthew J. Liberatore, and Robert L. Nydick. "A Survey of Operations Research Models and Applications in Homeland Security," *Interfaces* 36 (November–December 2006): 514–529.

Solutions to Selected Problems

14 (a) total revenue = $300; total variable cost = $160

   (b) BEP = 50; total revenue = $750

16 BEP = 4.28

18 $5.80

20 BEP = 96; total revenue = $4,800

Solutions to Self-Tests

1. c
2. d
3. b
4. b
5. c
6. c
7. d
8. c
9. d
10. a
11. a
12. quantitative analysis
13. defining the problem
14. schematic model
15. algorithm

Probability Concepts and Applications

LEARNING OBJECTIVES

After completing this chapter, students will be able to:

1. Understand the basic foundations of probability analysis.
2. Describe statistically dependent and independent events.
3. Use Bayes' theorem to establish posterior probabilities.
4. Describe and provide examples of both discrete and continuous random variables.
5. Explain the difference between discrete and continuous probability distributions.
6. Calculate expected values and variances and use the normal table.

1 Introduction

Life would be simpler if we knew without doubt what was going to happen in the future. The outcome of any decision would depend only on how logical and rational the decision was. If you lost money in the stock market, it would be because you failed to consider all the information or to make a logical decision. If you got caught in the rain, it would be because you simply forgot your umbrella. You could always avoid building a plant that was too large, investing in a company that would lose money, running out of supplies, or losing crops because of bad weather. There would be no such thing as a risky investment. Life would be simpler, but boring.

It wasn't until the sixteenth century that people started to quantify risks and to apply this concept to everyday situations. Today, the idea of risk or probability is a part of our lives. "There is a 40% chance of rain in Omaha today." "The Florida State University Seminoles are favored 2 to 1 over the Louisiana State University Tigers this Saturday." "There is a 50–50 chance that the stock market will reach an all-time high next month."

A probability is a numerical statement about the chance that an event will occur.

*A **probability** is a numerical statement about the likelihood that an event will occur.* In this chapter we examine the basic concepts, terms, and relationships of probability and probability distributions that are useful in solving many quantitative analysis problems. You can see that the study of quantitative analysis would be quite difficult without it.

2 Fundamental Concepts

There are two basic rules regarding the mathematics of probability:

People often misuse the two basic rules of probabilities when they use such statements as, "I'm 110% sure we're going to win the big game."

1. The probability, P, of any event or state of nature occurring is greater than or equal to 0 and less than or equal to 1. That is,

$$0 \leq P(\text{event}) \leq 1 \tag{1}$$

A probability of 0 indicates that an event is never expected to occur. A probability of 1 means that an event is always expected to occur.

2. The sum of the simple probabilities for all possible outcomes of an activity must equal 1. Both of these concepts are illustrated in Example 1.

EXAMPLE 1: TWO RULES OF PROBABILITY Demand for white latex paint at Diversey Paint and Supply has always been 0, 1, 2, 3, or 4 gallons per day. (There are no other possible outcomes and when one occurs, no other can.) Over the past 200 working days, the owner notes the following frequencies of demand.

QUANTITY DEMANDED (GALLONS)	NUMBER OF DAYS
0	40
1	80
2	50
3	20
4	10
	Total 200

If this past distribution is a good indicator of future sales, we can find the probability of each possible outcome occurring in the future by converting the data into percentages of the total:

QUANTITY DEMANDED	PROBABILITY
0	0.20 (=40/200)
1	0.40 (=80/200)
2	0.25 (=50/200)
3	0.10 (=20/200)
4	0.05 (=10/200)
	Total 1.00(=200/200)

Thus, the probability that sales are 2 gallons of paint on any given day is $P(2\,\text{gallons}) = 0.25 = 25\%$. The probability of any level of sales must be greater than or equal to 0 and less than or equal to 1. Since 0, 1, 2, 3, and 4 gallons exhaust all possible events or outcomes, the sum of their probability values must equal 1.

Types of Probability

There are two different ways to determine probability: the **objective approach** and the **subjective approach**.

OBJECTIVE PROBABILITY Example 1 provides an illustration of objective probability assessment. The probability of any paint demand level is the *relative frequency* of occurrence of that demand in a large number of trial observations (200 days, in this case). In general,

$$P(\text{event}) = \frac{\text{Number of occurrences of the event}}{\text{Total number of trials or outcomes}}$$

Objective probability can also be set using what is called the **classical** or **logical method**. Without performing a series of trials, we can often logically determine what the probabilities of various events should be. For example, the probability of tossing a fair coin once and getting a head is

$$P(\text{head}) = \frac{1}{2} \quad \longleftarrow \textit{Number of ways of getting a head}$$
$$\longleftarrow \textit{Number of possible outcomes (head or tail)}$$

Similarly, the probability of drawing a spade out of a deck of 52 playing cards can be logically set as

$$P(\text{spade}) = \frac{13}{52} \quad \longleftarrow \textit{Number of chances of drawing a spade}$$
$$\longleftarrow \textit{Number of possible outcomes}$$
$$= \frac{1}{4} = 0.25 = 25\%$$

SUBJECTIVE PROBABILITY When logic and past history are not appropriate, probability values can be assessed *subjectively*. The accuracy of subjective probabilities depends on the experience and judgment of the person making the estimates. A number of probability values cannot be determined unless the subjective approach is used. What is the probability that the price of gasoline will be more than $4 in the next few years? What is the probability that our economy will be in a severe depression in 2015? What is the probability that you will be president of a major corporation within 20 years?

There are several methods for making subjective probability assessments. Opinion polls can be used to help in determining subjective probabilities for possible election returns and potential political candidates. In some cases, experience and judgment must be used in making subjective assessments of probability values. A production manager, for example, might believe that the probability of manufacturing a new product without a single defect is 0.85. In the Delphi method, a panel of experts is assembled to make their predictions of the future.

Where do probabilities come from? Sometimes they are subjective and based on personal experiences. Other times they are objectively based on logical observations such as the roll of a die. Often, probabilities are derived from historical data.

3 Mutually Exclusive and Collectively Exhaustive Events

Events are said to be **mutually exclusive** if only one of the events can occur on any one trial. They are called **collectively exhaustive** if the list of outcomes includes every possible outcome. Many common experiences involve events that have both of these properties. In tossing a coin, for example, the possible outcomes are a head or a tail. Since both of them cannot occur on any one toss, the outcomes head and tail are mutually exclusive. Since obtaining a head and obtaining a tail represent every possible outcome, they are also collectively exhaustive.

EXAMPLE 2: ROLLING A DIE Rolling a die is a simple experiment that has six possible outcomes, each listed in the following table with its corresponding probability:

OUTCOME OF ROLL	PROBABILITY
1	$\frac{1}{6}$
2	$\frac{1}{6}$
3	$\frac{1}{6}$
4	$\frac{1}{6}$
5	$\frac{1}{6}$
6	$\frac{1}{6}$
	Total 1

MODELING IN THE REAL WORLD

Liver Transplants in the United States

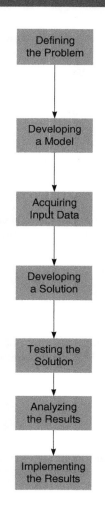

Defining the Problem

The scarcity of liver organs for transplants has reached critical levels in the United States; 1,131 individuals died in 1997 while waiting for a transplant. With only 4,000 liver donations per year, there are 10,000 patients on the waiting list, with 8,000 being added each year. There is a need to develop a model to evaluate policies for allocating livers to terminally ill patients who need them.

Developing a Model

Doctors, engineers, researchers, and scientists worked together with Pritsker Corp. consultants in the process of creating the liver allocation model, called ULAM. One of the model's jobs would be to evaluate whether to list potential recipients on a national basis or regionally.

Acquiring Input Data

Historical information was available from the United Network for Organ Sharing (UNOS), from 1990 to 1995. The data were then stored in ULAM. "Poisson" probability processes described the arrivals of donors at 63 organ procurement centers and arrival of patients at 106 liver transplant centers.

Developing a Solution

ULAM provides probabilities of accepting an offered liver, where the probability is a function of the patient's medical status, the transplant center, and the quality of the offered liver. ULAM also models the daily probability of a patient changing from one status of criticality to another.

Testing the Solution

Testing involved a comparison of the model output to actual results over the 1992–1994 time period. Model results were close enough to actual results that ULAM was declared valid.

Analyzing the Results

ULAM was used to compare more than 100 liver allocation policies and was then updated in 1998, with more recent data, for presentation to Congress.

Implementing the Results

Based on the projected results, the UNOS committee voted 18–0 to implement an allocation policy based on regional, not national, waiting lists. This decision is expected to save 2,414 lives over an 8-year period.

Source: Based on A. A. B. Pritsker. "Life and Death Decisions," *OR/MS Today* (August 1998): 22–28.

These events are both mutually exclusive (on any roll, only one of the six events can occur) and are also collectively exhaustive (one of them must occur and hence they total in probability to 1).

EXAMPLE 3: DRAWING A CARD You are asked to draw one card from a deck of 52 playing cards. Using a logical probability assessment, it is easy to set some of the relationships, such as

$$P(\text{drawing a 7}) = \frac{4}{52} = \frac{1}{13}$$
$$P(\text{drawing a heart}) = \frac{13}{52} = \frac{1}{4}$$

We also see that these events (drawing a 7 and drawing a heart) are *not* mutually exclusive since a 7 of hearts can be drawn. They are also *not* collectively exhaustive since there are other cards in the deck besides 7s and hearts.

You can test your understanding of these concepts by going through the following cases:

DRAWS	MUTUALLY EXCLUSIVE?	COLLECTIVELY EXHAUSTIVE?
1. Draw a spade and a club	Yes	No
2. Draw a face card and a number card	Yes	Yes
3. Draw an ace and a 3	Yes	No
4. Draw a club and a nonclub	Yes	Yes
5. Draw a 5 and a diamond	No	No
6. Draw a red card and a diamond	No	No

Adding Mutually Exclusive Events

Often we are interested in whether one event *or* a second event will occur. This is often called the *union* of two events. When these two events are mutually exclusive, the law of addition is simply as follows:

$$P(\text{event } A \text{ or event } B) = P(\text{event } A) + P(\text{event } B)$$

or, more briefly,

$$P(A \text{ or } B) = P(A) + P(B) \tag{2}$$

For example, we just saw that the events of drawing a spade or drawing a club out of a deck of cards are mutually exclusive. Since $P(\text{spade}) = {}^{13}\!/_{52}$ and $P(\text{club}) = {}^{13}\!/_{52}$, the probability of drawing either a spade or a club is

$$
\begin{aligned}
P(\text{spade or club}) &= P(\text{spade}) + P(\text{club}) \\
&= {}^{13}\!/_{52} + {}^{13}\!/_{52} \\
&= {}^{26}\!/_{52} = {}^{1}\!/_{2} = 0.50 = 50\%
\end{aligned}
$$

The *Venn diagram* in Figure 1 depicts the probability of the occurrence of mutually exclusive events.

Law of Addition for Events That Are Not Mutually Exclusive

When two events are not mutually exclusive, Equation 2 must be modified to account for double counting. The correct equation reduces the probability by subtracting the chance of both events occurring together:

$$P(\text{event } A \text{ or event } B) = P(\text{event } A) + P(\text{event } B)$$
$$-P(\text{event } A \text{ and event } B \text{ both occurring})$$

This can be expressed in shorter form as

$$P(A \text{ or } B) = P(A) + P(B) - P(A \text{ and } B) \tag{3}$$

Figure 2 illustrates this concept of subtracting the probability of outcomes that are common to both events. When events are mutually exclusive, the area of overlap, called the *intersection*, is 0, as shown in Figure 1.

FIGURE 1

Addition Law for Events that are Mutually Exclusive

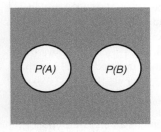

$P(A \text{ or } B) = P(A) + P(B)$

FIGURE 2

Addition Law for Events that are Not Mutually Exclusive

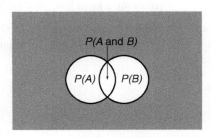

$P(A \text{ or } B) = P(A) + P(B) - P(A \text{ and } B)$

The formula for adding events that are not mutually exclusive is P(A *or* B) = P(A) + P(B) − P(A *and* B). *Do you understand why we subtract* P(A *and* B)?

Let us consider the events drawing a 5 and drawing a diamond out of the card deck. These events are not mutually exclusive, so Equation 3 must be applied to compute the probability of either a 5 or a diamond being drawn:

$$P(\text{five } or \text{ diamond}) = P(\text{five}) + P(\text{diamond}) - P(\text{five } and \text{ diamond})$$
$$= \frac{4}{52} + \frac{13}{52} - \frac{1}{52}$$
$$= \frac{16}{52} = \frac{4}{13}$$

4   Statistically Independent Events

Events may be either **independent** or **dependent**. When they are *independent*, the occurrence of one event has no effect on the probability of occurrence of the second event. Let us examine four sets of events and determine which are independent:

1. (a) Your education   ⎫ *Dependent events*
   (b) Your income level ⎬ Can you explain why?

2. (a) Draw a jack of hearts from a full 52-card deck ⎫
   (b) Draw a jack of clubs from a full 52-card deck   ⎬ *Independent events*

3. (a) Chicago Cubs win the National League pennant ⎫
   (b) Chicago Cubs win the World Series   ⎬ *Dependent events*

4. (a) Snow in Santiago, Chile ⎫ *Independent events*
   (b) Rain in Tel Aviv, Israel ⎬

The three types of probability under both statistical independence and statistical dependence are (1) marginal, (2) joint, and (3) conditional. When events are independent, these three are very easy to compute, as we shall see.

A marginal probability is the probability of an event occurring.

A *marginal* (or a *simple*) *probability* is just the probability of an event occurring. For example, if we toss a fair die, the marginal probability of a 2 landing face up is $P(\text{die is a }2) = \frac{1}{6} = 0.166$. Because each separate toss is an independent event (that is, what we get on the first toss has absolutely no effect on any later tosses), the marginal probability for each possible outcome is $\frac{1}{6}$.

A joint probability is the product of marginal probabilities.

The **joint probability** of two or more independent events occurring is the product of their marginal or simple probabilities. This may be written as

$$P(AB) = P(A) \times P(B) \tag{4}$$

where

$P(AB)$ = joint probability of events A and B occuring together, or one after the other
$P(A)$ = marginal probability of event A
$P(B)$ = marginal probability of event B

The probability, for example, of tossing a 6 on the first roll of a die and a 2 on the second roll is

$$P(6 \text{ on first and 2 on second roll})$$
$$= P(\text{tossing a 6}) \times P(\text{tossing a 2})$$
$$= \frac{1}{6} \times \frac{1}{6} = \frac{1}{36}$$
$$= 0.028$$

A conditional probability is the probability of an event occurring given that another event has taken place.

The third type, **conditional probability**, is expressed as $P(B|A)$, or "the probability of event B, given that event A has occurred." Similarly, $P(A|B)$ would mean "the conditional probability of event A, given that event B has taken place." Since events are independent the occurrence of one in no way affects the outcome of another, $P(A|B) = P(A)$ and $P(B|A) = P(B)$.

EXAMPLE 4: PROBABILITIES WHEN EVENTS ARE INDEPENDENT A bucket contains 3 black balls and 7 green balls. We draw a ball from the bucket, replace it, and draw a second ball. We can determine the probability of each of the following events occurring:

1. A black ball is drawn on the first draw:

$$P(B) = 0.30 \ \textit{(This is a marginal probability.)}$$

2. Two green balls are drawn:

$$P(GG) = P(G) \times P(G) = (0.7)(0.7) = 0.49$$

(This is a joint probability for two independent events.)

3. A black ball is drawn on the second draw if the first draw is green:

$$P(B|G) = P(B) = 0.30 \ \textit{(This is a conditional probability but equal to the marginal because the two draws are independent events.)}$$

4. A green ball is drawn on the second draw if the first draw was green:

$$P(G|G) = P(G) = 0.70 \ \textit{(This is a conditional probability, as in event 3.)}$$

5 Statistically Dependent Events

When events are statistically dependent, the occurrence of one event affects the probability of occurrence of some other event. Marginal, conditional, and joint probabilities exist under dependence as they did under independence, but the form of the latter two are changed.

A **marginal probability** is computed exactly as it was for independent events. Again, the marginal probability of the event A occurring is denoted $P(A)$.

Calculating a **conditional probability** under dependence is somewhat more involved than it is under independence. The formula for the conditional probability of A, given that event B has taken place, is stated as

$$P(A|B) = \frac{P(AB)}{P(B)} \tag{5}$$

From Equation 5, the formula for a joint probability is

$$P(AB) = P(A|B)P(B) \tag{6}$$

EXAMPLE 5: PROBABILITIES WHEN EVENTS ARE DEPENDENT Assume that we have an urn containing 10 balls of the following descriptions:

4 are white (W) and lettered (L).

2 are white (W) and numbered (N).

3 are yellow (Y) and lettered (L).

1 is yellow (Y) and numbered (N).

You randomly draw a ball from the urn and see that it is yellow. What, then, is the probability that the ball is lettered? (See Figure 3.)

Since there are 10 balls, it is a simple matter to tabulate a series of useful probabilities:

$$P(WL) = {}^4\!/_{10} = 0.4 \qquad P(YL) = {}^3\!/_{10} = 0.3$$

$$P(WN) = {}^2\!/_{10} = 0.2 \qquad P(YN) = {}^1\!/_{10} = 0.1$$

$$P(W) = {}^6\!/_{10} = 0.6, \ \text{or} \ P(W) = P(WL) + P(WN) = 0.4 + 0.2 = 0.6$$

$$P(L) = {}^7\!/_{10} = 0.7, \ \text{or} \ P(L) = P(WL) + P(YL) = 0.4 + 0.3 = 0.7$$

$$P(Y) = {}^4\!/_{10} = 0.4, \ \text{or} \ P(Y) = P(YL) + P(YN) = 0.3 + 0.1 = 0.4$$

$$P(N) = {}^3\!/_{10} = 0.3, \ \text{or} \ P(N) = P(WN) + P(YN) = 0.2 + 0.1 = 0.3$$

FIGURE 3

Dependent Events of Example 5

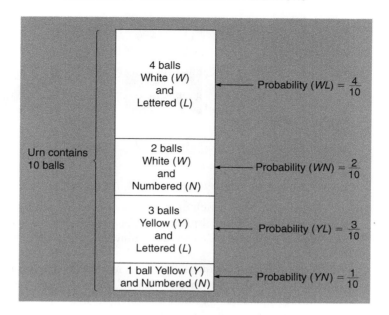

We can now calculate the conditional probability that the ball drawn is lettered, given that it is yellow:

$$P(L|Y) = \frac{P(YL)}{P(Y)} = \frac{0.3}{0.4} = 0.75$$

This equation shows that we divided the probability of *yellow* and *lettered* balls (3 out of 10) by the probability of yellow balls (4 out of 10). There is a 0.75 probability that the yellow ball that you drew is lettered.

We can use the joint probability formula to verify that $P(YL) = 0.3$, which was obtained by inspection in Example 5 by multiplying $P(L|Y)$ times $P(Y)$:

$$P(YL) = P(L|Y) \times P(Y) = (0.75)(0.4) = 0.3$$

EXAMPLE 6: JOINT PROBABILITIES WHEN EVENTS ARE DEPENDENT Your stockbroker informs you that if the stock market reaches the 12,500-point level by January, there is a 70% probability that Tubeless Electronics will go up in value. Your own feeling is that there is only a 40% chance of the market average reaching 12,500 points by January. Can you calculate the probability that *both* the stock market will reach 12,500 points *and* the price of Tubeless Electronics will go up?

Let M represent the event of the stock market reaching the 12,500 level, and let T be the event that Tubeless goes up in value. Then

$$P(MT) = P(T|M) \times P(M) = (0.70)(0.40) = 0.28$$

Thus, there is only a 28% chance that *both* events will occur.

6   Revising Probabilities with Bayes' Theorem

Bayes' theorem is used to incorporate additional information as it is made available and help create revised or *posterior probabilities*. This means that we can take new or recent data and then revise and improve upon our old probability estimates for an event (see Figure 4). Let us consider the following example.

EXAMPLE 7: POSTERIOR PROBABILITIES A cup contains two dice identical in appearance. One, however, is fair (unbiased) and the other is loaded (biased). The probability of rolling a 3 on the fair die is $\frac{1}{6}$, or 0.166. The probability of tossing the same number on the loaded die is 0.60.

FIGURE 4
Using Bayes' Process

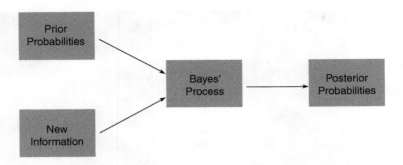

We have no idea which die is which, but select one by chance and toss it. The result is a 3. Given this additional piece of information, can we find the (revised) probability that the die rolled was fair? Can we determine the probability that it was the loaded die that was rolled?

The answer to these questions is yes, and we do so by using the formula for joint probability under statistical dependence and Bayes' theorem. First, we take stock of the information and probabilities available. We know, for example, that since we randomly selected the die to roll, the probability of it being fair or loaded is 0.50:

$$P(\text{fair}) = 0.50 \quad P(\text{loaded}) = 0.50$$

We also know that

$$P(3|\text{fair}) = 0.166 \quad P(3|\text{loaded}) = 0.60$$

Next, we compute joint probabilities $P(3 \text{ and fair})$ and $P(3 \text{ and loaded})$ using the formula $P(AB) = P(A|B) \times P(B)$:

$$P(3 \text{ and fair}) = P(3|\text{fair}) \times P(\text{fair})$$
$$= (0.166)(0.50) = 0.083$$

$$P(3 \text{ and loaded}) = P(3|\text{loaded}) \times P(\text{loaded})$$
$$= (0.60)(0.50) = 0.300$$

A 3 can occur in combination with the state "fair die" or in combination with the state "loaded die." The sum of their probabilities gives the unconditional or marginal probability of a 3 on the toss, namely, $P(3) = 0.083 + 0.300 = 0.383$.

If a 3 does occur, and if we do not know which die it came from, the probability that the die rolled was the fair one is

$$P(\text{fair}|3) = \frac{P(\text{fair and } 3)}{P(3)} = \frac{0.083}{0.383} = 0.22$$

The probability that the die rolled was loaded is

$$P(\text{loaded}|3) = \frac{P(\text{loaded and } 3)}{P(3)} = \frac{0.300}{0.383} = 0.78$$

These two conditional probabilities are called the **revised** or **posterior probabilities** for the next roll of the die.

Before the die was rolled in the preceding example, the best we could say was that there was a 50–50 chance that it was fair (0.50 probability) and a 50–50 chance that it was loaded. After one roll of the die, however, we are able to revise our **prior probability** estimates. The new posterior estimate is that there is a 0.78 probability that the die rolled was loaded and only a 0.22 probability that it was not.

Using a table is often helpful in performing the calculations associated with Bayes Theorem. Table 1 provides the general layout for this, and Table 2 provides this specific example.

TABLE 1

Tabular Form of Bayes Calculations Given that Event B has Occurred

STATE OF NATURE	P(B | STATE OF NATURE)	PRIOR PROBABILITY	JOINT PROBABILITY	POSTERIOR PROBABILITY
A	$P(B\|A)$	$\times P(A)$	$= P(B \text{ and } A)$	$P(B \text{ and } A)/P(B) = P(A\|B)$
A'	$P(B\|A')$	$\times P(A')$	$= P(B \text{ and } A')$	$P(B \text{ and } A')/P(B) = P(A'\|B)$
			$\overline{P(B)}$	

TABLE 2

Bayes Calculations Given that a 3 is Rolled in Example 7

STATE OF NATURE	P(3 | STATE OF NATURE)	PRIOR PROBABILITY	JOINT PROBABILITY	POSTERIOR PROBABILITY
Fair die	0.166	$\times 0.5$	$= 0.083$	$0.083/0.383 = 0.22$
Loaded die	0.600	$\times 0.5$	$= 0.300$	$0.300/0.383 = 0.78$
			$\overline{P(3) = 0.383}$	

General Form of Bayes' Theorem

Another way to compute revised probabilities is with Bayes' Theorem.

Revised probabilities can also be computed in a more direct way using a general form for **Bayes' theorem**:

$$P(A|B) = \frac{P(B|A)P(A)}{P(B|A)P(A) + P(B|A')P(A')} \tag{7}$$

where

$A' = $ the complement of the event A;
for example, if A is the event "fair die," then A' is "loaded die"

We originally saw in Equation 5 the conditional probability of event A, given event B, is

$$P(A|B) = \frac{P(AB)}{P(B)}$$

A Presbyterian minister, Thomas Bayes (1702–1761), did the work leading to this theorem.

Thomas Bayes derived his theorem from this. Appendix 1 shows the mathematical steps leading to Equation 7. Now let's return to Example 7.

Although it may not be obvious to you at first glance, we used this basic equation to compute the revised probabilities. For example, if we want the probability that the fair die was rolled given the first toss was a 3, namely, $P(\text{fair die} \mid 3 \text{ rolled})$, we can let

event "fair die" replace A in Equation 7

event "loaded die" replace A' in Equation 7

event "3 rolled" replace B in Equation 7

We can then rewrite Equation 7 and solve as follows:

$$P(\text{fair die}|3 \text{ rolled})$$
$$= \frac{P(3|\text{fair})P(\text{fair})}{P(3|\text{fair})P(\text{fair}) + P(3|\text{loaded})P(\text{loaded})}$$
$$= \frac{(0.166)(0.50)}{(0.166)(0.50) + (0.60)(0.50)}$$
$$= \frac{0.083}{0.383} = 0.22$$

This is the same answer that we computed in Example 7. Can you use this alternative approach to show that $P(\text{loaded die} \mid 3 \text{ rolled}) = 0.78$? Either method is perfectly acceptable, but we may find that Equation 7 or the tabular approach is easier to apply.

7 Further Probability Revisions

Although one revision of prior probabilities can provide useful posterior probability estimates, additional information can be gained from performing the experiment a second time. If it is financially worthwhile, a decision maker may even decide to make several more revisions.

EXAMPLE 8: A SECOND PROBABILITY REVISION Returning to Example 7, we now attempt to obtain further information about the posterior probabilities as to whether the die just rolled is fair or loaded. To do so, let us toss the die a second time. Again, we roll a 3. What are the further revised probabilities?

To answer this question, we proceed as before, with only one exception. The probabilities $P(\text{fair}) = 0.50$ and $P(\text{loaded}) = 0.50$ remain the same, but now we must compute $P(3,3 \mid \text{fair}) = (0.166)(0.166) = 0.027$ and $P(3,3 \mid \text{loaded}) = (0.6)(0.6) = 0.36$. With these joint probabilities of two 3s on successive rolls, given the two types of dice, we may revise the probabilities:

$$P(3, 3 \text{ and fair}) = P(3, 3 \mid \text{fair}) \times P(\text{fair})$$
$$= (0.027)(0.5) = 0.013$$

$$P(3, 3 \text{ and loaded}) = P(3, 3 \mid \text{loaded}) \times P(\text{loaded})$$
$$= (0.36)(0.5) = 0.18$$

Thus, the probability of rolling two 3s, a marginal probability, is $0.013 + 0.18 = 0.193$, the sum of the two joint probabilities:

$$P(\text{fair} \mid 3, 3) = \frac{P(3, 3 \text{ and fair})}{P(3, 3)}$$
$$= \frac{0.013}{0.193} = 0.067$$

$$P(\text{loaded} \mid 3, 3) = \frac{P(3, 3 \text{ and loaded})}{P(3, 3)}$$
$$= \frac{0.18}{0.193} = 0.933$$

 IN ACTION **Flight Safety and Probability Analysis**

With the horrific events of September 11, 2001, and the use of airplanes as weapons of mass destruction, airline safety has become an even more important international issue. How can we reduce the impact of terrorism on air safety? What can be done to make air travel safer overall? One answer is to evaluate various air safety programs and to use probability theory in the analysis of the costs of these programs.

Determining airline safety is a matter of applying the concepts of objective probability analysis. The chance of getting killed in a scheduled domestic flight is about 1 in 5 million. This is probability of about .0000002. Another measure is the number of deaths per passenger mile flown. The number is about 1 passenger per billion passenger miles flown, or a probability of about .000000001. Without question, flying is safer than many other forms of transportation, including driving. For a typical weekend, more people are killed in car accidents than a typical air disaster.

Analyzing new airline safety measures involves costs and the subjective probability that lives will be saved. One airline expert proposed a number of new airline safety measures. When the costs involved and probability of saving lives were taken into account, the result was about a $1 billion cost for every life saved on average. Using probability analysis will help determine which safety programs will result in the greatest benefit, and these programs can be expanded.

In addition, some proposed safety issues are not completely certain. For example, a Thermal Neutron Analysis device to detect explosives at airports had a probability of .15 of giving a false alarm, resulting in a high cost of inspection and long flight delays. This would indicate that money should be spent on developing more reliable equipment for detecting explosives. The result would be safer air travel with fewer unnecessary delays.

Without question, the use of probability analysis to determine and improve flight safety is indispensable. Many transportation experts hope that the same rigorous probability models used in the airline industry will some day be applied to the much more deadly system of highways and the drivers who use them.

Sources: Based on Robert Machol. "Flying Scared," *OR/MS Today* (October 1997): 32–37; and Arnold Barnett. "The Worst Day Ever," *OR/MS Today* (December 2001): 28–31.

What has this second roll accomplished? Before we rolled the die the first time, we knew only that there was a 0.50 probability that it was either fair or loaded. When the first die was rolled in Example 7, we were able to revise these probabilities:

$$\text{probability the die is fair} = 0.22$$
$$\text{probability the die is loaded} = 0.78$$

Now, after the second roll in Example 8, our refined revisions tell us that

$$\text{probability the die is fair} = 0.067$$
$$\text{probability the died is loaded} = 0.933$$

This type of information can be extremely valuable in business decision making.

8 Random Variables

We have just discussed various ways of assigning probability values to the outcomes of an experiment. Let us now use this probability information to compute the expected outcome, variance, and standard deviation of the experiment. This can help select the best decision among a number of alternatives.

A **random variable** assigns a real number to every possible outcome or event in an experiment. It is normally represented by a letter such as X or Y. When the outcome itself is numerical or quantitative, the outcome numbers can be the random variable. For example, consider refrigerator sales at an appliance store. The number of refrigerators sold during a given day can be the random variable. Using X to represent this random variable, we can express this relationship as follows:

$$X = \text{number of refrigerators sold during the day}$$

In general, whenever the experiment has quantifiable outcomes, it is beneficial to define these quantitative outcomes as the random variable. Examples are given in Table 3.

When the outcome itself is not numerical or quantitative, it is necessary to define a random variable that associates each outcome with a unique real number. Several examples are given in Table 4.

There are two types of random variables: *discrete random variables* and *continuous random variables*. Developing probability distributions and making computations based on these distributions depends on the type of random variable.

A random variable is a **discrete random variable** if it can assume only a finite or limited set of values. Which of the random variables in Table 3 are discrete random variables? Looking at Table 3, we can see that stocking 50 Christmas trees, inspecting 600 items, and sending out 5,000 letters are all examples of discrete random variables. Each of these random variables can assume only a finite or limited set of values. The number of Christmas trees sold, for example, can only be integer numbers from 0 to 50. There are 51 values that the random variable X can assume in this example.

Try to develop a few more examples of discrete random variables to be sure you understand this concept.

TABLE 3 Examples of Random Variables

EXPERIMENT	OUTCOME	RANDOM VARIABLES	RANGE OF RANDOM VARIABLES
Stock 50 Christmas trees	Number of Christmas trees sold	$X =$ number of Christmas trees sold	$0, 1, 2, \ldots, 50$
Inspect 600 items	Number of acceptable items	$Y =$ number of acceptable items	$0, 1, 2, \ldots, 600$
Send out 5,000 sales letters	Number of people responding to the letters	$Z =$ number of people responding to the letters	$0, 1, 2, \ldots, 5{,}000$
Build an apartment building	Percent of building completed after 4 months	$R =$ percent of building completed after 4 months	$0 \leq R \leq 100$
Test the lifetime of a lightbulb (minutes)	Length of time the bulb lasts up to 80,000 minutes	$S =$ time the bulb burns	$0 \leq S \leq 80{,}000$

TABLE 4

Random Variables for Outcomes that are Not Numbers

EXPERIMENT	OUTCOME		RANGE OF RANDOM VARIABLES	RANDOM VARIABLES
Students respond to a questionnaire	Strongly agree (SA) Agree (A) Neutral (N) Disagree (D) Strongly disagree (SD)	$X = \begin{cases} \\ \\ \\ \\ \end{cases}$	5 if SA 4 if A 3 if N 2 if D 1 if SD	1, 2, 3, 4, 5
One machine is inspected	Defective Not defective	$Y = \begin{cases} \\ \end{cases}$	0 if defective 1 if not defective	0, 1
Consumers respond to how they like a product	Good Average Poor	$Z = \begin{cases} \\ \\ \end{cases}$	3 if good 2 if average 1 if poor	1, 2, 3

A **continuous random variable** is a random variable that has an infinite or an unlimited set of values. Are there any examples of continuous random variables in Table 3 or 4? Looking at Table 3, we can see that testing the lifetime of a lightbulb is an experiment that can be described with a continuous random variable. In this case, the random variable, S, is the time the bulb burns. It can last for 3,206 minutes, 6,500.7 minutes, 251.726 minutes, or any other value between 0 and 80,000 minutes. In most cases, the range of a continuous random variable is stated as: lower value $\leq S \leq$ upper value, such as $0 \leq S \leq 80,000$. The random variable R in Table 3 is also continuous. Can you explain why?

9   Probability Distributions

Earlier we discussed the probability values of an event. We now explore the properties of **probability distributions**. We see how popular distributions, such as the normal, Poisson, binomial, and exponential probability distributions, can save us time and effort. Since a random variable may be *discrete* or *continuous*, we consider each of these types separately.

Probability Distribution of a Discrete Random Variable

When we have a *discrete random variable*, there is a probability value assigned to each event. These values must be between 0 and 1, and they must sum to 1. Let's look at an example.

The 100 students in Pat Shannon's statistics class have just completed a math quiz that he gives on the first day of class. The quiz consists of five very difficult algebra problems. The grade on the quiz is the number of correct answers, so the grades theoretically could range from 0 to 5. However, no one in this class received a score of 0, so the grades ranged from 1 to 5. The random variable X is defined to be the grade on this quiz, and the grades are summarized in Table 5. This discrete probability distribution was developed using the relative frequency approach presented earlier.

TABLE 5

Probability Distribution for Quiz Scores

RANDOM VARIABLE (X)-SCORE	NUMBER	PROBABILITY $P(X)$
5	10	0.1 = 10/100
4	20	0.2 = 20/100
3	30	0.3 = 30/100
2	30	0.3 = 30/100
1	10	0.1 = 10/100
	Total 100	1.0 = 100/100

The distribution follows the three rules required of all probability distributions: (1) the events are mutually exclusive and collectively exhaustive, (2) the individual probability values are between 0 and 1 inclusive, and (3) the total of the probability values sum to 1.

Although listing the probability distribution as we did in Table 5 is adequate, it can be difficult to get an idea about characteristics of the distribution. To overcome this problem, the probability values are often presented in graph form. The graph of the distribution in Table 5 is shown in Figure 5.

The graph of this probability distribution gives us a picture of its shape. It helps us identify the central tendency of the distribution, called the mean or **expected value**, and the amount of variability or spread of the distribution, called the **variance**.

Expected Value of a Discrete Probability Distribution

The expected value of a discrete distribution is a weighted average of the values of the random variable.

Once we have established a probability distribution, the first characteristic that is usually of interest is the *central tendency* of the distribution. The expected value, a measure of central tendency, is computed as the weighted average of the values of the random variable:

$$E(X) = \sum_{i=1}^{n} X_i P(X_i)$$

$$= X_1 P(X_1) + X_2 P(X_2) + \cdots + X_n P(X_n) \tag{8}$$

where

$$X_i = \text{random variable's possible values}$$
$$P(X_i) = \text{probability of each of the random variable's possible values}$$
$$\sum_{i=1}^{n} = \text{summation sign indicating we are adding all } n \text{ possible values}$$
$$E(X) = \text{expected value or mean of the random variable}$$

The expected value or mean of any discrete probability distribution can be computed by multiplying each possible value of the random variable, X_i, times the probability, $P(X_i)$, that outcome will occur and summing the results, $\sum$. Here is how the expected value can be computed for the quiz scores:

$$E(X) = \sum_{i=1}^{5} X_i P(X_i)$$

$$= X_1 P(X_1) + X_2 P(X_2) + X_3 P(X_3) + X_4 P(X_4) + X_5 P(X_5)$$
$$= (5)(0.1) + (4)(0.2) + (3)(0.3) + (2)(0.3) + (1)(0.1)$$
$$= 2.9$$

The expected value of 2.9 is the mean score on the quiz.

FIGURE 5

Probability Distribution for Dr. Shannon's Class

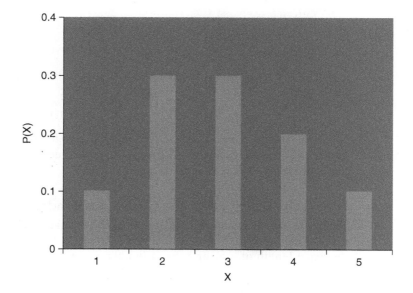

35

Variance of a Discrete Probability Distribution

In addition to the central tendency of a probability distribution, most people are interested in the variability or the spread of the distribution. If the variability is low, it is much more likely that the outcome of an experiment will be close to the average or expected value. On the other hand, if the variability of the distribution is high, which means that the probability is spread out over the various random variable values, there is less chance that the outcome of an experiment will be close to the expected value.

A probability distribution is often described by its mean and variance. Even if most of the men in class (or the United States) have heights between 5 feet 6 inches and 6 feet 2 inches, there is still some small probability of outliers.

The *variance* of a probability distribution is a number that reveals the overall spread or dispersion of the distribution. For a discrete probability distribution, it can be computed using the following equation:

$$\sigma^2 = \text{Variance} = \sum_{i=1}^{n} [X_i - E(X)]^2 P(X_i) \qquad (9)$$

where

$$X_i = \text{random variable's possible values}$$
$$E(X) = \text{expected value of the random variable}$$
$$[X_i - E(X)] = \text{difference between each value of the random variable and the expected value}$$
$$P(X_i) = \text{probability of each possible value of the random variable}$$

To compute the variance, each value of the random variable is subtracted from the expected value, squared, and multiplied times the probability of occurrence of that value. The results are then summed to obtain the variance. Here is how this procedure is done for Dr. Shannon's quiz scores:

$$\text{variance} = \sum_{i=1}^{5} [X_i - E(X)]^2 P(X_i)$$

$$\text{variance} = (5 - 2.9)^2(0.1) + (4 - 2.9)^2(0.2) + (3 - 2.9)^2(0.3) + (2 - 2.9)^2(0.3)$$
$$+ (1 - 2.9)^2(0.1)$$
$$= (2.1)^2(0.1) + (1.1)^2(0.2) + (0.1)^2(0.3) + (-0.9)^2(0.3) + (-1.9)^2(0.1)$$
$$= 0.441 + 0.242 + 0.003 + 0.243 + 0.361$$
$$= 1.29$$

A related measure of dispersion or spread is the **standard deviation**. This quantity is also used in many computations involved with probability distributions. The standard deviation is just the square root of the variance:

$$\sigma = \sqrt{\text{Variance}} = \sqrt{\sigma^2} \qquad (10)$$

where

$$\sqrt{} = \text{square root}$$
$$\sigma = \text{standard deviation}$$

The standard deviation for the random variable X in the example is

$$\sigma = \sqrt{\text{Variance}}$$
$$= \sqrt{1.29} = 1.14$$

These calculations are easily performed in Excel. Program 1A shows the inputs and formulas in Excel for calculating the mean, variance, and standard deviation in this example. Program 1B provides the output for this example.

Probability Distribution of a Continuous Random Variable

There are many examples of *continuous random variables*. The time it takes to finish a project, the number of ounces in a barrel of butter, the high temperature during a given day, the exact length of a given type of lumber, and the weight of a railroad car of coal are all

PROGRAM 1A

Formulas in an Excel Spreadsheet for the Dr. Shannon Example

	A	B	C	D
1	X	P(X)	XP(X)	$(X - E(X))^2 P(X)$
2	5	0.1	=A2*B2	=(A2-$C$7)^2*B2
3	4	0.2	=A3*B3	=(A3-$C$7)^2*B3
4	3	0.3	=A4*B4	=(A4-$C$7)^2*B4
5	2	0.3	=A5*B5	=(A5-$C$7)^2*B5
6	1	0.1	=A6*B6	=(A6-$C$7)^2*B6
7		E(X) = ΣXP(X) =	=SUM(C2:C6)	=SUM(D2:D6)
8				=SQRT(D7)

PROGRAM 1B

Excel Output for the Dr. Shannon Example

	A	B	C	D	E	F
1	X	P(X)	XP(X)	$(X - E(X))^2 P(X)$		
2	5	0.1	0.5	0.441		
3	4	0.2	0.8	0.242		
4	3	0.3	0.9	0.003		
5	2	0.3	0.6	0.243		
6	1	0.1	0.1	0.361		
7		E(X) = ΣXP(X) =	2.9	1.290	= Variance	
8				1.136	= Standard deviation	

examples of continuous random variables. Since random variables can take on an infinite number of values, the fundamental probability rules for continuous random variables must be modified.

As with discrete probability distributions, the sum of the probability values must equal 1. Because there are an infinite number of values of the random variables, however, the probability of each value of the random variable must be 0. If the probability values for the random variable values were greater than 0, the sum would be infinitely large.

A probability density function, $f(X)$, is a mathematical way of describing the probability distribution.

With a continuous probability distribution, there is a continuous mathematical function that describes the probability distribution. This function is called the **probability density function** or simply the **probability function**. It is usually represented by $f(X)$. When working with continuous probability distributions, the probability function can be graphed, and the area underneath the curve represents probability. Thus, to find any probability, we simply find the area under the curve associated with the range of interest.

We now look at the sketch of a sample density function in Figure 6. This curve represents the probability density function for the weight of a particular machined part. The weight could vary from 5.06 to 5.30 grams, with weights around 5.18 grams being the most likely. The shaded area represents the probability the weight is between 5.22 and 5.26 grams.

If we wanted to know the probability of a part weighing exactly 5.1300000 grams, for example, we would have to compute the area of a line of width 0. Of course, this would be 0. This result may seem strange, but if we insist on enough decimal places of accuracy, we are bound to find that the weight differs from 5.1300000 grams *exactly*, be the difference ever so slight.

FIGURE 6
Sample Density Function

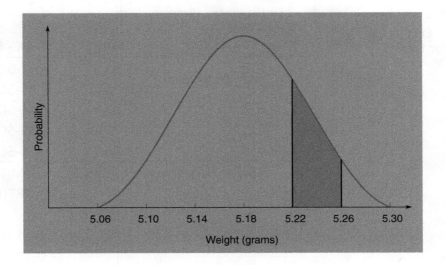

This is important because it means that, for any continuous distribution, the probability does not change if a single point is added to the range of values that is being considered. In Figure 6 this means the following probabilities are all exactly the same:

$$P(5.22 < X < 5.26) = P(5.22 < X \leq 5.26) = P(5.22 \leq X < 5.26)$$
$$= P(5.22 \leq X \leq 5.26)$$

The inclusion or exclusion of either endpoint (5.22 or 5.26) has no impact on the probability.

In this section we have investigated the fundamental characteristics and properties of probability distributions in general. In the next three sections we introduce three important continuous distributions—the normal distribution, the F distribution, and the exponential distribution—and two discrete distributions—the Poisson distribution and the binomial distribution.

10   The Binomial Distribution

Many business experiments can be characterized by the **Bernoulli process**. The probability of obtaining specific outcomes in a Bernoulli process is described by the binomial probability distribution. In order to be a Bernoulli process, an experiment must have the following characteristics:

1. Each trial in a Bernoulli process has only two possible outcomes. These are typically called a success and a failure, although examples might be yes or no, heads or tails, pass or fail, defective or good, and so on.
2. The probability stays the same from one trial to the next.
3. The trials are statistically independent.
4. The number of trials is a positive integer.

A common example of this process is tossing a coin.

The **binomial distribution** is used to find the probability of a specific number of successes out of n trials of a Bernoulli process. To find this probability, it is necessary to know the following:

$$n = \text{the number of trials}$$
$$p = \text{the probability of a success on any single trial}$$

We let

$$r = \text{the number of successes}$$
$$q = 1 - p = \text{the probability of a failure}$$

TABLE 6

Binomial Probability Distribution for $n = 5$ and $p = 0.50$

NUMBER OF HEADS (r)	PROBABILITY $= \dfrac{5!}{r!(5-r)!}(0.5)^r(0.5)^{5-r}$
0	$0.03125 = \dfrac{5!}{0!(5-0)!}(0.5)^0(0.5)^{5-0}$
1	$0.15625 = \dfrac{5!}{1!(5-1)!}(0.5)^1(0.5)^{5-1}$
2	$0.31250 = \dfrac{5!}{2!(5-2)!}(0.5)^2(0.5)^{5-2}$
3	$0.31250 = \dfrac{5!}{3!(5-3)!}(0.5)^3(0.5)^{5-3}$
4	$0.15625 = \dfrac{5!}{4!(5-4)!}(0.5)^4(0.5)^{5-4}$
5	$0.03125 = \dfrac{5!}{5!(5-5)!}(0.5)^5(0.5)^{5-5}$

The binomial formula is

$$\text{Probability of } r \text{ successes in } n \text{ trials} = \frac{n!}{r!(n-r)!}p^r q^{n-r} \tag{11}$$

The symbol ! means factorial, and $n! = n(n-1)(n-\,)\dots(1)$. For example,

$$4! = (4)(3)(2)(1) = 24$$

Also, $1! = 1$, and $0! = 1$ by definition.

Solving Problems with the Binomial Formula

A common example of a binomial distribution is the tossing of a coin and counting the number of heads. For example, if we wished to find the probability of 4 heads in 5 tosses of a coin, we would have

$$n = 5, r = 4, p = 0.5, \quad \text{and} \quad q = 1 - 0.5 = 0.5$$

Thus,

$$P(4 \text{ successes in 5 trials}) = \frac{5!}{4!(5-4)!}0.5^4 0.5^{5-4}$$

$$= \frac{5(4)(3)(2)(1)}{4(3)(2)(1)(1!)}(0.0625)(0.5) = 0.15625$$

Thus, the probability of 4 heads in 5 tosses of a coin is 0.15625 or about 16%.

Using Equation 11, it is also possible to find the entire probability distribution (all the possible values for r and the corresponding probabilities) for a binomial experiment. The probability distribution for the number of heads in 5 tosses of a fair coin is shown in Table 6 and then graphed in Figure 7.

FIGURE 7

Binomial Probability Distribution for $n = 5$ and $p = 0.50$

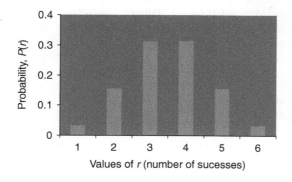

Solving Problems with Binomial Tables

MSA Electronics is experimenting with the manufacture of a new type of transistor that is very difficult to mass produce at an acceptable quality level. Every hour a supervisor takes a random sample of 5 transistors produced on the assembly line. The probability that any one transistor is defective is considered to be 0.15. MSA wants to know the probability of finding 3, 4, or 5 defectives if the true percentage defective is 15%.

For this problem, $n = 5$, $p = 0.15$, and $r = 3, 4,$ or 5. Although we could use the formula for each of these values, it is easier to use binomial tables for this. To find these probabilities, we look through the $n = 5$ section and find the $p = 0.15$ column. In the row where $r = 3$, we see 0.0244. Thus, $P(r = 3) = 0.0244$. Similarly, $P(r = 4) = 0.0022$, and $P(r = 5) = 0.0001$. By adding these three probabilities we have the probability that the number of defects is 3 or more:

$$P(3 \text{ or more defects}) = P(3) + P(4) + P(5)$$
$$= 0.0244 + 0.0022 + 0.0001 = 0.0267$$

The expected value (or mean) and the variance of a binomial random variable may be easily found. These are

$$\text{Expected value (mean)} = np \tag{12}$$

$$\text{Variance} = np(1 - p) \tag{13}$$

TABLE 7   A Sample Table for the Binomial Distribution

		P									
n	r	0.05	0.10	0.15	0.20	0.25	0.30	0.35	0.40	0.45	0.50
1	0	0.9500	0.9000	0.8500	0.8000	0.7500	0.7000	0.6500	0.6000	0.5500	0.5000
	1	0.0500	0.1000	0.1500	0.2000	0.2500	0.3000	0.3500	0.4000	0.4500	0.5000
2	0	0.9025	0.8100	0.7225	0.6400	0.5625	0.4900	0.4225	0.3600	0.3025	0.2500
	1	0.0950	0.1800	0.2500	0.3200	0.3750	0.4200	0.4550	0.4800	0.4950	0.5000
	2	0.0025	0.0100	0.0225	0.0400	0.0625	0.0900	0.1225	0.1600	0.2025	0.2500
3	0	0.8574	0.7290	0.6141	0.5120	0.4219	0.3430	0.2746	0.2160	0.1664	0.1250
	1	0.1354	0.2430	0.3251	0.3840	0.4219	0.4410	0.4436	0.4320	0.4084	0.3750
	2	0.0071	0.0270	0.0574	0.0960	0.1406	0.1890	0.2389	0.2880	0.3341	0.3750
	3	0.0001	0.0010	0.0034	0.0080	0.0156	0.0270	0.0429	0.0640	0.0911	0.1250
4	0	0.8145	0.6561	0.5220	0.4096	0.3164	0.2401	0.1785	0.1296	0.0915	0.0625
	1	0.1715	0.2916	0.3685	0.4096	0.4219	0.4116	0.3845	0.3456	0.2995	0.2500
	2	0.0135	0.0486	0.0975	0.1536	0.2109	0.2646	0.3105	0.3456	0.3675	0.3750
	3	0.0005	0.0036	0.0115	0.0256	0.0469	0.0756	0.1115	0.1536	0.2005	0.2500
	4	0.0000	0.0001	0.0005	0.0016	0.0039	0.0081	0.0150	0.0256	0.0410	0.0625
5	0	0.7738	0.5905	0.4437	0.3277	0.2373	0.1681	0.1160	0.0778	0.0503	0.0313
	1	0.2036	0.3281	0.3915	0.4096	0.3955	0.3602	0.3124	0.2592	0.2059	0.1563
	2	0.0214	0.0729	0.1382	0.2048	0.2637	0.3087	0.3364	0.3456	0.3369	0.3125
	3	0.0011	0.0081	0.0244	0.0512	0.0879	0.1323	0.1811	0.2304	0.2757	0.3125
	4	0.0000	0.0005	0.0022	0.0064	0.0146	0.0284	0.0488	0.0768	0.1128	0.1563
	5	0.0000	0.0000	0.0001	0.0003	0.0010	0.0024	0.0053	0.0102	0.0185	0.0313
6	0	0.7351	0.5314	0.3771	0.2621	0.1780	0.1176	0.0754	0.0467	0.0277	0.0156
	1	0.2321	0.3543	0.3993	0.3932	0.3560	0.3025	0.2437	0.1866	0.1359	0.0938
	2	0.0305	0.0984	0.1762	0.2458	0.2966	0.3241	0.3280	0.3110	0.2780	0.2344
	3	0.0021	0.0146	0.0415	0.0819	0.1318	0.1852	0.2355	0.2765	0.3032	0.3125
	4	0.0001	0.0012	0.0055	0.0154	0.0330	0.0595	0.0951	0.1382	0.1861	0.2344
	5	0.0000	0.0001	0.0004	0.0015	0.0044	0.0102	0.0205	0.0369	0.0609	0.0938
	6	0.0000	0.0000	0.0000	0.0001	0.0002	0.0007	0.0018	0.0041	0.0083	0.0156

The expected value and variance for the MSA Electronics example are computed as follows:

$$\text{Expected value} = np = 5(0.15) = 0.75$$
$$\text{Variance} = np(1 - p) = 5(0.15)(0.85) = 0.6375$$

Programs 2A and 2B illustrate how Excel is used for binomial probabilities.

PROGRAM 2A

Function in an Excel 2010 Spreadsheet for Binomial Probabilities

	A		
1	**The Binomial D**		
2	X = random variable fc		
3	n= 5		number of t
4	p= 0.5		probability of a succes
5	r= 4		specific number of successes
6			
7	Cumulative probabilit P(X ≤ r) =	=BINOM.DIST(B5,B3,B4,TRUE)
8	Probability of exactly P(X = r) =	=BINOM.DIST(B5,B3,B4,FALSE)

Using the cell references eliminates the need to retype the formula if you change a parameter such as p or r.

The function BINOM.DIST (r,n,p,TRUE) returns the cumulative probability.

PROGRAM 2B

Excel Output for the Binomial Example

	A	B	C
1	**The Binomial Distribution**		
2	X = random variable for number of successes		
3	n=	5	number of trials
4	p=	0.5	probability of a succes
5	r=	4	specific number of successes
6			
7	Cumulative probability	P(X ≤ r) =	0.96875
8	Probability of exactly r successes	P(X = r) =	0.15625

11 The Normal Distribution

The normal distribution affects a large number of processes in our lives (for example, filling boxes of cereal with 32 ounces of corn flakes). Each normal distribution depends on the mean and standard deviation.

One of the most popular and useful continuous probability distributions is the **normal distribution**. The probability density function of this distribution is given by the rather complex formula

$$f(X) = \frac{1}{\sigma\sqrt{2\pi}} e^{\frac{-(x-\mu)^2}{2\sigma^2}} \tag{14}$$

The normal distribution is specified completely when values for the mean, μ, and the standard deviation, σ, are known. Figure 8 shows several different normal distributions with the same standard deviation and different means. As shown, differing values of μ will shift the average or center of the normal distribution. The overall shape of the distribution remains the same. On the other hand, when the standard deviation is varied, the normal curve either flattens out or becomes steeper. This is shown in Figure 9.

As the standard deviation, σ, becomes smaller, the normal distribution becomes steeper. When the standard deviation becomes larger, the normal distribution has a tendency to flatten out or become broader.

FIGURE 8
Normal Distribution with Different Values for μ

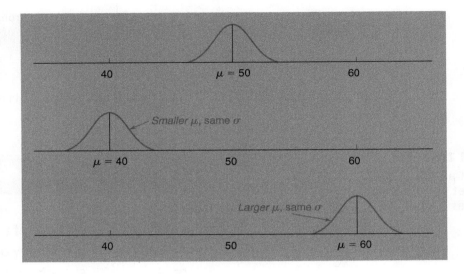

IN ACTION   **Probability Assessments of Curling Champions**

Probabilities are used every day in sporting activities. In many sporting events, there are questions involving strategies that must be answered to provide the best chance of winning the game. In baseball, should a particular batter be intentionally walked in key situations at the end of the game? In football, should a team elect to try for a two-point conversion after a touchdown? In soccer, should a penalty kick ever be aimed directly at the goal keeper? In curling, in the last round, or "end" of a game, is it better to be behind by one point and have the hammer or is it better to be ahead by one point and not have the hammer? An attempt was made to answer this last question.

In curling, a granite stone, or "rock," is slid across a sheet of ice 14 feet wide and 146 feet long. Four players on each of two teams take alternating turns sliding the rock, trying to get it as close as possible to the center of a circle called the "house." The team with the rock closest to this scores points. The team that is behind at the completion of a round or end has the advantage in

the next end by being the last team to slide the rock. This team is said to "have the hammer." A survey was taken of a group of experts in curling, including a number of former world champions. In this survey, about 58% of the respondents favored having the hammer and being down by one going into the last end. Only about 42% preferred being ahead and not having the hammer.

Data were also collected from 1985 to 1997 at the Canadian Men's Curling Championships (also called the Brier). Based on the results over this time period, it is better to be ahead by one point and not have the hammer at the end of the ninth end rather than be behind by one and have the hammer, as many people prefer. This differed from the survey results. Apparently, world champions and other experts preferred to have more control of their destiny by having the hammer even though it put them in a worse situation.

Source: Based on Keith A. Willoughby and Kent J. Kostuk. "Preferred Scenarios in the Sport of Curling," *Interfaces* 34, 2 (March–April 2004): 117–122.

Area Under the Normal Curve

Because the normal distribution is symmetrical, its midpoint (and highest point) is at the mean. Values on the X axis are then measured in terms of how many standard deviations they lie from the mean. As you may recall from our earlier discussion of probability distributions, the area under the curve (in a continuous distribution) describes the probability that a random variable has a value in a specified interval. When dealing with the uniform distribution, it is easy to compute the area between any points a and b. The normal distribution requires mathematical calculations beyond the scope of this chapter, but tables that provide areas or probabilities are readily available.

Using the Standard Normal Table

When finding probabilities for the normal distribution, it is best to draw the normal curve and shade the area corresponding to the probability being sought. The normal distribution table can then be used to find probabilities by following two steps.

Step 1. Convert the normal distribution to what we call a *standard normal distribution*. A standard normal distribution has a mean of 0 and a standard deviation of 1. All normal tables

←–Less Than
>–Greater Than

FIGURE 9

Normal Distribution with Different Values for σ

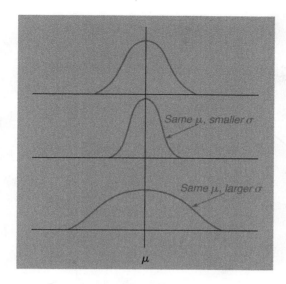

Same μ, smaller σ

Same μ, larger σ

μ

are set up to handle random variables with $\mu = 0$ and $\sigma = 1$. Without a standard normal distribution, a different table would be needed for each pair of μ and σ values. We call the new standard random variable Z. The value for Z for any normal distribution is computed from this equation:

$$Z = \frac{X - \mu}{\sigma} \qquad (15)$$

where

X = value of the random variable we want to measure

μ = mean of the distribution

σ = standard deviation of the distribution

Z = number of standard deviations from X to the mean, μ

For example, if $\mu = 100, \sigma = 15$, and we are interested in finding the probability that the random variable X is less than 130, we want $P(X < 130)$:

$$Z = \frac{X - \mu}{\sigma} = \frac{130 - 100}{15}$$

$$= \frac{30}{15} = 2 \text{ standard deviations}$$

This means that the point X is 2.0 standard deviations to the right of the mean. This is shown in Figure 10.

Step 2. Look up the probability from a table of normal curve areas. Table 8, which also appears as Appendix A, is such a table of areas for the standard normal distribution. It is set up to provide the area under the curve to the left of any specified value of Z.

Let's see how Table 8 can be used. The column on the left lists values of Z, with the second decimal place of Z appearing in the top row. For example, for a value of $Z = 2.00$ as just computed, find 2.0 in the left-hand column and 0.00 in the top row. In the body of the table, we find that the area sought is 0.97725, or 97.7%. Thus,

$$P(X < 130) = P(Z < 2.00) = 97.7\%$$

This suggests that if the mean IQ score is 100, with a standard deviation of 15 points, the probability that a randomly selected person's IQ is less than 130 is 97.7%. This is also the probability that the IQ is less than or equal to 130. To find the probability that the IQ is greater than 130, we simply note that this is the complement of the previous event and the total area under the curve (the total probability) is 1. Thus,

$$P(X > 130) = 1 - P(X \le 130) = 1 - P(Z \le 2) = 1 - 0.97725 = 0.02275$$

FIGURE 10

Normal Distribution Showing the Relationship Between Z Values and X Values

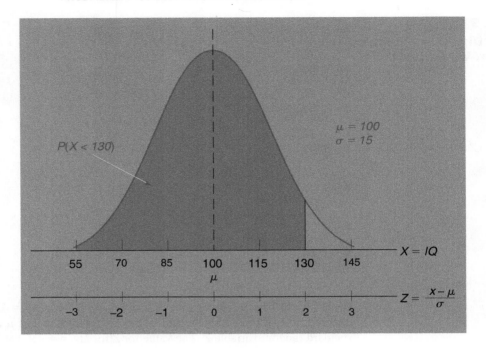

To be sure you understand the concept of symmetry in Table 8, try to find the probability such as **P(X < 85)**. *Note that the standard normal table shows only positive Z values.*

While Table 8 does not give negative Z values, the symmetry of the normal distribution can be used to find probabilities associated with negative Z values. For example, $P(Z < -2) = P(Z > 2)$.

To feel comfortable with the use of the standard normal probability table, we need to work a few more examples. We now use the Haynes Construction Company as a case in point.

Haynes Construction Company Example

Haynes Construction Company builds primarily three- and four-unit apartment buildings (called triplexes and quadraplexes) for investors, and it is believed that the total construction time in days follows a normal distribution. The mean time to construct a triplex is 100 days, and the standard deviation is 20 days. Recently, the president of Haynes Construction signed a contract to complete a triplex in 125 days. Failure to complete the triplex in 125 days would result in severe penalty fees. What is the probability that Haynes Construction will not be in violation of their construction contract? The normal distribution for the construction of triplexes is shown in Figure 11.

To compute this probability, we need to find the shaded area under the curve. We begin by computing Z for this problem:

$$Z = \frac{X - \mu}{\sigma}$$

$$= \frac{125 - 100}{20}$$

$$= \frac{25}{20} = 1.25$$

Looking in Table 8 for a Z value of 1.25, we find an area under the curve of 0.89435. (We do this by looking up 1.2 in the left-hand column of the table and then moving to the 0.05 column to find the value for $Z = 1.25$.) Therefore, the probability of not violating the contract is 0.89435, or about an 89% chance.

Now let us look at the Haynes problem from another perspective. If the firm finishes this triplex in 75 days or less, it will be awarded a bonus payment of $5,000. What is the probability that Haynes will receive the bonus?

TABLE 8   Standardized Normal Distribution Function

Z	0.00	0.01	0.02	0.03	0.04	0.05	0.06	0.07	0.08	0.09
				AREA UNDER THE NORMAL CURVE						
0.0	.50000	.50399	.50798	.51197	.51595	.51994	.52392	.52790	.53188	.53586
0.1	.53983	.54380	.54776	.55172	.55567	.55962	.56356	.56749	.57142	.57535
0.2	.57926	.58317	.58706	.59095	.59483	.59871	.60257	.60642	.61026	.61409
0.3	.61791	.62172	.62552	.62930	.63307	.63683	.64058	.64431	.64803	.65173
0.4	.65542	.65910	.66276	.66640	.67003	.67364	.67724	.68082	.68439	.68793
0.5	.69146	.69497	.69847	.70194	.70540	.70884	.71226	.71566	.71904	.72240
0.6	.72575	.72907	.73237	.73536	.73891	.74215	.74537	.74857	.75175	.75490
0.7	.75804	.76115	.76424	.76730	.77035	.77337	.77637	.77935	.78230	.78524
0.8	.78814	.79103	.79389	.79673	.79955	.80234	.80511	.80785	.81057	.81327
0.9	.81594	.81859	.82121	.82381	.82639	.82894	.83147	.83398	.83646	.83891
1.0	.84134	.84375	.84614	.84849	.85083	.85314	.85543	.85769	.85993	.86214
1.1	.86433	.86650	.86864	.87076	.87286	.87493	.87698	.87900	.88100	.88298
1.2	.88493	.88686	.88877	.89065	.89251	.89435	.89617	.89796	.89973	.90147
1.3	.90320	.90490	.90658	.90824	.90988	.91149	.91309	.91466	.91621	.91774
1.4	.91924	.92073	.92220	.92364	.92507	.92647	.92785	.92922	.93056	.93189
1.5	.93319	.93448	.93574	.93699	.93822	.93943	.94062	.94179	.94295	.94408
1.6	.94520	.94630	.94738	.94845	.94950	.95053	.95154	.95254	.95352	.95449
1.7	.95543	.95637	.95728	.95818	.95907	.95994	.96080	.96164	.96246	.96327
1.8	.96407	.96485	.96562	.96638	.96712	.96784	.96856	.96926	.96995	.97062
1.9	.97128	.97193	.97257	.97320	.97381	.97441	.97500	.97558	.97615	.97670
2.0	.97725	.97784	.97831	.97882	.97932	.97982	.98030	.98077	.98124	.98169
2.1	.98214	.98257	.98300	.98341	.98382	.98422	.98461	.98500	.98537	.98574
2.2	.98610	.98645	.98679	.98713	.98745	.98778	.98809	.98840	.98870	.98899
2.3	.98928	.98956	.98983	.99010	.99036	.99061	.99086	.99111	.99134	.99158
2.4	.99180	.99202	.99224	.99245	.99266	.99286	.99305	.99324	.99343	.99361
2.5	.99379	.99396	.99413	.99430	.99446	.99461	.99477	.99492	.99506	.99520
2.6	.99534	.99547	.99560	.99573	.99585	.99598	.99609	.99621	.99632	.99643
2.7	.99653	.99664	.99674	.99683	.99693	.99702	.99711	.99720	.99728	.99736
2.8	.99744	.99752	.99760	.99767	.99774	.99781	.99788	.99795	.99801	.99807
2.9	.99813	.99819	.99825	.99831	.99836	.99841	.99846	.99851	.99856	.99861
3.0	.99865	.99869	.99874	.99878	.99882	.99886	.99889	.99893	.99896	.99900
3.1	.99903	.99906	.99910	.99913	.99916	.99918	.99921	.99924	.99926	.99929
3.2	.99931	.99934	.99936	.99938	.99940	.99942	.99944	.99946	.99948	.99950
3.3	.99952	.99953	.99955	.99957	.99958	.99960	.99961	.99962	.99964	.99965
3.4	.99966	.99968	.99969	.99970	.99971	.99972	.99973	.99974	.99975	.99976
3.5	.99977	.99978	.99978	.99979	.99980	.99981	.99981	.99982	.99983	.99983
3.6	.99984	.99985	.99985	.99986	.99986	.99987	.99987	.99988	.99988	.99989
3.7	.99989	.99990	.99990	.99990	.99991	.99991	.99992	.99992	.99992	.99992
3.8	.99993	.99993	.99993	.99994	.99994	.99994	.99994	.99995	.99995	.99995
3.9	.99995	.99995	.99996	.99996	.99996	.99996	.99996	.99996	.99997	.99997

Source: Richard I. Levin and Charles A. Kirkpatrick. *Quantitative Approaches to Management*, 4th ed. Copyright © 1978, 1975, 1971, 1965 by McGraw-Hill, Inc. Used with permission of the McGraw-Hill Book Company.

FIGURE 11
Normal Distribution for Haynes Construction

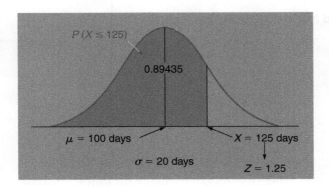

Figure 12 illustrates the probability we are looking for in the shaded area. The first step is again to compute the Z value:

$$Z = \frac{X - \mu}{\sigma}$$
$$= \frac{75 - 100}{20}$$
$$= \frac{-25}{20} = -1.25$$

This Z value indicates that 75 days is −1.25 standard deviations to the left of the mean. But the standard normal table is structured to handle only positive Z values. To solve this problem, we observe that the curve is symmetric. The probability that Haynes will finish in *75 days or less is equivalent* to the probability that it will finish in *more than 125 days*. A moment ago (in Figure 11) we found the probability that Haynes will finish in less than 125 days. That value is 0.89435. So the probability it takes more than 125 days is

$$P(X > 125) = 1.0 - P(X \leq 125)$$
$$= 1.0 - 0.89435 = 0.10565$$

Thus, the probability of completing the triplex in 75 days or less is 0.10565, or about 11%.

One final example: What is the probability that the triplex will take between 110 and 125 days? We see in Figure 13 that

$$P(110 < X < 125) = P(X \leq 125) - P(X < 110)$$

That is, the shaded area in the graph can be computed by finding the probability of completing the building in 125 days or less *minus* the probability of completing it in 110 days or less.

FIGURE 12
Probability that Haynes will Receive the Bonus by Finishing in 75 Days or Less

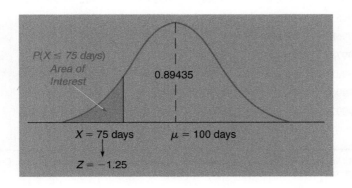

FIGURE 13

Probability that Haynes will Complete in 110 to 125 Days

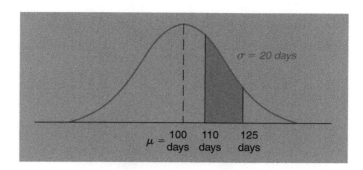

Recall that $P(X \leq 125 \text{ days})$ is equal to 0.89435. To find $P(X < 110 \text{ days})$, we follow the two steps developed earlier:

1.
$$Z = \frac{X - \mu}{\sigma} = \frac{110 - 100}{20} = \frac{10}{20}$$
$$= 0.5 \text{ standard deviations}$$

2. From Table 8, the area for $Z = 0.50$ is 0.69146. So the probability the triplex can be completed in less than 110 days is 0.69146. Finally,

$$P(110 \leq X \leq 125) = 0.89435 - 0.69146 = 0.20289$$

The probability that it will take between 110 and 125 days is about 20%.

PROGRAM 3A

Function in an Excel 2010 Spreadsheet for the Normal Distribution Example

	A	B
1	**Normal distribution - X is a**	
2	with mean, μ, and standar(	
3	μ =	100
4	σ =	20
5	x =	75
6	P(X ≤ x) =	=NORM.DIST(B5,B3,B4,TRUE)
7	P(X > x) =	=1-B6

PROGRAM 3B

Excel Output for the Normal Distribution Example

	A	B	C	D
1	**Normal distribution - X is a normal random variable**			
2	with mean, μ, and standard deviation, σ.			
3	μ =	100		
4	σ =	20		
5	x =	75		
6	P(X ≤ x) =	0.10565		
7	P(X > x) =	0.89435		

47

FIGURE 14

Approximate Probabilities from the Empirical Rule

Figure 14 is very important, and you should comprehend the meanings of ±1, 2, and 3 standard deviation symmetrical areas.

Managers often speak of 95% and 99% confidence intervals, which roughly refer to ±2 and 3 standard deviation graphs.

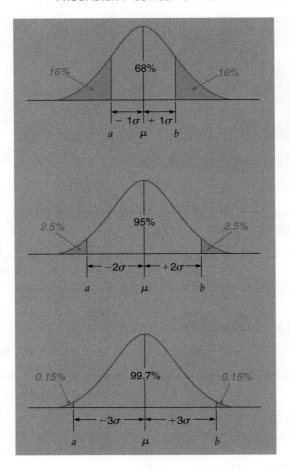

The Empirical Rule

While the probability tables for the normal distribution can provide precise probabilities, many situations require less precision. The empirical rule was derived from the normal distribution and is an easy way to remember some basic information about normal distributions. The empirical rule states that for a normal distribution

approximately 68% of the values will be within 1 standard deviation of the mean

approximately 95% of the values will be within 2 standard deviations of the mean

almost all (about 99.7%) of the values will be within 3 standard deviations of the mean

Figure 14 illustrates the empirical rule. The area from point *a* to point *b* in the first drawing represents the probability, approximately 68%, that the random variable will be within 1 standard deviation of the mean. The middle drawing illustrates the probability, approximately 95%, that the random variable will be within 2 standard deviations of the mean. The last drawing illustrates the probability, about 99.7% (almost all), that the random variable will be within 3 standard deviations of the mean.

12 The *F* Distribution

The **F distribution** is a continuous probability distribution that is helpful in testing hypotheses about variances. The *F* distribution will be used when regression models are tested for significance. Figure 15 provides a graph of the *F* distribution. As with a graph for any continuous distribution, the area underneath the curve represents probability. Note that for a large value of *F*, the probability is very small.

FIGURE 15
The *F* Distribution

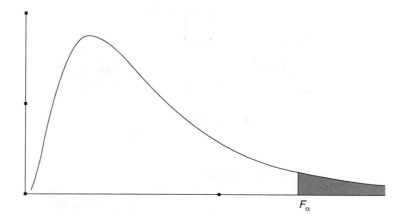

The *F* statistic is the ratio of two sample variances from independent normal distributions. Every *F* distribution has two sets of degrees of freedom associated with it. One of the degrees of freedom is associated with the numerator of the ratio, and the other is associated with the denominator of the ratio. The degrees of freedom are based on the sample sizes used in calculating the numerator and denominator.

Appendix *F* Distribution Values provides values of *F* associated with the upper tail of the distribution for certain probabilities (denoted by α) and degrees of freedom for the numerator (df_1) and degrees of freedom for the denominator (df_2).

To find the *F* value that is associated with a particular probability and degrees of freedom, refer to the same appendix. The following notation will be used:

$$df_1 = \text{degrees of freedom for the numerator}$$

$$df_2 = \text{degrees of freedom for the denominator}$$

Consider the following example:

$$df_1 = 5$$
$$df_2 = 6$$
$$\alpha = 0.05$$

From the appendix we get

$$F_{\alpha, df1, df2} = F_{0.05, 5, 6} = 4.39$$

This means

$$P(F > 4.39) = 0.05$$

The probability is very low (only 5%) that the *F* value will exceed 4.39. There is a 95% probability that it will not exceed 4.39. This is illustrated in Figure 16. The appendix also provides *F* values associated with $\alpha = 0.01$. Programs 4A and 4B illustrate Excel functions for the *F* distribution.

FIGURE 16

***F* Value for 0.05 Probability with 5 and 6 Degrees of Freedom**

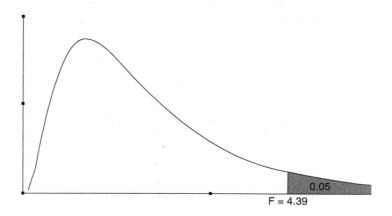

PROGRAM 4A

Functions in an Excel 2010 Spreadsheet for the *F* Distribution

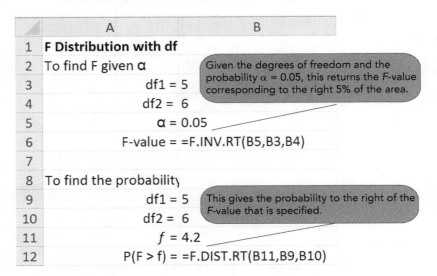

	A	B
1	**F Distribution with df**	
2	To find F given α	
3	df1 = 5	
4	df2 = 6	
5	α = 0.05	
6	F-value = =F.INV.RT(B5,B3,B4)	
7		
8	To find the probability	
9	df1 = 5	
10	df2 = 6	
11	f = 4.2	
12	P(F > f) = =F.DIST.RT(B11,B9,B10)	

Given the degrees of freedom and the probability α = 0.05, this returns the *F*-value corresponding to the right 5% of the area.

This gives the probability to the right of the *F*-value that is specified.

PROGRAM 4B

Excel Output for the *F* Distribution

	A	B	C	D	E
1	**F Distribution with df1 and df2 degrees of freedom**				
2	To find F given α				
3	df1 =	5			
4	df2 =	6			
5	α =	0.05			
6	F-value =	4.39			
7					
8	To find the probability to the right of a calculated value, *f*				
9	df1 =	5			
10	df2 =	6			
11	*f* =	4.2			
12	P(F > f) =	0.0548			

13 The Exponential Distribution

The *exponential distribution*, also called the **negative exponential distribution**, is used in dealing with queuing problems. The exponential distribution often describes the time required to service a customer. The exponential distribution is a continuous distribution. Its probability function is given by

$$f(X) = \mu e^{-\mu x} \tag{16}$$

where

X = random variable (service times)

μ = average number of units the service facility can handle in a specific period of time

e = 2.718 (the base of the natural logarithm)

FIGURE 17
Exponential Distribution

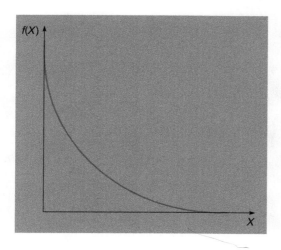

The general shape of the exponential distribution is shown in Figure 17. Its expected value and variance can be shown to be

$$\text{Expected value} = \frac{1}{\mu} = \text{Average service time} \tag{17}$$

$$\text{Variance} = \frac{1}{\mu^2} \tag{18}$$

As with any other continuous distribution, probabilities are found by determining the area under the curve. For the normal distribution, we found the area by using a table of probabilities. For the exponential distribution, the probabilities can be found using the exponent key on a calculator with the formula below. The probability that an exponentially distributed time (X) required to serve a customer is less than or equal to time t is given by the formula

$$P(X \leq t) = 1 - e^{-\mu t} \tag{19}$$

The time period used in describing μ determines the units for the time t. For example, if μ is the average number served per hour, the time t must be given in hours. If μ is the average number served per minute, the time t must be given in minutes.

Arnold's Muffler Example

Arnold's Muffler Shop installs new mufflers on automobiles and small trucks. The mechanic can install new mufflers at a rate of about three per hour, and this service time is exponentially distributed. What is the probability that the time to install a new muffler would be $1/2$ hour or less? Using Equation 19 we have

X = exponentially distributed service time

μ = average number that can be served per time period = 3 per hour

t = $1/2$ hour = 0.5 hour

$$P(X \leq 0.5) = 1 - e^{-3(0.5)} = 1 - e^{-1.5} = 1 - 0.2231 = 0.7769$$

Figure 18 shows the area under the curve from 0 to 0.5 to be 0.7769. Thus, there is about a 78% chance the time will be no more than 0.5 hour and about a 22% chance that the time will be longer than this. Similarly, we could find the probability that the service time is no more 1/3 hour or 2/3 hour, as follows:

$$P\left(X \leq \frac{1}{3}\right) = 1 - e^{-3\left(\frac{1}{3}\right)} = 1 - e^{-1} = 1 - 0.3679 = 0.6321$$

$$P\left(X \leq \frac{2}{3}\right) = 1 - e^{-3\left(\frac{2}{3}\right)} = 1 - e^{-2} = 1 - 0.1353 = 0.8647$$

FIGURE 18

Probability That the Mechanic Will Install a Muffler in 0.5 Hour

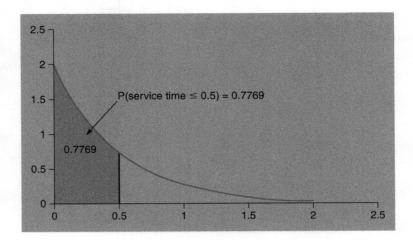

While Equation 19 provides the probability that the time (X) is less than or equal to a particular value t, the probability that the time is greater than a particular value t is found by observing that these two events are complementary. For example, to find the probability that the mechanic at Arnold's Muffler Shop would take longer than 0.5 hour, we have

$$P(X > 0.5) = 1 - P(X \le 0.5) = 1 - 0.7769 = 0.2231$$

Programs 5A and 5B illustrate how a function in Excel can find exponential probabilities.

PROGRAM 5A

Function in an Excel Spreadsheet for the Exponential Distribution

	A	B	C
1	**Exponential distrib**		
2	Average number	3	per hour
3	$t =$	0.5	hours
4	$P(X \le t) =$	=EXPON.DIST(B3,B2,TRUE)	
5	$P(X > t) =$	=1-B4	
6			
7			

PROGRAM 5B

Excel Output for the Exponential Distribution

	A	B	C
1	**Exponential distribution - the random variable (X) is time**		
2	Average number per time period = μ =	3	per hour
3	$t =$	0.5000	hours
4	$P(X \le t) =$	0.7769	
5	$P(X > t) =$	0.2231	

14   The Poisson Distribution

The Poisson probability distribution is used in many queuing models to represent arrival patterns.

An important **discrete probability distribution** is the **Poisson distribution**.[1] We examine it because of its key role in complementing the exponential distribution in queuing theory. The distribution describes situations in which customers arrive independently during a certain time interval, and the number of arrivals depends on the length of the time interval. Examples are

---

[1] This distribution, derived by Simeon Denis Poisson in 1837, is pronounced "pwah-sahn."

patients arriving at a health clinic, customers arriving at a bank window, passengers arriving at an airport, and telephone calls going through a central exchange.

The formula for the Poisson distribution is

$$P(X) = \frac{\lambda^x e^{-\lambda}}{X!} \tag{20}$$

where

$$P(X) = \text{probability of exactly } X \text{ arrivals or occurrences}$$

$$\lambda = \text{average number of arrivals per unit of time (the mean arrival rate),}$$
pronounced "lambda"

$$e = 2.718, \text{ the base of the natural logarithm}$$

$$X = \text{number of occurrences } (0, 1, 2, \dots)$$

The mean and variance of the Poisson distribution are equal and are computed simply as

$$\text{Expected value} = \lambda \tag{21}$$

$$\text{Variance} = \lambda \tag{22}$$

If $\lambda = 2$, we find $e^{-2} = 0.1353$. The Poisson probabilities that X is 0, 1, and 2 when $\lambda = 2$ are as follows:

$$P(X) = \frac{e^{-\lambda} \lambda^x}{X!}$$

$$P(0) = \frac{e^{-2} 2^0}{0!} = \frac{(0.1353)1}{1} = 0.1353 \approx 14\%$$

$$P(1) = \frac{e^{-2} 2^1}{1!} = \frac{e^{-2} 2}{1} = \frac{0.1353(2)}{1} = 0.2706 \approx 27\%$$

$$P(2) = \frac{e^{-2} 2^2}{2!} = \frac{e^{-2} 4}{2(1)} = \frac{0.1353(4)}{2} = 0.2706 \approx 27\%$$

These probabilities, as well as others for $\lambda = 2$ and $\lambda = 4$, are shown in Figure 19. Notice that the chances that 9 or more customers will arrive in a particular time period are virtually nil. Programs 6A and 6B illustrate how Excel can be used to find Poisson probabilities.

It should be noted that the exponential and Poisson distributions are related. If the number of occurrences per time period follows a Poisson distribution, then the time between occurrences follows an exponential distribution. For example, if the number of phone calls arriving at a customer service center followed a Poisson distribution with a mean of 10 calls per hour, the time between each phone call would be exponentially distributed with a mean time between calls of $\frac{1}{10}$ hour (6 minutes).

FIGURE 19
Sample Poisson Distributions with $\lambda = 2$ and $\lambda = 4$

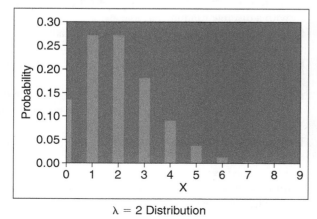

$\lambda = 2$ Distribution

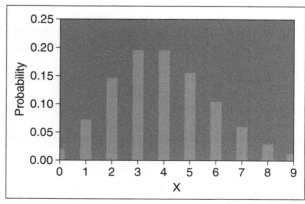

$\lambda = 4$ Distribution

PROGRAM 6A

Functions in an Excel 2010 Spreadsheet for the Poisson Distribution

	A	B	C
1	Poisson d		
2	λ = 2		per hour
3	X	P(X)	P(X ≤ x)
4	0	=POISSON.DIST(A4,$B$2,FALSE)	=POISSON.DIST(A4,$B$2,TRUE)
5	1	=POISSON.DIST(A5,$B$2,FALSE)	=POISSON.DIST(A5,$B$2,TRUE)
6	2	=POISSON.DIST(A6,$B$2,FALSE)	=POISSON.DIST(A6,$B$2,TRUE)

PROGRAM 6B

Excel Output for the Poisson Distribution

	A	B	C	D	E	F
1	Poisson distribution - X is the number of occurrences per time period					
2	λ =	2	per hour			
3	X	P(X)	P(X ≤ x)			
4	0	0.1353	0.1353			
5	1	0.2707	0.4060			
6	2	0.2707	0.6767			

Summary

This chapter presents the fundamental concepts of probability and probability distributions. Probability values can be obtained objectively or subjectively. A single probability value must be between 0 and 1, and the sum of all probability values for all possible outcomes must be equal to 1. In addition, probability values and events can have a number of properties. These properties include mutually exclusive, collectively exhaustive, statistically independent, and statistically dependent events. Rules for computing probability values depend on these fundamental properties. It is also possible to revise probability values when new information becomes available. This can be done using Bayes' theorem.

We also covered the topics of random variables, discrete probability distributions (such as Poisson and binomial), and continuous probability distributions (such as normal, *F*, and exponential). A probability distribution is any statement of a probability function having a set of collectively exhaustive and mutually exclusive events. All probability distributions follow the basic probability rules mentioned previously.

The topics presented here will be very important in many of the chapters to come. Basic probability concepts and distributions are used for decision theory, inventory control, Markov analysis, project management, simulation, and statistical quality control.

Glossary

Bayes' Theorem   A formula that is used to revise probabilities based on new information.

Bernoulli Process   A process with two outcomes in each of a series of independent trials in which the probabilities of the outcomes do not change.

Binomial Distribution   A discrete distribution that describes the number of successes in independent trials of a Bernoulli process.

Classical or **Logical Approach**   An objective way of assessing probabilities based on logic.

Collectively Exhaustive Events   A collection of all possible outcomes of an experiment.

Conditional Probability   The probability of one event occurring given that another has taken place.

Continuous Probability Distribution   A probability distribution with a continuous random variable.

Continuous Random Variable   A random variable that can assume an infinite or unlimited set of values.

Dependent Events   The situation in which the occurrence of one event affects the probability of occurrence of some other event.

Discrete Probability Distribution   A probability distribution with a discrete random variable.

Discrete Random Variable   A random variable that can only assume a finite or limited set of values.

Expected Value   The (weighted) average of a probability distribution.

F Distribution   A continuous probability distribution that is the ratio of the variances of samples from two independent normal distributions.

Independent Events   The situation in which the occurrence of one event has no effect on the probability of occurrence of a second event.

Joint Probability   The probability of events occurring together (or one after the other).

Marginal Probability   The simple probability of an event occurring.

Mutually Exclusive Events   A situation in which only one event can occur on any given trial or experiment.

Negative Exponential Distribution   A continuous probability distribution that describes the time between customer arrivals in a queuing situation.

Normal Distribution   A continuous bell-shaped distribution that is a function of two parameters, the mean and standard deviation of the distribution.

Poisson Distribution   A discrete probability distribution used in queuing theory.

Prior Probability   A probability value determined before new or additional information is obtained. It is sometimes called an a priori probability estimate.

Probability   A statement about the likelihood of an event occurring. It is expressed as a numerical value between 0 and 1, inclusive.

Probability Density Function   The mathematical function that describes a continuous probability distribution. It is represented by $f(X)$.

Probability Distribution   The set of all possible values of a random variable and their associated probabilities.

Random Variable   A variable that assigns a number to every possible outcome of an experiment.

Relative Frequency Approach   An objective way of determining probabilities based on observing frequencies over a number of trials.

Revised or **Posterior Probability**   A probability value that results from new or revised information and prior probabilities.

Standard Deviation   The square root of the variance.

Subjective Approach   A method of determining probability values based on experience or judgment.

Variance   A measure of dispersion or spread of the probability distribution.

Key Equations

(1) $0 \leq P(\text{event}) \leq 1$
A basic statement of probability.

(2) $P(A \text{ or } B) = P(A) + P(B)$
Law of addition for mutually exclusive events.

(3) $P(A \text{ or } B) = P(A) + P(B) - P(A \text{ and } B)$
Law of addition for events that are not mutually exclusive.

(4) $P(AB) = P(A)P(B)$
Joint probability for independent events.

(5) $P(A|B) = \dfrac{P(AB)}{p(B)}$
Conditional probability.

(6) $P(AB) = P(A|B)P(B)$
Joint probability for dependent events.

(7) $P(A|B) = \dfrac{P(B|A)P(A)}{P(B|A)P(A) + P(B|A')P(A')}$
Bayes' law in general form.

(8) $E(X) = \sum\limits_{i=1}^{n} X_i P(X_i)$
An equation that computes the expected value (mean) of a discrete probability distribution.

(9) $\sigma^2 = \text{Variance} = \sum\limits_{i=1}^{n} [X_i - E(X)]^2 P(X_i)$
An equation that computes the variance of a discrete probability distribution.

(10) $\sigma = \sqrt{\text{Variance}} = \sqrt{\sigma^2}$
An equation that computes the standard deviation from the variance.

(11) Probability of r successes in n trials $= \dfrac{n!}{r!(n-r)!} p^r q^{n-r}$
A formula that computes probabilities for the binomial probability distribution.

(12) Expected value (mean) $= np$
The expected value of the binomial distribution.

(13) Variance $= np(1 - p)$
The variance of the binomial distribution.

(14) $f(X) = \dfrac{1}{\sigma\sqrt{2\pi}} e^{\frac{-(x-\mu)^2}{2\sigma^2}}$
The density function for the normal probability distribution.

(15) $Z = \dfrac{X - \mu}{\sigma}$
An equation that computes the number of standard deviations, Z, the point X is from the mean μ.

(16) $f(X) = \mu e^{-\mu x}$
The exponential distribution.

(17) Expected value $= \dfrac{1}{\mu}$
The expected value of an exponential distribution.

(18) Variance $= \dfrac{1}{\mu^2}$
The variance of an exponential distribution.

(19) $P(X \leq t) = 1 - e^{-\mu t}$
Formula to find the probability that an exponential random variable (X) is less than or equal to time t.

(20) $P(X) = \dfrac{\lambda^x e^{-\lambda}}{X!}$
The Poisson distribution.

(21) Expected value $= \lambda$
The mean of a Poisson distribution.

(22) Variance $= \lambda$
The variance of a Poisson distribution.

Solved Problems

Solved Problem 1

In the past 30 days, Roger's Rural Roundup has sold either 8, 9, 10, or 11 lottery tickets. It never sold fewer than 8 or more than 11. Assuming that the past is similar to the future, find the probabilities for the number of tickets sold if sales were 8 tickets on 10 days, 9 tickets on 12 days, 10 tickets on 6 days, and 11 tickets on 2 days.

Solution

SALES	NO. DAYS	PROBABILITY
8	10	0.333
9	12	0.400
10	6	0.200
11	2	0.067
Total	30	1.000

Solved Problem 2

A class contains 30 students. Ten are female (F) and U.S. citizens (U); 12 are male (M) and U.S. citizens; 6 are female and non-U.S. citizens (N); 2 are male and non-U.S. citizens.

A name is randomly selected from the class roster and it is female. What is the probability that the student is a U.S. citizen?

Solution

$$P(FU) = {}^{10}/_{30} = 0.333$$
$$P(FN) = {}^{6}/_{30} = 0.200$$
$$P(MU) = {}^{12}/_{30} = 0.400$$
$$P(MN) = {}^{2}/_{30} = 0.067$$
$$P(F) = P(FU) + P(FN) = 0.333 + 0.200 = 0.533$$
$$P(M) = P(MU) + P(MN) = 0.400 + 0.067 = 0.467$$
$$P(U) = P(FU) + P(MU) = 0.333 + 0.400 = 0.733$$
$$P(N) = P(FN) + P(MN) = 0.200 + 0.067 = 0.267$$
$$P(U|F) = \frac{P(FU)}{P(F)} = \frac{0.333}{0.533} = 0.625$$

Solved Problem 3

Your professor tells you that if you score an 85 or better on your midterm exam, then you have a 90% chance of getting an A for the course. You think you have only a 50% chance of scoring 85 or better. Find the probability that *both* your score is 85 or better *and* you receive an A in the course.

Solution

$$P(A \text{ and } 85) = P(A|85) \times P(85) = (0.90)(0.50)$$
$$= 45\%$$

Solved Problem 4

A statistics class was asked if it believed that all tests on the Monday following the football game win over their archrival should be postponed automatically. The results were as follows:

Strongly agree	40
Agree	30
Neutral	20
Disagree	10
Strongly disagree	0
	100

Transform this into a numeric score, using the following random variable scale, and find a probability distribution for the results:

Strongly agree	5
Agree	4
Neutral	3
Disagree	2
Strongly disagree	1

Solution

OUTCOME	PROBABILITY, $P(X)$
Strongly agree (5)	$0.4 = 40/100$
Agree (4)	$0.3 = 30/100$
Neutral (3)	$0.2 = 20/100$
Disagree (2)	$0.1 = 10/100$
Strongly disagree (1)	$0.0 = 0/100$
Total	$1.0 = 100/100$

Solved Problem 5

For Solved Problem 4, let X be the numeric score. Compute the expected value of X.

Solution

$$E(X) = \sum_{i=1}^{5} X_i P(X_i) = X_1 P(X_1) + X_2 P(X_2)$$
$$+ X_3 P(X_3) + X_4 P(X_4) + X_5 P(X_5)$$
$$= 5(0.4) + 4(0.3) + 3(0.2) + 2(0.1) + 1(0)$$
$$= 4.0$$

Solved Problem 6

Compute the variance and standard deviation for the random variable X in Solved Problems 4 and 5.

Solution

$$\text{Variance} = \sum_{i=1}^{5} (x_i - E(x))^2 P(x_i)$$
$$= (5 - 4)^2(0.4) + (4 - 4)^2(0.3) + (3 - 4)^2(0.2) + (2 - 4)^2(0.1) + (1 - 4)^2(0.0)$$
$$= (1)^2(0.4) + (0)^2(0.3) + (-1)^2(0.2) + (-2)^2(0.1) + (-3)^2(0.0)$$
$$= 0.4 + 0.0 + 0.2 + 0.4 + 0.0 = 1.0$$

The standard deviation is

$$\sigma = \sqrt{\text{Variance}} = \sqrt{1} = 1$$

Solved Problem 7

A candidate for public office has claimed that 60% of voters will vote for her. If 5 registered voters were sampled, what is the probability that exactly 3 would say they favor this candidate?

Solution

We use the binomial distribution with $n = 5$, $p = 0.6$, and $r = 3$:

$$P(\text{exactly 3 successes in 5 trials}) = \frac{n!}{r!(n-r)!}p^r q^{n-r} = \frac{5!}{3!(5-3)!}(0.6)^3(0.4)^{5-3} = 0.3456$$

Solved Problem 8

The length of the rods coming out of our new cutting machine can be said to approximate a normal distribution with a mean of 10 inches and a standard deviation of 0.2 inch. Find the probability that a rod selected randomly will have a length

(a) of less than 10.0 inches
(b) between 10.0 and 10.4 inches
(c) between 10.0 and 10.1 inches
(d) between 10.1 and 10.4 inches
(e) between 9.6 and 9.9 inches
(f) between 9.9 and 10.4 inches
(g) between 9.886 and 10.406 inches

Solution

First compute the standard normal distribution, the Z value:

$$Z = \frac{X - \mu}{\sigma}$$

Next, find the area under the curve for the given Z value by using a standard normal distribution table.

(a) $P(X < 10.0) = 0.50000$
(b) $P(10.0 < X < 10.4) = 0.97725 - 0.50000 = 0.47725$
(c) $P(10.0 < X < 10.1) = 0.69146 - 0.50000 = 0.19146$
(d) $P(10.1 < X < 10.4) = 0.97725 - 0.69146 = 0.28579$
(e) $P(9.6 < X < 9.9) = 0.97725 - 0.69146 = 0.28579$
(f) $P(9.9 < X < 10.4) = 0.19146 + 0.47725 = 0.66871$
(g) $P(9.886 < X < 10.406) = 0.47882 + 0.21566 = 0.69448$

Self-Test

- Before taking the self-test, refer to the learning objectives at the beginning of the chapter, the notes in the margins, and the glossary at the end of the chapter.
- Use the key at the end of the chapter to correct your answers.
- Restudy pages that correspond to any questions that you answered incorrectly or material you feel uncertain about.

1. If only one event may occur on any one trial, then the events are said to be
   a. independent.
   b. exhaustive.
   c. mutually exclusive.
   d. continuous.
2. New probabilities that have been found using Bayes' theorem are called
   a. prior probabilities.
   b. posterior probabilities.
   c. Bayesian probabilities.
   d. joint probabilities.
3. A measure of central tendency is
   a. expected value.
   b. variance.
   c. standard deviation.
   d. all of the above.
4. To compute the variance, you need to know the
   a. variable's possible values.
   b. expected value of the variable.
   c. probability of each possible value of the variable.
   d. all of the above.
5. The square root of the variance is the
   a. expected value.
   b. standard deviation.
   c. area under the normal curve.
   d. all of the above.
6. Which of the following is an example of a discrete distribution?
   a. the normal distribution
   b. the exponential distribution
   c. the Poisson distribution
   d. the Z distribution
7. The total area under the curve for any continuous distribution must equal
   a. 1.
   b. 0.
   c. 0.5.
   d. none of the above.
8. Probabilities for all the possible values of a discrete random variable
   a. may be greater than 1.
   b. may be negative on some occasions.
   c. must sum to 1.
   d. are represented by area underneath the curve.

9. In a standard normal distribution, the mean is equal to
   a. 1.
   b. 0.
   c. the variance.
   d. the standard deviation.
10. The probability of two or more independent events occurring is the
    a. marginal probability.
    b. simple probability.
    c. conditional probability.
    d. joint probability.
    e. all of the above.
11. In the normal distribution, 95.45% of the population lies within
    a. 1 standard deviation of the mean.
    b. 2 standard deviations of the mean.
    c. 3 standard deviations of the mean.
    d. 4 standard deviations of the mean.
12. If a normal distribution has a mean of 200 and a standard deviation of 10, 99.7% of the population falls within what range of values?
    a. 170–230
    b. 180–220
    c. 190–210
    d. 175–225
    e. 170–220
13. If two events are mutually exclusive, then the probability of the intersection of these two events will equal
    a. 0.
    b. 0.5.
    c. 1.0.
    d. cannot be determined without more information.
14. If $P(A) = 0.4$ and $P(B) = 0.5$ and $P(A \text{ and } B) = 0.2$, then $P(B|A) =$
    a. 0.80.
    b. 0.50.
    c. 0.10
    d. 0.40.
    e. none of the above.
15. If $P(A) = 0.4$ and $P(B) = 0.5$ and $P(A \text{ and } B) = 0.2$, then $P(A \text{ or } B) =$
    a. 0.7.
    b. 0.9.
    c. 1.1.
    d. 0.2.
    e. none of the above.

Discussion Questions and Problems

Discussion Questions

1   What are the two basic laws of probability?

2   What is the meaning of mutually exclusive events? What is meant by collectively exhaustive? Give an example of each.

3   Describe the various approaches used in determining probability values.

4   Why is the probability of the intersection of two events subtracted in the sum of the probability of two events?

5   What is the difference between events that are dependent and events that are independent?

6   What is Bayes' theorem, and when can it be used?

7   Describe the characteristics of a Bernoulli process. How is a Bernoulli process associated with the binomial distribution?

8   What is a random variable? What are the various types of random variables?

9   What is the difference between a discrete probability distribution and a continuous probability distribution? Give your own example of each.

10   What is the expected value, and what does it measure? How is it computed for a discrete probability distribution?

11   What is the variance, and what does it measure? How is it computed for a discrete probability distribution?

12   Name three business processes that can be described by the normal distribution.

13   After evaluating student response to a question about a case used in class, the instructor constructed the following probability distribution. What kind of probability distribution is it?

RESPONSE	RANDOM VARIABLE, X	PROBABILITY
Excellent	5	0.05
Good	4	0.25
Average	3	0.40
Fair	2	0.15
Poor	1	0.15

Problems

• 14   A student taking Management Science 301 at East Haven University will receive one of the five possible grades for the course: A, B, C, D, or F. The distribution of grades over the past two years is as follows:

GRADE	NUMBER OF STUDENTS
A	80
B	75
C	90
D	30
F	25
	Total 300

If this past distribution is a good indicator of future grades, what is the probability of a student receiving a C in the course?

• 15   A silver dollar is flipped twice. Calculate the probability of each of the following occurring:
(a) a head on the first flip
(b) a tail on the second flip given that the first toss was a head
(c) two tails
(d) a tail on the first and a head on the second
(e) a tail on the first and a head on the second or a head on the first and a tail on the second
(f) at least one head on the two flips

• 16   An urn contains 8 red chips, 10 green chips, and 2 white chips. A chip is drawn and replaced, and then a second chip drawn. What is the probability of
(a) a white chip on the first draw?
(b) a white chip on the first draw and a red on the second?
(c) two green chips being drawn?
(d) a red chip on the second, given that a white chip was drawn on the first?

• 17   Evertight, a leading manufacturer of quality nails, produces 1-, 2-, 3-, 4-, and 5-inch nails for various uses. In the production process, if there is an overrun or the nails are slightly defective, they are placed in a common bin. Yesterday, 651 of the 1-inch nails, 243 of the 2-inch nails, 41 of the 3-inch nails, 451 of the 4-inch nails, and 333 of the 5-inch nails were placed in the bin.
(a) What is the probability of reaching into the bin and getting a 4-inch nail?
(b) What is the probability of getting a 5-inch nail?
(c) If a particular application requires a nail that is 3 inches or shorter, what is the probability of getting a nail that will satisfy the requirements of the application?

⁚ 18   Last year, at Northern Manufacturing Company, 200 people had colds during the year. One hundred

Note: ⍾ means the problem may be solved with QM for Windows; ✖ means the problem may be solved with Excel QM; and ⍾ means the problem may be solved with QM for Windows and/or Excel QM.

60

fifty-five people who did no exercising had colds, and the remainder of the people with colds were involved in a weekly exercise program. Half of the 1,000 employees were involved in some type of exercise.

(a) What is the probability that an employee will have a cold next year?

(b) Given that an employee is involved in an exercise program, what is the probability that he or she will get a cold next year?

(c) What is the probability that an employee who is not involved in an exercise program will get a cold next year?

(d) Are exercising and getting a cold independent events? Explain your answer.

: 19 The Springfield Kings, a professional basketball team, has won 12 of its last 20 games and is expected to continue winning at the same percentage rate. The team's ticket manager is anxious to attract a large crowd to tomorrow's game but believes that depends on how well the Kings perform tonight against the Galveston Comets. He assesses the probability of drawing a large crowd to be 0.90 should the team win tonight. What is the probability that the team wins tonight and that there will be a large crowd at tomorrow's game?

: 20 David Mashley teaches two undergraduate statistics courses at Kansas College. The class for Statistics 201 consists of 7 sophomores and 3 juniors. The more advanced course, Statistics 301, has 2 sophomores and 8 juniors enrolled. As an example of a business sampling technique, Professor Mashley randomly selects, from the stack of Statistics 201 registration cards, the class card of one student and then places that card back in the stack. If that student was a sophomore, Mashley draws another card from the Statistics 201 stack; if not, he randomly draws a card from the Statistics 301 group. Are these two draws independent events? What is the probability of

(a) a junior's name on the first draw?

(b) a junior's name on the second draw, given that a sophomore's name was drawn first?

(c) a junior's name on the second draw, given that a junior's name was drawn first?

(d) a sophomore's name on both draws?

(e) a junior's name on both draws?

(f) one sophomore's name and one junior's name on the two draws, regardless of order drawn?

: 21 The oasis outpost of Abu Ilan, in the heart of the Negev desert, has a population of 20 Bedouin tribesmen and 20 Farima tribesmen. El Kamin, a nearby oasis, has a population of 32 Bedouins and 8 Farima. A lost Israeli soldier, accidentally separated from his army unit, is wandering through the desert and arrives at the edge of one of the oases. The soldier has no idea which oasis he has found, but the first person he spots at a distance is a Bedouin. What is the probability that he wandered into Abu Ilan? What is the probability that he is in El Kamin?

: 22 The lost Israeli soldier mentioned in Problem 21 decides to rest for a few minutes before entering the desert oasis he has just found. Closing his eyes, he dozes off for 15 minutes, wakes, and walks toward the center of the oasis. The first person he spots this time he again recognizes as a Bedouin. What is the posterior probability that he is in El Kamin?

: 23 Ace Machine Works estimates that the probability its lathe tool is properly adjusted is 0.8. When the lathe is properly adjusted, there is a 0.9 probability that the parts produced pass inspection. If the lathe is out of adjustment, however, the probability of a good part being produced is only 0.2. A part randomly chosen is inspected and found to be acceptable. At this point, what is the posterior probability that the lathe tool is properly adjusted?

: 24 The Boston South Fifth Street Softball League consists of three teams: Mama's Boys, team 1; the Killers, team 2; and the Machos, team 3. Each team plays the other teams just once during the season. The win–loss record for the past 5 years is as follows:

WINNER	(1)	(2)	(3)
Mama's Boys (1)	X	3	4
The Killers (2)	2	X	1
The Machos (3)	1	4	X

Each row represents the number of wins over the past 5 years. Mama's Boys beat the Killers 3 times, beat the Machos 4 times, and so on.

(a) What is the probability that the Killers will win every game next year?

(b) What is the probability that the Machos will win at least one game next year?

(c) What is the probability that Mama's Boys will win exactly one game next year?

(d) What is the probability that the Killers will win fewer than two games next year?

: 25 The schedule for the Killers next year is as follows (refer to Problem 24):

Game 1: The Machos

Game 2: Mama's Boys

(a) What is the probability that the Killers will win their first game?

(b) What is the probability that the Killers will win their last game?

(c) What is the probability that the Killers will break even—win exactly one game?

(d) What is the probability that the Killers will win every game?

(e) What is the probability that the Killers will lose every game?

(f) Would you want to be the coach of the Killers?

: 26 The Northside Rifle team has two markspersons, Dick and Sally. Dick hits a bull's-eye 90% of the time, and Sally hits a bull's-eye 95% of the time.

(a) What is the probability that either Dick or Sally or both will hit the bull's-eye if each takes one shot?

(b) What is the probability that Dick and Sally will both hit the bull's-eye?

(c) Did you make any assumptions in answering the preceding questions? If you answered yes, do you think that you are justified in making the assumption(s)?

: 27 In a sample of 1,000 representing a survey from the entire population, 650 people were from Laketown, and the rest of the people were from River City. Out of the sample, 19 people had some form of cancer. Thirteen of these people were from Laketown.

(a) Are the events of living in Laketown and having some sort of cancer independent?

(b) Which city would you prefer to live in, assuming that your main objective was to avoid having cancer?

: 28 Compute the probability of "loaded die, given that a 3 was rolled," as shown in Example 7, this time using the general form of Bayes' theorem from Equation 7.

• 29 Which of the following are probability distributions? Why?

(a)

RANDOM VARIABLE X	PROBABILITY
2	0.1
−1	0.2
0	0.3
1	0.25
2	0.15

(b)

RANDOM VARIABLE Y	PROBABILITY
1	1.1
1.5	0.2
2	0.3
2.5	0.25
3	−1.25

(c)

RANDOM VARIABLE Z	PROBABILITY
1	0.1
2	0.2
3	0.3
4	0.4
5	0.0

• 30 Harrington Health Food stocks 5 loaves of Neutro-Bread. The probability distribution for the sales of Neutro-Bread is listed in the following table. How many loaves will Harrington sell on average?

NUMBER OF LOAVES SOLD	PROBABILITY
0	0.05
1	0.15
2	0.20
3	0.25
4	0.20
5	0.15

• 31 What are the expected value and variance of the following probability distribution?

RANDOM VARIABLE X	PROBABILITY
1	0.05
2	0.05
3	0.10
4	0.10
5	0.15
6	0.15
7	0.25
8	0.15

: 32 There are 10 questions on a true–false test. A student feels unprepared for this test and randomly guesses the answer for each of these.

(a) What is the probability that the student gets exactly 7 correct?

(b) What is the probability that the student gets exactly 8 correct?

(c) What is the probability that the student gets exactly 9 correct?

(d) What is the probability that the student gets exactly 10 correct?

(e) What is the probability that the student gets more than 6 correct?

: 33 Gary Schwartz is the top salesman for his company. Records indicate that he makes a sale on 70% of his sales calls. If he calls on four potential clients, what is the probability that he makes exactly 3 sales? What is the probability that he makes exactly 4 sales?

: 34 If 10% of all disk drives produced on an assembly line are defective, what is the probability that there will be exactly one defect in a random sample of 5 of these? What is the probability that there will be no defects in a random sample of 5?

: 35 Trowbridge Manufacturing produces cases for personal computers and other electronic equipment. The quality control inspector for this company believes that a particular process is out of control. Normally, only 5% of all cases are deemed defective due to discolorations. If 6 such cases are sampled, what is the probability that there will be 0 defective cases if the process is operating correctly? What is the probability that there will be exactly 1 defective case?

✘ : 36 Refer to the Trowbridge Manufacturing example in Problem 35. The quality control inspection procedure is to select 6 items, and if there are 0 or 1 defective cases in the group of 6, the process is said to be in control. If the number of defects is more than 1, the process is out of control. Suppose that the true proportion of defective items is 0.15. What is the probability that there will be 0 or 1 defects in a sample of 6 if the true proportion of defects is 0.15?

✘ : 37 An industrial oven used to cure sand cores for a factory manufacturing engine blocks for small cars is able to maintain fairly constant temperatures. The temperature range of the oven follows a normal distribution with a mean of 450°F and a standard deviation of 25°F. Leslie Larsen, president of the factory, is concerned about the large number of defective cores that have been produced in the past several months. If the oven gets hotter than 475°F, the core is defective. What is the probability that the oven will cause a core to be defective? What is the probability that the temperature of the oven will range from 460° to 470°F?

✘ : 38 Steve Goodman, production foreman for the Florida Gold Fruit Company, estimates that the average sale of oranges is 4,700 and the standard deviation is 500 oranges. Sales follow a normal distribution.
   (a) What is the probability that sales will be greater than 5,500 oranges?
   (b) What is the probability that sales will be greater than 4,500 oranges?
   (c) What is the probability that sales will be less than 4,900 oranges?
   (d) What is the probability that sales will be less than 4,300 oranges?

✘ : 39 Susan Williams has been the production manager of Medical Suppliers, Inc., for the past 17 years. Medical Suppliers, Inc., is a producer of bandages and arm slings. During the past 5 years, the demand for No-Stick bandages has been fairly constant. On the average, sales have been about 87,000 packages of No-Stick. Susan has reason to believe that the distribution of No-Stick follows a normal curve, with a standard deviation of 4,000 packages. What is the probability that sales will be less than 81,000 packages?

: 40 Armstrong Faber produces a standard number-two pencil called Ultra-Lite. Since Chuck Armstrong started Armstrong Faber, sales have grown steadily. With the increase in the price of wood products, however, Chuck has been forced to increase the price of the Ultra-Lite pencils. As a result, the demand for Ultra-Lite has been fairly stable over

the past 6 years. On the average, Armstrong Faber has sold 457,000 pencils each year. Furthermore, 90% of the time sales have been between 454,000 and 460,000 pencils. It is expected that the sales follow a normal distribution with a mean of 457,000 pencils. Estimate the standard deviation of this distribution. (*Hint:* Work backward from the normal table to find Z. Then apply Equation 15.)

: 41 The time to complete a construction project is normally distributed with a mean of 60 weeks and a standard deviation of 4 weeks.
   (a) What is the probability the project will be finished in 62 weeks or less?
   (b) What is the probability the project will be finished in 66 weeks or less?
   (c) What is the probability the project will take longer than 65 weeks?

: 42 A new integrated computer system is to be installed worldwide for a major corporation. Bids on this project are being solicited, and the contract will be awarded to one of the bidders. As a part of the proposal for this project, bidders must specify how long the project will take. There will be a significant penalty for finishing late. One potential contractor determines that the average time to complete a project of this type is 40 weeks with a standard deviation of 5 weeks. The time required to complete this project is assumed to be normally distributed.
   (a) If the due date of this project is set at 40 weeks, what is the probability that the contractor will have to pay a penalty (i.e., the project will not be finished on schedule)?
   (b) If the due date of this project is set at 43 weeks, what is the probability that the contractor will have to pay a penalty (i.e., the project will not be finished on schedule)?
   (c) If the bidder wishes to set the due date in the proposal so that there is only a 5% chance of being late (and consequently only a 5% chance of having to pay a penalty), what due date should be set?

: 43 Patients arrive at the emergency room of Costa Valley Hospital at an average of 5 per day. The demand for emergency room treatment at Costa Valley follows a Poisson distribution.
   (a) Using Appendix C, compute the probability of exactly 0, 1, 2, 3, 4, and 5 arrivals per day.
   (b) What is the sum of these probabilities, and why is the number less than 1?

: 44 Using the data in Problem 43, determine the probability of more than 3 visits for emergency room service on any given day.

: 45 Cars arrive at Carla's Muffler shop for repair work at an average of 3 per hour, following an exponential distribution.
   (a) What is the expected time between arrivals?
   (b) What is the variance of the time between arrivals?

46 A particular test for the presence of steroids is to be used after a professional track meet. If steroids are present, the test will accurately indicate this 95% of the time. However, if steroids are not present, the test will indicate this 90% of the time (so it is wrong 10% of the time and predicts the presence of steroids). Based on past data, it is believed that 2% of the athletes do use steroids. This test is administered to one athlete, and the test is positive for steroids. What is the probability that this person actually used steroids?

47 Market Researchers, Inc., has been hired to perform a study to determine if the market for a new product will be good or poor. In similar studies performed in the past, whenever the market actually was good, the market research study indicated that it would be good 85% of the time. On the other hand, whenever the market actually was poor, the market study incorrectly predicted it would be good 20% of the time. Before the study is performed, it is believed there is a 70% chance the market will be good. When Market Researchers, Inc. performs the study for this product, the results predict the market will be good. Given the results of this study, what is the probability that the market actually will be good?

48 Policy Pollsters is a market research firm specializing in political polls. Records indicate in past elections, when a candidate was elected, Policy Pollsters had accurately predicted this 80 percent of the time and they were wrong 20% of the time. Records also show for losing candidates, Policy Pollsters accurately predicted they would lose 90 percent of the time and they were only wrong 10% of the time. Before the poll is taken, there is a 50% chance of winning the election. If Policy Pollsters predicts a candidate will win the election, what is the probability that the candidate will actually win? If Policy Pollsters predicts that a candidate will lose the election, what is the probability that the candidate will actually lose?

49 Burger City is a large chain of fast-food restaurants specializing in gourmet hamburgers. A mathematical model is now used to predict the success of new restaurants based on location and demographic information for that area. In the past, 70% of all restaurants that were opened were successful. The mathematical model has been tested in the existing restaurants to determine how effective it is. For the restaurants that were successful, 90% of the time the model predicted they would be, while 10% of the time the model predicted a failure. For the restaurants that were not successful, when the mathematical model was applied, 20% of the time it incorrectly predicted a successful restaurant while 80% of the time it was accurate and predicted an unsuccessful restaurant. If the model is used on a new location and predicts the restaurant will be successful, what is the probability that it actually is successful?

50 A mortgage lender attempted to increase its business by marketing its subprime mortgage. This mortgage is designed for people with a less-than-perfect credit rating, and the interest rate is higher to offset the extra risk. In the past year, 20% of these mortgages resulted in foreclosure as customers defaulted on their loans. A new screening system has been developed to determine whether to approve customers for the subprime loans. When the system is applied to a credit application, the system will classify the application as "Approve for loan" or "Reject for loan." When this new system was applied to recent customers who had defaulted on their loans, 90% of these customers were classified as "Reject." When this same system was applied to recent loan customers who had not defaulted on their loan payments, 70% of these customers were classified as "Approve for loan."

(a) If a customer did not default on a loan, what is the probability that the rating system would have classified the applicant in the reject category?

(b) If the rating system had classified the applicant in the reject category, what is the probability that the customer would not default on a loan?

51 Use the F table in the appendix titled "F Distribution Values" to find the value of F for the upper 5% of the F distribution with
(a) $df_1 = 5, df_2 = 10$
(b) $df_1 = 8, df_2 = 7$
(c) $df_1 = 3, df_2 = 5$
(d) $df_1 = 10, df_2 = 4$

52 Use the F table in the appendix titled "F Distribution Values" to find the value of F for the upper 1% of the F distribution with
(a) $df_1 = 15, df_2 = 6$
(b) $df_1 = 12, df_2 = 8$
(c) $df_1 = 3, df_2 = 5$
(d) $df_1 = 9, df_2 = 7$

53 For each of the following F values, determine whether the probability indicated is greater than or less than 5%:
(a) $P(F_{3,4} > 6.8)$
(b) $P(F_{7,3} > 3.6)$
(c) $P(F_{20,20} > 2.6)$
(d) $P(F_{7,5} > 5.1)$
(e) $P(F_{7,5} < 5.1)$

54 For each of the following F values, determine whether the probability indicated is greater than or less than 1%:
(a) $P(F_{5,4} > 14)$
(b) $P(F_{6,3} > 30)$
(c) $P(F_{10,12} > 4.2)$
(d) $P(F_{2,3} > 35)$
(e) $P(F_{2,3} < 35)$

55 Nite Time Inn has a toll-free telephone number so that customers can call at any time to make a reservation. A typical call takes about 4 minutes to

complete, and the time required follows an exponential distribution. Find the probability that
(a) a call takes 3 minutes or less
(b) a call takes 4 minutes or less
(c) a call takes 5 minutes or less
(d) a call takes longer than 5 minutes

 56 During normal business hours on the east coast, calls to the toll-free reservation number of the Nite Time Inn arrive at a rate of 5 per minute. It has been determined that the number of calls per minute can be described by the Poisson distribution. Find the probability that in the next minute, the number of calls arriving will be
(a) exactly 5
(b) exactly 4

(c) exactly 3
(d) exactly 6
(e) less than 2

57 In the Arnold's Muffler example for the exponential distribution in this chapter, the average rate of service was given as 3 per hour, and the times were expressed in hours. Convert the average service rate to the number per minute and convert the times to minutes. Find the probabilities that the service times will be less than 1/2 hour, 1/3 hour, and 2/3 hour. Compare these probabilities to the probabilities found in the example.

Internet Homework Problems

See our Internet home page, at **www.pearsonhighered.com/render**, for additional homework problems, Problems 58 to 65.

Case Study

WTVX

WTVX, Channel 6, is located in Eugene, Oregon, home of the University of Oregon's football team. The station was owned and operated by George Wilcox, a former Duck (University of Oregon football player). Although there were other television stations in Eugene, WTVX was the only station that had a weatherperson who was a member of the American Meteorological Society (AMS). Every night, Joe Hummel would be introduced as the only weatherperson in Eugene who was a member of the AMS. This was George's idea, and he believed that this gave his station the mark of quality and helped with market share.

In addition to being a member of AMS, Joe was also the most popular person on any of the local news programs. Joe was always trying to find innovative ways to make the weather interesting, and this was especially difficult during the winter months when the weather seemed to remain the same over long periods of time. Joe's forecast for next month, for example, was that there would be a 70% chance of rain *every* day, and that what happens on one day (rain or shine) was not in any way dependent on what happened the day before.

One of Joe's most popular features of the weather report was to invite questions during the actual broadcast. Questions would be phoned in, and they were answered on the spot by Joe. Once a 10-year-old boy asked what caused fog, and Joe did an excellent job of describing some of the various causes.

Occasionally, Joe would make a mistake. For example, a high school senior asked Joe what the chances were of getting 15 days of rain in the next month (30 days). Joe made a quick calculation: $(70\%) \times (15 \text{ days}/30 \text{ days}) = (70\%)(1/2) = 35\%$. Joe quickly found out what it was like being wrong in a university town. He had over 50 phone calls from scientists, mathematicians, and other university professors, telling him that he had made a big mistake in computing the chances of getting 15 days of rain during the next 30 days. Although Joe didn't understand all of the formulas the professors mentioned, he was determined to find the correct answer and make a correction during a future broadcast.

Discussion Questions

1. What are the chances of getting 15 days of rain during the next 30 days?
2. What do you think about Joe's assumptions concerning the weather for the next 30 days?

Bibliography

Berenson, Mark, David Levine, and Timothy Krehbiel. *Basic Business Statistics*, 10th ed. Upper Saddle River, NJ: Prentice Hall, 2006.

Campbell, S. *Flaws and Fallacies in Statistical Thinking*. Upper Saddle River, NJ: Prentice Hall, 1974.

Feller, W. *An Introduction to Probability Theory and Its Applications*, Vols. 1 and 2. New York: John Wiley & Sons, Inc., 1957 and 1968.

Groebner, David, Patrick Shannon, Phillip Fry, and Kent Smith. *Business Statistics*, 8th ed. Upper Saddle River, NJ: Prentice Hall, 2011.

Hanke, J. E., A. G. Reitsch, and D. W. Wichern. *Business Forecasting*, 9th ed. Upper Saddle River, NJ: Prentice Hall, 2008.

Huff, D. *How to Lie with Statistics*. New York: W. W. Norton & Company, Inc., 1954.

Newbold, Paul, William Carlson, and Betty Thorne. *Statistics for Business and Economics*, 6th ed. Upper Saddle River, NJ: Prentice Hall, 2007.

Appendix 1: Derivation of Bayes' Theorem

We know that the following formulas are correct:

$$P(A|B) = \frac{P(AB)}{P(B)} \tag{1}$$

$$P(B|A) = \frac{P(AB)}{P(A)}$$

[which can be rewritten as $P(AB) = P(B|A)P(A)$] and $\qquad$ (2)

$$P(B|A') = \frac{P(A'B)}{P(A')}$$

[which can be rewritten as $P(A'B) = P(B|A')P(A')$]. $\qquad$ (3)

Furthermore, by definition, we know that

$$P(B) = P(AB) + P(A'B)$$
$$= P(B|A)P(A) + P(B|A')P(A') \tag{4}$$

from (2)   from (3)

Substituting Equations 2 and 4 into Equation 1, we have

$$P(A|B) = \frac{P(AB)}{P(B)}$$

from (2)

$$= \frac{P(B|A)P(A)}{P(B|A)P(A) + P(B|A')P(A')} \tag{5}$$

from (4)

This is the general form of Bayes' theorem, shown as Equation 7 in this chapter.

Appendix 2: Basic Statistics Using Excel

Statistical Functions

Many statistical functions are available in Excel 2010 and earlier versions. To see the complete list of available functions, from the Formulas tab in Excel 2010 or 2007, select *fx* (Insert Function) and select Statistical, as shown in Program 7. Scroll down the list to see all available functions. The names of some of these have changed slightly from Excel 2007 to Excel 2010. For example, the function to obtain a probability with the normal distribution was NORMDIST in Excel 2007, while the same function in Excel 2010 is NORM.DIST (a period was added between NORM and DIST).

PROGRAM 7

Accessing Statistical Functions in Excel 2010

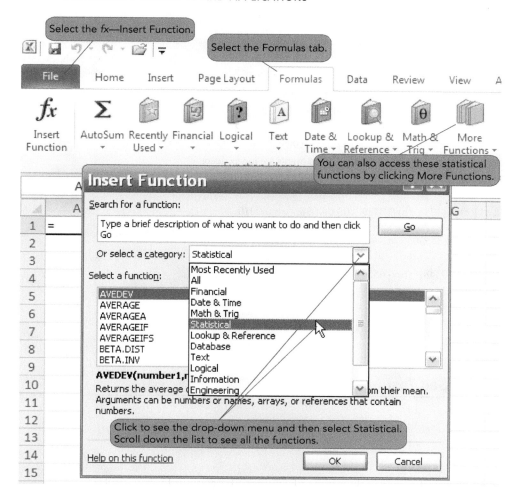

Summary Information

Other statistical procedures are available in the Analysis ToolPak, which is an add-in that comes with Excel. Analysis ToolPak quickly provides summary descriptive statistics and performs other statistical procedures such as regression.

Solutions to Selected Problems

14	0.30
16	(a) 0.10 (b) 0.04 (c) 0.25 (d) 0.40
18	(a) 0.20 (b) 0.09 (c) 0.31 (d) dependent
20	(a) 0.3 (b) 0.3 (c) 0.8 (d) 0.49 (e) 0.24 (f) 0.27
22	0.719
24	(a) 0.08 (b) 0.84 (c) 0.44 (d) 0.92
26	(a) 0.995 (b) 0.885 (c) Assumed events are independent
28	0.78
30	2.85
32	(a) 0.1172 (b) 0.0439 (c) 0.0098 (d) 0.0010 (e) 0.1719
34	0.328, 0.590
36	0.776
38	(a) 0.0548 (b) 0.6554 (c) 0.6554 (d) 0.2119
40	1829.27
42	(a) 0.5 (b) 0.27425 (c) 48.2
44	0.7365
46	0.162

Solutions to Self-Tests

1.	c
2.	b
3.	a
4.	d
5.	b
6.	c
7.	a
8.	c
9.	b
10.	d
11.	b
12.	a
13.	a
14.	b
15.	a

Decision Analysis

LEARNING OBJECTIVES

After completing this chapter, students will be able to:

1. List the steps of the decision-making process and describe the different types of decision-making environments.
2. Make decisions under uncertainty and under risk.
3. Use Excel to set up and solve problems involving decision tables.
4. Develop accurate and useful decision trees.
5. Use TreePlan to set up and analyze decision tree problems with Excel.
6. Revise probability estimates using Bayesian analysis.
7. Understand the importance and use of utility theory in decision making.

CHAPTER OUTLINE

Summary • Glossary • Solved Problems • Discussion Questions and Problems • Case Study: Ski Right • Case Study: Blake Electronics • Internet Case Studies

The companion website for this text is www.pearsonhighered.com/balakrishnan.

From Chapter 8 of *Managerial Decision Modeling with Spreadsheets*, Third Edition. Nagraj Balakrishnan, Barry Render, Ralph M. Stair, Jr.

1 Introduction

Decision analysis is an analytic and systematic way to tackle problems.

To a great extent, the successes and failures that a person experiences in life depend on the decisions that he or she makes. The development of the Mac computer, followed by the iPod, the iPhone, and now the iPad, made Steve Jobs a very wealthy person. In contrast, the person who designed the flawed tires at Firestone (which caused so many accidents with Ford Explorers in the late 1990s) probably did not have a great career at that company. Why and how did these people make their respective decisions? A single decision can make the difference between a successful career and an unsuccessful one. *Decision analysis* is an analytic and systematic approach to the study of decision making. In this chapter, we present decision models that are useful in helping managers make the best possible decisions.

A good decision is based on logic.

What makes the difference between good and bad decisions? In most practical situations, managers have to make decisions without knowing for sure which events will occur in the future. In such cases, a good decision can be defined as one that is based on logic, considers all possible decision alternatives, examines all available information about the future, and applies the decision modeling approach described in this chapter. Occasionally, due to the uncertainty of future events, a good decision could result in an unfavorable outcome. But if a decision is made properly, it is still a good decision.

A bad decision does not consider all alternatives.

In contrast, a bad decision is one that is not based on logic, does not use all available information, does not consider all alternatives, and does not employ appropriate decision modeling techniques. If you make a bad decision but are lucky enough that a favorable outcome occurs, you have still made a bad decision. Although occasionally good decisions yield bad results, in the long run, using decision analysis will result in successful outcomes.

2 The Five Steps in Decision Analysis

Whether you are deciding about signing up for next semester's classes, buying a new computer, or building a multimillion-dollar factory, the steps in making a good decision are basically the same:

Five Steps of Decision Making

1. Clearly define the problem at hand.
2. List *all* possible decision alternatives.
3. Identify the possible future outcomes for each decision alternative.
4. Identify the payoff (usually profit or cost) for each combination of alternatives and outcomes.
5. Select one of the decision analysis modeling techniques discussed in this chapter. Apply the decision model and make your decision.

Thompson Lumber Company Example

We use the case of Thompson Lumber Company as an example to illustrate the use of the five decision analysis steps. John Thompson is the founder and president of Thompson Lumber Company, a profitable firm located in Portland, Oregon.

The first step is to define the problem.

STEP 1 In the first step, John identifies his decision-making problem as whether to expand his business by manufacturing and marketing a new product, backyard storage sheds.

The second step is to list alternatives.

STEP 2 The second step is to generate the complete list of decision alternatives available to the decision maker. In decision analysis, a **decision alternative** is defined as a course of action that is available to the decision maker. There is no limit to the number of decision alternatives that a problem can have. The decision maker has total control over which decision alternative he or she chooses and must choose exactly one of the alternatives listed in the problem.

In Thompson Lumber's case, let us assume that John decides that his alternatives are as follows: (1) build a large plant to manufacture the storage sheds, (2) build a small plant to manufacture the storage sheds, or (3) build no plant at all (i.e., not develop the new product line and keep his business at its current size).

One of the biggest mistakes that decision makers make in practice is to leave out important decision alternatives. For example, suppose John had left out the alternative to build no plant at all. It could well turn out that based on all the issues in the decision-making problem, the best decision for him would have been to not expand his business. However, by not including that alternative among his choices, John would have been unable to select that decision. In general, it is important to remember that while a particular decision alternative may sometimes appear to be inappropriate on the surface, it may turn out to be an excellent choice when all issues in the problem are considered.

The third step is to identify possible outcomes.

STEP 3 The third step involves identifying all possible future **outcomes** for each decision alternative. In decision analysis, outcomes are also known as *states of nature*. There is no limit to the number of outcomes that can be listed for a decision alternative, and each alternative can have its own unique set of outcomes. Exactly one of the listed outcomes will occur for a specific decision alternative. However, the decision maker has little or no control over which outcome will occur.

In Thompson Lumber's case, suppose John determines that all three of his decision alternatives have the same three possible outcomes: (1) Demand for the sheds will be high, (2) demand for the sheds will be moderate, or (3) demand for the sheds will be low.

As with decision alternatives, a common mistake in practice is to forget about some of the possible outcomes. Optimistic decision makers may tend to ignore bad outcomes under the mistaken assumption that they will not happen, whereas pessimistic managers may discount a favorable outcome. If we don't consider all possibilities, we will not make a logical decision, and the results may be undesirable.

The fourth step is to list payoffs.

STEP 4 The fourth step is to define the measurable output resulting from each possible combination of decision alternative and outcome. That is, we need to identify the output that will result if we choose a specific decision alternative, and a particular outcome then occurs. In decision analysis, we call these outputs *payoffs*, regardless of whether they denote profit or cost. Payoffs can also be nonmonetary (e.g., number of units sold, number of workers needed).

In Thompson Lumber's case, let us assume that John wants to use net profits to measure his payoffs. He has already evaluated the potential profits associated with the various combinations of alternatives and outcomes, as follows:

- If John decides to build a large plant, he thinks that with high demand for sheds, the result would be a net profit of $200,000 to his firm. The net profit would, however, be only $100,000 if demand were moderate. If demand were low, there would actually be a net loss of $120,000. Payoffs are also called **conditional values** because, for example, John receiving a profit of $200,000 is conditional upon both his building a large factory and having high demand.
- If he builds a small plant, the results would be a net profit of $90,000 if there were high demand for sheds, a net profit of $50,000 if there were moderate demand, and a net loss of $20,000 if there were low demand.
- Finally, doing nothing would result in $0 payoff in any demand scenario.

During the fourth step, the decision maker can construct decision or payoff tables.

The easiest way to present payoff values is by constructing a *payoff table*, or **decision table**. A payoff table for John's conditional profit values is shown in Table 1. All the decision alternatives are listed down the left side of this table, and all the possible outcomes are listed across the top. The body of the table contains the actual payoffs (profits, in this case).

The last step is to select and apply a decision analysis model.

STEP 5 The last step is to select a decision analysis model and apply it to the data to help make the decision. The types of decision models available for selection depends on the environment in which we are operating and the amount of uncertainty and risk involved. The model specifies the criteria to be used in choosing the best decision alternative.

TABLE 1
Payoff Table for Thompson Lumber

	OUTCOMES		
ALTERNATIVES	**HIGH DEMAND**	**MODERATE DEMAND**	**LOW DEMAND**
Build large plant	$200,000	$100,000	−$120,000
Build small plant	$ 90,000	$ 50,000	−$ 20,000
No plant	$ 0	$ 0	$ 0

3 Types of Decision-Making Environments

The types of decisions people make depend on how much knowledge or information they have about the problem scenario. There are three decision-making environments, as described in the following sections.

The consequence of every alternative is known in decision making under certainty.

TYPE 1: DECISION MAKING UNDER CERTAINTY In the environment of **decision making under certainty**, decision makers know for sure (i.e., with certainty) the payoff for every decision alternative. Typically, this means that there is only one outcome for each alternative. Naturally, decision makers will select the alternative that will result in the best payoff. The mathematical programming approaches are all examples of decision modeling techniques suited for decision making under certainty.

Let's see how decision making under certainty could affect Thompson Lumber's problem. In this environment, we assume that John knows exactly what will happen in the future. For example, if he knows with certainty that demand for storage sheds will be high, what should he do? Looking at John's conditional profit values in Table 1, it is clear in this case that he should build the large plant, which has the highest profit, $200,000.

In real-world cases, however, few managers would be fortunate enough to have complete information and knowledge about the outcomes under consideration. In most situations, managers would either have no information at all about the outcomes, or, at best, have probabilistic information about future outcomes. These are the second and third types of decision-making environments.

Probabilities are not known in decision making under uncertainty.

TYPE 2: DECISION MAKING UNDER UNCERTAINTY In **decision making under uncertainty**, decision makers have no information at all about the various outcomes. That is, they do not know the likelihood (or probability) that a specific outcome will occur. For example, it is impossible to predict the probability that the Democratic Party will control the U.S. Congress 25 years from now. Likewise, it may be impossible in some cases to assess the probability that a new product or undertaking will be successful.

There are several decision models available to handle decision-making problems under uncertainty. These are explained in section 4.

Probabilities are known in decision making under risk.

TYPE 3: DECISION MAKING UNDER RISK In **decision making under risk**, decision makers have some knowledge regarding the probability of occurrence of each outcome. The probability could be a precise measure (e.g., the probability of being dealt an ace from a deck of cards is exactly $\frac{1}{13}$) or an estimate (e.g., the probability that it will rain tomorrow is 0.40). Regardless of how the probabilities are determined, in decision making under risk, decision makers attempt to identify the alternative that optimizes their *expected* payoff.

IN ACTION **Decision Analysis Helps American Airlines Assess Uncertainty of Bid Quotes**

American Airlines, Inc. (AA) is the world's largest airline in passenger miles transported with annual revenue of over $21 billion. Although its primary goal is to transport passengers, AA has to also manage ancillary functions such as full-truckload (FTL) freight shipment of maintenance equipment and in-flight service items. The inventory value of these goods as they move point to point worldwide can be over $1 billion at any given time.

Each year AA has approximately 500 requests for quotes (RFQs) in the bid process for its FTL point-to-point freight shipment routes. AA needed a should-cost model to assess these quotes to ensure that it does not overpay its FTL suppliers. Working

with researchers at North Carolina State University, AA developed a decision tree–based analysis that estimates reasonable costs for these shipments. The fully expanded decision tree for this problem has nearly 60,000 end points.

AA has now used this decision tree model on more than 20 RFQs to prioritize its contractual opportunities and obtain accurate assessments of the FTL costs, thus minimizing the risk of overpaying its FTL suppliers.

Source: Based on M. J. Bailey et al. "American Airlines Uses Should-Cost Modeling to Assess the Uncertainty of Bids for Its Full-Truckload Shipment Routes," *Interfaces* 41, 2 (March–April 2011): 194–196.

Decision analysis models for business problems in this environment typically employ one of two criteria: (1) maximization of expected monetary value or (2) minimization of expected opportunity loss. We study models using both criteria for decision making under risk in section 5.

4 Decision Making Under Uncertainty

Probabilities of outcomes are not known.

As noted previously, an environment of decision making under uncertainty exists when a manager cannot assess the probabilities of the different outcomes with confidence or when virtually no probability data are available. In this section, we discuss the following five different decision-making criteria to handle such situations:

1. Maximax
2. Maximin
3. Criterion of realism
4. Equally likely
5. Minimax regret

In discussing these criteria here, we assume that all payoffs represent profits. That is, we prefer higher payoffs to smaller ones. If the payoffs represent costs (i.e., we prefer smaller payoffs to higher ones), some of the criteria would need to be used differently. To avoid this confusion, an easy option is to convert costs in a payoff table to profits by multiplying all cost values by –1. This way, we can apply the criteria as discussed here for all problems, regardless of whether the payoffs represent profits or costs.

The first four criteria can be computed directly from the decision (payoff) table, whereas the minimax regret criterion requires use of the opportunity loss table (which we compute subsequently). Let us look at each of the five criteria and apply them to the Thompson Lumber example. Remember that the decision-making environment assumes that John has no probability information about the three outcomes—high demand, moderate demand, and low demand for storage sheds.

Maximax Criterion

Maximax is an optimistic approach.

The **maximax** criterion selects the decision alternative that *maxi*mizes the *max*imum payoff over all alternatives. We first locate the maximum payoff for each alternative and then select the alternative with the highest value among these maximum payoffs. Because this criterion takes an extremely rosy view of the future and locates the alternative with the overall highest possible payoff, it is also called the *optimistic* criterion.

In Table 2 we see that John's maximax choice is the first alternative, build large plant. The $200,000 payoff is the maximum of the maximum payoffs (i.e., $200,000, $90,000, and $0) for each decision alternative.

Maximin Criterion

Maximin is a pessimistic approach.

The opposite of the maximax criterion is the **maximin** criterion, which takes an extremely conservative view of the future. For this reason, it is also called the *pessimistic* criterion. The maximin criterion finds the alternative that *maxi*mizes the *min*imum payoff over all decision alternatives. We first locate the minimum payoff for each alternative and then select the alternative with the highest value among those minimum payoffs.

TABLE 2
Thompson Lumber's Maximax Decision

| ALTERNATIVES | OUTCOMES | | | MAXIMUM FOR ALTERNATIVE |
	HIGH DEMAND	MODERATE DEMAND	LOW DEMAND	
Build large plant	$200,000	$100,000	–$120,000	$200,000 → Maximax
Build small plant	$ 90,000	$ 50,000	–$ 20,000	$ 90,000
No plant	$ 0	$ 0	$ 0	$ 0

TABLE 3
Thompson Lumber's Maximin Decision

	OUTCOMES			
ALTERNATIVES	**HIGH DEMAND**	**MODERATE DEMAND**	**LOW DEMAND**	**MINIMUM FOR ALTERNATIVE**
Build large plant	$200,000	$100,000	−$120,000	−$120,000
Build small plant	$ 90,000	$ 50,000	−$ 20,000	−$ 20,000
No plant	$ 0	$ 0	$ 0	$ 0 → Maximin

John's maximin choice, no plant, is shown in Table 3. The $0 payoff is the maximum of the minimum payoffs (i.e., −$120,000, −$20,000, and $0) for each alternative.

Criterion of Realism (Hurwicz)

The criterion of realism uses the weighted average approach.

Decision makers are seldom extreme optimists or extreme pessimists. Because most tend to be somewhere in between the two extremes, the *criterion of realism* (or *Hurwicz*) decision criterion offers a compromise between optimistic and pessimistic decisions. In this criterion, we use a parameter called the **coefficient of realism** to measure the decision maker's level of optimism regarding the future. This coefficient, denoted by α, has a value between 0 and 1. An α value of 0 implies that the decision maker is totally pessimistic about the future, while an α value of 1 implies that the decision maker is totally optimistic about the future. The advantage of this approach is that it allows the decision maker to build in personal feelings about relative optimism and pessimism. The formula is as follows:

$$\text{Realism payoff for alternative} = \alpha \times (\text{Maximum payoff for alternative}) + (1 - \alpha) \times (\text{Minimum payoff for alternative}) \tag{1}$$

Because the realism payoff is just a weighted average for the maximum and minimum payoffs (where α is the weight), this criterion is also called the *weighted average* criterion.

Suppose we identify John Thompson's coefficient of realism to be $\alpha = 0.45$. That is, John is a slightly pessimistic person (note that $\alpha = 0.5$ implies a strictly neutral person). Under this situation, his best decision would be to build a small plant. As shown in Table 4, this alternative has the highest realism payoff, at $29,500 [= 0.45 \times \$90,000 + 0.55 \times (-\$20,000)]$.

Equally Likely (Laplace) Criterion

The equally likely criterion selects the highest average alternative.

The **equally likely** (or *Laplace*) criterion finds the decision alternative that has the highest average payoff. We first calculate the average payoff for each alternative and then pick the alternative with the maximum average payoff. Note that the Laplace approach essentially assumes that all the outcomes are equally likely to occur.

The equally likely choice for Thompson Lumber is the first alternative, build a large plant. This strategy, as shown in Table 5, has a maximum average payoff of $60,000 over all alternatives.

Minimax Regret Criterion

Minimax regret is based on opportunity loss.

The final decision criterion that we discuss is based on **opportunity loss**, also called *regret*. Opportunity loss is defined as the difference between the optimal payoff and the actual payoff received. In other words, it's the amount lost by *not* picking the best alternative.

TABLE 4
Thompson Lumber's Criterion of Realism Decision ($\alpha = 0.45$)

	OUTCOMES			
ALTERNATIVES	**HIGH DEMAND**	**MODERATE DEMAND**	**LOW DEMAND**	**WT. AVG. ($\alpha = 0.45$) FOR ALTERNATIVE**
Build large plant	$200,000	$100,000	−$120,000	$24,000
Build small plant	$ 90,000	$ 50,000	−$ 20,000	$29,500 → Realism
No plant	$ 0	$ 0	$ 0	$ 0

TABLE 5
Thompson Lumber's
Equally Likely Decision

handwritten: 200,000+100,000 + (-120,000) ÷ 3
handwritten: 90,000+50,000 + (-20,000) ÷ 3

ALTERNATIVES	OUTCOMES			AVERAGE FOR ALTERNATIVE
	HIGH DEMAND	MODERATE DEMAND	LOW DEMAND	
Build large plant	$200,000	$100,000	−$120,000	$60,000 → Equally likely
Build small plant	$ 90,000	$ 50,000	−$ 20,000	$40,000
No plant	$ 0	$ 0	$ 0	$ 0

handwritten: Highest avel payof

We first develop the opportunity loss table from the payoff table.

Minimax regret finds the alternative that *mini*mizes the *max*imum opportunity loss within each alternative.

To use this criterion, we need to first develop the opportunity loss table. This is done by determining the opportunity loss of not choosing the best alternative for each outcome. To do so, we subtract each payoff for a specific outcome from the *best* payoff for that outcome. For example, the best payoff with high demand in Thompson Lumber's payoff table is $200,000 (corresponding to building a large plant). Hence, we subtract all payoffs for that outcome (i.e., in that column) from $200,000. Likewise, the best payoffs with moderate demand and low demand are $100,000 and $0, respectively. We therefore subtract all payoffs in the second column from $100,000 and all payoffs in the third column from $0. Table 6 illustrates these computations and shows John's complete opportunity loss table.

Once the opportunity loss table has been constructed, we locate the maximum opportunity loss (regret) for each alternative. We then pick the alternative with the smallest value among these maximum regrets. As shown in Table 7, John's minimax regret choice is the second alternative, build a small plant. The regret of $110,000 is the minimum of the maximum regrets (i.e., $120,000, $110,000, and $200,000) over all three alternatives.

Using Excel to Solve Decision-Making Problems under Uncertainty

As just demonstrated in the Thompson Lumber example, calculations for the different criteria in decision making under uncertainty are fairly straightforward. In most cases, we can perform these calculations quickly even by hand. However, if we wish, we can easily construct Excel spreadsheets to calculate these results for us. Screenshot 1A shows the relevant formulas for the different decision criteria in the Thompson Lumber example. The results are shown in Screenshot 1B.

File: 8-1.xls

TABLE 6   Opportunity Loss Table for Thompson Lumber

ALTERNATIVES	OUTCOMES		
	HIGH DEMAND	MODERATE DEMAND	LOW DEMAND
Build large plant	$200,000 − $200,000 = $ 0	$100,000 − $100,000 = $ 0	$0 − (−$120,000) = $120,000
Build small plant	$200,000 − $ 90,000 = $110,000	$100,000 − $ 50,000 = $ 50,000	$0 − (−$ 20,000) = $ 20,000
No plant	$200,000 − $ 0 = $200,000	$100,000 − $ 0 = $100,000	$0 − $ 0 = $ 0

TABLE 7
Thompson Lumber's
Minimax Regret
Decision

ALTERNATIVES	OUTCOMES			MAXIMUM FOR ALTERNATIVE
	HIGH DEMAND	MODERATE DEMAND	LOW DEMAND	
Build large plant	$ 0	$ 0	$120,000	$120,000
Build small plant	$110,000	$ 50,000	$ 20,000	$110,000 → Minimax
No plant	$200,000	$100,000	$ 0	$200,000

SCREENSHOT 1A **Formula View of Excel Layout for Thompson Lumber: Decision Making under Uncertainty**

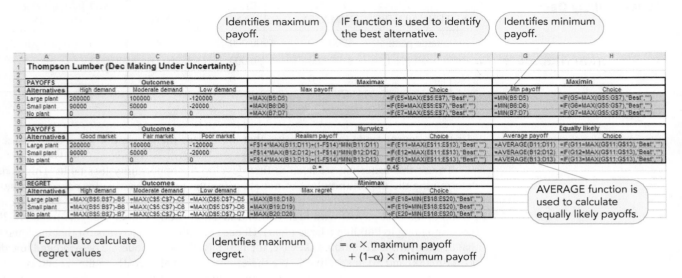

SCREENSHOT 1B **Excel Solution for Thompson Lumber: Decision Making under Uncertainty**

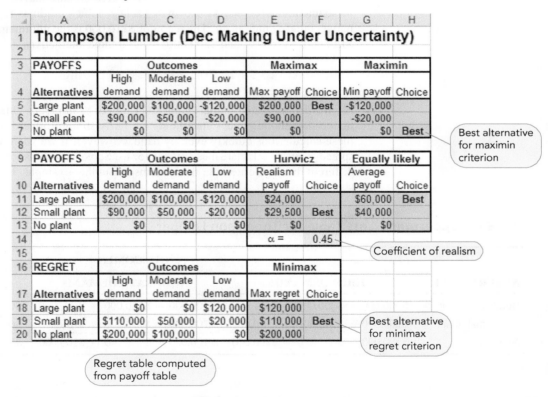

Excel Notes

- The Companion Website for this text, at www.pearsonhighered.com/balakrishnan, contains the Excel file for each sample problem discussed here. The relevant file name is shown in the margin next to each example.
- For clarity, our Excel layouts in this chapter are color coded as follows:
  - *Input cells*, where we enter the problem data, are shaded yellow.
  - *Output cells*, where the results are shown, are shaded green.

Excel worksheets can be created easily to solve decision-making problems under uncertainty.

Note that the number of decision alternatives and the number of outcomes would vary from problem to problem. The formulas shown in Screenshot 1A can, however, easily be modified to accommodate any changes in these parameters.

5 Decision Making under Risk

In many real-world situations, it is common for the decision maker to have some idea about the probabilities of occurrence of the different outcomes. These probabilities may be based on the decision maker's personal opinions about future events or on data obtained from market surveys, expert opinions, and so on. As noted previously, when the probability of occurrence of each outcome can be assessed, the problem environment is called *decision making under risk*.

In this section we consider one of the most popular methods of making decisions under risk: selecting the alternative with the highest expected monetary value. We also look at the concepts of expected opportunity loss and expected value of perfect information.

Expected Monetary Value

EMV *is the weighted average of possible payoffs for each alternative.*

Given a decision table with payoffs and probability assessments, we can determine the **expected monetary value (EMV)** for each alternative. The EMV for an alternative is computed as the *weighted average* of all possible payoffs for that alternative, where the weights are the probabilities of the different outcomes. That is,

$$
\begin{aligned}
\text{EMV (Alternative } i) = & \ (\text{Payoff of first outcome}) \\
& \times (\text{Probability of first outcome}) \\
& + (\text{Payoff of second outcome}) \\
& \times (\text{Probability of second outcome}) \\
& + \cdots + (\text{Payoff of last outcome}) \\
& \times (\text{Probability of last outcome}) \quad (2)
\end{aligned}
$$

In Thompson Lumber's case, let us assume that John has used his knowledge of the storage shed industry to specify that the probabilities of high demand, moderate demand, and low demand are 0.3, 0.5, and 0.2, respectively. Under this scenario, which alternative would give him the greatest EMV? To determine this, we compute the EMV for each alternative, as shown in Table 8. The largest EMV, $86,000, results from the first alternative, build a large plant.

Observe that the EMV represents the long-run *average* payoff, while the *actual* payoff from a decision will be one of the payoffs listed in the decision table. That is, the EMV of $86,000 does not mean that John will actually realize a profit of $86,000 if he builds a large plant. Nevertheless, the EMV is widely used as an acceptable criterion to compare decision alternatives in many business decisions because companies make similar decisions on a repeated basis over time.

TABLE 8 Thompson Lumber's EMV Decision

	OUTCOMES			
ALTERNATIVES	**HIGH DEMAND**	**MODERATE DEMAND**	**LOW DEMAND**	**EMV FOR ALTERNATIVE**
Build large plant	$200,000	$100,000	−$120,000	$200,000 × 0.3 + $100,000 × 0.5 + (−$120,000) × 0.2 = $86,000
Build small plant	$ 90,000	$ 50,000	−$ 20,000	$90,000 × 0.3 + $50,000 × 0.5 + (−$20,000) × 0.2 = $48,000
No plant	$ 0	$ 0	$ 0	$0 × 0.3 + $0 × 0.5 + $0 × 0.2 = $ 0
Probabilities	0.3	0.5	0.2	

Expected Opportunity Loss

EOL is the expected cost of not picking the best solution.

An alternative approach in decision making under risk is to minimize **expected opportunity loss (EOL)**. Recall from section 4 that opportunity loss, also called regret, refers to the difference between the optimal payoff and the actual payoff received. The EOL for an alternative is computed as the weighted average of all possible regrets for that alternative, where the weights are the probabilities of the different outcomes. That is,

$$
\begin{aligned}
\text{EOL (Alternative } i) = \ & (\text{Regret of first outcome}) \\
& \times (\text{Probability of first outcome}) \\
& + (\text{Regret of second outcome}) \\
& \times (\text{Probability of second outcome}) \\
& + \cdots + (\text{Regret of last outcome}) \\
& \times (\text{Probability of last outcome}) \quad (3)
\end{aligned}
$$

Minimum EOL will always result in the same decision as the maximum EMV.

The EOL values for Thompson Lumber's problem are computed as shown in Table 9. Using minimum EOL as the decision criterion, the best decision would be the first alternative, build a large plant, with an EOL of $24,000. It is important to note that the minimum EOL will *always* result in the same decision alternative as the maximum EMV.

Expected Value of Perfect Information

John Thompson has been approached by Scientific Marketing, Inc., a market research firm, with a proposal to help him make the right decision regarding the size of the new plant. Scientific claims that its analysis will tell John with *certainty* whether the demand for storage sheds will be high, moderate, or low. In other words, it will change John's problem environment from one of decision making under risk to one of decision making under certainty. Obviously, this information could prevent John from making an expensive mistake. Scientific would charge $30,000 for the information. What should John do? Should he hire Scientific to do the marketing study? Is the information worth $30,000? If not, what is it worth?

EVPI places an upper bound on what to pay for any information.

We call the type of information offered by Scientific *perfect information* because it is certain (i.e., it is never wrong). Although such perfect information is almost never available in practice, determining its value can be very useful because it places an upper bound on what we should be willing to spend on *any* information. In what follows, we therefore investigate two related issues: the **expected value with perfect information (EVwPI)** and the **expected value of perfect information (EVPI)**.

The EVwPI is the expected payoff if we have perfect information *before* a decision has to be made. Clearly, if we knew for sure that a particular outcome was going to occur, we would choose the alternative that yielded the best payoff for that outcome. Unfortunately, until we get

TABLE 9 Thompson Lumber's EOL Decision

| | OUTCOMES | | | |
ALTERNATIVES	HIGH DEMAND	MODERATE DEMAND	LOW DEMAND	EOL FOR ALTERNATIVE
Build large plant	$ 0	$ 0	$120,000	$0 × 0.3 + $0 × 0.5 + $120,000 × 0.2 = $ 24,000
Build small plant	$110,000	$ 50,000	$ 20,000	$110,000 × 0.3 + $50,000 × 0.5 + $20,000 × 0.2 = $ 62,000
No plant	$200,000	$100,000	$ 0	$200,000 × 0.3 + $100,000 × 0.5 + $0 × 0.2 = $110,000
Probabilities	0.3	0.5	0.2	

this information, we don't know for sure which outcome is going to occur. Hence, to calculate the EVwPI value, we choose the best payoff for each outcome and multiply it by the probability of occurrence of that outcome. That is,

$$
\begin{aligned}
\text{EVwPI} = {} & (\text{Best payoff of first outcome}) \\
& \times (\text{Probability of first outcome}) \\
& + (\text{Best payoff of second outcome}) \\
& \times (\text{Probability of second outcome}) \\
& + \cdots + (\text{Best payoff of last outcome}) \\
& \times (\text{Probability of last outcome})
\end{aligned} \tag{4}
$$

EVPI *is the expected value with perfect information minus the maximum EMV.*

We then compute the EVPI as the EVwPI minus the expected value *without* information, namely, the maximum EMV. That is,

$$
\text{EVPI} = \text{EVwPI} - \text{Maximum EMV} \tag{5}
$$

By referring to Table 8, we can calculate the EVPI for John as follows:

1. The best payoff for the outcome high demand is \$200,000, associated with building a large plant. The best payoff for moderate demand is \$100,000, again associated with building a large plant. Finally, the best payoff for low demand is \$0, associated with not building a plant. Hence,

$$
\text{EVwPI} = \$200,000 \times 0.3 + \$100,000 \times 0.5 + \$0 \times 0.20 = \$110,000
$$

That is, if we had perfect information, we would expect an *average* payoff of \$110,000 if the decision could be repeated many times.

2. Recall from Table 8 that the maximum EMV, or the best expected value *without* information, is \$86,000. Hence,

$$
\text{EVPI} = \text{EVwPI} - \text{Maximum EMV} = \$110,000 - \$86,000 = \$24,000
$$

EVPI = *Minimum EOL*

Thus, the most John should pay for perfect information is \$24,000. Because Scientific Marketing wants \$30,000 for its analysis, John should reject the offer. It is important to note that the following relationship always holds: EVPI = Minimum EOL. Referring to Thompson Lumber's example, we see that EVPI = Minimum EOL = \$24,000.

Using Excel to Solve Decision-Making Problems under Risk

File: 8-2.xls

Just as with decision making under uncertainty, calculations for finding the EMV, EOL, EVwPI, and EVPI in decision making under risk are also fairly straightforward. In most small cases, we can perform these calculations quickly even by hand. However, if we wish, we can once again easily construct Excel spreadsheets to calculate these values for us. Screenshot 2A shows the relevant formulas to solve the Thompson Lumber example. The results are shown in Screenshot 2B.

As with Screenshot 1A, note that the number of decision alternatives and number of outcomes would vary from problem to problem. The formulas shown in Screenshot 2A can, however, be easily modified to accommodate any changes in these parameters.

6 Decision Trees

Any problem that can be presented in a decision table can also be graphically illustrated in a *decision tree*. A decision tree consists of nodes (or points) and arcs (or lines), just like a network. We illustrate the construction and use of decision trees using the Thompson Lumber example.

SCREENSHOT 2A Formula View of Excel Layout for Thompson Lumber: Decision Making under Risk

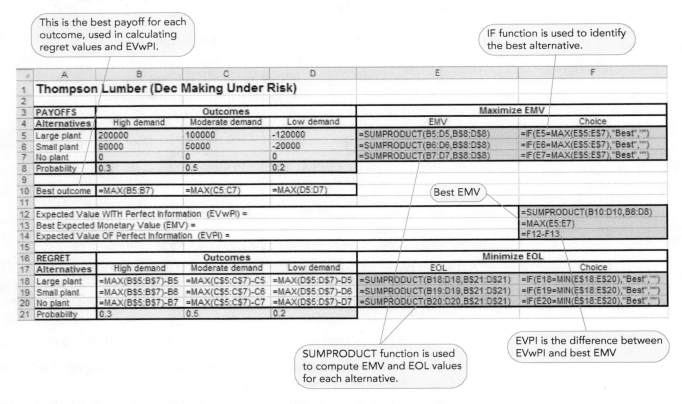

This is the best payoff for each outcome, used in calculating regret values and EVwPI.

IF function is used to identify the best alternative.

Best EMV

SUMPRODUCT function is used to compute EMV and EOL values for each alternative.

EVPI is the difference between EVwPI and best EMV

SCREENSHOT 2B Excel Solution for Thompson Lumber: Decision Making under Risk

Best EMV choice is large plant

Known probability for each outcome

EVPI = minimum EOL

Best EOL choice is same as best EMV choice.

IN ACTION — Designing U.S. Army Installations Using Decision Analysis

Prior to 2002, army installations at about 100 major bases in the United States were managed by five U.S. Army organizations. In October 2002, the Installation Management Agency (IMA) was established to centrally manage all installations worldwide. The IMA's objective was to ensure a standard delivery of services and resources to all installations while reducing costs and redundancies.

Within the United States, the IMA was set up to use four regions to manage all continental U.S. installations. Based partly on concerns from Congress, the army wanted an analysis to verify if the IMA's use of four regions was indeed appropriate. Researchers from the U.S. Military Academy used decision analysis to evaluate several regional alternatives (i.e., using anywhere from just 1 up to 8 regions), measuring how well each alternative would perform the functions. The measures captured the effectiveness and efficiency of the regional organization for each function.

The analyses showed that four regions was an appropriate number to manage installations effectively. The use of a decision analysis framework to develop both qualitative and quantitative models of this problem helped provide a sound analysis to senior army decision makers.

Source: Based on T. E. Trainor et al. "The US Army Uses Decision Analysis in Designing Its US Installation Regions," *Interfaces* 37, 3 (May–June 2007): 253–264.

Decision trees contain decision nodes and outcome nodes.

A decision tree presents the decision alternatives and outcomes in a sequential manner. All decision trees are similar in that they contain *decision nodes* and *outcome nodes*. These nodes are represented using the following symbols:

□ = A *decision* node. Arcs (lines) originating from a decision node denote all decision alternatives available to the decision maker at that node. Of these, the decision maker must select only one alternative.

○ = An *outcome* node. Arcs (lines) originating from an outcome node denote all outcomes that could occur at that node. Of these, only one outcome will actually occur.

A decision tree usually begins with a decision node.

Although it is possible for a decision tree to begin with an outcome node, most trees begin with a decision node. In Thompson Lumber's case, this decision node indicates that John has to decide among his three alternatives: building a large plant, a small plant, or no plant. Each alternative is represented by an arc originating from this decision node. Once John makes this decision, one of three possible outcomes (high demand, moderate demand, or low demand) will occur. The simple decision tree to represent John's decision is shown in Figure 1.

Observe that all alternatives available to John are shown as arcs originating from a decision node (□). Likewise, at each outcome node (○), all possible outcomes that could occur if John chooses that decision alternative are shown as arcs. The payoffs resulting from each alternative and outcome combination are shown at the end of each relevant path in the tree. For example, if John chooses to build a large plant and demand turns out to be high, the resulting payoff is $200,000.

FIGURE 1
Decision Tree for Thompson Lumber

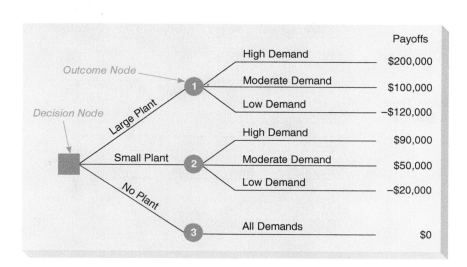

Folding Back a Decision Tree

We fold back a decision tree to identify the best decision.

The process by which a decision tree is analyzed to identify the optimal decision is referred to as *folding back* the decision tree. We start with the payoffs (i.e., the right extreme of the tree) and work our way back to the first decision node. In folding back the decision tree, we use the following two rules:

- At each outcome node, we compute the expected payoff, using the probabilities of all possible outcomes at that node and the payoffs associated with those outcomes.
- At each decision node, we select the alternative that yields the better expected payoff. If the expected payoffs represent profits, we select the alternative with the largest value. In contrast, if the expected payoffs represent costs, we select the alternative with the smallest value.

The EMV is calculated at each outcome node.

The complete decision tree for Thompson Lumber is presented in Figure 2. For convenience, the probability of each outcome is shown in parentheses next to each outcome. The EMV at each outcome node is then calculated and placed by that node. The EMV at node 1 (if John decides to build a large plant) is $86,000, and the EMV at node 2 (if John decides to build a small plant) is $48,000. Building no plant has, of course, an EMV of $0.

At this stage, the decision tree for Thompson Lumber has been folded back to just the first decision node and the three alternatives (arcs) originating from it. That is, all outcome nodes and the outcomes from these nodes have been examined and collapsed into the EMVs. The reduced decision tree for Thompson Lumber is shown in Figure 3.

The best alternative is selected at a decision node.

Using the rule stated earlier for decision nodes, we now select the alternative with the highest EMV. In this case, it corresponds to the alternative to build a large plant. The resulting EMV is $86,000.

FIGURE 2
Complete Decision Tree for Thompson Lumber

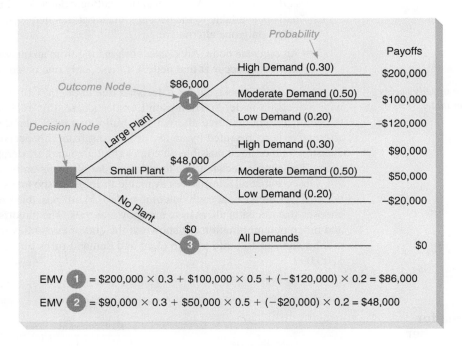

EMV ① = $200,000 × 0.3 + $100,000 × 0.5 + (−$120,000) × 0.2 = $86,000

EMV ② = $90,000 × 0.3 + $50,000 × 0.5 + (−$20,000) × 0.2 = $48,000

FIGURE 3
Reduced Decision Tree for Thompson Lumber

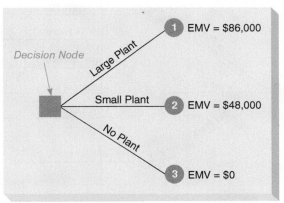

7   Using Treeplan to Solve Decision Tree Problems with Excel

TreePlan is an Excel add-in for solving decision tree problems.

We can use TreePlan, an add-in for Excel, to set up and solve decision tree problems. The TreePlan program consists of a single Excel add-in file, *Treeplan.xla*, which can be copied from this text Companion Website to your hard disk.

Loading TreePlan

There are two ways of loading TreePlan in Excel.

To load and enable TreePlan in Excel, you can use either of the two approaches described in the following sections.

LOADING MANUALLY Each time you run Excel, you can load TreePlan manually, as follows:

M1. Click File | Open and use the file browse window to find the *Treeplan.xla* file on your hard disk.

M2. Open the file. Note that you will not see anything new on your Excel spreadsheet at this time. Also, depending on your macro settings for Excel (click File | Help | Options | Trust Center | Trust Center Settings | Macro Settings to see your settings), Excel may ask if you want to enable macros in the file. You must enable macros to use TreePlan.

M3. Under the Add-Ins tab in Excel, you will see a menu command called Decision Tree.

LOADING AUTOMATICALLY You have to load automatically only once, as follows:

A1. Copy the *Treeplan.xla* file to your hard drive.

A2. Open Excel. Click File | Options | Add-Ins. In the Manage window, select Excel Add-Ins and click Go.

A3. Click Browse and use the file browse window to locate and select the *Treeplan.xla* file. Then click OK.

A4. You will see an option named TreePlan Decision Tree in the Add-In list. Make sure the box next to this option is checked. Click OK. *Note:* To subsequently prevent TreePlan from loading automatically, repeat step A2 and uncheck the box next to this add-in.

A5. Under the Add-Ins tab in Excel, you will see a menu command called Decision Tree. *Note:* You must enable macros to use TreePlan (see step M2 for details).

Creating a Decision Tree Using TreePlan

Once you have installed and loaded TreePlan, you can use the following six steps to set up and solve a decision tree problem: (1) start the program; (2) begin a new tree; (3) add nodes and branches; (4) change titles, probabilities, and payoffs; (5) identify the best decision; and (6) make minor formatting changes. On the next several pages, we illustrate these six steps using the Thompson Lumber problem. Recall that we saw the complete decision tree for this problem in Figure 2.

Select Add-Ins | Decision Tree in Excel to start TreePlan.

STEP 1: START TREEPLAN Start Excel and open a blank worksheet. Place the cursor in any blank cell (say, cell A1). Select Decision Tree from the Add-Ins tab in Excel. *Note:* If you don't see the Add-Ins tab or the Decision Tree menu command as a choice within this tab, you have to install TreePlan, as discussed in the preceding section.

File: 8-3.xls, sheet: 8-3A

STEP 2: START A NEW TREE Select New Tree. As shown in Screenshot 3A, this creates an initial decision tree with a single decision node (in cell B5, if the cursor was placed in cell A1). Two alternatives (named Alternative 1 and Alternative 2) are automatically created at this node.

The TreePlan menu that appears depends on the location of the cursor.

STEP 3: ADD NODES AND BRANCHES We now modify the basic decision tree in Screenshot 3A to reflect our full decision problem. To do so, we use TreePlan menus. To bring up the menu, we either select Add-Ins | Decision Tree or press the Control (Ctrl), Shift, and T keys at the same time. The TreePlan menu that is displayed each time depends on the location of the cursor when we bring up the menu, as follows:

- If the cursor is at a node in the tree (such as cell B5 in Screenshot 3A), the menu shown in Screenshot 3B(a) is displayed.
- If the cursor is at a terminal point in the tree (such as cells F3 and F8 in Screenshot 3A), the menu shown in Screenshot 3B(b) is displayed.
- If the cursor is at any other location in the spreadsheet, the menu shown in Screenshot 3B(c) is displayed.

SCREENSHOT 3A
Initial Decision Tree from TreePlan

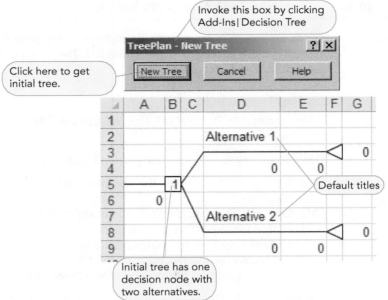

Invoke this box by clicking Add-Ins| Decision Tree

Click here to get initial tree.

Default titles

Initial tree has one decision node with two alternatives.

SCREENSHOT 3B
TreePlan Menus

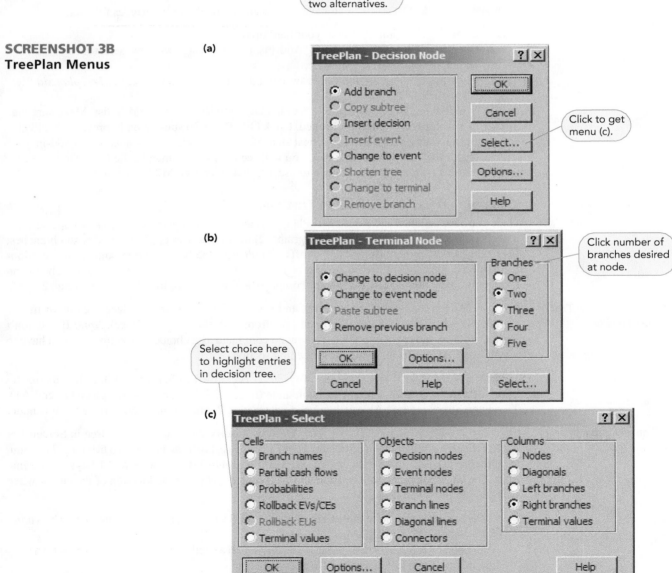

(a)

Click to get menu (c).

(b)

Click number of branches desired at node.

Select choice here to highlight entries in decision tree.

(c)

For the Thompson Lumber example, we begin by placing the cursor in cell B5 and bringing up the menu in Screenshot 3B(a). We then select Add Branch and click OK to get the third decision branch (named Decision 3).

Next, we move the cursor to the end of the branch for Decision 1 (i.e., to cell F3 in Screenshot 3A) and bring up the menu in Screenshot 3B(b). We first select Change to Event Node. (Note that TreePlan refers to outcome nodes as *event nodes*.) Then we select Three under Branches to add three outcome arcs to this outcome node. When we click OK, the program creates three arcs, named Event 4, Event 5, and Event 6, respectively. Because these are outcomes, we need to associate probability values with the events. TreePlan automatically assigns equal probability values by default. In this case, because there are three events, the default value assigned is 1/3 (shown as 0.33333).

Each time we add more decision alternatives or outcomes to a decision tree, TreePlan automatically repositions the tree on the Excel worksheet to make it fit better. We next move the cursor to the end of the branch for Decision 2 and repeat the preceding step to create Event 7, Event 8, and Event 9. The structure of the decision tree, shown in Screenshot 3C, is now similar to that of the tree in Figure 2.

STEP 4: CHANGE TITLES, PROBABILITIES, AND PAYOFFS We can change the default titles for all arcs in the decision tree to reflect the Thompson Lumber example. For example, we

TreePlan refers to outcome nodes as event nodes.

File: 8-3.xls, sheet: 8-3C

Titles can be changed in TreePlan, if desired.

SCREENSHOT 3C Complete Decision Tree Using TreePlan for Thompson Lumber

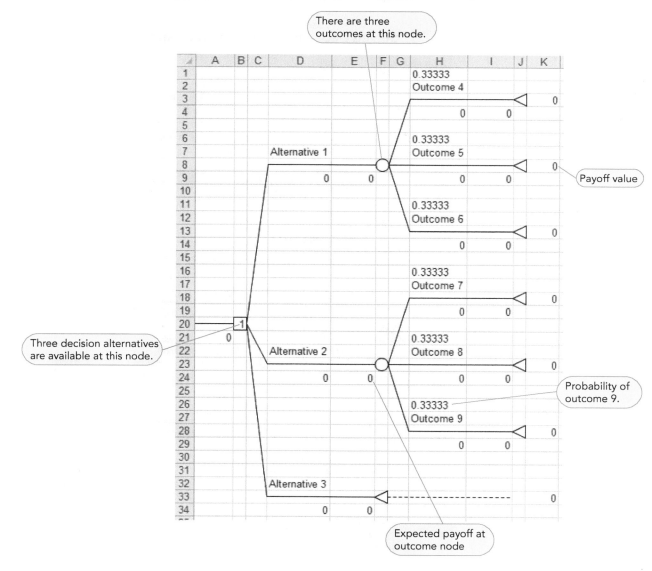

can replace Decision 1 (in cell D7 of Screenshot 3C) with Large plant. Likewise, we can replace Event 4 (in cell H2 of Screenshot 3C) with High demand. The changes are shown in Screenshot 3D.

Next, we change the default probability values on the event arcs to the correct values. Finally, we enter the payoffs. TreePlan allows us to enter these values in two ways:

There are two ways of entering payoffs in TreePlan.

File: 8-3.xls, sheet: 8-3D

- We can directly enter the payoffs at the end of each path in the decision tree. That is, we can enter the appropriate payoff values in cells K3, K8, K13, K18, K23, K28, and K33 (see Screenshot 3D).
- We can allow TreePlan to compute the payoffs. Each time we create an arc (a decision alternative or outcome) in TreePlan, it assigns a default payoff of zero to that branch. We can edit these payoffs (or costs) for all alternatives and outcomes. For example, we leave cell D9 at $0 (default value) because there is no cost specified for building a large plant. However, we change the entry in cell H4 to $200,000 to reflect the payoff if demand turns out to be high. TreePlan adds these two entries (in cells D9 and H4) automatically and reports it as the payoff in cell K3. We can do likewise for all other payoffs in John's tree.

TreePlan writes formulas in the appropriate cells as the tree is created.

STEP 5: IDENTIFY THE BEST DECISION TreePlan automatically writes formulas into the appropriate cells as the tree is created and structured. For example, TreePlan writes the following formula in cell E9 (which computes the EMV of building a large plant) of Screenshot 3D:

$$=IF(ABS(1-SUM(H1, H6, H11)) <= 0.00001, SUM(H1*I4, H6*I9, H11*I14), NA())$$

SCREENSHOT 3D   Solved Decision Tree Using TreePlan for Thompson Lumber

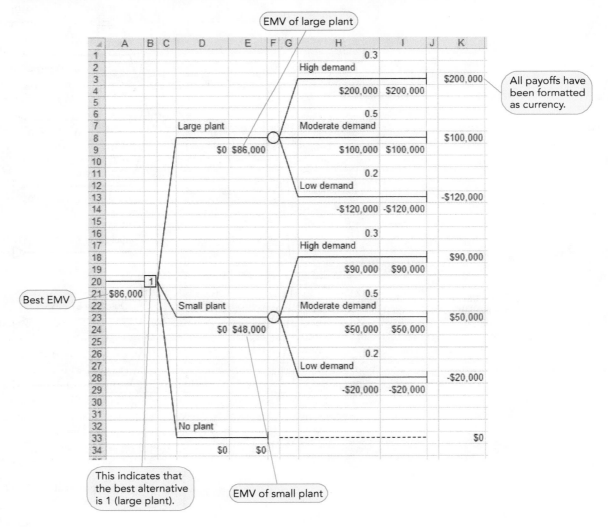

IN ACTION — Decision Analysis Helps Solve Airport Ground Delay Problems

One of the most frustrating aspects of air travel is rushing to the airport only to find out that your flight has been delayed. Often triggered by what is called the Ground-Delay Program (GDP), the Federal Aviation Administration (FAA) keeps flights from departing when the air traffic or weather at the destination is unfavorable.

Decisions involving GDP are classic problems in decision analysis. At the heart of such a problem, there are two decision alternatives: allow the flight to depart or do not allow the flight to depart. In choosing from these alternatives, the decision maker has to consider several unknown future outcomes, such as the weather, expected air traffic, and a variety of other factors that could develop at the destination. These factors could delay or prevent a flight from landing safely.

The original GDP system was administered by the FAA. The FAA monitored existing imbalances between demand and capacity at given airports to determine whether a ground delay was warranted and justified at other airports that fed into it. Some experts, however, claimed that the FAA lacked current and accurate information. In some cases, the FAA relied on the published airline schedules, which were subject to change and inaccuracies. This resulted in the inefficient use of arrival resources and unnecessary ground delays at some airports. To overcome some of these problems, a decision analysis model was developed.

Using decision analysis models can improve not only information flow but also performance. Before the initiative, 51% of flights left on time. Afterward, 66% left on time. In addition to conserving fuel and improving utilization of arrival resources, these types of initiatives can save travelers a tremendous amount of frustration and lost time.

Source: Based on K. Chang, et al. "Enhancements to the FAA Ground-Delay Program Under Collaborative Decision Making," *Interfaces* 31, 1 (January–February 2001): 57–76.

The ABS part of the formula verifies that the sum of probabilities of all outcomes at a given outcome node equals 1. The second part (SUM) computes the EMV using the appropriate payoffs and probability values. The EMVs are shown next to the outcome nodes. For example, cell E9 shows an EMV of $86,000 for the large plant.

Once all expected values have been computed, TreePlan then selects the optimal decision alternative at each decision node. The selection is indicated within that node. For example, the 1 within the decision node in cell B20 indicates that the first alternative (i.e., large plant) is the best choice for Thompson Lumber. The best EMV of $86,000 is shown next to this decision node (in cell A21).

If the payoffs denote costs, we can click Options in any of the TreePlan menus (see Screenshot 3B) to change the selection criterion from maximizing profits to minimizing costs. In this case, TreePlan will select the decision alternative with the smallest expected costs.

STEP 6: MAKE MINOR FORMATTING CHANGES If desired, we can add titles, format payoffs to be shown as dollar values, change number of decimals shown, and make other cosmetic changes to the tree, as shown in Screenshot 3D.

8 Decision Trees for Multistage Decision-Making Problems

Multistage decision problems involve a sequence of decision alternatives and outcomes.

The Thompson Lumber problem discussed so far is a single-stage problem. That is, John has to choose a decision alternative, which is followed by an outcome. Depending on the alternative chosen and the outcome that occurs, John gets a payoff, and the problem ends there.

In many cases, however, the decision-making scenario is a multistage problem. In such cases, the decision maker must evaluate and make a set of **sequential decisions** up front (i.e., before the first decision is implemented). However, the decisions are actually implemented in a sequential manner, as follows. The problem usually begins with the decision maker implementing his or her initial decision. This is followed by an outcome. Depending on the initial decision and the outcome that occurs after it, the decision maker next implements his or her next decision. The alternatives for this follow-up decision may be different for different outcomes of the earlier decision. This decision, in turn, is followed by an outcome. The set of outcomes for this decision may be different from the set of outcomes for the earlier decision. This sequence could continue several more times, and the final payoff is a function of the sequence of decisions made and the outcomes that occurred at each stage of the problem.

At one or more stages in a problem, it is possible for a specific decision to have no outcomes following it. In such cases, the decision maker is immediately faced with the next decision. Likewise, at one or more stages in the problem, it is possible to have one outcome occur directly after another outcome without the decision maker facing a decision in between the two.

For multistage scenarios, decision tables are no longer convenient, and we are forced to analyze these problems using decision trees. Although we can, in theory, extend multistage scenarios to a sequence of as many decisions and outcomes as we wish, we will limit our discussion here to problems involving just two stages. To facilitate this discussion, let us consider an expanded version of the Thompson Lumber problem.

A Multistage Decision-Making Problem for Thompson Lumber

Before deciding about building a new plant, let's suppose John Thompson has been approached by Smart Services, another market research firm. Smart will charge John $4,000 to conduct a market survey. The results of the survey will indicate either positive or negative market conditions for storage sheds. What should John do?

John recognizes that Smart's market survey will not provide him with *perfect* information, but it may help him get a better feel for the outcomes nevertheless. The type of information obtained here is referred to either as *sample* information or *imperfect* information.

Recall from section 5 that we calculated John's EVPI as $24,000. That is, if the results of the market survey are going to be 100% accurate, John should be willing to pay up to $24,000 for the survey. Because Smart's survey will cost significantly less (only $4,000), it is at least worth considering further. However, given that it yields only imperfect information, how much is it actually worth? We determine this by extending the decision tree analysis for Thompson Lumber to include Smart's market survey.

Expanded Decision Tree for Thompson Lumber

John's new decision tree is represented in Figure 4. Let's take a careful look at this more complex tree. Note that all possible alternatives and outcomes are included in their logical sequence. This is one of the strengths of using decision trees in making decisions. The user is forced to examine all possible outcomes, including unfavorable ones. He or she is also forced to make decisions in a logical, sequential manner.

Examining the tree, we see that John's first decision point is whether to conduct Smart's market survey. If he chooses not to do the survey (i.e., the upper part of the tree), he is immediately faced with his second decision node: whether to build a large plant, a small plant, or no plant. The possible outcomes for each of these alternatives are high demand (0.3 probability), moderate demand (0.5 probability), and low demand (0.2 probability). The payoffs for each of the possible consequences are listed along the right side of the tree. As a matter of fact, this portion of John's tree in Figure 4 is identical to the simpler decision tree shown in Figure 2. Can you see why this is so?

The lower portion of Figure 4 reflects the decision to conduct the market survey. This decision has two possible outcomes—positive survey result or negative survey result—each with a specific probability. For now, let us assume that John knows these probabilities to be as follows: probability of 0.57 that the survey will indicate positive market conditions for storage sheds, and probability of 0.43 that the survey will indicate negative market conditions. An explanation of how these probabilities can be calculated in real-world situations is the topic of section 9.

Regardless of which survey outcome occurs, John is now faced with his next decision. Although the decision alternatives at this point could be different for different survey outcomes, let us assume in John's case that for both survey outcomes he has the same three alternatives: whether to build a large plant, a small plant, or no plant. Each alternative has the same three outcomes as before: high demand, moderate demand, and low demand. The key difference, however, is that the survey outcome (positive or negative) allows John to update the probabilities of the demand outcomes. For this reason, the probabilities shown in parentheses for these outcomes in Figure 4 are called *conditional probabilities*. An explanation of how these probabilities can be calculated in real-world situations is also presented in section 9. For now, let us assume that these probabilities have already been calculated and are available to John.

From Figure 4, we note, for example, that the probability of high demand for sheds, given a positive survey result, is 0.509. Note that this is higher than the 0.30 probability that John had estimated for high demand before the market survey. This increase in the probability is not surprising because you would, of course, expect a positive survey result to be a stronger

It is possible for one outcome (or alternative) to directly follow another outcome (or alternative).

Multistage decision problems are analyzed using decision trees.

EVPI is an upper bound on the value of sample information.

All outcomes and alternatives must be considered.

Many of the probabilities are conditional probabilities.

FIGURE 4 Expanded Decision Tree with Payoffs and Probabilities for Thompson Lumber

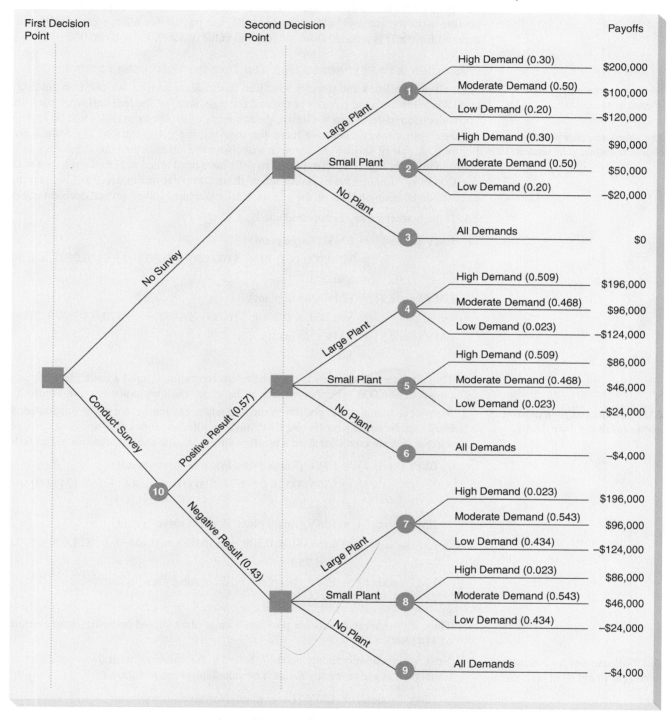

indicator of high demand. Don't forget, however, that any market research study is subject to error. Therefore, it is possible that Smart's market survey didn't result in very reliable information. In fact, as shown in Figure 4, demand for sheds could be moderate (with a probability of 0.468) or low (with a probability of 0.023), even if Smart's survey results are positive.

Likewise, we note in Figure 4 that if the survey results are negative, the probability of low demand for sheds increases from the 0.20 that John originally estimated to 0.434. However, because Smart's survey results are not perfect, there are nonzero probabilities of moderate and high demand for sheds, even if the survey results are negative. As shown in Figure 4, these values are 0.543 and 0.023, respectively.

The cost of the survey has to be included in the decision tree.

Finally, when we look to the payoff values in Figure 4, we note that the cost of the market survey ($4,000) has to be subtracted from every payoff in the lower portion of the tree (i.e., the portion with the survey). Thus, for example, the payoff for a large plant followed by high demand for sheds is reduced from the original value of $200,000 to $196,000.

Folding Back the Expanded Decision Tree for Thompson Lumber

We start by computing the EMV of each branch.

With all probabilities and payoffs specified in the decision tree, we can start folding back the tree. We begin with the payoffs at the end (or right side) of the tree and work back toward the initial decision node. When we finish, the sequence of decisions to make will be known.

The alternative that should be chosen is indicated by slashes (//).

For your convenience, we have summarized the computations for John's problem in Figure 5. A pair of slashes (//) through a decision branch indicates the alternative selected at a decision node. In Figure 5, all expected payoffs have been noted next to the relevant nodes on the decision tree. Although we explain each of these computations in detail below, you may find it easier to do all computations on the tree itself after you have solved several decision tree problems:

1. If the market survey is *not* conducted,

$$\text{EMV (node 1)} = \text{EMV (Large plant)}$$
$$= \$200,000 \times 0.30 + \$100,000 \times 0.50 + (-\$120,000) \times 0.20$$
$$= \$86,000$$
$$\text{EMV (node 2)} = \text{EMV (Small plant)}$$
$$= \$90,000 \times 0.30 + \$50,000 \times 0.50 + (-\$20,000) \times 0.20 = \$48,000$$
$$\text{EMV (node 3)} = \text{EMV (No plant)}$$
$$= \$0$$

Thus, if the market survey is not conducted, John should build a large plant, for an expected payoff of $86,000. As expected, this is the same result we saw earlier, in Figure 2.

EMV calculations for a positive survey result are done first.

2. Now let us examine the portion of the tree where the market survey is conducted. Working backward from the payoffs, we first consider outcome nodes 4, 5, and 6. All calculations at these nodes are conditional on a positive survey result. The calculations are as follows:

$$\text{EMV (node 4)} = \text{EMV (Large plant} \mid \text{Positive survey result)}$$
$$= \$196,000 \times 0.509 + \$96,000 \times 0.468 + (-\$124,000) \times 0.023$$
$$= \$141,840$$
$$\text{EMV (node 5)} = \text{EMV (Small plant} \mid \text{Positive survey result)}$$
$$= \$86,000 \times 0.509 + \$46,000 \times 0.468 + (-\$24,000) \times 0.023$$
$$= \$64,750$$
$$\text{EMV (node 6)} = \text{EMV (No plant} \mid \text{Positive survey result)}$$
$$= -\$4,000$$

Thus, if the survey results are positive, a large plant should be built, for an expected payoff of $141,840.

EMV calculations for a negative survey result are done next.

3. Next, we consider outcome nodes 7, 8, and 9. All calculations at these nodes are conditional on a negative survey result. The calculations are as follows:

$$\text{EMV (node 7)} = \text{EMV (Large plant} \mid \text{Negative survey result)}$$
$$= \$196,000 \times 0.023 + \$96,000 \times 0.543 + (-\$124,000) \times 0.434$$
$$= \$2,820$$
$$\text{EMV (node 8)} = \text{EMV (Small plant} \mid \text{Negative survey result)}$$
$$= \$86,000 \times 0.023 + \$46,000 \times 0.543 + (-\$24,000) \times 0.434$$
$$= \$16,540$$
$$\text{EMV (node 9)} = \text{EMV (No plant} \mid \text{Negative survey result)}$$
$$= -\$4,000$$

Thus, given a negative survey result, John should build a small plant, with an expected payoff of $16,540.

FIGURE 5 **Thompson Lumber's Expanded Decision Tree, with EMVs Shown**

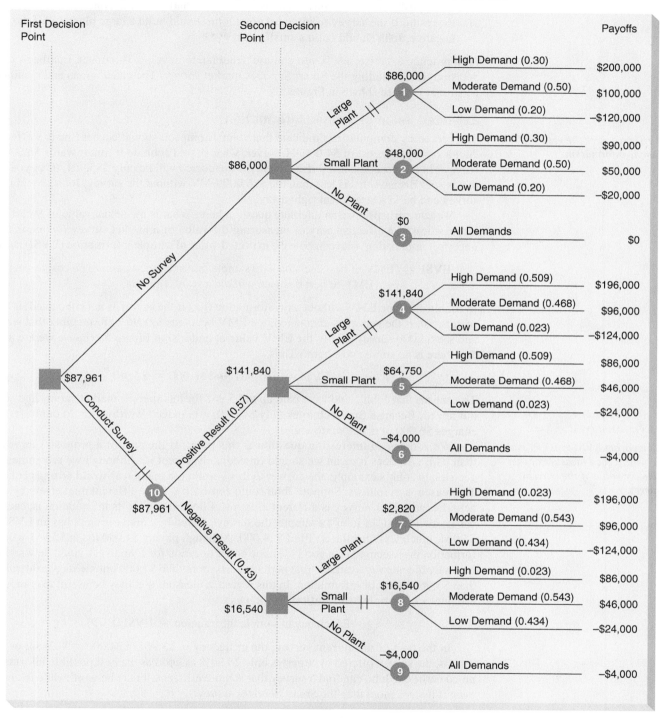

We continue working backward to the origin, computing EMV values.

4. Continuing on the lower portion of the tree and moving backward, we next consider outcome node 10. At this node, we compute the expected value if we conduct the market survey, as follows:

$$\text{EMV (node 10)} = \text{EMV (Conduct survey)}$$
$$= \$141,840 \times 0.57 + \$16,540 \times 0.43 = \$87,961$$

5. Finally, we consider the initial decision node. At this node, we compare the EMV of not conducting the survey with the EMV of conducting the survey. Because the EMV of

$87,961 if we conduct the survey is higher than the $86,000 EMV if the survey is not conducted, John's decision should be to accept Smart's offer to conduct a survey and await the result. If the survey result is positive, John should build a large plant; but if the result is negative, John should build a small plant.

As a practice exercise, see if you can use TreePlan to develop Thompson Lumber's complete decision tree, including the Smart Services market survey. The calculations and results should be similar to those shown in Figure 5.

Expected Value of Sample Information

EVSI measures the value of sample information.

The preceding computations indicate that John Thompson should accept Smart's offer to conduct a survey at a cost of $4,000. However, what should John do if Smart wants $6,000 for the survey? In this case, the EMV if the survey is conducted will be only $85,961. (Can you see why this is so?) Because this is less than the $86,000 EMV without the survey, John should reject the survey and build a large plant right away.

We can perhaps pose an alternate question here: What is the actual value of Smart's survey information? An effective way of measuring the value of a market survey (which is typically imperfect information) is to compute the **expected value of sample information (EVSI)**, as follows:

EVSI = (EMV of best decision *with* sample information, *assuming* no cost to get it)
    − (EMV of best decision *without* any information)   (6)

In John's case, the EMV without any information (i.e., if the survey is not conducted) is $86,000. In contrast, if the survey is conducted, the EMV becomes $91,961. (Remember that we need to add the $4,000 survey cost to the EMV value at node 10 in Figure 5 because we are assuming that there is no survey cost here.) Thus,

$$\text{EVSI} = \$91,961 - \$86,000 = \$5,961$$

This means that John could have paid up to $5,961 for this *specific* market survey and still come out ahead. Because Smart charges only $4,000, it is indeed worthwhile. In contrast, if Smart charges $6,000, it is not worthwhile.

Comparing EVSI to EVPI may provide a good measure of the relative value of the current survey.

We address an interesting question at this point: If the cost of a proposed survey is less than its EVSI, does it mean we should immediately accept it? Although we recommended this decision in John's example, the answer to this question in many real-world settings could be no. The reason is as follows. Suppose John could approach *several* different market survey firms for help. Because each survey is different in terms of how imperfect its information is, each survey has its own EVSI. In John's example, the survey offered by Smart Services has an EVSI of only $5,961, much less than the EVPI of $24,000. Although paying $4,000 to get $5,961 worth of information may seem to be a good idea, the better question for John to ask could be whether there is some *other* survey available that perhaps costs more than $4,000 but yields considerably more than $5,961 worth of information. In this regard, a measure that may be useful to compute is the **efficiency of sample information**, as follows:

$$\text{Efficiency of sample information} = \text{EVSI/EVPI} \qquad (7)$$

In the case of the current survey, the efficiency is $5,961/$24,000 = 0.2484, or 24.84%. That is, the survey offered by Smart is only 24.84% as good as the best possible information. As noted earlier, if John can find a survey that is more efficient, it may be worthwhile to consider it, even if it costs more than the Smart Services survey.

9   Estimating Probability Values Using Bayesian Analysis

Bayes' theorem allows decision makers to revise probability values.

In discussing Thompson Lumber's multistage decision problem (see Figure 5), we assumed that the following event and conditional probabilities were available to John with regard to the survey offered by Smart Services:

$P($Positive survey result$)$	$= P(\text{PS})$	$= 0.570$
$P($Negative survey result$)$	$= P(\text{NS})$	$= 0.430$
$P($High demand $\mid$ Positive survey result$)$	$= P(\text{HD}\mid\text{PS})$	$= 0.509$

$$P(\text{Moderate demand} \mid \text{Positive survey result}) = P(\text{MD} \mid \text{PS}) = 0.468$$
$$P(\text{Low demand} \mid \text{Positive survey result}) = P(\text{LD} \mid \text{PS}) = 0.023$$
$$P(\text{High demand} \mid \text{Negative survey result}) = P(\text{HD} \mid \text{NS}) = 0.023$$
$$P(\text{Moderate demand} \mid \text{Negative survey result}) = P(\text{MD} \mid \text{NS}) = 0.543$$
$$P(\text{Low demand} \mid \text{Negative survey result}) = P(\text{LD} \mid \text{NS}) = 0.443$$

In practice, as illustrated in this section, John would have computed these probabilities using Bayes' theorem on data regarding the performance of Smart Services on past surveys. Bayes' theorem allows decision makers to incorporate additional information (e.g., past performance) to revise their probability estimates of various outcomes.

Calculating Revised Probabilities

Prior probabilities are estimates before the market survey.

In order to evaluate the reliability of the survey, John asks Smart Services to provide him with information regarding its performance on past surveys. Specifically, he wants to know how many similar surveys the company has conducted in the past, what it predicted each time, and what the actual result turned out to be eventually in each case. Let's assume that Smart has data on 75 past surveys that it has conducted. In these 75 surveys, Smart had predicted high demand in 30 cases, moderate demand in 15 cases, and low demand in 30 cases. These data are summarized in Table 10.

Table 10 reveals, for example, that in 29 of 30 past cases where a product's demand subsequently turned out to be high, Smart's surveys had predicted positive market conditions. That is, the probability of positive survey results, given high demand, $P(\text{PS} \mid \text{HD})$, is 0.967. Likewise, in 7 of 15 past cases where a product's demand subsequently turned out to be moderate, Smart's surveys had predicted negative market conditions. That is, the probability of negative survey results, given moderate demand, $P(\text{NS} \mid \text{MD})$, is 0.467. How does John use this information to gauge the accuracy of Smart's survey in his specific case?

Revised probabilities are determined using the prior probabilities and the market survey information.

Recall that without any market survey information, John's current probability estimates of high, moderate, and low demand are $P(\text{HD}) = 0.30$, $P(\text{MD}) = 0.50$, and $P(\text{LD}) = 0.20$, respectively. These are referred to as *prior* probabilities. Based on the survey performance information in Table 10, we compute John's revised, or *posterior*, probabilities—namely, $P(\text{HD} \mid \text{PS})$, $P(\text{MD} \mid \text{PS})$, $P(\text{LD} \mid \text{PS})$, $P(\text{HD} \mid \text{NS})$, $P(\text{MD} \mid \text{NS})$, and $P(\text{LD} \mid \text{NS})$. This computation, using the formula for Bayes' theorem, proceeds as follows:

$$P(HD \mid PS) = \frac{P(PS \text{ and } HD)}{P(PS)} = \frac{P(PS \mid HD) \times P(HD)}{P(PS)}$$

$$= \frac{P(PS \mid HD) \times P(HD)}{P(PS \mid HD) \times P(HD) + P(PS \mid MD) \times P(MD) + P(PS \mid LD) \times P(LD)}$$

$$= \frac{0.967 \times 0.30}{0.967 \times 0.30 + 0.533 \times 0.50 + 0.067 \times 0.20} = \frac{0.290}{0.570} = 0.509$$

We can calculate conditional probabilities using a probability table.

The other five revised probabilities (i.e., $P(\text{MD} \mid \text{PS})$, $P(\text{LD} \mid \text{PS})$, etc.) can also be computed in a similar manner. However, as you can see, Bayes' formula is rather cumbersome and somewhat difficult to follow intuitively. For this reason, it is perhaps easier in practice to compute these revised probabilities by using a probability table. We show these calculations in Table 11 for the case where the survey result is positive and in Table 12 for the case where the survey result is negative.

TABLE 10
Reliability of the Smart Services Survey in Predicting Actual Outcomes

WHEN ACTUAL OUTCOME WAS	SURVEY RESULT WAS	
	POSITIVE (PS)	**NEGATIVE (NS)**
High demand (**HD**)	$P(\text{PS} \mid \text{HD}) = 29/30 = 0.967$	$P(\text{NS} \mid \text{HD}) = 1/30 = 0.033$
Moderate demand (**MD**)	$P(\text{PS} \mid \text{MD}) = 8/15 = 0.533$	$P(\text{NS} \mid \text{MD}) = 7/15 = 0.467$
Low demand (**LD**)	$P(\text{PS} \mid \text{LD}) = 2/30 = 0.067$	$P(\text{NS} \mid \text{LD}) = 28/30 = 0.933$

TABLE 11 Probability Revisions, Given a Positive Survey Result (PS)

OUTCOME	CONDITIONAL PROB. $P(\text{PS} \mid \text{OUTCOME})$		PRIOR PROB.		JOINT PROB.	REVISED PROB. $P(\text{OUTCOME} \mid \text{PS})$
High demand (**HD**)	0.967	×	0.30	=	0.290	0.290/0.57 = 0.509
Moderate demand (**MD**)	0.533	×	0.50	=	0.267	0.267/0.57 = 0.468
Low demand (**LD**)	0.067	×	0.20	=	0.013	0.013/0.57 = 0.023
	$P(\text{PS}) = P(\text{Positive Survey}) =$				0.570	1.000

TABLE 12 Probability Revisions, Given a Negative Survey Result (NS)

OUTCOME	CONDITIONAL PROB. $P(\text{NS} \mid \text{OUTCOME})$		PRIOR PROB.		JOINT PROB.	REVISED PROB. $P(\text{OUTCOME} \mid \text{NS})$
High demand (**HD**)	0.033	×	0.30	=	0.010	0.010/0.43 = 0.023
Moderate demand (**MD**)	0.467	×	0.50	=	0.233	0.233/0.43 = 0.543
Low demand (**LD**)	0.933	×	0.20	=	0.187	0.187/0.43 = 0.434
	$P(\text{NS}) = P(\text{Negative Survey}) =$				0.430	1.000

The calculations in Table 11 are as follows. For any outcome, such as high demand (HD), we know the conditional probability, $P(\text{PS} \mid \text{HD})$, and the prior probability, $P(\text{HD})$. Using Equation 6 of Appendix Probability Concepts and Applications, we can compute the joint probability, $P(\text{PS and HD})$, as the product of the conditional and prior probabilities. After we repeat this computation for the other two outcomes (moderate demand and low demand), we add the three joint probabilities—$P(\text{PS and HD}) + P(\text{PS and MD}) + P(\text{PS and LD})$—to determine $P(\text{PS})$. Observe that this computation is the same as that in the denominator of the Bayes' theorem formula. After we have computed $P(\text{PS})$, we can use Equation 5 of Appendix Probability Concepts and Applications to compute the revised probabilities $P(\text{HD} \mid \text{PS})$, $P(\text{MD} \mid \text{PS})$, and $P(\text{LD} \mid \text{PS})$. Table 12 shows similar calculations when the survey result is negative. As you can see, the probabilities obtained here are the same ones we used earlier in Figure 5.

 IN ACTION Using Utility and Decision Trees in Hip Replacement

Should you or a family member undergo a somewhat dangerous surgery for an illness, or is it better to manage the illness medically by using drugs? Should a health care firm put a new drug on its list of approved medicines? What medical procedures should the government reimburse? Individuals and institutions face medical treatment decision problems from a variety of perspectives. For example, the decision an individual patient faces is driven by the medical treatment that best describes the patient's attitudes about risk (utility) and quality of life over the rest of his or her life.

One common application of utility theory decision tree modeling in medicine is total hip replacement surgery for patients with severe arthritis of the hip. Several hundred thousand hip replacements are performed per year in North America. Although this surgery is mostly successful, the treatment decision for an individual patient can be difficult. Although surgery offers the potential of increased quality of life, it also carries the risk of death.

A decision tree analysis helps define all the time-sequenced outcomes that can occur in dealing with arthritis of the hip. Conservative management using medication is a surgical alternative, but the disease is degenerative, and a worsening condition is inevitable. A successful surgery, which restores full function, is likely, but uncertainty exists even then. First, infection can cause the new prosthetic hip to fail. Or the new hip may fail over time due to breakage or malfunction. Both cases require a revision surgery, whose risks are greater than the first surgery. Decision trees and utility theory help patients first assess their personal risk levels and then allow them to compute life expectancy based on sex and race.

Source: Based on G. Hazen, J. Pellissier, and J. Sounderpandian. "Stochastic Tree Models in Medical Decision Making," *Interfaces* 28, 4 (July–August 1998): 64–80.

Potential Problems in Using Survey Results

In using past performance to gauge the reliability of a survey's results, we typically base our probabilities only on those cases in which a decision to take some course of action is actually made. For example, we can observe demand only in cases where the product was actually introduced after the survey was conducted. Unfortunately, there is no way to collect information about the demand in situations in which the decision after the survey was to not introduce the product. This implies that conditional probability information is not quite always as accurate as we would like it to be. Nevertheless, calculating conditional probabilities helps to refine the decision-making process and, in general, to make better decisions. For this reason, the use of Bayesian analysis in revising prior probabilities is very popular in practice.

10   Utility Theory

EMV is not always the best criterion to use to make decisions.

So far we have used monetary values to make decisions in all our examples. In practice, however, using money to measure the value of a decision could sometimes lead to bad decisions. The reason for this is that different people value money differently at different times. For example, having $100 in your pocket may mean a lot to you today, when you are a student, but may be relatively unimportant in a few years, when you are a wealthy businessperson. This implies that while you may be unwilling to bet $100 on a risky project today, you may be more than willing to do so in a few years. Unfortunately, when we use monetary values to make decisions, we do not account for these perceptions of risk in our model.

Here's another example to drive home this point. Assume that you are the holder of a lottery ticket. In a few moments, a fair coin will be flipped. If it comes up tails, you win $100,000. If it comes up heads, you win nothing. Now suppose a wealthy person offers you $35,000 for your ticket before the coin is flipped. What should you do? According to a decision based on monetary values, as shown in the decision tree in Figure 6, you should reject the offer and hold on to your ticket because the EMV of $50,000 is greater than the offer of $35,000. In reality, what would *you* do? It is likely that many people would take the guaranteed $35,000 in exchange for a risky shot at $100,000. (In fact, many would probably be willing to settle for a lot less than $35,000.) Of course, just how low a specific individual would go is a matter of personal preference because, as noted earlier, different people value money differently. This example, however, illustrates how basing a decision on EMV may not be appropriate.

One way to get around this problem and incorporate a person's attitude toward risk in the model is through **utility theory**. In the next section we explore first how to measure a person's utility function and then how to use utility measures in decision making.

FIGURE 6
Decision Tree for a Lottery Ticket

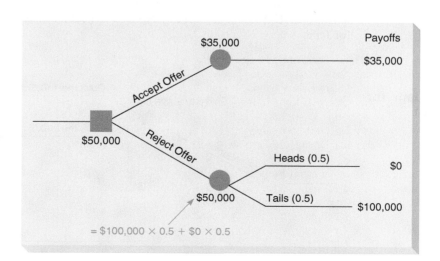

Measuring Utility and Constructing a Utility Curve

Utility function converts a person's value for money and attitudes toward risk into a dimensionless number between 0 and 1.

Using a utility function is a way of converting a person's value for money and attitudes toward risk into a dimensionless number between 0 and 1. There are three important issues to note at this stage:

- Each person has his or her own utility function. It is therefore critical in any problem to determine the utility function for the decision maker in that problem.
- A person's utility function could change over time as his or her economic and other conditions change. Recall the earlier example about how important $100 is to you today as opposed to how important it may be to you in a few years. A person's utility function should therefore be updated periodically.
- A person may have different utility functions for different magnitudes of money. For example, most people tend to be very willing to take risks when the monetary amounts involved are small. (After all, we're all willing to buy a $1 lottery ticket, even when we know very well that we're unlikely to win anything.) However, the same people tend to be unwilling to take risks with larger monetary amounts. (Would you be willing to buy a $1,000 lottery ticket even if the potential top prize were $1 billion?) This implies that we should consider a person's utility function only over the relevant range of monetary values involved in the specific problem at hand.

Let us use an example to study how we can determine a person's utility function.

We assign the worst payoff a utility of 0 and the best payoff a utility of 1.

JANE DICKSON'S UTILITY FUNCTION Jane Dickson would like to construct a utility function to reveal her preference for monetary amounts between $0 and $50,000. We start assessing Jane's utility function by assigning a utility value of 0 to the worst payoff and a utility value of 1 to the best payoff. That is, $U(\$0) = 0$ and $U(\$50,000) = 1$. Monetary values between these two payoffs will have utility values between 0 and 1. To determine these utilities, we begin by posing the following gamble to Jane, as outlined in Figure 7:

> You have a 50% chance at getting $0 and a 50% chance at getting $50,000. That is, the EMV of this gamble is $25,000. What is the minimum guaranteed amount that you will accept in order to walk away from this gamble? In other words, what is the minimum amount that will make you indifferent between alternative 1 (gamble between $0 and $50,000) and alternative 2 (obtain this amount for sure).

Certainty equivalent is the minimum guaranteed amount you are willing to accept to avoid the risk associated with a gamble.

The answer to this question may vary from person to person, and it is called the **certainty equivalent** between the two payoff values ($0 and $50,000, in this case). Let's suppose Jane is willing to settle for $15,000. (Some of you may have settled for less, while others may have wanted more.) That is, Jane is willing to accept a guaranteed payoff of $15,000 to avoid the risk associated with a potential payoff of $50,000. The implication is that from a utility perspective (i.e., with respect to Jane's attitudes toward risk and value for money), the expected value between $0 and $50,000 is only $15,000, and not the $25,000 we calculated in Figure 7. In otherwords, $U(\$15,000) = U(\$0) \times 0.5 + U(\$50,000) \times 0.5 = 0 \times 0.5 + 1 \times 0.5 = 0.5$ for Jane.

FIGURE 7
Gamble Posed to Jane for Utility Assessment

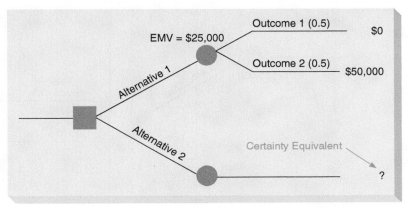

We repeat the gamble in Figure 7, except that the two monetary amounts presented to Jane in the gamble are $15,000 and $50,000. The EMV is $32,500. Let's suppose Jane is willing to settle for a certainty equivalent of $27,000. This implies that for Jane, $U(\$27,000) = U(\$15,000) \times 0.5 + U(\$50,000) \times 0.5 = 0.5 \times 0.5 + 1 \times 0.5 = 0.75$.

We repeat the gamble in Figure 7 again, this time with monetary amounts of $0 and $15,000. The EMV is $7,500. Let's suppose Jane is willing to settle for a certainty equivalent of $6,000. This implies that for Jane, $U(\$6,000) = U(\$0) \times 0.5 + U(\$15,000) \times 0.5 = 0 \times 0.5 + 0.5 \times 0.5 = 0.25$.

A utility curve plots utility values versus monetary values.

At this stage, we know the monetary values associated with utilities of 0, 0.25, 0.5, 0.75, and 1 for Jane. If necessary, we can continue this process several more times to find additional utility points. For example, we could present the gamble between $27,000 (with a utility of 0.75) and $50,000 (with a utility of 1) to determine the monetary value associated with a utility of $0.875 = (0.75 \times 0.5 + 1 \times 0.5)$. However, the five assessments shown here are usually enough to get an idea of Jane's feelings toward risk. Perhaps the easiest way to view Jane's utility function is to construct a **utility curve** that plots utility values (Y-axis) versus monetary values (X-axis). This is shown in Figure 8. In the figure, the assessed utility points of $0, $6,000, $15,000, $27,000, and $50,000 are obtained from the preceding discussion, while the rest of the curve is eyeballed in. As noted earlier, it is usually enough to know five points on the curve in order to get a reasonable approximation.

Jane's utility curve is typical of a risk avoider. A **risk avoider** is a decision maker who gets less utility or pleasure from a greater risk and tends to avoid situations in which high losses might occur. As monetary value increases on her utility curve, the utility increases at a slower rate. Another way to characterize a person's attitude toward risk is to compute the risk premium, defined as

$$\text{Risk premium} = (\text{EMV of gamble}) - (\text{Certainty equivalent}) \tag{8}$$

Risk premium *is the EMV that a person is willing to give up in order to avoid the risk associated with a gamble.*

The **risk premium** represents the monetary amount that a decision maker is willing to give up in order to avoid the risk associated with a gamble. For example, Jane's risk premium in the first gamble between $0 and $50,000 is computed as $25,000 - $15,000 = $10,000. That is, Jane is willing to give up $10,000 to avoid the uncertainty associated with a gamble. Likewise, she is willing to give up $5,500 (=$32,500 - $27,000) to avoid the risk of gambling between $15,000 and $50,000.

Clearly, a person who is more averse to risk will be willing to give up an even larger amount to avoid the uncertainty. In contrast, a person who is a risk seeker will insist on getting a certainty

FIGURE 8
Utility Curve for Jane Dickson

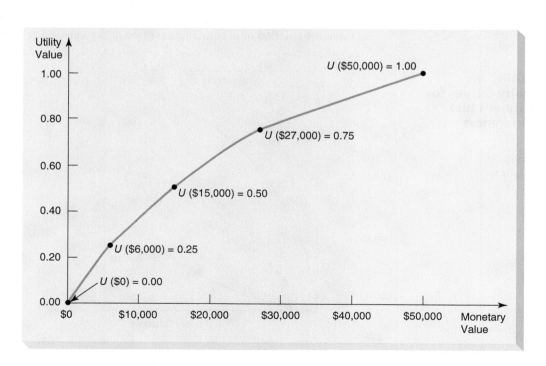

equivalent that is greater than the EMV in order to walk away from a gamble. Such a person will therefore have a negative risk premium. Finally, a person who is risk neutral will always specify a certainty equivalent that is exactly equal to the EMV. Based on the preceding discussion, we can now define the following three preferences for risk:

- Risk avoider or risk-averse person: Risk premium > 0
- Risk indifferent or risk-neutral person: Risk premium $= 0$
- Risk seeker or risk-prone person: Risk premium < 0

A risk neutral person has a utility curve that is a straight line.

Figure 9 illustrates the utility curves for all three risk preferences. As shown in the figure, a person who is a **risk seeker** has an opposite-shaped utility curve to that of a risk avoider. This type of decision maker gets more utility from a greater risk and a higher potential payoff. As monetary value increases on his or her utility curve, the utility increases at an increasing rate. A person who is **risk neutral** has a utility curve that is a straight line.

The shape of a person's utility curve depends on the specific decision being considered, the person's psychological frame of mind, and how the person feels about the future. As noted earlier, it may well be that a person has one utility curve for some situations and a completely different curve for others. In practice, most people are likely to be risk seekers when the monetary amounts involved are small (recall the earlier comment about buying a $1 lottery ticket) but tend to become risk avoiders as the monetary amounts increase. The exact monetary amount at which a specific individual switches from being a risk seeker to a risk avoider is, of course, a matter of personal preference.

EXPONENTIAL UTILITY FUNCTION If a person is a risk avoider, it is possible to use curve-fitting techniques to fit an equation to the utility curve. This makes it convenient to determine the person's utility for any monetary value within the appropriate range. Looking at the utility curve in Figure 9 for a risk avoider, it is apparent that the curve can be approximated by an exponential function. The equation would be as follows:

$$U(X) = 1 - e^{-X/R} \tag{9}$$

where e is the exponential constant (equal to 2.7182), X represents the monetary value, and R is a parameter that controls the shape of the person's utility curve. As R increases, the utility curve becomes flatter (corresponding to a decision maker who is less risk averse).

Utility as a Decision-Making Criterion

Utility values replace monetary values.

Once we have determined a decision maker's utility curve, how do we use it in making decisions? We construct the decision tree and make all prior and revised probability estimates and computations as before. However, instead of using monetary values as payoffs, we now replace all monetary payoffs with the appropriate utility values. We then fold back the decision tree, using the criterion of maximizing expected utility values. Let's look at an example.

FIGURE 9
Utility Curves for Different Risk Preferences

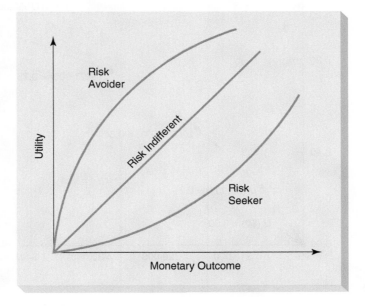

FIGURE 10
**Decision Tree Using EMV
for Mark Simkin**

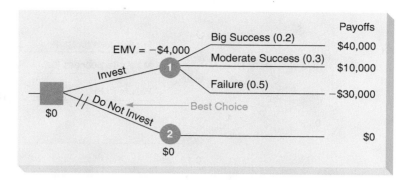

Mark Simkin has an opportunity to invest in a new business venture. If the venture is a big success, Mark will make a profit of $40,000. If the venture is a moderate success, Mark will make a profit $10,000. If the venture fails, Mark will lose his investment of $30,000. Mark estimates the venture's chances as 20% for big success, 30% for moderate success, and 50% for failure. Should Mark invest in the venture?

Mark's alternatives are displayed in the tree shown in Figure 10. Using monetary values, the EMV at node 1 is $40,000 \times 0.2 + $10,000 \times 0.3 + (-$30,000) \times 0.5 = -$4,000$. Because this is smaller than the EMV of $0 at node 2, Mark should turn down the venture and invest his money elsewhere.

Now let's view the same problem from a utility perspective. Using the procedure outlined earlier, Mark is able to construct a utility curve showing his preference for monetary amounts between $40,000 and −$30,000 (the best and worst payoffs in his problem). This curve, shown in Figure 11, indicates that within this monetary range Mark is a risk seeker (i.e., a gambler).

Mark's objective is to maximize expected utility.

From Figure 11, we note the following utility values for Mark: $U(-$30,000) = 0$, $U($0) = 0.15$, $U($10,000) = 0.30$, and $U($40,000) = 1$. Substituting these values in the decision tree in Figure 10 in place of the monetary values, we fold back the tree to maximize Mark's expected utility. The computations are shown in Figure 12.

Using expected utility may lead to a decision that is different from the one suggested by EMV.

Using utility values, the expected utility at node 1 is 0.29, which is greater than the utility of 0.15 at node 2. This implies that Mark should invest his money in the venture. As you can

FIGURE 11 Utility Curve for Mark Simkin

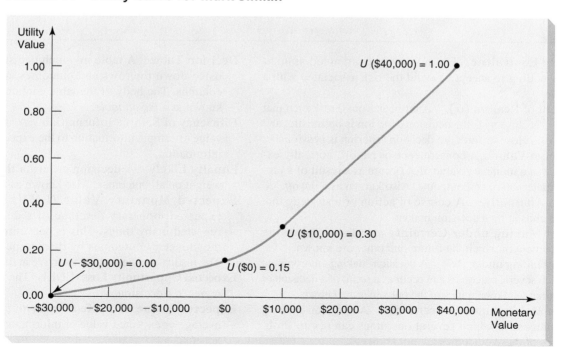

FIGURE 12
Decision Tree Using Utility Values for Mark Simkin

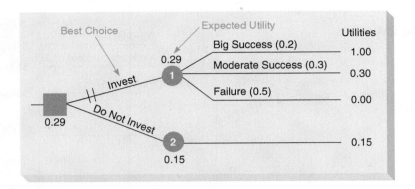

see, this is the opposite of the decision suggested if EMV had been used, and it clearly illustrates how using utilities instead of monetary values may lead to different decisions in the same problem. In Mark's case, the utility curve indicates that he is a risk seeker, and the choice of investing in the venture certainly reflects his preference for risk.

Summary

This chapter introduces the topic of decision analysis, which is an analytic and systematic approach to studying decision making. We first indicate the steps involved in making decisions in three different environments: (1) decision making under certainty, (2) decision making under uncertainty, and (3) decision making under risk. For decision problems under uncertainty, we identify the best alternatives, using criteria such as maximax, maximin, criterion of realism, equally likely, and minimax regret. For decision problems under risk, we discuss the computation and use of the expected monetary value (EMV), expected opportunity loss (EOL), and expected value of perfect information (EVPI).

We also illustrate the use of Excel to solve decision analysis problems.

Decision trees are used for larger decision problems in which decisions must be made in sequence. In this case, we compute the expected value of sample information (EVSI). Bayesian analysis is used to revise or update probability values. We also discuss how decision trees can be set up and solved using TreePlan, an Excel add-in.

When it is inappropriate to use monetary values, utility theory can be used to assign a utility value to each decision payoff. In such cases, we compute expected utilities and select the alternative with the highest utility value.

Glossary

Certainty Equivalent The minimum guaranteed amount one is willing to accept to avoid the risk associated with a gamble.

Coefficient of Realism (α). A number from 0 to 1 such that when α is close to 1, the decision criterion is optimistic, and when α is close to zero, the decision criterion is pessimistic.

Conditional Value A consequence or payoff, normally expressed in a monetary value, that occurs as a result of a particular alternative and outcome. Also known as a *payoff.*

Decision Alternative A course of action or a strategy that can be chosen by a decision maker.

Decision Making under Certainty A decision-making environment in which the future outcomes are known.

Decision Making under Risk A decision-making environment in which several outcomes can occur as a result of a decision or an alternative. Probabilities of the outcomes are known.

Decision Making under Uncertainty A decision-making environment in which several outcomes can occur. Probabilities of these outcomes are not known.

Decision Table A table in which decision alternatives are listed down the rows and outcomes are listed across the columns. The body of the table contains the payoffs. Also known as a *payoff table.*

Efficiency of Sample Information A ratio of the expected value of sample information to the expected value of perfect information.

Equally Likely A decision criterion that places an equal weight on all outcomes. Also known as *Laplace.*

Expected Monetary Value (EMV) The average or expected monetary outcome of a decision if it can be repeated many times. This is determined by multiplying the monetary outcomes by their respective probabilities. The results are then added to arrive at the EMV.

Expected Opportunity Loss (EOL) The average or expected regret of a decision.

Expected Value of Perfect Information (EVPI) The average or expected value of information if it is completely accurate.

Expected Value of Sample Information (EVSI)   The average or expected value of imperfect or survey information.

Expected Value with Perfect Information (EVwPI)   The average or expected value of the decision if the decision maker knew what would happen ahead of time.

Maximax   An optimistic decision-making criterion. This is the alternative with the highest possible return.

Maximin   A pessimistic decision-making criterion that maximizes the minimum outcome. It is the best of the worst possible outcomes.

Minimax Regret   A decision criterion that minimizes the maximum opportunity loss.

Opportunity Loss   The amount you would lose by not picking the best alternative. For any outcome, this is the difference between the consequences of any alternative and the best possible alternative. Also called *regret*.

Outcome   An occurrence over which a decision maker has little or no control. Also known as a state-of-nature.

Risk Avoider   A person who avoids risk. As the monetary value increases on the utility curve, the utility increases at a decreasing rate. This decision maker gets less utility for a greater risk and higher potential returns.

Risk Neutral   A person who is indifferent toward risk. The utility curve for a risk-neutral person is a straight line.

Risk Premium   The monetary amount that a person is willing to give up in order to avoid the risk associated with a gamble.

Risk Seeker   A person who seeks risk. As the monetary value increases on the utility curve, the utility increases at an increasing rate. This decision maker gets more pleasure for a greater risk and higher potential returns.

Sequential Decisions   Decisions in which the outcome of one decision influences other decisions.

Utility Curve   A graph or curve that illustrates the relationship between utility and monetary values. When this curve has been constructed, utility values from the curve can be used in the decision-making process.

Utility Theory   A theory that allows decision makers to incorporate their risk preference and other factors into the decision-making process.

Solved Problems

Solved Problem 1

Cal Bender and Becky Addison are undergraduates in business at Central College. In an attempt to make extra money, Cal and Becky have decided to look into the possibility of starting a small company that would provide word-processing services to students who need term papers or other reports prepared in a professional manner. They have identified three strategies. Strategy 1 is to invest in a fairly expensive microcomputer system with a high-quality laser printer. In a good market, they should be able to obtain a net profit of $10,000 over the next two years. If the market is bad, they could lose $8,000. Strategy 2 is to purchase a cheaper system. With a good market, they could get a return during the next two years of $8,000. With a bad market, they could incur a loss of $4,000. Their final strategy, strategy 3, is to do nothing. Cal is basically a risk taker, whereas Becky tries to avoid risk.

a. Which decision criterion should Cal use? What would Cal's decision be?
b. Which decision criterion should Becky use? What decision would Becky make?
c. If Cal and Becky were indifferent to risk, which decision criterion should they use? What would be the decision?

Solution

The problem is one of decision making under uncertainty. To answer the specific questions, it is helpful to construct a decision table showing the alternatives, outcomes, and payoffs, as follows:

ALTERNATIVE	GOOD MARKET	BAD MARKET
Expensive system	$10,000	–$8,000
Cheaper system	$ 8,000	–$4,000
Do nothing	$ 0	$ 0

a. Cal should use the maximax, or optimistic, decision criterion. The maximum payoffs for the three alternatives are $10,000, $8,000, and $0, respectively. Hence, Cal should select the expensive system.

b. Becky should use the maximin, or pessimistic, decision criterion. The minimum payoffs for the three alternatives are −$8,000, −$4,000, and $0, respectively. Hence, Becky should choose to do nothing.

c. If Cal and Becky are indifferent to risk, they should use the equally likely criterion. The average payoffs for the three alternatives are $1,000, $2,000, and $0, respectively. Hence, their decision would be to select the cheaper system.

Solved Problem 2

Maria Rojas is considering the possibility of opening a small dress shop on Fairbanks Avenue, a few blocks from the university. She has located a good mall that attracts students. Her options are to open a small shop, a medium-sized shop, or no shop at all. The market for a dress shop can be good, average, or bad. The probabilities for these three possibilities are 0.2 for a good market, 0.5 for an average market, and 0.3 for a bad market. The net profit or loss for the medium-sized and small shops for the various market conditions are given in the following payoff table:

| | OUTCOMES | | |
ALTERNATIVE	GOOD MARKET	AVERAGE MARKET	BAD MARKET
Small shop	$ 75,000	$25,000	−$40,000
Medium-sized shop	$100,000	$35,000	−$60,000
No shop	$ 0	$ 0	$ 0
Probabilities	0.2	0.5	0.3

Building no shop at all yields no loss and no gain. What do you recommend?

Solution

The problem can be solved by computing the EMV for each alternative, as follows:

EMV(Small shop)   = $75,000 × 0.2 + $25,000 × 0.5 + (−$40,000) × 0.3 = $15,500

EMV(Medium shop) = $100,000 × 0.2 + $35,000 × 0.5 + (−$60,000) × 0.3 = $19,500

EMV(No shop)   = $0

As can be seen, the best decision is to build the medium-sized shop. The EMV for this alternative is $19,500.

Solved Problem 3

Monica Britt has enjoyed sailing small boats since she was 7 years old, when her mother started sailing with her. Today Monica is considering the possibility of starting a company to produce small sailboats for the recreational market. Unlike other mass-produced sailboats, however, these boats will be made specifically for children between the ages of 10 and 15. The boats will be of the highest quality and extremely stable, and the sail size will be reduced to prevent problems with capsizing.

Because of the expense involved in developing the initial molds and acquiring the necessary equipment to produce fiberglass sailboats for young children, Monica has decided to conduct a pilot study to make sure that the market for the sailboats will be adequate. She estimates that the pilot study will cost her $10,000. Furthermore, the pilot study can be either successful or not successful. Her basic decisions are to build a large manufacturing facility, a small manufacturing facility, or no facility at all. With a favorable market, Monica can expect to make $90,000 from the large facility or $60,000 from the smaller facility. If the market is unfavorable, however, Monica estimates that she would lose $30,000 with a large facility, whereas she would lose only $20,000 with the small facility. Monica estimates that the probability of a favorable market, given a successful pilot study result, is 0.8. The probability of an unfavorable market, given an unsuccessful pilot study result, is estimated to be 0.9. Monica feels there is a 50–50 chance that the pilot study will be successful. Of course, Monica could bypass the pilot study and simply make the decision whether to build a large plant, a small plant, or no facility at all. Without doing any testing in a pilot study, she estimates the probability of a successful market is 0.6. What do you recommend?

Solution

The decision tree for Monica's problem is shown in Figure 13. The tree shows all alternatives, outcomes, probability values, payoffs, and EMVs. The expected value computations at the various nodes are as follows:

$$
\begin{aligned}
\text{EMV(Node 1)} &= \$60{,}000 \times 0.6 + (-\$20{,}000) \times 0.4 = \$28{,}000 \\
\text{EMV(Node 2)} &= \$90{,}000 \times 0.6 + (-\$30{,}000) \times 0.3 = \$42{,}000 \\
\text{EMV(Node 3)} &= \$0 \\
\text{EMV(Node 4)} &= \$50{,}000 \times 0.8 + (-\$30{,}000) \times 0.2 = \$34{,}000 \\
\text{EMV(Node 5)} &= \$80{,}000 \times 0.8 + (-\$40{,}000) \times 0.2 = \$56{,}000 \\
\text{EMV(Node 6)} &= -\$10{,}000 \\
\text{EMV(Node 7)} &= \$50{,}000 \times 0.1 + (-\$30{,}000) \times 0.9 = -\$22{,}000 \\
\text{EMV(Node 8)} &= \$80{,}000 \times 0.1 + (-\$40{,}000) \times 0.9 = -\$28{,}000 \\
\text{EMV(Node 9)} &= -\$10{,}000 \\
\text{EMV(Node 10)} &= \$56{,}000 \times 0.5 + (-\$10{,}000) \times 0.5 = \$23{,}000
\end{aligned}
$$

Monica's optimal solution is to *not* conduct the pilot study and construct the large plant directly. The EMV of this decision is $42,000.

Solved Problem 4

Developing a small driving range for golfers of all abilities has long been a desire of John Jenkins. John, however, believes that the chance of a successful driving range is only about 40%. A friend of John's has suggested that he conduct a survey in the community to get a better feel for the demand for such a facility. There is a 0.9 probability that the survey result will be positive if the driving range will be successful. Furthermore, it is estimated that there is a 0.8 probability that the survey result will be negative if indeed the driving range will be unsuccessful. John would like to determine the chances of a successful driving range, given a positive result from the survey.

Solution

This problem requires the use of Bayes' theorem. Before we start to solve the problem, we will define the following terms:

$P(S)$ = probability of successful driving range

$P(U)$ = probability of unsuccessful driving range

$P(P|S)$ = probability survey result will be positive given a successful driving range

$P(N|S)$ = probability survey result will be negative given a successful driving range

$P(P|U)$ = probability survey result will be positive given an unsuccessful driving range

$P(N|U)$ = probability survey result will be negative given an unsuccessful driving range

Now, we can summarize what we know:

$$
\begin{aligned}
P(S) &= 0.4 \\
P(P|S) &= 0.9 \\
P(N|U) &= 0.8
\end{aligned}
$$

FIGURE 13 Complete Decision Tree for Monica Britt

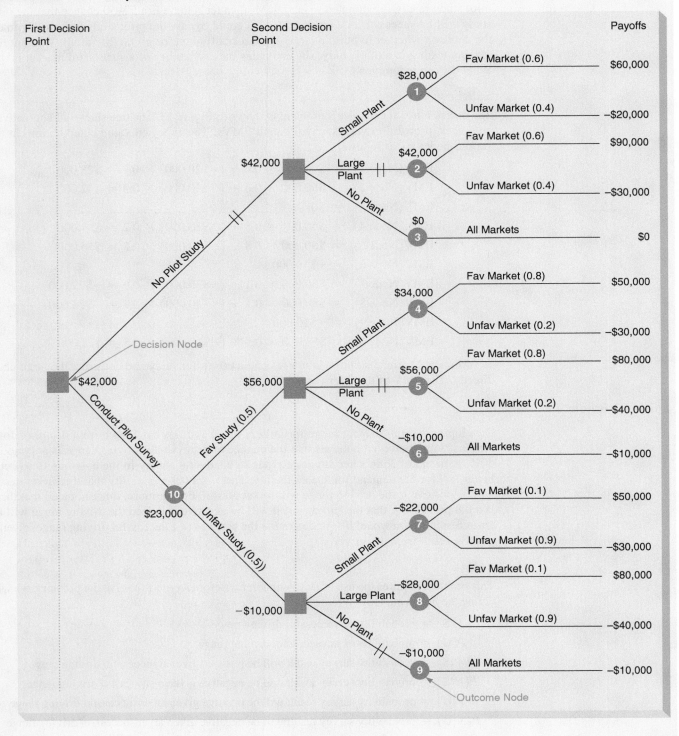

From this information we can compute three additional probabilities needed to solve the problem:

$$P(U) = 1 - P(S) = 1 - 0.4 = 0.6$$
$$P(U|S) = 1 - P(P|S) = 1 - 0.9 = 0.1$$
$$P(P|U) = 1 - P(N|U) = 1 - 0.8 = 0.2$$

Now we can put these values into Bayes' theorem to compute the desired revised probability given a positive survey result, as shown in the following table:

OUTCOME	CONDITIONAL PROBABILITY $P(P \mid$ OUTCOME$)$		PRIOR PROBABILITY OF OUTCOME		JOINT PROBABILITY $P(P$ and OUTCOME$)$	POSTERIOR PROBABILITY
Successful driving range (S)	0.9	$\times$	0.4	$=$	0.36	$0.36/0.48 = 0.75$
Unsuccessful driving range (U)	0.2	$\times$	0.6	$=$	0.12	$0.12/0.48 = 0.25$
					0.48	

The probability of a successful driving range, given a positive survey result is $P(S|P) = P(P \text{ and } S)/P(S) = 0.36/0.48$, or 0.75.

Discussion Questions and Problems

Discussion Questions

1 Give an example of a good decision that you made that resulted in a bad outcome. Also give an example of a bad decision that you made that had a good outcome. Why was each decision good or bad?

2 Describe what is involved in the decision-making process.

3 What is an alternative? What is an outcome?

4 Discuss the differences between decision making under certainty, decision making under risk, and decision making under uncertainty.

5 State the meanings of EMV and EVPI.

6 Under what conditions is a decision tree preferable to a decision table?

7 What is the difference between prior and posterior probabilities?

8 What is the purpose of Bayesian analysis? Describe how you would use Bayesian analysis in the decision-making process.

9 What is the purpose of utility theory?

10 Briefly discuss how a utility function can be assessed. What is a standard gamble, and how is it used in determining utility values?

11 How is a utility curve used in selecting the best decision for a particular problem?

12 What is a risk seeker? What is a risk avoider? How do the utility curves for these types of decision makers differ?

Problems

13 In the environment of increased competition, a fitness club executive is considering the purchase of additional equipment. His alternatives, outcomes, and payoffs (profits) are shown in the following table:

EQUIPMENT	FAVORABLE MARKET	UNFAVORABLE MARKET
Acme	$400,000	−$175,000
Standard	$280,000	−$ 90,000
High Pro	$ 95,000	−$ 15,000

(a) If the executive is an optimistic decision maker, which alternative will he likely choose?

(b) If the executive is a pessimistic decision maker, which alternative will he likely choose?

(c) Market research suggests the chance of a favorable market for fitness clubs is 76%. If the executive uses this analysis, which alternative will he likely choose?

14 Steve's Mountain Bicycle Shop is considering three options for its facility next year. Steve can expand his current shop, move to a larger facility, or make no change. With a good market, the annual payoff would be $76,000 if he expands, $90,000 if he moves, and $40,000 if he does nothing. With an average market, his payoffs will be $30,000, $41,000, and $15,000, respectively. With a poor market, his payoff will be −$17,000, −$28,000, and $4,000, respectively.

(a) Which option should Steve choose if he uses the maximax criterion?

(b) Which option should Steve choose if he uses the maximin criterion?

(c) Which option should Steve choose if he uses the equally likely criterion?

(d) Which option should Steve choose if he uses the criterion of realism with $\alpha = 0.4$?

(e) Which option should Steve choose if he uses the minimax regret criterion?

15 Steve (see Problem 14) has gathered some additional information. The probabilities of good, average, and poor markets are 0.25, 0.45, and 0.3, respectively.

(a) Using EMVs, what option should Steve choose? What is the maximum EMV?

(b) Using EOL, what option should Steve choose? What is the minimum EOL?

(c) Compute the EVPI and show that it is the same as the minimum EOL.

16 Debbie Gibson is considering three investment options for a small inheritance that she has just received—stocks, bonds, and money market. The return on her investment will depend on the performance of the economy, which can be strong, average, or weak. The returns for each possible combination are shown in the following table:

INVESTMENT	STRONG	AVERAGE	WEAK
Stocks	12%	6%	−10%
Bonds	7%	4%	1%
Money market	4%	3%	2%

Assume that Debbie will choose only one of the investment options.

(a) Which investment should Debbie choose if she uses the maximax criterion?

(b) Which investment should Debbie choose if she uses the maximin criterion?

(c) Which investment should Debbie choose if she uses the equally likely criterion?

(d) Which investment should Debbie choose if she uses the criterion of realism with $\alpha = 0.5$?

(e) Which investment should Debbie choose if she uses the minimax regret criterion?

17 After reading about economic predictions, Debbie Gibson (see Problem 16) has assigned the probability that the economy will be strong, average, and weak at 0.2, 0.35, and 0.45, respectively.

(a) Using EMVs, what option should Debbie choose? What is the maximum EMV?

(b) Using EOL, what option should Debbie choose? What is the minimum EOL?

(c) Compute the EVPI and show that it is the same as the minimum EOL.

18 A hospital administrator in Portland is trying to determine whether to build a large wing onto the existing hospital, a small wing, or no wing at all. If the population of Portland continued to grow, a large wing could return $225,000 to the hospital each year. If the small wing were built, it would return $90,000 to the hospital each year if the population continued to grow. If the population of Portland remained the same, the hospital would encounter a loss of $125,000 if the large wing were built. Furthermore, a loss of $65,000 would be realized if the small wing were constructed and the population remained the same. It is unknown whether Portland's population will grow in the near future.

(a) Construct a decision table.

(b) Using the equally likely criterion, determine the best alternative.

(c) The chairman of the hospital's board has advised using a coefficient of realism of 0.7 in determining the best alternative. What is the best decision according to this criterion?

19 Shaq Bryant sells newspapers on Sunday mornings in an area surrounded by three busy churches. Assume that Shaq's demand can either be for 100, 300, or 500 newspapers, depending on traffic and weather. Shaq has the option to order 100, 300, or 500 newspapers from his supplier. Shaq pays $1.25 for each newspaper he orders and sells each for $2.50.

(a) How many papers should Shaq order if he chooses the maximax criterion?

(b) How many papers should Shaq order if he chooses the maximin criterion?

(c) How many papers should Shaq order if he chooses the equally likely criterion?

(d) How many papers should Shaq order if he chooses the criterion of realism with $\alpha = 0.45$?

(e) How many papers should Shaq order if he chooses the minimax regret criterion?

20 Shaq (see Problem 19) has done some research and discovered that the probabilities for demands of 100, 300, and 500 newspapers are 0.4, 0.35, and 0.25, respectively.

(a) Using EMVs, how many papers should Shaq order?

(b) Using EOL, how many papers should Shaq order?

(c) Compute Shaq's EVwPI and EVPI.

21 The Boatwright Sauce Company is a small manufacturer of several different sauces to use in food products. One of the products is a blended sauce mix that is sold to retail outlets. Joy Boatwright must decide how many cases of this mix to manufacture each month. The probability that the demand will be six cases is 0.1, for seven cases is 0.5, for eight cases is 0.3, and for nine cases is 0.1. The cost of every case is $55, and the price that Joy gets for each case is $90. Unfortunately, any cases not sold by the end of the month are of no value, due to spoilage. How many cases of sauce should Joy manufacture each month?

22 Waldo Books needs to decide how many copies of a new hardcover release to purchase for its shelves. The store has assumed that demand will be 50, 100, 150, or 200 copies next month, and it needs to decide whether to order 50, 100, 150, or 200 books for this period. Each book costs Waldo $20 and can be sold for $30. Waldo can sell any unsold books back to the supplier for $4.

(a) Which option should Waldo choose if it uses the maximax criterion?

(b) Which option should Waldo choose if it uses the maximin criterion?

(c) Which option should Waldo choose if it uses the equally likely criterion?

(d) Which option should Waldo choose if it uses the criterion of realism with $\alpha = 0.7$?

(e) Which option should Waldo choose if it uses the minimax regret criterion?

23 After researching the market, Waldo Books (see Problem 21) has concluded that the probabilities of selling 50, 100, 150, and 200 books next month are 0.2, 0.35, 0.25, and 0.2, respectively.

(a) Using EMVs, how many books should Waldo order?

(b) Using EOL, how many books should Waldo order?

(c) Compute Waldo's EVwPI and EVPI.

24 A souvenir retailer has an opportunity to establish a new location inside a large airport. The annual returns will depend primarily on the size of the space she rents and if the economy will be favorable. The retailer has worked with the airport concession commission, and has projected the following possible annual earnings associated with renting a small, medium, large, or very large space:

SIZE	GOOD ECONOMY	FAIR ECONOMY	POOR ECONOMY
Small	$ 70,000	$28,000	-$ 14,000
Medium	$112,000	$42,000	-$ 28,000
Large	$140,000	$42,000	-$ 56,000
Very large	$420,000	$35,000	-$224,000

(a) What is the souvenir retailer's maximax decision?

(b) What is her maximin decision?

(c) What is her equally likely decision?

(d) What is her criterion of realism decision, using $\alpha = 0.8$?

(e) What is her minimax regret decision?

25 An ambulance driver has three major routes from the hospital base station to the university, to which he makes several trips weekly. The traffic patterns are, however, very complex. Under good conditions, Broad Street is the fastest route. When Broad is congested,

one of the other routes, either Drexel Avenue or the expressway, is usually preferable. Over the past two months, the driver has tried each route several times, under different traffic conditions. This information is summarized (in minutes of travel time to work) in the following table:

ROUTE	NO CONGESTION	MILD CONGESTION	SEVERE CONGESTION
Broad Street	10	21	30
Drexel Avenue	13	17	23
Expressway	20	21	20

In the past 50 days, the driver has encountered severe traffic congestion 10 days and mild traffic congestion 20 days. Assume that the past 50 days are typical of traffic conditions.

(a) Which route should the driver take? Remember that we want to find the fastest route.

(b) If the ambulance had a traffic scanner to accurately inform the driver of the level of congestion in this part of town, how much time could he potentially save?

26 A group of medical professionals is considering constructing a private clinic. If patient demand for the clinic is high, the physicians could realize a net profit of $100,000. If the demand is low, they could lose $40,000. Of course, they don't have to proceed at all, in which case there is no cost. In the absence of any market data, the best the physicians can guess is that there is a 50–50 chance that demand will be good.

(a) Construct a decision tree to help analyze this problem. What should the medical professionals do?

(b) The physicians have been approached by a market research firm that offers to perform a study of the market at a fee of $5,000. The market researchers claim that their experience enables them to use Bayes' theorem to make the following statements of probability:

probability of high demand given a positive study result = 0.82

probability of low demand given a positive study result = 0.18

probability of high demand given a negative study result = 0.11

probability of low demand given a negative study result = 0.89

probability of a positive study result = 0.55

probability of a negative study result = 0.45

Expand the decision tree in part (a) to reflect the options now open with the market study. What should the medical professionals do now?

(c) What is the maximum amount the physicians would be willing to pay for the market study?

(d) What is the efficiency of the market study's information?

27 In Problem 26, you helped a group of medical professionals analyze a decision, using EMV as the decision criterion. This group has also assessed its utility for money: $U(-\$45,000) = 0, U(-\$40,000) = 0.1$, $U(-\$5,000) = 0.7$, $U(\$0) = 0.9$, $U(\$95,000) = 0.99$, and $U(\$100,000) = 1$.

(a) Are the medical professionals risk seekers or risk avoiders? Justify your answer.

(b) Use expected utility as the decision criterion and determine the best decision for the medical professionals (including the option to use the market research firm).

28 Jerry Young is thinking about opening a bicycle shop in his hometown. Jerry loves to take his own bike on 50-mile trips with his friends, but he believes that any small business should be started only if there is a good chance of making a profit. Jerry can open a small shop, a large shop, or no shop at all. Because there will be a five-year lease on the building that Jerry is thinking about using, he wants to make sure that he makes the correct decision.

Jerry has done some analysis about the profitability of the bicycle shop. If Jerry builds the large bicycle shop, he will earn $60,000 if the market is good, but he will lose $40,000 if the market is bad. The small shop will return a $30,000 profit in a good market and a $10,000 loss in a bad market. At the present time, he believes that there is a 59% chance that the market will be good.

Jerry also has the option of hiring his old marketing professor for $5,000 to conduct a marketing research study. If the study is conducted, the results could be either favorable or unfavorable. It is estimated that there is a 0.6 probability that the survey will be favorable. Furthermore, there is a 0.9 probability that the market will be good, given a favorable outcome from the study. However, the marketing professor has warned Jerry that there is only a probability of 0.12 of a good market if the marketing research results are not favorable.

(a) Develop a decision tree for Jerry and help him decide what he should do.

(b) How much is the marketing professor's information worth? What is the efficiency of this information?

29 A manufacturer buys valves from two suppliers. The quality of the valves from the suppliers is as follows:

PERCENTAGE DEFECTIVE	PROBABILITY FOR SUPPLIER A	PROBABILITY FOR SUPPLIER B
1	0.60	0.30
3	0.25	0.40
5	0.15	0.30

For example, the probability of getting a batch of valves that are 1% defective from supplier A is 0.60. Because the manufacturer orders 10,000 valves per order, this would mean that there is a 0.6 probability of getting 100 defective valves out of the 10,000 valves if supplier A is used to fill the order. A defective valve can be repaired for 60 cents. Although the quality of supplier B is lower, it will sell an order of 10,000 valves for $37 less than supplier A.

(a) Develop a decision tree to help the manufacturer decide which supplier it should use.

(b) For how much less would supplier B have to sell an order of 10,000 valves than supplier A for the manufacturer to be indifferent between the two suppliers?

30 After observing the heavy snow that his town received the previous winter, Ajay Patel, an enterprising student, plans to offer a snow-clearing service in his neighborhood this winter. If he invests in a new heavy-duty blower, Ajay forecasts a profit of $700 if snowfall this winter is heavy, a profit of $200 if it is moderate, and a loss of $900 if it is light. As per the current weather forecasts, the probabilities of heavy, moderate, and light snowfall this winter are 0.4, 0.3, and 0.3, respectively.

Rather than purchase a new blower, Ajay could get his father's blower repaired and just accept smaller jobs. Under this option, Ajay estimates a profit of $350 for a heavy snowfall, a profit of $100 for a moderate snowfall, and a loss of $150 for a light snowfall. Ajay, of course, has the option of choosing neither of these options.

The local weather expert, Samantha Adams, is Ajay's good friend. For $50, she is willing to run sophisticated weather models on her computer and tell Ajay whether she expects this winter to be unseasonably cold. For the sake of solving this problem, assume that the following information is available. There is a 45% chance that Samantha will predict this winter to be unseasonably cold. If she does say this, the probabilities of heavy, moderate, and light snowfall are revised to 0.7, 0.25, and 0.05, respectively. On the other hand, if she predicts that this winter will not be unseasonably cold, these probabilities are revised to 0.15, 0.33, and 0.52, respectively.

Draw the decision tree for the situation faced by Ajay. Fold back the tree and determine the strategy you would recommend he follow. What is the efficiency of Samantha's information?

31 Oscar Weng is planning to raise funds to pay for a scouting trip by running a concession stand during tomorrow's high school soccer game. Oscar needs to decide whether to rent a large insulated thermos from the local rental store and sell cocoa at the game or to rent a large refrigerated container and sell lemonade.

Unfortunately, Oscar does not have the resources to rent both items. Sales depend on whether it is sunny or rainy during the game. If the weather is sunny, Oscar will make a profit of $60 from lemonade but only $20 from cocoa. If, however, it is rainy, Oscar will make a profit of $80 from cocoa but only break even if he brings lemonade. Based on the local newspaper's prediction, Oscar thinks there is a 60% chance of it being sunny tomorrow.

Oscar's older brother Elmo, who has earned the Meteorology Badge, claims he can predict the weather more accurately than the newspaper. For only $4, he offers to study the weather and tell Oscar if there is a "good chance" or "bad chance" of it being sunny tomorrow. Assume that the following data are available about the accuracy of the brother's information:

- The probability that he will say "good chance" is 0.7.
- If he says "good chance," then there is a 0.83 probability that it will actually be sunny tomorrow.
- If he says "bad chance," then there is only a 0.25 probability that it will actually be sunny tomorrow.

(a) Draw the complete decision tree for Oscar's problem and fold it back to help him decide what he should do.

(b) How much is his brother's information actually worth to Oscar?

32 You have been hired by the No Flight Golf Company, and your first task is to decide whether to market a new golf ball utilizing breakthrough technology and, if so, determine the price. The payoff of your decision will be affected by whether your competitor will market similar balls and the price of their golf balls after you go to market. The cost to market the golf balls is $80,000, and the probability that your competitor will enter the market is 0.75. The following table describes the payoffs of each pricing combination, assuming that No Flight will have competition:

| | **COMPETITOR'S PRICE** | | |
OUR PRICE	**HIGH**	**MEDIUM**	**LOW**
High	$400,000	$250,000	$ 25,000
Medium	$475,000	$325,000	$175,000
Low	$350,000	$250,000	$125,000

If No Flight sets its price high, the probability that the competition will set its price high, medium, and low is 0.3, 0.55, and 0.15, respectively. If No Flight sets its price medium, the probability that the competition will set its price high, medium, and low is 0.2, 0.7, and 0.1, respectively. Finally, if No Flight sets its price low, the probability that the competition

will set its price high, medium, and low is 0.15, 0.25, and 0.6, respectively.

If No Flight has no competition for its new golf balls, its expected payoff for setting the price high, medium, and low is $600,000, $500,000, and $400,000, respectively, excluding marketing costs. Do you recommend marketing the new golf balls? If so, what is your pricing recommendation?

33 Your regular tennis partner has made a friendly wager with you. The two of you will play out one point in which you can serve. The loser pays the winner $100. If your first serve is not in play, you get a second serve. If your second serve is not in play, you lose the point. You have two kinds of serves: a hard one and a soft one. You know that your hard serve is in play 65% of the time and, when it is in play, you win the point 75% of the time. You put your soft serve in play 88% of the time and, when it is in play, you win the point 27% of the time. Should you accept the wager? If so, should you use your hard or soft serve?

34 Rob Johnson is a product manager for Diamond Chemical. The firm is considering whether to launch a new product line that will require building a new facility. The technology required to produce the new product is yet untested. If Rob decides to build the new facility and the process is successful, Diamond Chemical will realize a profit of $675,000. If the process does not succeed, the company will lose $825,000. Rob estimates that there is a 0.6 probability that the process will succeed.

Rob can also decide to build a pilot plant for $60,000 to test the new process before deciding to build the full-scale facility. If the pilot plant succeeds, Rob feels the chance of the full-scale facility succeeding is 85%. If the pilot plant fails, Rob feels the chance of the full-scale facility succeeding is only 20%. The probability that the pilot plant will succeed is estimated at 0.6. Structure this problem with a decision tree and advise Rob what to do.

35 Rob Johnson (see Problem 34) has some revised information concerning the accuracy of the pilot plant probabilities. According to his new information, the probability that the pilot plant will be successful, given that the full-scale facility will work, is 0.8. The probability that the pilot plant will fail, given that the full-scale facility will fail, is 0.85. Calculate the posterior probabilities and reevaluate the decision tree from Problem 34. Does this new information affect Diamond Chemical's original decision?

36 You are reconsidering your analysis of the tennis wager between you and your partner (see Problem 33) and have decided to incorporate utility theory into the decision making process.

The following table describes your utility values for various payoffs:

MONETARY VALUE	UTILITY
−$100	0.00
−$ 50	0.50
$ 0	0.80
$ 50	0.95
$100	1.00

(a) Redo Problem 35 using this information.
(b) How can you best describe your attitude toward risk? Justify your answer.

37 Shamrock Oil owns a parcel of land that has the potential to be an underground oil field. It will cost $500,000 to drill for oil. If oil does exist on the land, Shamrock will realize a payoff of $4,000,000 (not including drilling costs). With current information, Shamrock estimates that there is a 0.2 probability that oil is present on the site. Shamrock also has the option of selling the land as is for $400,000, without further information about the likelihood of oil being present. A third option is to perform geological tests at the site, which would cost $100,000. There is a 30% chance that the test results will be positive, after which Shamrock can sell the land for $650,000 or drill the land, with a 0.65 probability that oil exists. If the test results are negative, Shamrock can sell the land for $50,000 or drill the land, with a 0.05 probability that oil exists. Using a decision tree, recommend a course of action for Shamrock Oil.

38 Shamrock Oil (see Problem 37) has some revised information concerning the accuracy of the geological test probabilities. According to this new information, the probability that the test will be positive, given that oil is present in the ground, is 0.85. The probability that the test will be negative, given that oil is not present, is 0.75. Calculate the posterior probabilities and reevaluate the decision tree from Problem 37. Does this new information affect Shamrock Oil's original decision?

39 Shamrock Oil (see Problem 37) has decided to rely on utility theory to assist in the decision concerning the oil field. The following table describes its utility function; all monetary values are in thousands of dollars:

MONETARY VALUE	UTILITY
−$ 600	0.00
−$ 500	0.03
−$ 50	0.10
$ 400	0.15
$ 550	0.17
$3,400	0.90
$3,500	1.00

(a) Redo Problem 37 using this information.
(b) How can you best describe Shamrock Oil's attitude toward risk? Justify your answer.

40 Jim Sellers is thinking about producing a new type of electric razor for men. If the market is good, he would get a return of $140,000, but if the market for this new type of razor is poor, he would lose $84,000. Because Ron Bush is a close friend of Jim Sellers, Jim is considering the possibility of using Bush Marketing Research to gather additional information about the market for the razor. Ron has suggested two options to Jim. The first alternative is a sophisticated questionnaire that would be administered to a test market. It will cost $5,000. The second alternative is to run a pilot study. This would involve producing a limited number of the new razors and trying to sell them in two cities that are typical of American cities. The pilot study is more accurate but is also more expensive. It will cost $20,000. Ron has suggested that it would be a good idea for Jim to conduct either the questionnaire or the pilot before making the decision concerning whether to produce the new razor. But Jim is not sure if the value of either option is worth the cost.

For the sake of solving this problem, assume that Jim has the following probability estimates available: the probability of a successful market without performing the questionnaire or pilot study is 0.5, the probability of a successful market given a positive questionnaire result is 0.78, the probability of a successful market given a negative questionnaire result is 0.27, the probability of a successful market given a positive pilot study result is 0.89, and the probability of a successful market given a negative pilot study result is 0.18. Further, the probability of a positive questionnaire result is 0.45 and the probability of a positive pilot study result is also 0.45.

(a) Draw the decision tree for this problem and identify the best decision for Jim.
(b) What is the value of the questionnaire's information? What is its efficiency?
(c) What is the value of the pilot study's information? What is its efficiency?

41 Jim Sellers (see Problem 40) has been able to estimate his utility for a number of different values, and he would like to use these utility values in making his decision. The utility values are $U(-\$104,000) = 0$, $U(-\$89,000) = 0.5$, $U(-\$84,000) = 0.55$, $U(-\$20,000) = 0.7$, $U(-\$5,000) = 0.8$, $U(\$0) = 0.81$, $U(\$120,000) = 0.9$, $U(\$135,000) = 0.95$, and $U(\$140,000) = 1$.

(a) Solve Problem 40(a) again using utility values.
(b) Is Jim a risk avoider or risk seeker? Justify your answer.

42 Jason Scott has applied for a mortgage to purchase a house, and he will go to settlement in two months.

His loan can be locked in now at the current market interest rate of 7% and a cost of $1,000. He also has the option of waiting one month and locking in the rate available at that time at a cost of $500. Finally, he can choose to accept the market rate available at settlement in two months at no cost. Assume that interest rates will either increase by 0.5% (0.3 probability), remain unchanged (0.5 probability), or decrease by 0.5% (0.2 probability) at the end one month.

Rates can also increase, remain unchanged, or decrease by another 0.5% at the end on the second month. If rates increase after one month, the probability that they will increase, remain unchanged, and decrease at the end of the second month is 0.5, 0.25, and 0.25, respectively. If rates remain unchanged after one month, the probability that they will increase, remain unchanged, and decrease at the end of the second month is 0.25, 0.5, and 0.25, respectively. If rates decrease after one month, the probability that they will increase, remain unchanged, and decrease at the end of the second month is 0.25, 0.25, and 0.5, respectively.

Assuming that Jason will stay in the house for 5 years, each 0.5% increase in the interest rate of his mortgage will cost him $2,400. Each 0.5% decrease in the rate will likewise save him $2,400. What strategy would you recommend?

43 Jason Scott (see Problem 42) has decided to incorporate utility theory into his decision with his mortgage application. The following table describes Jason's utility function:

MONETARY VALUE	UTILITY
−$4,800	0.00
−$2,900	0.10
−$2,400	0.12
−$1,000	0.15
−$ 500	0.19
$ 0	0.21
$1,900	0.26
$2,400	0.30
$4,800	1.00

(a) How can you best describe Jason's attitude toward risk? Justify your answer.
(b) Will the use of utilities affect Jason's original decision in Problem 42?

44 An investor is deciding whether to build a retail store. If she invests in the store and it is successful, she expects a return of $100,000 in the first year. If the store is not successful, she will suffer a loss of $80,000. She guesses that the probability that the store will be a success is 0.6.

To remove some of the uncertainty from this decision, the investor tries to establish more information, but this market research will cost $20,000. If she spends this money, she will have more confidence in her investment. There is a 0.6 probability that this information will be favorable; if it is, the likelihood that the store will be a success increases to 0.9. If the information is not favorable, the likelihood that the store will be a success reduces to only 0.2. Of course, she can elect to do nothing.
(a) What do you recommend?
(b) How much is the information worth? What is its efficiency?

45 Replace all monetary values in Problem 44 with the following utilities:

MONETARY VALUE	UTILITY
$100,000	1.00
$ 80,000	0.40
$ 0	0.20
−$ 20,000	0.10
−$ 80,000	0.05
−$100,000	0.00

(a) What do you recommend, based on expected utility?
(b) Is the investor a risk seeker or a risk avoider? Justify your answer.

46 The Jamis Corporation is involved with waste management. During the past 10 years it has become one of the largest waste disposal companies in the Midwest, serving primarily Wisconsin, Illinois, and Michigan. Bob Jamis, president of the company, is considering the possibility of establishing a waste treatment plant in northern Mississippi. From past experience, Bob believes that a small plant would yield a $500,000 profit, regardless of the demand for the plant. The success of a medium-sized plant would depend on demand. With a low demand for waste treatment, Bob expects a $200,000 profit. A fair demand would yield a $700,000 profit, and a high demand would return $800,000. Although a large plant is much riskier than a medium-sized one, the potential rewards are much greater. With a high demand, a large plant would return $1,000,000. However, the plant would yield a profit of only $400,000 with a fair demand, and it would actually lose $200,000 with a low demand. Looking at the current economic conditions in northern Mississippi, Bob estimates that the probabilities of low, fair, and high demands are 0.15, 0.4, and 0.45, respectively.

Because of the large potential investment and the possibility of a loss, Bob has decided to hire a market research team that is based in Jackson, Mississippi. This team will perform a survey to get a better feel for the probability of a low, medium, or high demand for a waste treatment facility. The cost of the survey is $50,000, and the survey could result in three possible outcomes—low, fair, and high. To help Bob determine whether to go ahead with the survey, the marketing research firm has provided Bob with the following information regarding the conditional probabilities, i.e., P(Survey results | Possible outcomes):

	SURVEY RESULTS		
POSSIBLE OUTCOME	LOW	FAIR	HIGH
Low demand	0.7	0.2	0.1
Fair demand	0.4	0.5	0.1
High demand	0.1	0.3	0.6

For example, P(Low survey result | Low demand) = 0.7. What should Bob do?

47 Before market research was done, Peter Martin believed that there was a 50–50 chance that his food store would be a success. The research team determined that there was a 0.75 probability that the market research would be favorable, given a successful food store. Moreover, there was a 0.65 probability that the market research would be unfavorable, given an unsuccessful food store. This information is based on past experience.

(a) If the market research is favorable, what is Peter's revised probability of a successful food store?

(b) If the market research is unfavorable, what is Peter's revised probability of a successful food store?

48 A market research company has approached you about the possibility of using its services to help you decide whether to launch a new product. According to its customer portfolio, it has correctly predicted a favorable market for its clients' products 14 out of the last 16 times. It has also correctly predicted an unfavorable market for its clients' products 9 out of 11 times. Without this research company's help, you have estimated the probability of a favorable market

at 0.55. Calculate the posterior probabilities, using the track record of the research firm.

49 Lathum Consulting is an econometrics research firm that predicts the direction of the gross national product (GNP) during the next quarter. More specifically, it forecasts whether the GNP will grow, hold steady, or decline. The following table describes Lathum's track record from past predictions by displaying the probabilities of its predictions, given the actual outcome:

	GNP PREDICTION		
ACTUAL GNP	GROWTH	STEADY	DECLINE
Growth	0.75	0.08	0.05
Steady	0.18	0.80	0.12
Decline	0.07	0.12	0.83

For example, the chance that Lathum will predict that the GNP will grow when it actually is steady is 18%. Your company is considering a contract with Lathum Consulting to assist in predicting the direction of next quarter's GNP. Prior to enlisting Lathum's services, you have assessed the probability of the GNP growing, holding steady, and declining at 0.3, 0.45, and 0.25, respectively. Calculate the posterior probabilities, using the services of Lathum Consulting.

50 In the past few years, the traffic problems in Lynn McKell's hometown have gotten worse. Now, Broad Street is congested about half the time. The normal travel time to work for Lynn is only 15 minutes when she takes Broad Street and there is no congestion. With congestion, however, it takes Lynn 40 minutes to get to work using Broad Street. If Lynn decides to take the expressway, it takes 30 minutes, regardless of the traffic conditions. Lynn's utility for travel time is $U(15 \text{ minutes}) = 0.9$, $U(30 \text{ minutes}) = 0.7$, and $U(40 \text{ minutes}) = 0.2$.

(a) Which route will minimize Lynn's expected travel time?

(b) Which route will maximize Lynn's utility?

(c) When it comes to travel time, is Lynn a risk seeker or a risk avoider? Justify your answer.

Case Study

Ski Right

After retiring as a physician, Bob Guthrie became an avid downhill skier on the steep slopes of the Utah Rocky Mountains. As an amateur inventor, Bob was always looking for something new. With the recent deaths of several celebrity skiers, Bob knew he could use his creative mind to make

skiing safer and his bank account larger. He knew that many deaths on the slopes were caused by head injuries. Although ski helmets have been on the market for some time, most skiers considered them boring and basically ugly. As a physician, Bob knew that some type of new ski helmet was the answer.

Bob's biggest challenge was to invent a helmet that was attractive, safe, and fun to wear. Multiple colors, using the latest fashion designs, would be a must. After years of skiing, Bob knew that many skiers believed that how you looked on the slopes was more important than how you skied. His helmets would have to look good and fit in with current fashion trends. But attractive helmets were not enough. Bob had to make the helmets fun and useful. The name of the new ski helmet, Ski Right, was sure to be a winner. If Bob could come up with a good idea, he believed that there was a 20% chance that the market for the Ski Right helmet would be excellent. The chance of a good market should be 40%. Bob also knew that the market for his helmet could be only average (30% chance) or even poor (10% chance).

The idea of how to make ski helmets fun and useful came to Bob on a gondola ride to the top of a mountain. A busy executive on the gondola ride was on his cell phone, trying to complete a complicated merger. When the executive got off the gondola, he dropped the phone, and it was crushed by the gondola mechanism. Bob decided that his new ski helmet would have a built-in cell phone and an AM/FM stereo radio. All the electronics could be operated by a control pad worn on a skier's arm or leg.

Bob decided to try a small pilot project for Ski Right. He enjoyed being retired and didn't want a failure to cause him to go back to work. After some research, Bob found Progressive Products (PP). The company was willing to be a partner in developing the Ski Right and sharing any profits. If the market was excellent, Bob would net $5,000. With a good market, Bob would net $2,000. An average market would result in a loss of $2,000, and a poor market would mean Bob would be out $5,000.

Another option for Bob was to have Leadville Barts (LB) make the helmet. The company had extensive experience in making bicycle helmets. PP would then take the helmets made by LB and do the rest. Bob had a greater risk. He estimated that he could lose $10,000 in a poor market or $4,000 in an average

market. A good market for Ski Right would result in a $6,000 profit for Bob, and an excellent market would mean a $12,000 profit.

A third option for Bob was to use TalRad (TR), a radio company in Tallahassee, Florida. TR had extensive experience in making military radios. LB could make the helmets, and PP could do the rest. Again, Bob would be taking on greater risk. A poor market would mean a $15,000 loss, and an average market would mean a $10,000 loss. A good market would result in a net profit of $7,000 for Bob. An excellent market would return $13,000.

Bob could also have Celestial Cellular (CC) develop the cell phones. Thus, another option was to have CC make the phones and have PP do the rest of the production and distribution. Because the cell phone was the most expensive component of the helmet, Bob could lose $30,000 in a poor market. He could lose $20,000 in an average market. If the market was good or excellent, Bob would see a net profit of $10,000 or $30,000, respectively.

Bob's final option was to forget about PP entirely. He could use LB to make the helmets, CC to make the phones, and TR to make the AM/FM stereo radios. Bob could then hire some friends to assemble everything and market the finished Ski Right helmets. With this final alternative, Bob could realize a net profit of $55,000 in an excellent market. Even if the market were just good, Bob would net $20,000. An average market, however, would mean a loss of $35,000. If the market was poor, Bob would lose $60,000.

Discussion Questions

1. What do you recommend?
2. What is the opportunity loss for this problem?
3. Compute the expected value of perfect information.
4. Was Bob completely logical in how he approached this decision problem?

Case Study

Blake Electronics

In 1969, Steve Blake founded Blake Electronics in Long Beach, California, to manufacture resistors, capacitors, inductors, and other electronic components. During the Vietnam War, Steve was a radio operator, and it was during this time that he became proficient at repairing radios and other communications equipment. Steve viewed his four-year experience with the army with mixed feelings. He hated army life, but that experience gave him the confidence and the initiative to start his own electronics firm.

Over the years, Steve kept the business relatively unchanged. By 1984, total annual sales were in excess of $2 million. In 1988, Steve's son, Jim, joined the company after finishing high school and two years of courses in electronics at Long Beach Community College. Jim had always been aggressive in high school athletics, and he became even more aggressive as general sales manager of Blake Electronics. This aggressiveness

bothered Steve, who was more conservative. Jim would make deals to supply companies with electronic components before he bothered to find out if Blake Electronics had the ability or capacity to produce the components. On several occasions, this behavior caused the company some embarrassing moments when Blake Electronics was unable to produce the electronic components for companies with which Jim had made deals.

In 1992, Jim started to go after government contracts for electronic components. By 1994, total annual sales had increased to more than $10 million, and the number of employees exceeded 200. Many of these employees were electronics specialists and graduates of electrical engineering programs from top colleges and universities. But Jim's tendency to stretch Blake Electronics to contracts continued as well, and by 2001, Blake Electronics had a reputation with government agencies as a company that could not deliver what it promised. Almost overnight,

FIGURE 14
Master Control Center

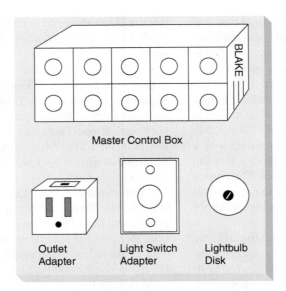

Master Control Box

Outlet
Adapter

Light Switch
Adapter

Lightbulb
Disk

government contracts stopped, and Blake Electronics was left with an idle workforce and unused manufacturing equipment. This high overhead started to melt away profits, and in 2003, Blake Electronics was faced with the possibility of sustaining a loss for the first time in its history.

In 2005, Steve decided to look at the possibility of manufacturing electronic components for home use. Although this was a totally new market for Blake Electronics, Steve was convinced that this was the only way to keep Blake Electronics from dipping into the red. The research team at Blake Electronics was given the task of developing new electronic devices for home use. The first idea from the research team was the Master Control Center. The basic components for this system are shown in Figure 14.

The heart of the system is the master control box. This unit, which would have a retail price of $250, has two rows of five buttons. Each button controls one light or appliance and can be set as either a switch or a rheostat. When set as a switch, a light finger touch on the bottom either turns a light or appliance on or off. When set as a rheostat, a finger touching the bottom controls the intensity of the light. Leaving your finger on the button makes the light go through a complete cycle, ranging from off to bright and back to off again.

To allow for maximum flexibility, each master control box is powered by two D-sized batteries that can last up to a year, depending on usage. In addition, the research team has developed three versions of the master control box—versions A, B, and C. If a family wants to control more than 10 lights or appliances, another master control box can be purchased.

The lightbulb disk, which would have a retail price of $2.50, is controlled by the master control box and is used to control the intensity of any light. A different disk is available for each button position for all three master control boxes. By inserting the lightbulb disk between the lightbulb and the socket, the appropriate button on the master control box can completely control the intensity of the light. If a standard light switch is used, it must be on at all times for the master control box to work.

One disadvantage of using a standard light switch is that only the master control box can be used to control the particular light. To avoid this problem, the research team developed a special light switch adapter that would sell for $15. When this device is installed either the master control box or the light switch adapter can be used to control the light.

When used to control appliances other than lights, the master control box must be used in conjunction with one or more outlet adapters. The adapters are plugged in to a standard wall outlet, and the appliance is then plugged in to the adapter. Each outlet adapter has a switch on top that allows the appliance to be controlled from the master control box or the outlet adapter. The price of each outlet adapter would be $25.

The research team estimated that it would cost $500,000 to develop the equipment and procedures needed to manufacture the master control box and accessories. If successful, this venture could increase sales by approximately $2 million. But would the master control boxes be a successful venture? With a 60% chance of success estimated by the research team, Steve has serious doubts about trying to market the master control boxes even though he liked the basic idea. Because of his reservations, Steve decided to send requests for proposals (RFPs) for additional marketing research to 30 marketing research companies in southern California.

The first RFP to come back was from a small company called Marketing Associates, Inc. (MAI), which would charge $100,000 for the survey. According to its proposal, MAI has been in business for about three years and has conducted about 100 marketing research projects. MAI's major strengths appeared to be individual attention to each account, experienced staff, and fast work. Steve was particularly interested in one part of the proposal, which revealed MAI's success record with previous accounts. This is shown in Table 13.

The only other proposal to be returned was by a branch office of Iverstine and Kinard, one of the largest marketing research firms in the country. The cost for a complete survey would be $300,000. Although the proposal did not contain the

TABLE 13
Success Figures for MAI

	SURVEY RESULTS		
OUTCOME	FAVORABLE	UNFAVORABLE	TOTAL
Successful venture	35	20	55
Unsuccessful venture	15	30	45

same success record as MAI, the proposal from Iverstine and Kinard did contain some interesting information. The chance of getting a favorable survey result, given a successful venture, was 90%. On the other hand, the chance of getting an unfavorable survey result, given an unsuccessful venture, was 80%. Thus, it appeared to Steve that Iverstine and Kinard would be able to predict the success or failure of the master control boxes with a great amount of certainty.

Steve pondered the situation. Unfortunately, the two marketing research teams gave different types of information in their proposals. Steve concluded that there would be no way that the two proposals could be compared unless he got additional information from Iverstine and Kinard. Furthermore, Steve wasn't sure what he would do with the information and whether it would be worth the expense of hiring one of the marketing research firms.

Discussion Questions

1. Does Steve need additional information from Iverstine and Kinard?

2. What would you recommend?

 Internet Case Studies

See the Companion Website for this text, at www.pearsonhighered.com/balakrishnan, for additional case studies.

Brief Solutions to Odd-Numbered End-of-Chapter Problems

13 (a) Maximax; Acme; $400,000. (b) Maximin; High Pro; −$15,000. (c) Acme, EMV = $262,000.

15 (a) Move shop, EMV = $32,550. (b) Move shop, EOL = $7,200. (c) EVPI = $7,200.

17 (a) Bonds, EMV = 3.25%. (b) Bonds, EOL = 2.15%. (c) EVPI = 2.15%.

19 (a) 500. (b) 100. (c) 300. (d) 100. (e) 300.

21 7 cases.

23 (a) 100. (b) 100. (c) EVwPI = $1,225. EVPI = $485.

25 (a) Drexel. (b) 0.60 minutes.

27 (a) Risk avoiders. (b) Expected utility = 0.90.

29 (a) Supplier A, Expected cost = $126. (b) $54.

31 (a) Expected profit = $50.36. Hire Elmo. (b) $10.36.

33 Expected payoff = $31.63. Accept wager.

35 Expected profit = $246,000. Build pilot.

37 Expected payoff = $565,000. Test land.

39 (a) Expected utility = 0.246. Test land. (b) Risk seeker.

41 (a) Expected utility = 0.823. Conduct questionnaire. (b) Risk avoider.

43 (a) Risk seeker. (b) No. Expected utility = 0.261.

45 (a) Expected utility = 0.62. Get information. (b) Risk seeker.

47 (a) 0.682. (b) 0.278.

49 Given growth prediction: 0.696, 0.250, 0.054. Given steady prediction: 0.058, 0.870, 0.072. Given decline prediction: 0.054, 0.195, 0.751.

Regression Models

LEARNING OBJECTIVES

After completing this chapter, students will be able to:

1. Identify variables and use them in a regression model.
2. Develop simple linear regression equations from sample data and interpret the slope and intercept.
3. Compute the coefficient of determination and the coefficient of correlation and interpret their meanings.
4. Interpret the *F* test in a linear regression model.
5. List the assumptions used in regression and use residual plots to identify problems.
6. Develop a multiple regression model and use it for prediction purposes.
7. Use dummy variables to model categorical data.
8. Determine which variables should be included in a multiple regression model.
9. Transform a nonlinear function into a linear one for use in regression.
10. Understand and avoid mistakes commonly made in the use of regression analysis.

CHAPTER OUTLINE

1 Introduction
2 Scatter Diagrams
3 Simple Linear Regression
4 Measuring the Fit of the Regression Model
5 Using Computer Software for Regression
6 Assumptions of the Regression Model

7 Testing the Model for Significance
8 Multiple Regression Analysis
9 Binary or Dummy Variables
10 Model Building
11 Nonlinear Regression
12 Cautions and Pitfalls in Regression Analysis

Summary • Glossary • Key Equations • Solved Problems • Self-Test • Discussion Questions and Problems

Case Study: North–South Airline • Bibliography

From Chapter 4 of *Quantitative Analysis for Management*, 11/e. Barry Render. Ralph M. Stair, Jr. Michael E. Hanna. Copyright © 2012 by Pearson Education. All rights reserved.

1 Introduction

Regression analysis is a very valuable tool for today's manager. Regression has been used to model such things as the relationship between level of education and income, the price of a house and the square footage, and the sales volume for a company relative to the dollars spent on advertising. When businesses are trying to decide which location is best for a new store or branch office, regression models are often used. Cost estimation models are often regression models. The applicability of regression analysis is virtually limitless.

Two purposes of regression analysis are to understand the relationship between variables and to predict the value of one based on the other.

There are generally two purposes for regression analysis. The first is to understand the relationship between variables such as advertising expenditures and sales. The second purpose is to predict the value of one variable based on the value of the other. Because of this, regression is a very important forecasting technique.

In this chapter, the simple linear regression model will first be developed, and then a more complex multiple regression model will be used to incorporate even more variables into our model. In any regression model, the variable to be predicted is called the **dependent variable** or **response variable**. The value of this is said to be dependent upon the value of an **independent variable**, which is sometimes called an **explanatory variable** or a **predictor variable**.

2 Scatter Diagrams

A scatter diagram is a graph of the data.

To investigate the relationship between variables, it is helpful to look at a graph of the data. Such a graph is often called a **scatter diagram** or a **scatter plot**. Normally the independent variable is plotted on the horizontal axis and the dependent variable is plotted on the vertical axis. The following example will illustrate this.

Triple A Construction Company renovates old homes in Albany. Over time, the company has found that its dollar volume of renovation work is dependent on the Albany area payroll. The figures for Triple A's revenues and the amount of money earned by wage earners in Albany for the past six years are presented in Table 1. Economists have predicted the local area payroll to be $600 million next year, and Triple A wants to plan accordingly.

Figure 1 provides a scatter diagram for the Triple A Construction data given in Table 1. This graph indicates that higher values for the local payroll seem to result in higher sales for the company. There is not a perfect relationship because not all the points lie in a straight line, but there is a relationship. A line has been drawn through the data to help show the relationship that exists between the payroll and sales. The points do not all lie on the line, so there would be some error involved if we tried to predict sales based on payroll using this or any other line. Many lines could be drawn through these points, but which one best represents the true relationship? Regression analysis provides the answer to this question.

TABLE 1

Triple A Construction Company Sales and Local Payroll

TRIPLE A'S SALES ($100,000s)	LOCAL PAYROLL ($100,000,000s)
6	3
8	4
9	6
5	4
4.5	2
9.5	5

FIGURE 1

Scatter Diagram of Triple A Construction Company Data

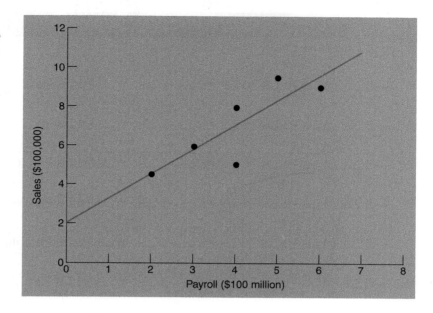

3   Simple Linear Regression

In any regression model, there is an implicit assumption (which can be tested) that a relationship exists between the variables. There is also some random error that cannot be predicted. The underlying simple linear regression model is

$$Y = \beta_0 + \beta_1 X + \epsilon \qquad (1)$$

where

The dependent variable is Y and the independent variable is X.

Y = dependent variable (response variable)
X = independent variable (predictor variable or explanatory variable)
β_0 = intercept (value of Y when $X = 0$)
β_1 = slope of regression line
ϵ = random error

Estimates of the slope and intercept are found from sample data.

The true values for the intercept and slope are not known, and therefore they are estimated using sample data. The regression equation based on sample data is given as

$$\hat{Y} = b_0 + b_1 X \qquad (2)$$

where

$\hat{Y}$ = predicted value of Y
b_0 = estimate of β_0, based on sample results
b_1 = estimate of β_1, based on sample results

In the Triple A Construction example, we are trying to predict the sales, so the dependent variable (Y) would be sales. The variable we use to help predict sales is the Albany area payroll, so this is the independent variable (X). Although any number of lines can be drawn through these points to show a relationship between X and Y in Figure 1, the line that will be chosen is the one that in some way minimizes the errors. Error is defined as

$$\text{Error} = (\text{Actual value}) - (\text{Predicted value})$$

$$e = Y - \hat{Y} \qquad (3)$$

The regression line minimizes the sum of the squared errors.

Since errors may be positive or negative, the average error could be zero even though there are extremely large errors—both positive and negative. To eliminate the difficulty of negative errors

TABLE 2

Regression Calculations for Triple A Construction

Y	X	$(X - \overline{X})^2$	$(X - \overline{X})(Y - \overline{Y})$
6	3	$(3 - 4)^2 = 1$	$(3 - 4)(6 - 7) = 1$
8	4	$(4 - 4)^2 = 0$	$(4 - 4)(8 - 7) = 0$
9	6	$(6 - 4)^2 = 4$	$(6 - 4)(9 - 7) = 4$
5	4	$(4 - 4)^2 = 0$	$(4 - 4)(5 - 7) = 0$
4.5	2	$(2 - 4)^2 = 4$	$(2 - 4)(4.5 - 7) = 5$
9.5	5	$(5 - 4)^2 = 1$	$(5 - 4)(9.5 - 7) = 2.5$
$\Sigma Y = 42$	$\Sigma X = 24$	$\Sigma(X - \overline{X})^2 = 10$	$\Sigma(X - \overline{X})(Y - \overline{Y}) = 12.5$
$\overline{Y} = 42/6 = 7$	$\overline{Y} = 24/6 = 4$		

canceling positive errors, the errors can be squared. The best regression line will be defined as the one with the minimum sum of the squared errors. For this reason, regression analysis is sometimes called **least-squares** regression.

Statisticians have developed formulas that we can use to find the equation of a straight line that would minimize the sum of the squared errors. The simple linear regression equation is

$$\hat{Y} = b_0 + b_1 X$$

The following formulas can be used to compute the intercept and the slope:

$$\overline{X} = \frac{\Sigma X}{n} = \text{average (mean) of } X \text{ values}$$

$$\overline{Y} = \frac{\Sigma Y}{n} = \text{average (mean) of } Y \text{ values}$$

$$b_1 = \frac{\Sigma(X - \overline{X})(Y - \overline{Y})}{\Sigma(X - \overline{X})^2} \tag{4}$$

$$b_0 = \overline{Y} - b_1\overline{X} \tag{5}$$

The preliminary calculations are shown in Table 2. There are other "shortcut" formulas that are helpful when doing the computations on a calculator, and these are presented in Appendix 1. They will not be shown here, as computer software will be used for most of the other examples in this chapter.

Computing the slope and intercept of the regression equation for the Triple A Construction Company example, we have

$$\overline{X} = \frac{\Sigma X}{6} = \frac{24}{6} = 4$$

$$\overline{Y} = \frac{\Sigma Y}{6} = \frac{42}{6} = 7$$

$$b_1 = \frac{\Sigma(X - \overline{X})(Y - \overline{Y})}{\Sigma(X - \overline{X})^2} = \frac{12.5}{10} = 1.25$$

$$b_0 = \overline{Y} - b_1\overline{X} = 7 - (1.25)(4) = 2$$

The estimated regression equation therefore is

$$\hat{Y} = 2 + 1.25X$$

or

$$\text{sales} = 2 + 1.25(\text{payroll})$$

If the payroll next year is $600 million ($X = 6$), then the predicted value would be

$$\hat{Y} = 2 + 1.25(6) = 9.5$$

or $950,000.

One of the purposes of regression is to understand the relationship among variables. This model tells us that for each $100 million (represented by X) increase in the payroll, we would expect the sales to increase by $125,000 since $b_1 = 1.25$ ($100,000s). This model helps Triple A Construction see how the local economy and company sales are related.

4 Measuring the Fit of the Regression Model

Deviations (errors) may be positive or negative.

A regression equation can be developed for any variables X and Y, even random numbers. We certainly would not have any confidence in the ability of one random number to predict the value of another random number. How do we know that the model is actually helpful in predicting Y based on X? Should we have confidence in this model? Does the model provide better predictions (smaller errors) than simply using the average of the Y values?

In the Triple A Construction example, sales figures (Y) varied from a low of 4.5 to a high of 9.5, and the mean was 7. If each sales value is compared with the mean, we see how far they deviate from the mean and we could compute a measure of the total variability in sales. Because Y is sometimes higher and sometimes lower than the mean, there may be both positive and negative deviations. Simply summing these values would be misleading because the negatives would cancel out the positives, making it appear that the numbers are closer to the mean than they actually are. To prevent this problem, we will use the sum of the **squares total (SST)** to measure the total variability in Y:

The SST measures the total variability in Y about the mean.

$$\text{SST} = \Sigma(Y - \overline{Y})^2 \tag{6}$$

If we did not use X to predict Y, we would simply use the mean of Y as the prediction, and the SST would measure the accuracy of our predictions. However, a regression line may be used to predict the value of Y, and while there are still errors involved, the sum of these squared errors will be less than the total sum of squares just computed. The sum of the squares error (SSE) is

The SSE measures the variability in Y about the regression line.

$$\text{SSE} = \Sigma e^2 = \Sigma(Y - \hat{Y})^2 \tag{7}$$

Table 3 provides the calculations for the Triple A Construction Example. The mean ($\overline{Y} = 7$) is compared to each value and we get

$$\text{SST} = 22.5$$

The prediction ($\hat{Y}$) for each observation is computed and compared to the actual value. This results in

$$\text{SSE} = 6.875$$

The SSE is much lower than the SST. Using the regression line has reduced the variability in the sum of squares by $22.5 - 6.875 = 15.625$. This is called the **sum of squares due to**

TABLE 3 Sum of Squares for Triple A Construction

Y	X	$(Y - \overline{Y})^2$	$\hat{Y}$	$(Y - \hat{Y})^2$	$(\hat{Y} - \overline{Y})^2$
6	3	$(6 - 7)^2 = 1$	$2 + 1.25(3) = 5.75$	0.0625	1.563
8	4	$(8 - 7)^2 = 1$	$2 + 1.25(4) = 7.00$	1	0
9	6	$(9 - 7)^2 = 4$	$2 + 1.25(6) = 9.50$	0.25	6.25
5	4	$(5 - 7)^2 = 4$	$2 + 1.25(4) = 7.00$	4	0
4.5	2	$(4.5 - 7)^2 = 6.25$	$2 + 1.25(2) = 4.50$	0	6.25
9.5	5	$(9.5 - 7)^2 = 6.25$	$2 + 1.25(5) = 8.25$	1.5625	1.563
		$\Sigma(Y - \overline{Y})^2 = 22.5$		$\Sigma(Y - \hat{Y})^2 = 6.875$	$\Sigma(\hat{Y} - \overline{Y})^2 = 15.625$
$\overline{Y} = 7$		$\text{SST} = 22.5$		$\text{SSE} = 6.875$	$\text{SSR} = 15.625$

FIGURE 2

Deviations from the Regression Line and from the Mean

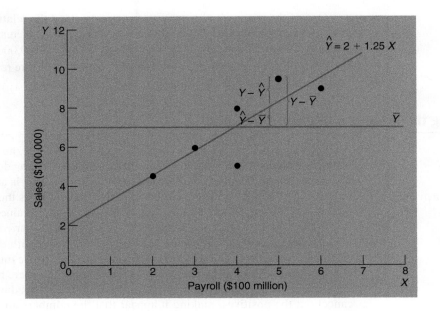

regression (SSR) and indicates how much of the total variability in Y is explained by the regression model. Mathematically, this can be calculated as

$$SSR = \Sigma(\hat{Y} - \overline{Y})^2 \tag{8}$$

Table 3 indicates

$$SSR = 15.625$$

There is a very important relationship between the sums of squares that we have computed:

$$(\text{Sum of squares total}) = (\text{Sum of squares due to regression}) + (\text{Sum of squares error})$$

$$SST = SSR + SSE \tag{9}$$

Figure 2 displays the data for Triple A Construction. The regression line is shown, as is a line representing the mean of the Y values. The errors used in computing the sums of squares are shown on this graph. Notice how the sample points are closer to the regression line than they are to the mean.

Coefficient of Determination

The SSR is sometimes called the explained variability in Y while the SSE is the unexplained variability in Y. The proportion of the variability in Y that is explained by the regression equation is called the **coefficient of determination** and is denoted by r^2. Thus,

$$r^2 = \frac{SSR}{SST} = 1 - \frac{SSE}{SST} \tag{10}$$

Thus, r^2 can be found using either the SSR or the SSE. For Triple A Construction, we have

$$r^2 = \frac{15.625}{22.5} = 0.6944$$

This means that about 69% of the variability in sales (Y) is explained by the regression equation based on payroll (X).

If every point in the sample were on the regression line (meaning all errors are 0), then 100% of the variability in Y could be explained by the regression equation, so $r^2 = 1$ and SSE $= 0$. The lowest possible value of r^2 is 0, indicating that X explains 0% of the variability in Y. Thus, r^2 can range from a low of 0 to a high of 1. In developing regression equations, a good model will have an r^2 value close to 1.

r^2 is the proportion of variability in Y that is explained by the regression equation.

If every point lies on the regression line, $r^2 = 1$ and SSE $= 0$.

FIGURE 3
Four Values of the Correlation Coefficient

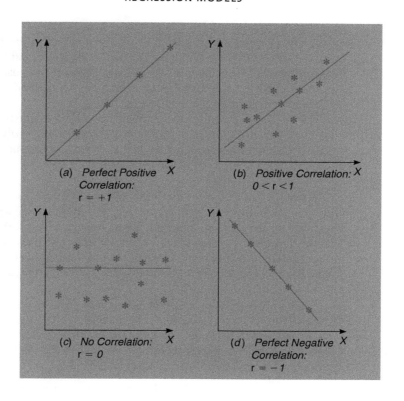

(a) Perfect Positive Correlation: $r = +1$

(b) Positive Correlation: $0 < r < 1$

(c) No Correlation: $r = 0$

(d) Perfect Negative Correlation: $r = -1$

Correlation Coefficient

Another measure related to the coefficient of determination is the **coefficient of correlation**. This measure also expresses the degree or strength of the linear relationship. It is usually expressed as r and can be any number between and including $+1$ and -1. Figure 3 illustrates possible scatter diagrams for different values of r. The value of r is the square root of r^2. It is negative if the slope is negative, and it is positive if the slope is positive. Thus,

$$r = \pm\sqrt{r^2} \tag{11}$$

The correlation coefficient ranges from -1 to $+1$.

For the Triple A Construction example with $r^2 = 0.6944$,

$$r = \sqrt{0.6944} = 0.8333$$

We know it is positive because the slope is $+1.25$.

 **IN ACTION** | **Multiple Regression Modeling at Canada's TransAlta Utilities**

TransAlta Utilities (TAU) is a $1.6 billion energy company operating in Canada, New Zealand, Australia, Argentina, and the United States. Headquartered in Alberta, Canada, TAU is that country's largest publicly owned utility. It serves 340,000 customers in Alberta through 57 customer-service facilities, each of which was staffed by 5 to 20 customer service linemen. The 270 linemen's jobs are to handle new connections and repairs and to patrol power lines and check substations. This existing system was not the result of some optimal central planning but was put in place incrementally as the company grew.

With help from the University of Alberta, TAU wanted to develop a causal model to decide how many linemen would be best assigned to each facility. The research team decided to build a multiple regression model with only three independent variables. The hardest part of the task was to select variables that were easy to quantify based on available data. In the end, the explanatory variables were number of urban customers, number of rural customers, and geographic size of a service area. The implicit assumptions in this model are that the time spent on customers is proportional to the number of customers; and the time spent on facilities (line patrol and substation checks) and travel are proportional to the size of the service region. By definition, the unexplained time in the model accounts for time that is not explained by the three variables (such as meetings, breaks, or unproductive time).

Not only did the results of the model please TAU managers, but the project (which included optimizing the number of facilities and their locations) saved $4 million per year.

Source: Based on E. Erkut, T. Myroon, and K. Strangway. "TransAlta Redesigns Its Service-Delivery Network," *Interfaces* (March–April 2000): 54–69.

5 Using Computer Software for Regression

Software such as QM for Windows (Appendix 2), Excel, and Excel QM (Appendix 3) is often used for regression calculations. We will rely on Excel for most of the calculations in the rest of this chapter. When using Excel to develop a regression model, the input and output for Excel 2007 and Excel 2010 are the same.

The Triple A Construction example will be used to illustrate how to develop a regression model in Excel 2010. Go to the *Data* tab and select *Data Analysis*, as shown in Program 1A. If *Data Analysis* does not appear, then the Excel add-in *Data Analysis* from the Analysis ToolPak must be enabled or activated. Once an add-in is activated, it will remain on the *Data* tab for future use.

When the *Data Analysis* window opens, scroll down to and highlight *Regression* and click *OK*, as illustrated in Program 1A. The Regression window will open, as shown in Program 1B, and you can input the *X* and *Y* ranges. Check the *Labels* box because the cells with the variable name were included in the first row of the *X* and *Y* ranges. To have the output presented on this page rather than on a new worksheet, select *Output Range* and give a cell address for the start of the output. Click the *OK* button, and the output appears in the output range specified.

Program 1C shows the intercept (2), slope (1.25), and other information that was previously calculated for the Triple A Construction example.

Errors are also called residuals.

The sums of squares are shown in the column headed by SS. Another name for *error* is **residual**. In Excel, the **sum of squares error** is shown as the sum of squares residual. The values in this output are the same values shown in Table 3:

$$\text{Sum of squares regression} = \text{SSR} = 15.625$$

$$\text{Sum of squares error (residual)} = \text{SSE} = 6.8750$$

$$\text{Sum of squares total} = \text{SST} = 22.5$$

The coefficient of determination (r^2) is shown to be 0.6944. The coefficient of correlation (r) is called *Multiple R* in the Excel output, and this is 0.8333.

PROGRAM 1A

Accessing the Regression Option in Excel 2010

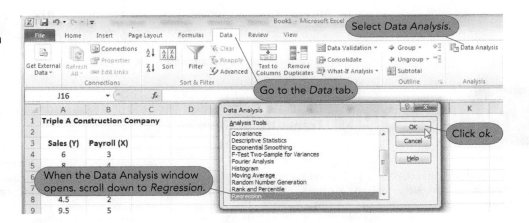

PROGRAM 1B
Data Input for Regression in Excel

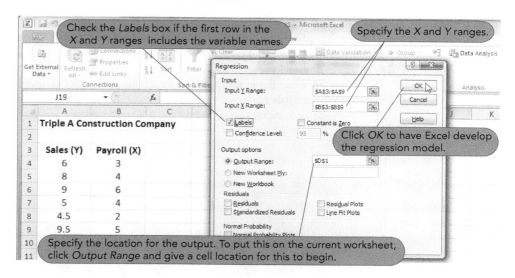

PROGRAM 1C
Excel Output for the Triple A Construction Example

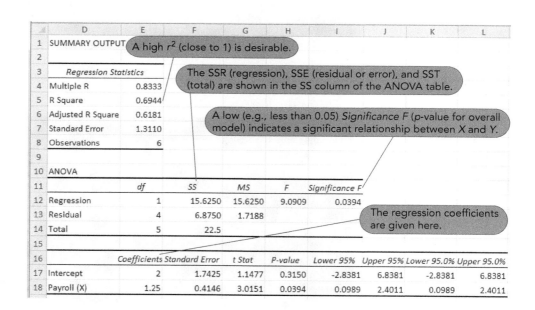

6 Assumptions of the Regression Model

If we can make certain assumptions about the errors in a regression model, we can perform statistical tests to determine if the model is useful. The following assumptions are made about the errors:

1. The errors are independent.
2. The errors are normally distributed.
3. The errors have a mean of zero.
4. The errors have a constant variance (regardless of the value of X).

A plot of the errors may highlight problems with the model.

It is possible to check the data to see if these assumptions are met. Often a plot of the residuals will highlight any glaring violations of the assumptions. When the errors (residuals) are plotted against the independent variable, the pattern should appear random.

Figure 4 presents some typical error patterns, with Figure 4A displaying a pattern that is expected when the assumptions are met and the model is appropriate. The errors are random and no discernible pattern is present. Figure 4B demonstrates an error pattern in which the errors increase as *X* increases, violating the constant variance assumption. Figure 4C shows errors con-

FIGURE 4A
Pattern of Errors Indicating Randomness

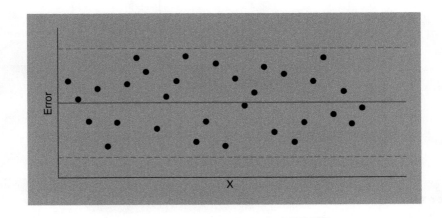

FIGURE 4B
Nonconstant Error Variance

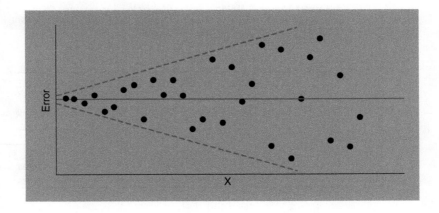

FIGURE 4C
Errors Indicate Relationship is Not Linear

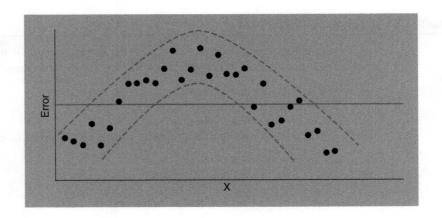

sistently increasing at first, and then consistently decreasing. A pattern such as this would indicate that the model is not linear and some other form (perhaps quadratic) should be used. In general, patterns in the plot of the errors indicate problems with the assumptions or the model specification.

Estimating the Variance

The error variance is estimated by the MSE.

While the errors are assumed to have constant variance (σ^2), this is usually not known. It can be estimated from the sample results. The estimate of σ^2 is the **mean squared error (MSE)** and is denoted by s^2. The MSE is the sum of squares due to error divided by the degrees of freedom:[*]

$$s^2 = \text{MSE} = \frac{\text{SSE}}{n - k - 1} \tag{12}$$

where

n = number of observations in the sample

k = number of independent variables

In this example, $n = 6$ and $k = 1$. So

$$s^2 = \text{MSE} = \frac{\text{SSE}}{n - k - 1} = \frac{6.8750}{6 - 1 - 1} = \frac{6.8750}{4} = 1.7188$$

From this we can estimate the standard deviation as

$$s = \sqrt{\text{MSE}} \tag{13}$$

This is called the **standard error of the estimate** or the *standard deviation of the regression*. In the example shown in Program 1D,

$$s = \sqrt{\text{MSE}} = \sqrt{1.7188} = 1.31$$

This is used in many of the statistical tests about the model. It is also used to find interval estimates for both Y and regression coefficients.[**]

7   Testing the Model for Significance

Both the MSE and r^2 provide a measure of accuracy in a regression model. However, when the sample size is too small, it is possible to get good values for both of these even if there is no relationship between the variables in the regression model. To determine whether these values are meaningful, it is necessary to test the model for significance.

To see if there is a linear relationship between X and Y, a statistical hypothesis test is performed. The underlying linear model was given in Equation 1 as

$$Y = \beta_0 + \beta_1 X + \epsilon$$

An F test is used to determine if there is a relationship between X and Y.

If $\beta_1 = 0$, then Y does not depend on X in any way. The null hypothesis says there is no linear relationship between the two variables (i.e., $\beta_1 = 0$). The alternate hypothesis is that there is a linear relationship (i.e., $\beta_1 \neq 0$). If the null hypothesis can be rejected, then we have proven that a linear relationship does exist, so X is helpful in predicting Y. The F distribution is used for testing this hypothesis. The appendix titled "F Distribution Values" contains values for the F distribution which can be used when calculations are performed by hand. The results of the test can also be obtained from both Excel and QM for Windows.

---

[*]See bibliography at end of this chapter for books with further details.

[**]The MSE is a common measure of accuracy in forecasting. When used with techniques besides regression, it is common to divide the SSE by n rather than $n - k - 1$.

The F statistic used in the hypothesis test is based on the MSE (seen in the previous section) and the mean squared regression (MSR). The MSR is calculated as

$$\text{MSR} = \frac{\text{SSR}}{k} \tag{14}$$

where

k = number of independent variables in the model

The F statistic is

$$F = \frac{\text{MSR}}{\text{MSE}} \tag{15}$$

Based on the assumptions regarding the errors in a regression model, this calculated F statistic is described by the F distribution with

degrees of freedom for the numerator = $\text{df}_1 = k$

degrees of freedom for the denominator = $\text{df}_2 = n - k - 1$.

where

k = the number of independent (X) variables

If the significance level for the F test is low, there is a relationship between X and Y.

If there is very little error, the denominator (MSE) of the F statistic is very small relative to the numerator (MSR), and the resulting F statistic would be large. This would be an indication that the model is useful. A significance level related to the value of the F statistic is then found. Whenever the F value is large, the significance level (p-value) will be low, indicating that it is extremely unlikely that this could have occurred by chance. When the F value is large (with a resulting small significance level), we can reject the null hypothesis that there is no linear relationship. This means that there is a linear relationship and the values of MSE and r^2 are meaningful.

The hypothesis test just described is summarized here:

Steps in Hypothesis Test for a Significant Regression Model

1. Specify null and alternative hypotheses:

$$H_0 : \beta_1 = 0$$
$$H_1 : \beta_1 \neq 0$$

2. Select the level of significance (α). Common values are 0.01 and 0.05.

3. Calculate the value of the test statistic using the formula

$$F = \frac{\text{MSR}}{\text{MSE}}$$

4. Make a decision using one of the following methods:
   (a) Reject the null hypothesis if the test statistic is greater than the F value from the table in the appendix titled "F Distribution Values". Otherwise, do not reject the null hypothesis:

   Reject if $F_{\text{calculated}} > F_{\alpha, \text{df}_1, \text{df}_2}$

   $\text{df}_1 = k$

   $\text{df}_2 = n - k - 1$

   (b) Reject the null hypothesis if the **observed significance level**, or **p-value**, is less than the level of significance (α). Otherwise, do not reject the null hypothesis:

   p-value = $P(F >$ calculated test statistic$)$

   Reject if p-value $< \alpha$

FIGURE 5

F Distribution for Triple A Construction Test for Significance

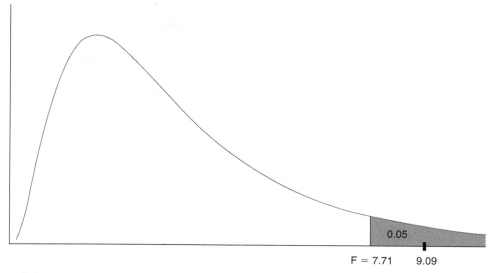

Triple A Construction Example

To illustrate the process of testing the hypothesis about a significant relationship, consider the Triple A Construction example. The appendix titled "*F* Distribution Values" will be used to provide values for the *F* distribution.

Step 1.

$$H_0 : \beta_1 = 0 \quad (\text{no linear relationship between } X \text{ and } Y)$$
$$H_1 : \beta_1 \neq 0 \quad (\text{linear relationship exists between } X \text{ and } Y)$$

Step 2.

$$\text{Select } \alpha = 0.05.$$

Step 3. Calculate the value of the test statistic. The MSE was already calculated to be 1.7188. The MSR is then calculated so that *F* can be found:

$$\text{MSR} = \frac{\text{SSR}}{k} = \frac{15.6250}{1} = 15.6250$$

$$F = \frac{\text{MSR}}{\text{MSE}} = \frac{15.6250}{1.7188} = 9.09$$

Step 4. (a) Reject the null hypothesis if the test statistic is greater than the *F* value from the table in the appendix titled "*F* Distribution Values."

$$\text{df}_1 = k = 1$$
$$\text{df}_2 = n - k - 1 = 6 - 1 - 1 = 4$$

The value of *F* associated with a 5% level of significance and with degrees of freedom 1 and 4 is found in the appendix titled "*F* Distribution Values". Figure 5 illustrates this:

$$F_{0.05,1,4} = 7.71$$
$$F_{\text{calculated}} = 9.09$$
$$\text{Reject } H_0 \text{ because } 9.09 > 7.71$$

Thus, there is sufficient data to conclude that there is a statistically significant relationship between *X* and *Y*, so the model is helpful. The strength of this relationship is measured by $r^2 = 0.69$. Thus, we can conclude that about 69% of the variability in sales (*Y*) is explained by the regression model based on local payroll (*X*).

The Analysis of Variance (ANOVA) Table

When software such as Excel or QM for Windows is used to develop regression models, the output provides the observed significance level, or *p*-value, for the calculated *F* value. This is then compared to the level of significance (α) to make the decision.

TABLE 4

Analysis of Variance (ANOVA) Table for Regression

	DF	SS	MS	F	SIGNIFICANCE F
Regression	k	SSR	MSR = SSR/k	MSR/MSE	$P(F > $ MSR/MSE$)$
Residual	$n - k - 1$	SSE	MSE = SSE/$(n-k-1)$		
Total	$n - 1$	SST			

Table 4 provides summary information about the ANOVA table. This shows how the numbers in the last three columns of the table are computed. The last column of this table, labeled Significance F, is the p-value, or observed significance level, which can be used in the hypothesis test about the regression model.

Triple A Construction ANOVA Example

The Excel output that includes the ANOVA table for the Triple A Construction data is shown in Program 1C. The observed significance level for $F = 9.0909$ is given to be 0.0394. This means

$$P(F > 9.0909) = 0.0394$$

Because this probability is less than 0.05 (α), we would reject the hypothesis of no linear relationship and conclude that there is a linear relationship between X and Y. Note in Figure 5 that the area under the curve to the right of 9.09 is clearly less than 0.05, which is the area to the right of the F value associated with a 0.05, level of signicance.

8 Multiple Regression Analysis

A multiple regression model has more than one independent variable.

The **multiple regression model** is a practical extension of the model we just observed. It allows us to build a model with several independent variables. The underlying model is

$$Y = \beta_0 + \beta_1 X_1 + \beta_2 X_2 + \cdots + \beta_k X_k + \epsilon \tag{16}$$

where

$$Y = \text{dependent variable (response variable)}$$
$$X_i = i\text{th independent variable (predictor variable or explanatory variable)}$$
$$\beta_0 = \text{intercept (value of } Y \text{ when all } X_i = 0)$$
$$\beta_i = \text{coefficient of the } i\text{th independent variable}$$
$$k = \text{number of independent variables}$$
$$\epsilon = \text{random error}$$

To estimate the values of these coefficients, a sample is taken and the following equation is developed:

$$\hat{Y} = b_0 + b_1 X_1 + b_2 X_2 + \cdots + b_k X_k \tag{17}$$

where

$$\hat{Y} = \text{predicted value of } Y$$
$$b_0 = \text{sample intercept (and is an estimate of } \beta_0)$$
$$b_i = \text{sample coefficient of } i\text{th variable (and is an estimate of } \beta_i)$$

Consider the case of Jenny Wilson Realty, a real estate company in Montgomery, Alabama. Jenny Wilson, owner and broker for this company, wants to develop a model to determine a suggested listing price for houses based on the size of the house and the age of the house. She selects a sample of houses that have sold recently in a particular area, and she records the selling price, the square footage of the house, the age of the house, and also the condition (good, excellent, or mint) of each house as shown in Table 5. Initially Jenny plans to use

TABLE 5

Jenny Wilson Real
Estate Data

SELLING PRICE ($)	SQUARE FOOTAGE	AGE	CONDITION
95,000	1,926	30	Good
119,000	2,069	40	Excellent
124,800	1,720	30	Excellent
135,000	1,396	15	Good
142,800	1,706	32	Mint
145,000	1,847	38	Mint
159,000	1,950	27	Mint
165,000	2,323	30	Excellent
182,000	2,285	26	Mint
183,000	3,752	35	Good
200,000	2,300	18	Good
211,000	2,525	17	Good
215,000	3,800	40	Excellent
219,000	1,740	12	Mint

only the square footage and age to develop a model, although she wants to save the information on condition of the house to use later. She wants to find the coefficients for the following multiple regression model:

$$\hat{Y} = b_0 + b_1 X_1 + b_2 X_2$$

where

$\hat{Y}$ = predicted value of dependent variable (selling price)

b_0 = Y intercept

X_1 and X_2 = value of the two independent variables (square footage and age), respectively

b_1 and b_2 = slopes for X_1 and X_2, respectively

Excel can be used to develop multiple regression models.

The mathematics of multiple regression becomes quite complex, so we leave formulas for b_0, b_1, and b_2 to regression textbooks.[*] Excel can be used to develop a multiple regression model just as it was used for a simple linear regression model. When entering the data in Excel, it is important that all of the independent variables are in adjoining columns to facilitate the input. From the *Data* tab in Excel, select *Data Analysis* and then *Regression*, as shown earlier, in Program 1A. This opens the regression window to allow the input, as shown in Program 2A. Note that the *X Range* includes the data in two columns (B and C) because there are two independent variables. The Excel output that Jenny Wilson obtains is shown in Program 2B, and it provides the following equation:

$$\hat{Y} = b_0 + b_1 X_1 + b_2 X_2$$
$$= 146,630.89 + 43.82 \, X_1 - 2898.69 \, X_2$$

Evaluating the Multiple Regression Model

A multiple regression model can be evaluated in a manner similar to the way a simple linear regression model is evaluated. Both the p-value for the F test and r^2 can be interpreted the same with multiple regression models as they are with simple linear regression models. However, as

---

[*]See, for example, Norman R. Draper and Harry Smith. *Applied Regression Analysis*, 3rd ed. New York: John Wiley & Sons, Inc., 1998.

there is more than one independent variable, the hypothesis that is being tested with the F test is that all the coefficients are equal to 0. If all these are 0, then none of the independent variables in the model is helpful in predicting the dependent variable.

PROGRAM 2A

Input Screen for the Jenny Wilson Realty Multiple Regression Example

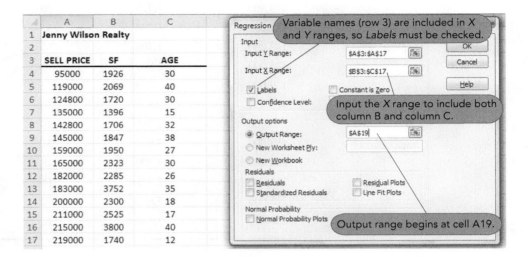

PROGRAM 2B

Output for the Jenny Wilson Realty Multiple Regression Example

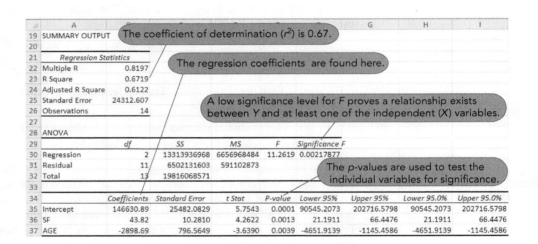

To determine which of the independent variables in a multiple regression model is significant, a significance test on the coefficient for each variable is performed. While statistics textbooks can provide the details of these tests, the results of these tests are automatically displayed in the Excel output. The null hypothesis is that the coefficient is 0 ($H_0: \beta_i = 0$) and the alternate hypothesis is that it is not zero ($H_1: \beta_i \neq 0$). The test statistic is calculated in Excel, and the p-value is given. If the p-value is lower than the level of significance (α), then the null hypothesis is rejected and it can be concluded that the variable is significant.

Jenny Wilson Realty Example

In the Jenny Wilson Realty example in Program 2B, the overall model is statistically significant and useful in predicting the selling price of the house because the p-value for the F test is 0.002. The r^2 value is 0.6719, so 67% of the variability in selling price for these houses can be explained by the regression model. However, there were two independent variables in the model—square footage and age. It is possible that one of these is significant and the other is not. The F test simply indicates that the model as a whole is significant.

Two significance tests can be performed to determine if square footage or age (or both) are significant. In Program 2B, the results of two hypothesis tests are provided. The first test for variable X_1 (square footage) is

$$H_0: \beta_1 = 0$$
$$H_1: \beta_1 \neq 0$$

Using a 5% level of significance ($\alpha = 0.05$), the null hypothesis is rejected because the p-value for this is 0.0013. Thus, square footage is helpful in predicting the price of a house.

Similarly, the variable X_2 (age) is tested using the Excel output, and the p-value is 0.0039. The null hypothesis is rejected because this is less than 0.05. Thus, age is also helpful in predicting the price of a house.

9 Binary or Dummy Variables

A dummy variable is also called an indicator variable or a binary variable.

All of the variables we have used in regression examples have been quantitative variables such as sales figures, payroll numbers, square footage, and age. These have all been easily measurable and have had numbers associated with them. There are many times when we believe a qualitative variable rather than a quantitative variable would be helpful in predicting the dependent variable Y. For example, regression may be used to find a relationship between annual income and certain characteristics of the employees. Years of experience at a particular job would be a quantitative variable. However, information regarding whether or not a person has a college degree might also be important. This would not be a measurable value or quantity, so a special variable called a **dummy variable** (or a **binary variable** or an **indicator variable**) would be used. A dummy variable is assigned a value of 1 if a particular condition is met (e.g., a person has a college degree), and a value of 0 otherwise.

Return to the Jenny Wilson Realty example. Jenny believes that a better model can be developed if the condition of the property is included. To incorporate the condition of the house into the model, Jenny looks at the information available (see Table 5), and sees that the three categories are good condition, excellent condition, and mint condition. Since these are not quantitative variables, she must use dummy variables. These are defined as

$$X_3 = 1 \text{ if house is in excellent condition}$$
$$= 0 \text{ otherwise}$$
$$X_4 = 1 \text{ if house is in mint condition}$$
$$= 0 \text{ otherwise}$$

The number of dummy variables must equal one less than the number of categories of a qualitative variable.

Notice there is no separate variable for "good" condition. If X_3 and X_4 are both 0, then the house cannot be in excellent or mint condition, so it must be in good condition. When using dummy variables, the number of variables must be 1 less than the number of categories. In this problem, there were three categories (good, excellent, and mint condition) so we must have two dummy variables. If we had mistakenly used too many variables and the number of dummy variables equaled the number of categories, then the mathematical computations could not be performed or would not give reliable values.

These dummy variables will be used with the two previous variables (X_1—square footage, and X_2—age) to try to predict the selling prices of houses for Jenny Wilson. Programs 3A and 3B provide the Excel input and output for this new data, and this shows how the dummy variables were coded. The significance level for the F test is 0.00017, so this model is statistically significant. The coefficient of determination (r^2) is 0.898, so this is a much better model than the previous one. The regression equation is

$$\hat{Y} = 121,658 + 56.43X_1 - 3,962X_2 + 33,162X_3 + 47,369X_4$$

This indicates that a house in excellent condition ($X_3 = 1$, $X_4 = 0$) would sell for about $33,162 more than a house in good condition ($X_3 = 0$, $X_4 = 0$). A house in mint condition ($X_3 = 0$, $X_4 = 1$) would sell for about $47,369 more than a house in good condition.

PROGRAM 3A

Input Screen for the Jenny Wilson Realty Example with Dummy Variables

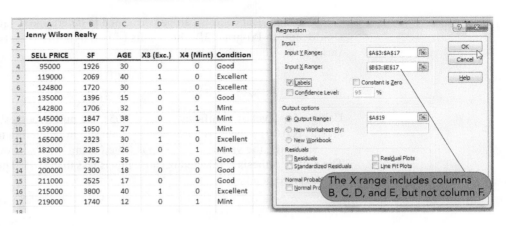

PROGRAM 3B

Output for the Jenny Wilson Realty Example with Dummy Variables

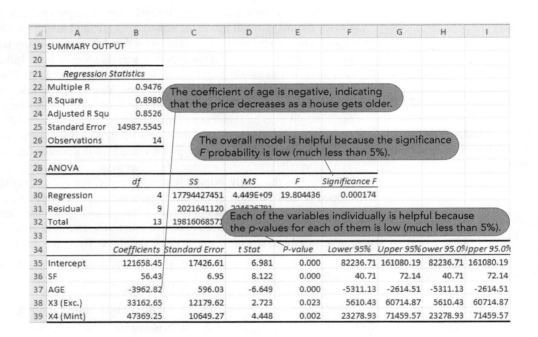

10 Model Building

The value of r^2 can never decrease when more variables are added to the model.

The adjusted r^2 may decrease when more variables are added to the model.

In developing a good regression model, possible independent variables are identified and the best ones are selected to be used in the model. The best model is a statistically significant model with a high r^2 and few variables.

As more variables are added to a regression model, r^2 will usually increase, and it cannot decrease. It is tempting to keep adding variables to a model to try to increase r^2. However, if too many independent variables are included in the model, problems can arise. For this reason, the **adjusted r^2** value is often used (rather than r^2) to determine if an additional independent variable is beneficial. The adjusted r^2 takes into account the number of independent variables in the model, and it is possible for the adjusted r^2 to decrease. The formula for r^2 is

$$r^2 = \frac{SSR}{SST} = 1 - \frac{SSE}{SST}$$

134

The adjusted r^2 is

$$\text{Adjusted } r^2 = 1 - \frac{\text{SSE}/(n - k - 1)}{\text{SST}/(n - 1)} \tag{18}$$

Notice that as the number of variables (k) increases, $n - k - 1$ will decrease. This causes $\text{SSE}/(n - k - 1)$ to increase, and consequently the adjusted r^2 will decrease unless the extra variable in the model causes a significant decrease in the SSE. Thus, the reduction in error (and SSE) must be sufficient to offset the change in k.

A variable should not be added to the model if it causes the adjusted r^2 *to decrease.*

As a general rule of thumb, if the adjusted r^2 increases when a new variable is added to the model, the variable should probably remain in the model. If the adjusted r^2 decreases when a new variable is added, the variable should not remain in the model. Other factors should also be considered when trying to build the model, but they are beyond the introductory level of this chapter.

STEPWISE REGRESSION While the process of model building may be tedious, there are many statistical software packages that include stepwise regression procedures to do this. **Stepwise regression** is an automated process to systematically add or delete independent variables from a regression model. A *forward stepwise procedure* puts the most significant variable in the model first and then adds the next variable that will improve the model the most, given that the first variable is already in the model. Variables continue to be added in this fashion until all the variables are in the model or until any remaining variables do not significantly improve the model. A *backwards stepwise procedure* begins with all independent variables in the model, and one-by-one the least helpful variables are deleted. This continues until only significant variables remain. Many variations of these stepwise models exist.

MULTICOLLINEARITY In the Jenny Wilson Realty example illustrated in Program 3B, we saw an r^2 of about 0.90 and an adjusted r^2 of 0.85. While other variables such as the size of the lot, the number of bedrooms, and the number of bathrooms might be related to the selling price of a house, we may not want to include these in the model. It is likely that these variables would be correlated with the square footage of the house (e.g., more bedrooms usually means a larger house), which is already included in the model. Thus, the information provided by these additional variables might be duplication of information already in the model.

Multicollinearity exists when a variable is correlated to other variables.

When an independent variable is correlated with one other independent variable, the variables are said to be **collinear**. If an independent variable is correlated with a combination of other independent variables, the condition of **multicollinearity** exists. This can create problems in interpreting the coefficients of the variables as several variables are providing duplicate information. For example, if two independent variables were monthly salary expenses for a company and annual salary expenses for a company, the information provided in one is also provided in the other. Several sets of regression coefficients for these two variables would yield exactly the same results. Thus, individual interpretation of these variables would be questionable, although the model itself is still good for prediction purposes. When multicollinearity exists, the overall F test is still valid, but the hypothesis tests related to the individual coefficients are not. A variable may appear to be significant when it is insignificant, or a variable may appear to be insignificant when it is significant.

11 Nonlinear Regression

The regression models we have seen are linear models. However, at times there exist nonlinear relationships between variables. Some simple variable transformations can be used to create an apparently linear model from a nonlinear relationship. This allows us to use Excel and other linear regression programs to perform the calculations. We will demonstrate this in the following example.

Transformations may be used to turn a nonlinear model into a linear model.

On every new automobile sold in the United States, the fuel efficiency (as measured by miles per gallon of gasoline (MPG) of the automobile is prominently displayed on the window sticker. The MPG is related to several factors, one of which is the weight of the automobile. Engineers at Colonel Motors, in an attempt to improve fuel efficiency, have been asked to study the impact of weight on MPG. They have decided that a regression model should be used to do this.

A sample of 12 new automobiles was selected, and the weight and MPG rating were recorded. Table 6 provides this data. A scatter diagram of this data in Figure 6A shows the weight and MPG. A linear regression line is drawn through the points. Excel was used to develop a simple linear regression equation to relate the MPG (Y) to the weight in 1,000 lb. (X_1) in the form

$$\hat{Y} = b_0 + b_1 X_1$$

TABLE 6
Automobile Weight vs. MPG

MPG	WEIGHT (1,000 LB.)	MPG	WEIGHT (1,000 LB.)
12	4.58	20	3.18
13	4.66	23	2.68
15	4.02	24	2.65
18	2.53	33	1.70
19	3.09	36	1.95
19	3.11	42	1.92

FIGURE 6A
Linear Model for MPG Data

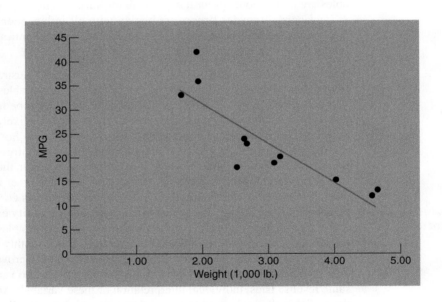

FIGURE 6B
Nonlinear Model for MPG Data

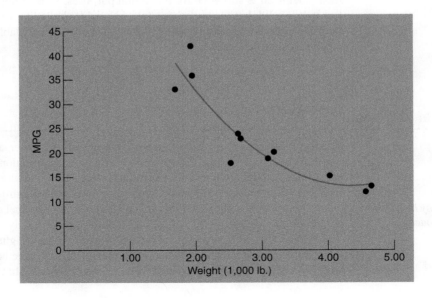

PROGRAM 4

Excel Output for Linear Regression Model with MPG Data

	A	B	C	D	E	F	G	H	I	J	K	L	M
1	Automobile Weight vs. MPG			SUMMARY OUTPUT									
2													
3	MPG (Y)	Weight (X1)		Regression Statistics									
4	12	4.58		Multiple R	0.8629								
5	13	4.66		R Square	0.7446								
6	15	4.02		Adjusted R Sc	0.7190								
7	18	2.53		Standard Erroi	5.0076								
8	19	3.09		Observations	12								
9	19	3.11											
10	20	3.18		ANOVA									
11	23	2.68			df	SS	MS	F	Significance F				
12	24	2.65		Regression	1	730.9090	730.9090	29.1480	0.0003				
13	33	1.70		Residual	10	250.7577	25.0758						
14	36	1.95		Total	11	981.6667							
15	42	1.92											
16					Coefficients	Standard Err	t Stat	p-value	Lower 95%	Upper 95%	Lower 95.0	Upper 95.0%	
17				Intercept	47.6193	4.8132	9.8936	0.0000	36.8950	58.3437	36.8950	58.3437	
18				Weight	-8.2460	1.5273	-5.3989	0.0003	-11.6491	-4.8428	-11.6491	-4.8428	

The Excel output is shown in Program 4. From this we get the equation

$$\hat{Y} = 47.6 - 8.2X_1$$

or

$$\text{MPG} = 47.6 - 8.2(\text{weight in 1,000 lb.})$$

The model is useful since the significance level for the F test is small and $r^2 = 0.7446$. However, further examination of the graph in Figure 6A brings into question the use of a linear model. Perhaps a nonlinear relationship exists, and maybe the model should be modified to account for this. A quadratic model is illustrated in Figure 6B. This model would be of the form

$$\text{MPG} = b_0 + b_1(\text{weight}) + b_2(\text{weight})^2$$

The easiest way to develop this model is to define a new variable

$$X_2 = (\text{weight})^2$$

This gives us the model

$$\hat{Y} = b_0 + b_1X_1 + b_2X_2$$

We can create another column in Excel, and again run the regression tool. The output is shown in Program 5. The new equation is

$$\hat{Y} = 79.8 - 30.2X_1 + 3.4X_2$$

The significance level for F is low (0.0002) so the model is useful, and $r^2 = 0.8478$. The adjusted r^2 increased from 0.719 to 0.814, so this new variable definitely improved the model.

A low significance value for F and a high r² are indications of a good model.

This model is good for prediction purposes. However, we should not try to interpret the coefficients of the variables due to the correlation between X_1 (weight) and X_2 (weight squared). Normally we would interpret the coefficient for X_1 as the change in Y that results from a 1-unit change in X_1, while holding all other variables constant. Obviously holding one variable constant while changing the other is impossible in this example since $X_2 = X_1^2$. If X_1

PROGRAM 5

Excel Output for Nonlinear Regression Model with MPG Data

	A	B	C	D	E	F	G	H	I	J	K	L
1	Automobile Weight vs. MPG			SUMMARY OUTPUT								
2												
3	MPG (Y)	Weight (X1)	WeightSq. (X2)	Regression Statistics								
4	12	4.58	20.98	Multiple R	0.9208							
5	13	4.66	21.72	R Square	0.8478							
6	15	4.02	16.16	Adjusted R Sc	0.8140							
7	18	2.53	6.40	Standard Erro	4.0745							
8	19	3.09	9.55	Observations	12							
9	19	3.11	9.67									
10	20	3.18	10.11	ANOVA								
11	23	2.68	7.18		df	SS	MS	F	Significance F			
12	24	2.65	7.02	Regression	2	832.2557	416.1278	25.0661	0.0002			
13	33	1.70	2.89	Residual	9	149.4110	16.6012					
14	36	1.95	3.80	Total	11	981.6667						
15	42	1.92	3.69									
16					Coefficient	Standard Err	t Stat	p-value	Lower 95%	Upper 95%	Lower 95.0	Upper 95.0%
17				Intercept	79.7888	13.5962	5.8685	0.0002	49.0321	110.5454	49.0321	110.5454
18				Weight	-30.2224	8.9809	-3.3652	0.0083	-50.5386	-9.9061	-50.5386	-9.9061
19				Weight2	3.4124	1.3811	2.4708	0.0355	0.2881	6.5367	0.2881	6.5367

changes, then X_2 must change also. This is an example of a problem that exists when multi-collinearity is present.

Other types of nonlinearities can be handled using a similar approach. A number of transformations exist that may help to develop a linear model from variables with nonlinear relationships.

12   Cautions and Pitfalls in Regression Analysis

This chapter has provided a brief introduction into regression analysis, one of the most widely used quantitative techniques in business. However, some common errors are made with regression models, so caution should be observed when using this.

If the assumptions are not met, the statistical tests may not be valid. Any interval estimates are also invalid, although the model can still be used for prediction purposes.

A high correlation does not mean one variable is causing a change in the other.

Correlation does not necessarily mean causation. Two variables (such as the price of automobiles and your annual salary) may be highly correlated to one another, but one is not causing the other to change. They may both be changing due to other factors such as the economy in general or the inflation rate.

If multicollinearity is present in a multiple regression model, the model is still good for prediction, but interpretation of individual coefficients is questionable. The individual tests on the regression coefficients are not valid.

The regression equation should not be used with values of X that are below the lowest value of X or above the highest value of X found in the sample.

Using a regression equation beyond the range of X is very questionable. A linear relationship may exist within the range of values of X in the sample. What happens beyond this range is unknown; the linear relationship may become nonlinear at some point. For example, there is usually a linear relationship between advertising and sales within a limited range. As more money is spent on advertising, sales tend to increase even if everything else is held constant. However, at some point, increasing advertising expenditures will have less impact on sales unless the company does other things to help, such as opening new markets or expanding the product offerings. If advertising is increased and nothing else changes, the sales will probably level off at some point.

Related to the limitation regarding the range of X is the interpretation of the intercept (b_0). Since the lowest value for X in a sample is often much greater than 0, the intercept is a point on the regression line beyond the range of X. Therefore, we should not be concerned if the t-test for this coefficient is not significant as we should not be using the regression equation to predict a value of Y when $X = 0$. This intercept is merely used in defining the line that fits the sample points the best.

Using the F test and concluding a linear regression model is helpful in predicting Y does not mean that this is the best relationship. While this model may explain much of the variability in Y, it is possible that a nonlinear relationship might explain even more. Similarly, if it is concluded that no linear relationship exists, another type of relationship could exist.

A significant F *value may occur even when the relationship is not strong.*

A statistically significant relationship does not mean it has any practical value. With large enough samples, it is possible to have a statistically significant relationship, but r^2 might be 0.01. This would normally be of little use to a manager. Similarly, a high r^2 could be found due to random chance if the sample is small. The F test must also show significance to place any value in r^2.

Summary

Regression analysis is an extremely valuable quantitative tool. Using scatter diagrams helps to see relationships between variables. The F test is used to determine if the results can be considered useful. The coefficient of determination (r^2) is used to measure the proportion of variability in Y that is explained by the regression model. The correlation coefficient measures the relationship between two variables.

Multiple regression involves the use of more than one independent variable. Dummy variables (binary or indicator variables) are used with qualitative or categorical data. Nonlinear models can be transformed into linear models.

We saw how to use Excel to develop regression models. Interpretation of computer output was presented, and several examples were provided.

Glossary

Adjusted r^2   A measure of the explanatory power of a regression model that takes into consideration the number of independent variables in the model.

Binary Variable   See Dummy Variable.

Coefficient of Correlation (r)   A measure of the strength of the relationship between two variables.

Coefficient of Determination (r^2)   The percent of the variability in the dependent variable (Y) that is explained by the regression equation.

Collinearity   A condition that exists when one independent variable is correlated with another independent variable.

Dependent Variable   The Y-variable in a regression model. This is what is being predicted.

Dummy Variable   A variable used to represent a qualitative factor or condition. Dummy variables have values of 0 or 1. This is also called a binary variable or an indicator variable.

Error.   The difference between the actual value (Y) and the predicted value ($\hat{Y}$).

Explanatory Variable   The independent variable in a regression equation.

Independent Variable   The X-variable in a regression equation. This is used to help predict the dependent variable.

Least Squares   A reference to the criterion used to select the regression line, to minimize the squared distances between the estimated straight line and the observed values.

Mean Squared Error (MSE)   An estimate of the error variance.

Multicollinearity   A condition that exists when one independent variable is correlated with other independent variables.

Multiple Regression Model   A regression model that has more than one independent variable.

Observed Significance Level   Another name for p-value.

p-Value   A probability value that is used when testing a hypothesis. The hypothesis is rejected when this is low.

Predictor Variable   Another name for explanatory variable.

Regression Analysis   A forecasting procedure that uses the least squares approach on one or more independent variables to develop a forecasting model.

Residual.   Another term for error.

Response Variable   The dependent variable in a regression equation.

Scatter Diagrams   Diagrams of the variable to be forecasted, plotted against another variable, such as time. Also called scatter plots.

Standard Error of the Estimate   An estimate of the standard deviation of the errors and is sometimes called the standard deviation of the regression.

Stepwise Regression   An automated process to systematically add or delete independent variables from a regression model.

Sum of Squares Error (SSE)   The total sum of the squared differences between each observation (Y) and the predicted value ($\hat{Y}$).

Sum of Squares Regression (SSR)   The total sum of the squared differences between each predicted value ($\hat{Y}$) and the mean ($\overline{Y}$).

Sum of Squares Total (SST)   The total sum of the squared differences between each observation (Y) and the mean ($\overline{Y}$).

Key Equations

(1) $Y = \beta_0 + \beta_1 X + \epsilon$
Underlying linear model for simple linear regression.

(2) $\hat{Y} = b_0 + b_1 X$
Simple linear regression model computed from a sample.

(3) $e = Y - \hat{Y}$
Error in regression model.

(4) $b_1 = \dfrac{\Sigma(X - \overline{X})(Y - \overline{Y})}{\Sigma(X - \overline{X})^2}$
Slope in the regression line.

(5) $b_0 = \overline{Y} - b_1\overline{X}$
The intercept in the regression line.

(6) $SST = \Sigma(Y - \overline{Y})^2$
Total sums of squares.

(7) $SSE = \Sigma e^2 = \Sigma(Y - \hat{Y})^2$
Sum of squares due to error.

(8) $SSR = \Sigma(\hat{Y} - \overline{Y})^2$
Sum of squares due to regression.

(9) $SST = SSR + SSE$
Relationship among sums of squares in regression.

(10) $r^2 = \dfrac{SSR}{SST} = 1 - \dfrac{SSE}{SST}$
Coefficient of determination.

(11) $r = \pm\sqrt{r^2}$
Coefficient of correlation. This has the same sign as the slope.

(12) $s^2 = MSE = \dfrac{SSE}{n - k - 1}$
An estimate of the variance of the errors in regression; n is the sample size and k is the number of independent variables.

(13) $s = \sqrt{MSE}$
An estimate of the standard deviation of the errors. Also called the standard error of the estimate.

(14) $\text{MSR} = \dfrac{\text{SSR}}{k}$

Mean square regression. k is the number of independent variables.

(15) $F = \dfrac{\text{MSR}}{\text{MSE}}$

F statistic used to test significance of overall regression model.

(16) $Y = \beta_0 + \beta_1 X_1 + \beta_2 X_2 + \cdots + \beta_k X_k + \epsilon$
Underlying model for multiple regression model.

(17) $\hat{Y} = b_0 + b_1 X_1 + b_2 X_2 + \cdots + b_k X_k$
Multiple regression model computed from a sample.

(18) $\text{Adjusted } r^2 = 1 - \dfrac{\text{SSE}/(n - k - 1)}{\text{SST}/(n - 1)}$

Adjusted r^2 used in building multiple regression models.

Solved Problems

Solved Problem 1

Judith Thompson runs a florist shop on the Gulf Coast of Texas, specializing in floral arrangements for weddings and other special events. She advertises weekly in the local newspapers and is considering increasing her advertising budget. Before doing so, she decides to evaluate the past effectiveness of these ads. Five weeks are sampled, and the advertising dollars and sales volume for each of these is shown in the following table. Develop a regression equation that would help Judith evaluate her advertising. Find the coefficient of determination for this model.

SALES ($1,000)	ADVERTISING ($100)
11	5
6	3
10	7
6	2
12	8

Solution

SALES Y	ADVERTISING X	$(X - \bar{X})^2$	$(X - \bar{X})(Y - \bar{Y})$
11	5	$(5 - 5)^2 = 0$	$(5 - 5)(11 - 9) = 0$
6	3	$(3 - 5)^2 = 4$	$(3 - 5)(6 - 9) = 6$
10	7	$(7 - 5)^2 = 4$	$(7 - 5)(10 - 9) = 2$
6	2	$(2 - 5)^2 = 9$	$(2 - 5)(6 - 9) = 9$
12	8	$(8 - 5)^2 = 9$	$(8 - 5)(12 - 9) = 9$
$\Sigma Y = 45$	$\Sigma X = 25$	$\Sigma(X - \bar{X})^2 = 26$	$\Sigma(X - \bar{X})(Y - \bar{Y}) = 26$
$\bar{Y} = 45/5$	$\bar{X} = 25/5$		
$= 9$	$= 5$		

$$b_1 = \frac{\Sigma(X - \bar{X})(Y - \bar{Y})}{\Sigma(X - \bar{X})^2} = \frac{26}{26} = 1$$

$$b_0 = \bar{Y} - b_1 \bar{X} = 9 - (1)(5) = 4$$

The regression equation is

$$\hat{Y} = 4 + 1X$$

To compute r^2, we use the following table:

Y	X	$\hat{Y} = 4 + 1X$	$(Y - \hat{Y})^2$	$(Y - \overline{Y})^2$
11	5	9	$(11 - 9)^2 = 4$	$(11 - 9)^2 = 4$
6	3	7	$(6 - 7)^2 = 1$	$(6 - 9)^2 = 9$
10	7	11	$(10 - 11)^2 = 1$	$(10 - 9)^2 = 1$
6	2	6	$(6 - 6)^2 = 0$	$(6 - 9)^2 = 9$
12	8	12	$(12 - 12)^2 = 0$	$(12 - 9)^2 = 9$
$\Sigma Y = 45$	$\Sigma X = 25$		$\Sigma(Y - \hat{Y})^2 = 6$	$\Sigma(Y - \overline{Y})^2 = 32$
$\overline{Y} = 9$	$\overline{X} = 5$		SSE	SST

The slope $(b_1 = 1)$ tells us that for each 1 unit increase in X (or \$100 in advertising), sales increase by 1 unit (or \$1,000). Also, $r^2 = 0.8125$ indicating that about 81% of the variability in sales can be explained by the regression model with advertising as the independent variable.

Solved Problem 2

Use Excel with the data in Solved Problem 1 to find the regression model. What does the F test say about this model?

Solution

Program 6 provides the Excel output for this problem. We see the equation is

$$\hat{Y} = 4 + 1X$$

The coefficient of determination (r^2) is shown to be 0.8125. The significance level for the F test is 0.0366, which is less than 0.05. This indicates the model is statistically significant. Thus, there is sufficient evidence in the data to conclude that the model is useful, and there is a relationship between X (advertising) and Y (sales).

PROGRAM 6

Excel Output for Solved Problem 2

	A	B	C	D	E	F	G	H	I	J
17	SUMMARY OUTPUT									
18										
19	*Regression Statistics*									
20	Multiple R	0.9014								
21	R Square	0.8125								
22	Adjusted R Squ	0.7500								
23	Standard Error	1.4142								
24	Observations	5								
25										
26	ANOVA									
27		*df*	*SS*	*MS*	*F*	*Significance F*				
28	Regression	1	26	26	13	0.03662				
29	Residual	3	6	2						
30	Total	4	32							
31										
32		*Coefficient*	*Standard E*	*t Stat*	*p-value*	*Lower 95%*	*Upper 9!*	*Lower 9!*	*Upper 95.0%*	
33	Intercept	4	1.5242	2.6244	0.0787	-0.8506	8.8506	-0.8506	8.8506	
34	Advertising ($100)	1	0.2774	3.6056	0.0366	0.1173	1.8827	0.1173	1.8827	

Self-Test

- Before taking the self-test, refer to the learning objectives at the beginning of the chapter, the notes in the margins, and the glossary at the end of the chapter.
- Use the key at the end of the chapter to correct your answers.
- Restudy pages that correspond to any questions that you answered incorrectly or material you feel uncertain about.

1. One of the assumptions in regression analysis is that
   a. the errors have a mean of 1.
   b. the errors have a mean of 0.
   c. the observations (Y) have a mean of 1.
   d. the observations (Y) have a mean of 0.
2. A graph of the sample points that will be used to develop a regression line is called
   a. a sample graph.
   b. a regression diagram.
   c. a scatter diagram.
   d. a regression plot.
3. When using regression, an error is also called
   a. an intercept.
   b. a prediction.
   c. a coefficient.
   d. a residual.
4. In a regression model, Y is called
   a. the independent variable.
   b. the dependent variable.
   c. the regression variable.
   d. the predictor variable.
5. A quantity that provides a measure of how far each sample point is from the regression line is
   a. the SSR.
   b. the SSE.
   c. the SST.
   d. the MSR.
6. The percentage of the variation in the dependent variable that is explained by a regression equation is measured by
   a. the coefficient of correlation.
   b. the MSE.
   c. the coefficient of determination.
   d. the slope.
7. In a regression model, if every sample point is on the regression line (all errors are 0), then
   a. the correlation coefficient would be 0.
   b. the correlation coefficient would be −1 or 1.
   c. the coefficient of determination would be −1.
   d. the coefficient of determination would be 0.
8. When using dummy variables in a regression equation to model a qualitative or categorical variable, the number of dummy variables should equal to
   a. the number of categories.
   b. one more than the number of categories.
   c. one less than the number of categories.
   d. the number of other independent variables in the model.
9. A multiple regression model differs from a simple linear regression model because the multiple regression model has more than one
   a. independent variable.
   b. dependent variable.
   c. intercept.
   d. error.
10. The overall significance of a regression model is tested using an F test. The model is significant if
    a. the F value is low.
    b. the significance level of the F value is low.
    c. the r^2 value is low.
    d. the slope is lower than the intercept.
11. A new variable should not be added to a multiple regression model if that variable causes
    a. r^2 to decrease.
    b. the adjusted r^2 to decrease.
    c. the SST to decrease.
    d. the intercept to decrease.
12. A good regression model should have
    a. a low r^2 and a low significance level for the F test.
    b. a high r^2 and a high significance level for the F test.
    c. a high r^2 and a low significance level for the F test.
    d. a low r^2 and a high significance level for the F test.

Discussion Questions and Problems

Discussion Questions

1 What is the meaning of least squares in a regression model?
2 Discuss the use of dummy variables in regression analysis.
3 Discuss how the coefficient of determination and the coefficient of correlation are related and how they are used in regression analysis.
4 Explain how a scatter diagram can be used to identify the type of regression to use.
5 Explain how the adjusted r^2 value is used in developing a regression model.
6 Explain what information is provided by the F test.
7 What is the SSE? How is this related to the SST and the SSR?
8 Explain how a plot of the residuals can be used in developing a regression model.

Problems

• 9 John Smith has developed the following forecasting model:

$$\hat{Y} = 36 + 4.3X_1$$

where

$\hat{Y}$ = Demand for K10 air conditioners

X_1 = the outside temperature (°F)

(a) Forecast the demand for K10 when the temperature is 70°F.

(b) What is the demand for a temperature of 80°F?

(c) What is the demand for a temperature of 90°F?

: 10 The operations manager of a musical instrument distributor feels that demand for bass drums may be related to the number of television appearances by the popular rock group Green Shades during the preceding month. The manager has collected the data shown in the following table:

DEMAND FOR BASS DRUMS	GREEN SHADES TV APPEARANCE
3	3
6	4
7	7
5	6
10	8
8	5

(a) Graph these data to see whether a linear equation might describe the relationship between the group's television shows and bass drum sales.

(b) Using the equations presented in this chapter, compute the SST, SSE, and SSR. Find the least squares regression line for these data.

(c) What is your estimate for bass drum sales if the Green Shades performed on TV six times last month?

: 11 Using the data in Problem 10, test to see if there is a statistically significant relationship between sales and TV appearances at the 0.05 level of significance. Use the formulas in this chapter.

: 12 Using computer software, find the least squares regression line for the data in Problem 10. Based on the F test, is there a statistically significant relationship between the demand for drums and the number of TV appearances?

: 13 Students in a management science class have just received their grades on the first test. The instructor has provided information about the first test grades in some previous classes as well as the final average for the same students. Some of these grades have been sampled and are as follows:

STUDENT	1	2	3	4	5	6	7	8	9
1st test grade	98	77	88	80	96	61	66	95	69
Final average	93	78	84	73	84	64	64	95	76

(a) Develop a regression model that could be used to predict the final average in the course based on the first test grade.

(b) Predict the final average of a student who made an 83 on the first test.

(c) Give the values of r and r^2 for this model. Interpret the value of r^2 in the context of this problem.

: 14 Using the data in Problem 13, test to see if there is a statistically significant relationship between the grade on the first test and the final average at the 0.05 level of significance. Use the formulas in this chapter.

: 15 Using computer software, find the least squares regression line for the data in Problem 13. Based on the F test, is there a statistically significant relationship between the first test grade and the final average in the course?

: 16 Steve Caples, a real estate appraiser in Lake Charles, Louisiana, has developed a regression model to help appraise residential housing in the Lake Charles area. The model was developed using recently sold homes in a particular neighborhood. The price (Y) of the house is based on the square footage (X) of the house. The model is

$$\hat{Y} = 13,473 + 37.65X$$

The coefficient of correlation for the model is 0.63.

(a) Use the model to predict the selling price of a house that is 1,860 square feet.

(b) A house with 1,860 square feet recently sold for $95,000. Explain why this is not what the model predicted.

(c) If you were going to use multiple regression to develop an appraisal model, what other quantitative variables might be included in the model?

(d) What is the coefficient of determination for this model?

: 17 Accountants at the firm Walker and Walker believed that several traveling executives submit unusually high travel vouchers when they return from business trips. The accountants took a sample of 200 vouchers submitted from the past year; they then developed the following multiple regression equation relating expected travel cost (Y) to number of days on the road (X_1) and distance traveled (X_2) in miles:

$$\hat{Y} = \$90.00 + \$48.50X_1 + \$0.40X_2$$

Note: ⚙ means the problem may be solved with QM for Windows; ✖ means the problem may be solved with Excel QM; and ⚙ means the problem may be solved with QM for Windows and/or Excel QM.

The coefficient of correlation computed was 0.68.

(a) If Thomas Williams returns from a 300-mile trip that took him out of town for five days, what is the expected amount that he should claim as expenses?

(b) Williams submitted a reimbursement request for $685; what should the accountant do?

(c) Comment on the validity of this model. Should any other variables be included? Which ones? Why?

 : 18　Thirteen students entered the undergraduate business program at Rollins College 2 years ago. The following table indicates what their grade-point averages (GPAs) were after being in the program for 2 years and what each student scored on the SAT exam (maximum 2400) when he or she was in high school. Is there a meaningful relationship between grades and SAT scores? If a student scores a 1200 on the SAT, what do you think his or her GPA will be? What about a student who scores 2400?

STUDENT	SAT SCORE	GPA	STUDENT	SAT SCORE	GPA
A	1263	2.90	H	1443	2.53
B	1131	2.93	I	2187	3.22
C	1755	3.00	J	1503	1.99
D	2070	3.45	K	1839	2.75
E	1824	3.66	L	2127	3.90
F	1170	2.88	M	1098	1.60
G	1245	2.15			

 : 19　Bus and subway ridership in Washington, D.C., during the summer months is believed to be heavily tied to the number of tourists visiting the city. During the past 12 years, the following data have been obtained:

YEAR	NUMBER OF TOURISTS (1,000,000s)	RIDERSHIP (100,000s)
1	7	15
2	2	10
3	6	13
4	4	15
5	14	25
6	15	27
7	16	24
8	12	20
9	14	27
10	20	44
11	15	34
12	7	17

(a) Plot these data and determine whether a linear model is reasonable.

(b) Develop a regression model.

(c) What is expected ridership if 10 million tourists visit the city?

(d) If there are no tourists at all, explain the predicted ridership.

 : 20　Use computer software to develop a regression model for the data in Problem 19. Explain what this output indicates about the usefulness of this model.

 : 21　The following data give the starting salary for students who recently graduated from a local university and accepted jobs soon after graduation. The starting salary, grade-point average (GPA), and major (business or other) are provided.

SALARY	$29,500	$46,000	$39,800	$36,500
GPA	3.1	3.5	3.8	2.9
Major	Other	Business	Business	Other

SALARY	$42,000	$31,500	$36,200
GPA	3.4	2.1	2.5
Major	Business	Other	Business

(a) Using a computer, develop a regression model that could be used to predict starting salary based on GPA and major.

(b) Use this model to predict the starting salary for a business major with a GPA of 3.0.

(c) What does the model say about the starting salary for a business major compared to a non-business major?

(d) Do you believe this model is useful in predicting the starting salary? Justify your answer, using information provided in the computer output.

 : 22　The following data give the selling price, square footage, number of bedrooms, and age of houses that have sold in a neighborhood in the past 6 months. Develop three regression models to predict the selling price based upon each of the other factors individually. Which of these is best?

SELLING PRICE($)	SQUARE FOOTAGE	BEDROOMS	AGE (YEARS)
64,000	1,670	2	30
59,000	1,339	2	25
61,500	1,712	3	30
79,000	1,840	3	40
87,500	2,300	3	18
92,500	2,234	3	30
95,000	2,311	3	19
113,000	2,377	3	7

(Continued on next page)

SELLING PRICE($)	SQUARE FOOTAGE	BEDROOMS	AGE (YEARS)
115,000	2,736	4	10
138,000	2,500	3	1
142,500	2,500	4	3
144,000	2,479	3	3
145,000	2,400	3	1
147,500	3,124	4	0
144,000	2,500	3	2
155,500	4,062	4	10
165,000	2,854	3	3

: 23 Use the data in Problem 22 and develop a regression model to predict selling price based on the square footage and number of bedrooms. Use this to predict the selling price of a 2,000-square-foot house with 3 bedrooms. Compare this model with the models in Problem 22. Should the number of bedrooms be included in the model? Why or why not?

: 24 Use the data in Problem 22 and develop a regression model to predict selling price based on the square footage, number of bedrooms, and age. Use this to predict the selling price of a 10-year-old, 2,000-square-foot house with 3 bedrooms.

: 25 Tim Cooper plans to invest money in a mutual fund that is tied to one of the major market indices, either the S&P 500 or the Dow Jones Industrial Average. To obtain even more diversification, Tim has thought about investing in both of these. To determine whether investing in two funds would help, Tim decided to take 20 weeks of data and compare the two markets. The closing price for each index is shown in the table below:

WEEK	1	2	3	4	5	6	7
DJIA	10,226	10,473	10,452	10,442	10,471	10,213	10,187
S&P	1,107	1,141	1,135	1,139	1,142	1,108	1,110

WEEK	8	9	10	11	12	13	14
DJIA	10,240	10,596	10,584	10,619	10,628	10,593	10,488
S&P	1,121	1,157	1,145	1,144	1,146	1,143	1,131

WEEK	15	16	17	18	19	20
DJIA	10,568	10,601	10,459	10,410	10,325	10,278
S&P	1,142	1,140	1,122	1,108	1,096	1,089

Develop a regression model that would predict the DJIA based on the S&P 500 index. Based on this model, what would you expect the DJIA to be when the S&P is 1,100? What is the correlation coefficient (r) between the two markets?

: 26 The total expenses of a hospital are related to many factors. Two of these factors are the number of beds in the hospital and the number of admissions. Data were collected on 14 hospitals, as shown in the table below:

HOSPITAL	NUMBER OF BEDs	ADMISSIONS (100s)	TOTAL EXPENSES (MILLIONS)
1	215	77	57
2	336	160	127
3	520	230	157
4	135	43	24
5	35	9	14
6	210	155	93
7	140	53	45
8	90	6	6
9	410	159	99
10	50	18	12
11	65	16	11
12	42	29	15
13	110	28	21
14	305	98	63

Find the best regression model to predict the total expenses of a hospital. Discuss the accuracy of this model. Should both variables be included in the model? Why or why not?

: 27 A sample of 20 automobiles was taken, and the miles per gallon (MPG), horsepower, and total weight were recorded. Develop a linear regression model to predict MPG, using horsepower as the only independent variable. Develop another model with weight as the independent variable. Which of these two models is better? Explain.

MPG	HORSEPOWER	WEIGHT
44	67	1,844
44	50	1,998
40	62	1,752
37	69	1,980
37	66	1,797
34	63	2,199
35	90	2,404
32	99	2,611
30	63	3,236
28	91	2,606
26	94	2,580
26	88	2,507

(Continued on next page)

MPG	HORSEPOWER	WEIGHT
25	124	2,922
22	97	2,434
20	114	3,248
21	102	2,812
18	114	3,382
18	142	3,197
16	153	4,380
16	139	4,036

: 28   Use the data in Problem 27 to develop a multiple linear regression model. How does this compare with each of the models in Problem 27?

: 29   Use the data in Problem 27 to find the best quadratic regression model. (There is more than one to consider.) How does this compare to the models in Problems 27 and 28?

: 30   A sample of nine public universities and nine private universities was taken. The total cost for the year (including room and board) and the median SAT score (maximum total is 2400) at each school were recorded. It was felt that schools with higher median SAT scores would have a better reputation and would charge more tuition as a result of that. The data is in the table below. Use regression to help answer the following questions based on this sample data. Do schools with higher SAT scores charge more in tuition and fees? Are private schools more expensive than public schools when SAT scores are

CATEGORY	TOTAL COST ($)	MEDIAN SAT
Public	21,700	1990
Public	15,600	1620
Public	16,900	1810
Public	15,400	1540
Public	23,100	1540
Public	21,400	1600
Public	16,500	1560
Public	23,500	1890
Public	20,200	1620
Private	30,400	1630
Private	41,500	1840
Private	36,100	1980
Private	42,100	1930
Private	27,100	2130
Private	34,800	2010
Private	32,100	1590
Private	31,800	1720
Private	32,100	1770

taken into consideration? Discuss how accurate you believe these results are using information related the regression models.

31   In 2008, the total payroll for the New York Yankees was $209.1 million, while the total payroll for the Tampa Bay Rays was about $43.8 million, or about one-fifth that of the Yankees. Many people have suggested that some teams are able to buy winning seasons and championships by spending a lot of money on the most talented players available. The table below lists the payrolls (in millions of dollars) for all 14 Major League Baseball teams in the American League as well as the total number of victories for each in the 2008 season:

TEAM	PAYROLL ($MILLIONS)	NUMBER OF VICTORIES
New York Yankees	209.1	89
Detroit Tigers	138.7	74
Boston Red Sox	133.4	95
Chicago White Sox	121.2	89
Cleveland Indians	79.0	81
Baltimore Orioles	67.2	68
Oakland Athletics	48.0	75
Los Angeles Angels	119.2	100
Seattle Mariners	118.0	61
Toronto Blue Jays	98.6	86
Minnesota Twins	62.2	88
Kansas City Royals	58.2	75
Tampa Bay Rays	43.8	97
Texas Rangers	68.2	79

Develop a regression model to predict the total number of victories based on the payroll of a team. Based on the results of the computer output, discuss how accurate this model is. Use the model to predict the number of victories for a team with a payroll of $79 million.

: 32   In 2009, the New York Yankees won 103 baseball games during the regular season. The table on the next page lists the number of victories (W), the earned-run-average (ERA), and the batting average (AVG) of each team in the American League. The ERA is one measure of the effectiveness of the pitching staff, and a lower number is better. The batting average is one measure of effectiveness of the hitters, and a higher number is better.

(a) Develop a regression model that could be used to predict the number of victories based on the ERA.

(b) Develop a regression model that could be used to predict the number of victories based on the batting average.

TEAM	W	ERA	AVG
New York Yankees	103	4.26	0.283
Los Angeles Angels	97	4.45	0.285
Boston Red Sox	95	4.35	0.270
Minnesota Twins	87	4.50	0.274
Texas Rangers	87	4.38	0.260
Detroit Tigers	86	4.29	0.260
Seattle Mariners	85	3.87	0.258
Tampa Bay Rays	84	4.33	0.263
Chicago White Sox	79	4.14	0.258
Toronto Blue Jays	75	4.47	0.266
Oakland Athletics	75	4.26	0.262
Cleveland Indians	65	5.06	0.264
Kansas City Royals	65	4.83	0.259
Baltimore Orioles	64	5.15	0.268

MONTH	DJIA	STOCK 1	STOCK 2
1	11,168	48.5	32.4
2	11,150	48.2	31.7
3	11,186	44.5	31.9
4	11,381	44.7	36.6
5	11,679	49.3	36.7
6	12,081	49.3	38.7
7	12,222	46.1	39.5
8	12,463	46.2	41.2
9	12,622	47.7	43.3
10	12,269	48.3	39.4
11	12,354	47.0	40.1
12	13,063	47.9	42.1
13	13,326	47.8	45.2

(c) Which of the two models is better for predicting the number of victories?

(d) Develop a multiple regression model that includes both ERA and batting average. How does this compare to the previous models?

: 33 The closing stock price for each of two stocks was recorded over a 12-month period. The closing price for the Dow Jones Industrial Average (DJIA) was also recorded over this same time period. These values are shown in the following table:

(a) Develop a regression model to predict the price of stock 1 based on the Dow Jones Industrial Average.

(b) Develop a regression model to predict the price of stock 2 based on the Dow Jones Industrial Average.

(c) Which of the two stocks is most highly correlated to the Dow Jones Industrial Average over this time period?

Case Study

North–South Airline

In January 2008, Northern Airlines merged with Southeast Airlines to create the fourth largest U.S. carrier. The new North–South Airline inherited both an aging fleet of Boeing 727-300 aircraft and Stephen Ruth. Stephen was a tough former Secretary of the Navy who stepped in as new president and chairman of the board.

Stephen's first concern in creating a financially solid company was maintenance costs. It was commonly surmised in the airline industry that maintenance costs rise with the age of the aircraft. He quickly noticed that historically there had been a significant difference in the reported B727-300 maintenance costs (from ATA Form 41s) both in the airframe and engine areas between Northern Airlines and Southeast Airlines, with Southeast having the newer fleet.

On February 12, 2008, Peg Jones, vice president for operations and maintenance, was called into Stephen's office and asked to study the issue. Specifically, Stephen wanted to know whether the average fleet age was correlated to direct airframe maintenance costs, and whether there was a relationship between average fleet age and direct engine maintenance costs.

Peg was to report back by February 26 with the answer, along with quantitative and graphical descriptions of the relationship.

Peg's first step was to have her staff construct the average age of Northern and Southeast B727-300 fleets, by quarter, since the introduction of that aircraft to service by each airline in late 1993 and early 1994. The average age of each fleet was calculated by first multiplying the total number of calendar days each aircraft had been in service at the pertinent point in time by the average daily utilization of the respective fleet to total fleet hours flown. The total fleet hours flown was then divided by the number of aircraft in service at that time, giving the age of the "average" aircraft in the fleet.

The average utilization was found by taking the actual total fleet hours flown on September 30, 2007, from Northern and Southeast data, and dividing by the total days in service for all aircraft at that time. The average utilization for Southeast was 8.3 hours per day, and the average utilization for Northern was 8.7 hours per day. Because the available cost data were calculated for each yearly period ending at the end of the first quarter, average fleet age was calculated at the same points in time.

The fleet data are shown in the following table. Airframe cost data and engine cost data are both shown paired with fleet average age in that table.

Discussion Question

1. Prepare Peg Jones's response to Stephen Ruth.

Note: Dates and names of airlines and individuals have been changed in this case to maintain confidentiality. The data and issues described here are real.

North–South Airline Data for Boeing 727-300 Jets

YEAR	NORTHERN AIRLINE DATA			SOUTHEAST AIRLINE DATA		
	AIRFRAME COST PER AIRCRAFT($)	ENGINE COST PER AIRCRAFT($)	AVERAGE AGE (HOURS)	AIRFRAME COST PER AIRCRAFT($)	ENGINE COST PER AIRCRAFT($)	AVERAGE AGE (HOURS)
2001	51.80	43.49	6,512	13.29	18.86	5,107
2002	54.92	38.58	8,404	25.15	31.55	8,145
2003	69.70	51.48	11,077	32.18	40.43	7,360
2004	68.90	58.72	11,717	31.78	22.10	5,773
2005	63.72	45.47	13,275	25.34	19.69	7,150
2006	84.73	50.26	15,215	32.78	32.58	9,364
2007	78.74	79.60	18,390	35.56	38.07	8,259

Bibliography

Berenson, Mark L., David M. Levine, and Timothy C. Kriehbiel. *Basic Business Statistics: Concepts and Applications*, 11th ed. Upper Saddle River, NJ: Prentice Hall, 2009.

Black, Ken. *Business Statistics: For Contemporary Decision Making*, 6th ed. John Wiley & Sons, Inc., 2010.

Draper, Norman R., and Harry Smith. *Applied Regression Analysis*, 3rd ed. New York: John Wiley & Sons, Inc., 1998.

Kutner, Michael, John Neter, Chris J. Nachtsheim, and William Wasserman. *Applied Linear Regression Models,* 4th ed., Boston; New York: McGraw-Hill/Irwin, 2004.

Mendenhall, William, and Terry L. Sincich. *A Second Course in Statistics: Regression Analysis*, 6th ed., Upper Saddle River, NJ: Prentice Hall, 2004.

Appendix 1 Formulas for Regression Calculations

When performing regression calculations by hand, there are other formulas that can make the task easier and are mathematically equivalent to the ones presented in the chapter. These, however, make it more difficult to see the logic behind the formulas and to understand what the results actually mean.

When using these formulas, it helps to set up a table with the columns shown in Table 7, which has the Triple A Construction Company data that was used earlier in the chapter. The sample size (n) is 6. The totals for all columns are shown, and the averages for X and Y are calculated. Once this is done, we can use the following formulas for computations in a simple linear regression model (one independent variable). The simple linear regression equation is again given as

$$\hat{Y} = b_0 + b_1 X$$

Slope of regression equation:

$$b_1 = \frac{\Sigma XY - n\overline{XY}}{\Sigma X^2 - n\overline{X}^2}$$

$$b_1 = \frac{180.5 - 6(4)(7)}{106 - 6(4^2)} = 1.25$$

TABLE 7

Preliminary Calculations for Triple A Construction

Y	X	Y^2	X^2	XY
6	3	$6^2 = 36$	$3^2 = 9$	$3(6) = 18$
8	4	$8^2 = 64$	$4^2 = 16$	$4(8) = 32$
9	6	$9^2 = 81$	$6^2 = 36$	$6(9) = 54$
5	4	$5^2 = 25$	$4^2 = 16$	$4(5) = 20$
4.5	2	$4.5^2 = 20.25$	$2^2 = 4$	$2(4.5) = 9$
9.5	5	$9.5^2 = 90.25$	$5^2 = 25$	$5(9.5) = 47.5$
$\Sigma Y = 42$	$\Sigma X = 24$	$\Sigma Y^2 = 316.5$	$\Sigma X^2 = 106$	$\Sigma XY = 180.5$
$\overline{Y} = 42/6 = 7$	$\overline{X} = 24/6 = 4$			

Intercept of regression equation:

$$b_0 = \overline{Y} - b_1\overline{X}$$
$$b_0 = 7 - 1.25(4) = 2$$

Sum of squares of the error:

$$\text{SSE} = \Sigma Y^2 - b_0\Sigma Y - b_1\Sigma XY$$
$$\text{SSE} = 316.5 - 2(42) - 1.25(180.5) = 6.875$$

Estimate of the error variance:

$$s^2 = \text{MSE} = \frac{\text{SSE}}{n-2}$$
$$s^2 = \frac{6.875}{6-2} = 1.71875$$

Estimate of the error standard deviation:

$$s = \sqrt{\text{MSE}}$$
$$s = \sqrt{1.71875} = 1.311$$

Coefficient of determination:

$$r^2 = 1 - \frac{\text{SSE}}{\Sigma Y^2 - n\overline{Y}^2}$$
$$r^2 = 1 - \frac{6.875}{316.5 - 6(7^2)} = 0.6944$$

This formula for the correlation coefficient automatically determines the sign of r. This could also be found by taking the square root of r^2 and giving it the same sign as the slope:

$$r = \frac{n\Sigma XY - \Sigma X\Sigma Y}{\sqrt{[n\Sigma X^2 - (\Sigma X)^2][n\Sigma Y^2 - (\Sigma Y)^2]}}$$
$$r = \frac{6(180.5) - (24)(42)}{\sqrt{[6(106) - 24^2][6(316.5) - 42^2]}} = 0.833$$

Appendix 2   Regression Models Using QM for Windows

The use of QM for Windows to develop a regression model is very easy. We will use the Triple A Construction Company data to illustrate this. After starting QM for Windows, under *Modules* we select *Forecasting*. To enter the problem we select *New* and specify *Least Squares—Simple and Multiple Regression,* as illustrated in Program 7A. This opens the window shown in Program 7B. We enter the number of observations, which is 6 in this example. There is only 1 independent (*X*) variable. When *OK* is clicked, a window opens and the data is input as shown in Program 7C. After entering the data, click *Solve,* and the forecasting results are shown as in Program 7D. The equation as well as other information is provided on this screen. Additional output is available by clicking the *Window* option on the toolbar.

Recall that the MSE is an estimate of the error variance (σ^2), and the square root of this is the standard error of the estimate. The formula presented in the chapter and used in Excel is

$$MSE = SSE/(n - k - 1)$$

where *n* is the sample size and *k* is the number of independent variables. This is an unbiased estimate of σ^2. In QM for Windows, the mean squared error is computed as

$$MSE = SSE/n$$

This is simply the average error and is a biased estimate of σ^2. The standard error shown in Program 7D is not the square root of the MSE in the output, but rather is found using the denominator of $n - 2$. If this standard error is squared, you get the MSE we saw earlier in the Excel output.

PROGRAM 7A

Initial Input Screen for QM for *File—New—Least Squares–Simple and Multiple Regression*

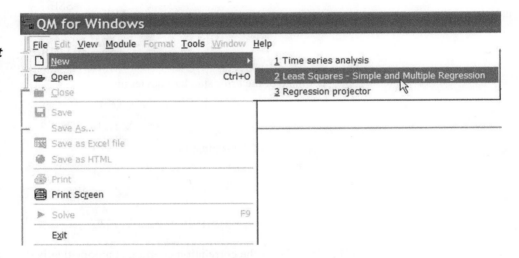

PROGRAM 7B

Second Input Screen for QM for Windows

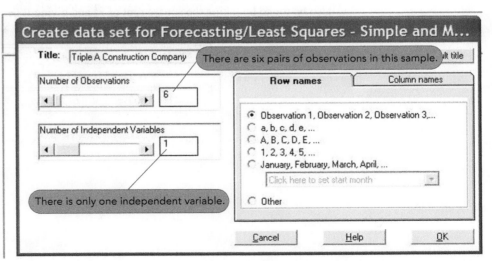

The *F* test was used to test a hypothesis about the overall effectiveness of the model. To see the ANOVA table, after the problem has been solved, select *Window—ANOVA Summary*, and the screen shown in Program 7E will be displayed.

PROGRAM 7C

Data Input for Triple A Construction Example

	Triple A construction	
	Dpndnt var, Y	X1
Observation 1	6	3
Observation 2	8	4
Observation 3	9	6
Observation 4	5	4
Observation 5	4.5	2
Observation 6	9.5	5

PROGRAM 7D

QM for Windows Output for Triple A Construction Data

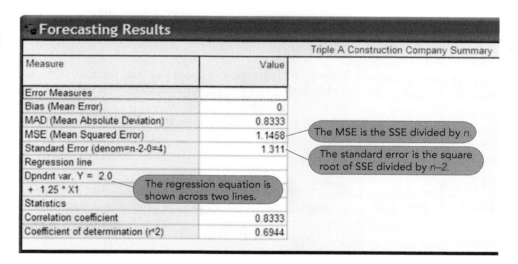

Forecasting Results

Triple A Construction Company Summary

Measure	Value
Error Measures	
Bias (Mean Error)	0.
MAD (Mean Absolute Deviation)	0.8333
MSE (Mean Squared Error)	1.1458
Standard Error (denom=n-2-0=4)	1.311
Regression line	
Dpndnt var, Y = 2.0 + 1.25 * X1	
Statistics	
Correlation coefficient	0.8333
Coefficient of determination (r^2)	0.6944

The MSE is the SSE divided by *n*.

The standard error is the square root of SSE divided by *n–2*.

The regression equation is shown across two lines.

PROGRAM 7E

ANOVA Summary Output in QM for Windows

ANOVA Summary

Triple A construction solution

	Sum	Degrees of Freedom	Mean square
SSR (Sum of squares due to regression)	15.625	1	15.625
SSE (Sum of the squared error)	6.875	4	1.7188
SST (Sum of the squares total)	22.5	5	
F statistic	9.0909		
Probability	0.0394		

Appendix 3 Regression Analysis in Excel QM or Excel 2007

Excel QM

Perhaps the easiest way to do regression analysis in Excel (either 2007 or 2010) is to use Excel QM, which is available on the companion website for this book. Once Excel QM has been installed as an add-in to Excel, go to the *Add-Ins* tab and click *Excel QM*, as shown in Program 8A. When the menu appears, point the cursor at *Forecasting*, and the options will appear. Click on *Multiple Regression*, as shown in Program 8A, for either simple or multiple regression models.

A window will open, as shown in Program 8B. Enter the number of past observations and the number of independent (*X*) variables. You can also enter a name or title for the problem. To enter the data for the Triple A Construction example in this chapter, enter 6 for the past periods (observations) and 1 for the number of independent variables. This will initialize the size of the spreadsheet, and the spreadsheet will appear as presented in Program 8C.

The shaded area under Y and x 1 will be empty, but the data are entered in this shaded area, and the calculations are automatically performed. In Program 8C, the intercept is 2 (the coefficient in the Y column) and the slope is 1.25 (the coefficient in the x 1 column), resulting in the regression equation

$$Y = 2 + 1.25X$$

which is the equation found earlier in this chapter.

Excel 2007

When doing regression in Excel (without the Excel QM add-in), the *Data Analysis* add-in is used in both Excel 2010 and Excel 2007. The steps and illustrations for Excel 2010 provided earlier in this chapter also apply to Excel 2007. However, the procedure to enable or activate this or any other Excel add-in varies, depending on which of the two versions of Excel is being used.

PROGRAM 8A
Using Excel QM for Regression

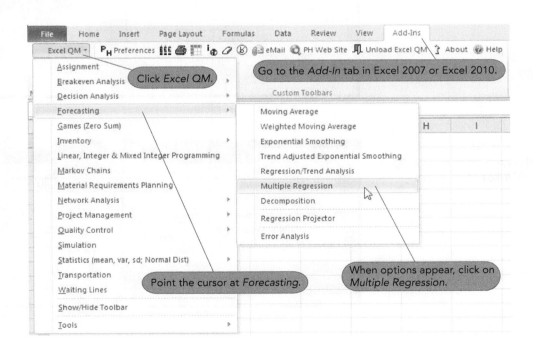

PROGRAM 8B

Initializing the
Spreadsheet in Excel QM

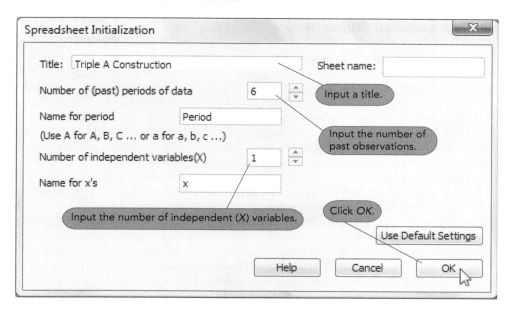

PROGRAM 8C

Input and Results for
Regression in Excel QM

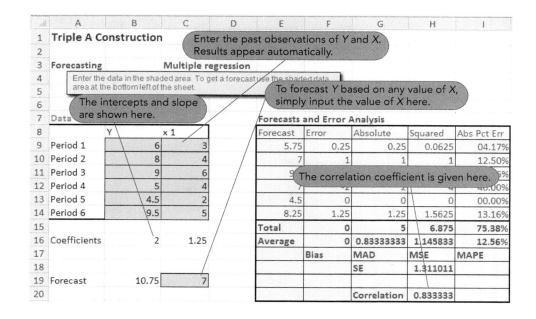

Solutions to Selected Problems

10 (b) SST = 29.5 SSE = 12 SSR = 17.5 $\hat{Y} = 1 + 1.0X$
(c) $\hat{Y} = 7$

12 (a) $\hat{Y} = 1 + 1X$

16 (a) \$83,502   (b) The model predicts the average price for a house this size.   (c) Age, number of bedrooms, lot size   (d) 0.3969

18 For $X = 1200$, $\hat{Y} = 2.35$ for $X = 2400$, $\hat{Y} = 3.67$

22 The model with just *age* is best because it has the highest $r^2(0.78)$.

24 $\hat{Y} = 82{,}185.6 + 25.94X_1 - 2151.74X_2 - 1711.54X_3$;
X_1 = sq. ft., X_2 = bedrooms, X_3 = age
(a) $\hat{Y} = 82{,}185.6 + 25.94(2000) - 2151.74(3) - 1711.54(10) = \$110{,}495$ (rounded)

26 Best model is $\hat{Y} = 1.518 + 0.669X$;
$\hat{Y}$ = expenses (millions), X = admissions (100s).
$r^2 = 0.974$. The adjusted r^2 decreases when number of beds is added, so only admissions should be used.

28 $\hat{Y} = 57.686 - 0.166X_1 - 0.005X_2$; $\hat{Y}$ = mpg,
X_1 = horsepower, X_2 = weight. This is better—both r^2 and adjusted r^2 are higher.

Solutions to Self-Tests

1. b
2. c
3. d
4. b
5. b
6. c
7. b
8. c
9. a
10. b
11. b
12. c

Forecasting

From Chapter 5 of *Quantitative Analysis for Management,* 11/e. Barry Render. Ralph M. Stair, Jr. Michael E. Hanna. Copyright © 2012 by Pearson Education. All rights reserved.

1　Introduction

Every day, managers make decisions without knowing what will happen in the future. Inventory is ordered though no one knows what sales will be, new equipment is purchased though no one knows the demand for products, and investments are made though no one knows what profits will be. Managers are always trying to reduce this uncertainty and to make better estimates of what will happen in the future. Accomplishing this is the main purpose of forecasting.

There are many ways to forecast the future. In numerous firms (especially smaller ones), the entire process is subjective, involving seat-of-the-pants methods, intuition, and years of experience. There are also many *quantitative* forecasting models, such as moving averages, exponential smoothing, trend projections, and least squares regression analysis.

The following steps can help in the development of a forecasting system. While steps 5 and 6 may not be as relevant if a qualitative model is selected in step 4, data are certainly necessary for the quantitative forecasting models presented in this chapter.

Eight Steps to Forecasting

1. Determine the use of the forecast—what objective are we trying to obtain?
2. Select the items or quantities that are to be forecasted.
3. Determine the time horizon of the forecast—is it 1 to 30 days (short term), 1 month to 1 year (medium term), or more than 1 year (long term)?
4. Select the forecasting model or models.
5. Gather the data or information needed to make the forecast.
6. Validate the forecasting model.
7. Make the forecast.
8. Implement the results.

These steps present a systematic way of initiating, designing, and implementing a forecasting system. When the forecasting system is to be used to generate forecasts regularly over time, data must be collected routinely, and the actual computations or procedures used to make the forecast can be done automatically.

No single method is superior. Whatever works best should be used.

There is seldom a single superior forecasting method. One organization may find regression effective, another firm may use several approaches, and a third may combine both quantitative and subjective techniques. Whatever tool works best for a firm is the one that should be used.

2　Types of Forecasts

The three categories of models are time series, causal, and qualitative.

In this chapter we consider forecasting models that can be classified into one of three categories: time-series models, causal models, and qualitative models (see Figure 1).

Time-Series Models

Time-series models attempt to predict the future by using historical data. These models make the assumption that what happens in the future is a function of what has happened in the past. In other words, time-series models look at what has happened over a period of time and use a series of past data to make a forecast. Thus, if we are forecasting weekly sales for lawn mowers, we use the past weekly sales for lawn mowers in making the forecast.

The time-series models we examine in this chapter are moving average, exponential smoothing, trend projections, and decomposition. Regression analysis can be used in trend projections and in one type of decomposition model. The primary emphasis of this chapter is time series forecasting.

Causal Models

Causal models incorporate the variables or factors that might influence the quantity being forecasted into the forecasting model. For example, daily sales of a cola drink might depend on the season, the average temperature, the average humidity, whether it is a weekend or a weekday, and so on. Thus, a causal model would attempt to include factors for temperature, humidity, season, day of the week, and so on. Causal models may also include past sales data as time-series models do, but they include other factors as well.

FIGURE 1
Forecasting Models

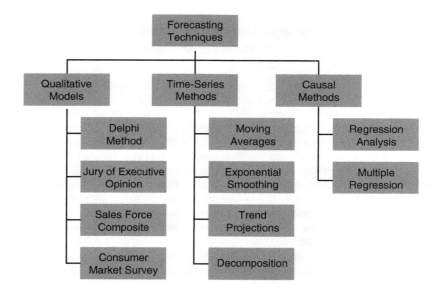

Our job as quantitative analysts is to develop the best statistical relationship between sales or the variable being forecast and the set of independent variables. The most common quantitative causal model is regression analysis. Regression models demonstrate how to predict the selling price of a house based on characteristics such as size, age, and condition of the house. Other causal models do exist, and many of them are based on regression analysis.

Qualitative Models

Whereas time-series and causal models rely on quantitative data, **qualitative models** attempt to incorporate judgmental or subjective factors into the forecasting model. Opinions by experts, individual experiences and judgments, and other subjective factors may be considered. Qualitative models are especially useful when subjective factors are expected to be very important or when accurate quantitative data are difficult to obtain.

Here is a brief overview of four different qualitative forecasting techniques:

Overview of four qualitative or judgmental approaches: Delphi, jury of executive opinion, sales force composite, and consumer market survey.

1. *Delphi method.* This iterative group process allows experts, who may be located in different places, to make forecasts. There are three different types of participants in the **Delphi** process: decision makers, staff personnel, and respondents. The **decision making group** usually consists of 5 to 10 experts who will be making the actual forecast. The staff personnel assist the decision makers by preparing, distributing, collecting, and summarizing a series of questionnaires and survey results. The respondents are a group of people whose judgments are valued and are being sought. This group provides inputs to the decision makers before the forecast is made.

   In the Delphi method, when the results of the first questionnaire are obtained, the results are summarized and the questionnaire is modified. Both the summary of the results and the new questionnaire are then sent to the same respondents for a new round of responses. The respondents, upon seeing the results from the first questionnaire, may view things differently and may modify their original responses. This process is repeated with the hope that a consensus is reached.

2. *Jury of executive opinion.* This method takes the opinions of a small group of high-level managers, often in combination with statistical models, and results in a group estimate of demand.

3. *Sales force composite.* In this approach, each salesperson estimates what sales will be in his or her region; these forecasts are reviewed to ensure that they are realistic and are then combined at the district and national levels to reach an overall forecast.

4. *Consumer market survey.* This method solicits input from customers or potential customers regarding their future purchasing plans. It can help not only in preparing a forecast but also in improving product design and planning for new products.

IN ACTION

Hurricane Landfall Location Forecasts and the Mean Absolute Deviation

Scientists at the National Hurricane Center (NHC) of the National Weather Service have the very difficult job of predicting where the eye of a hurricane will hit land. Accurate forecasts are extremely important to coastal businesses and residents who need to prepare for a storm or perhaps even evacuate. They are also important to local government officials, law enforcement agencies, and other emergency responders who will provide help once a storm has passed. Over the years, the NHC has tremendously improved the forecast accuracy (measured by the mean absolute deviation [MAD]) in predicting the actual landfall location for hurricanes that originate in the Atlantic Ocean.

The NHC provides forecasts and periodic updates of where the hurricane eye will hit land. Such landfall location predictions are

recorded when a hurricane is 72 hours, 48 hours, 36 hours, 24 hours, and 12 hours away from actually reaching land. Once the hurricane has come ashore, these forecasts are compared to the actual landfall location, and the error (in miles) is recorded. At the end of the hurricane season, the errors for all the hurricanes in that year are used to calculate the MAD for each type of forecast (12 hours away, 24 hour away, etc.). The graph below shows how the landfall location forecast has improved since 1989. During the early 1990s, the landfall forecast when the hurricane was 48 hours away had an MAD close to 200 miles; in 2009, this number was down to about 75 miles. Clearly, there has been vast improvement in forecast accuracy, and this trend is continuing.

Source: Based on National Hurricane Center, http://www.nhc.noaa.gov.

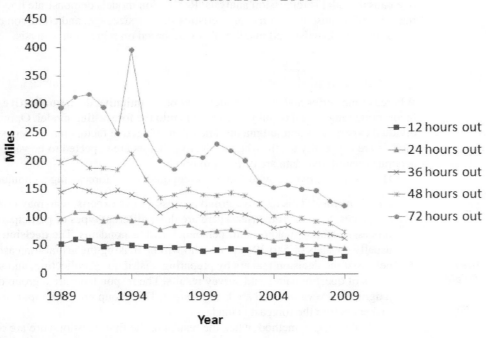

3 Scatter Diagrams and Time Series

A scatter diagram helps obtain ideas about a relationship.

As with regression models, **scatter diagrams** are very helpful when forecasting time series. A scatter diagram for a time series may be plotted on a two-dimensional graph with the horizontal axis representing the time period. The variable to be forecast (such as sales) is placed on the vertical axis. Let us consider the example of a firm that needs to forecast sales for three different products.

Wacker Distributors notes that annual sales for three of its products—television sets, radios, and compact disc players—over the past 10 years are as shown in Table 1. One simple way to examine these historical data, and perhaps to use them to establish a forecast, is to draw a scatter diagram for each product (Figure 2). This picture, showing the relationship between sales of a product and time, is useful in spotting trends or cycles. An exact mathematical model that describes the situation can then be developed if it appears reasonable to do so.

TABLE 1
Annual Sales of Three Products

YEAR	TELEVISION SETS	RADIOS	COMPACT DISC PLAYERS
1	250	300	110
2	250	310	100
3	250	320	120
4	250	330	140
5	250	340	170
6	250	350	150
7	250	360	160
8	250	370	190
9	250	380	200
10	250	390	190

FIGURE 2
Scatter Diagram for Sales

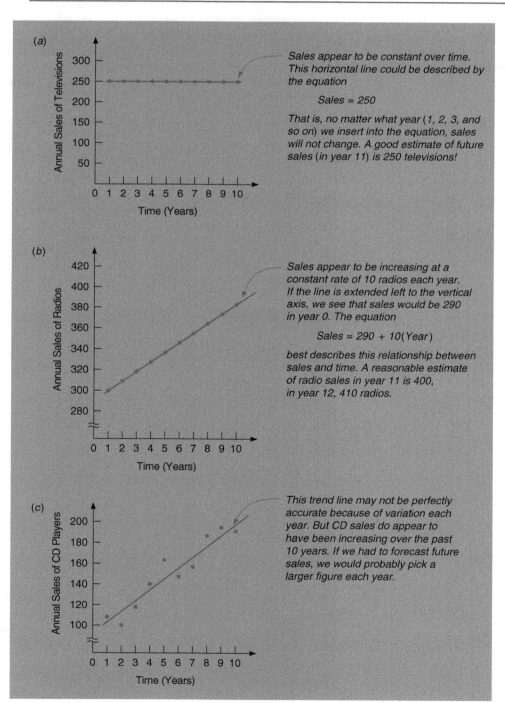

(a)

Sales appear to be constant over time. This horizontal line could be described by the equation

$$Sales = 250$$

That is, no matter what year (1, 2, 3, and so on) we insert into the equation, sales will not change. A good estimate of future sales (in year 11) is 250 televisions!

(b)

Sales appear to be increasing at a constant rate of 10 radios each year. If the line is extended left to the vertical axis, we see that sales would be 290 in year 0. The equation

$$Sales = 290 + 10(Year)$$

best describes this relationship between sales and time. A reasonable estimate of radio sales in year 11 is 400, in year 12, 410 radios.

(c)

This trend line may not be perfectly accurate because of variation each year. But CD sales do appear to have been increasing over the past 10 years. If we had to forecast future sales, we would probably pick a larger figure each year.

4 Measures of Forecast Accuracy

We discuss several different forecasting models in this chapter. To see how well one model works, or to compare that model with other models, the forecasted values are compared with the actual or observed values. The forecast error (or deviation) is defined as follows:

$$\text{Forecast error} = \text{Actual value} - \text{Forecast value}$$

One measure of accuracy is the **mean absolute deviation (MAD)**. This is computed by taking the sum of the absolute values of the individual forecast errors and dividing by the numbers of errors (n):

$$\text{MAD} = \frac{\sum |\text{forecast error}|}{n} \tag{1}$$

Consider the Wacker Distributors sales of CD players shown in Table 1. Suppose that in the past, Wacker had forecast sales for each year to be the sales that were actually achieved in the previous year. This is sometimes called a **naïve model**. Table 2 gives these forecasts as well as the absolute value of the errors. In forecasting for the next time period (year 11), the forecast would be 190. Notice that there is no error computed for year 1 since there was no forecast for this year, and there is no error for year 11 since the actual value of this is not yet known. Thus, the number of **errors** (n) is 9.

The naïve forecast for the next period is the actual value observed in the current period.

From this, we see the following:

$$\text{MAD} = \frac{\sum |\text{forecast error}|}{n} = \frac{160}{9} = 17.8$$

This means that on the average, each forecast missed the actual value by 17.8 units.

Other measures of the accuracy of historical errors in forecasting are sometimes used besides the MAD. One of the most common is the **mean squared error (MSE)**, which is the average of the squared errors:[*]

$$\text{MSE} = \frac{\sum (\text{error})^2}{n} \tag{2}$$

TABLE 2

Computing the Mean Absolute Deviation (MAD)

YEAR	ACTUAL SALES OF CD PLAYERS	FORECAST SALES	ABSOLUTE VALUE OF ERRORS (DEVIATION), |ACTUAL–FORECAST|
1	110	—	—
2	100	110	|100 − 110| = 10
3	120	100	|120 − 100| = 20
4	140	120	|140 − 120| = 20
5	170	140	|170 − 140| = 30
6	150	170	|150 − 170| = 20
7	160	150	|160 − 150| = 10
8	190	160	|190 − 160| = 30
9	200	190	|200 − 190| = 10
10	190	200	|190 − 200| = 10
11	—	190	—

Sum of |errors| = 160

MAD = 160/9 = 17.8

[*]In regression analysis, the MSE formula is usually adjusted to provide an unbiased estimator of the error variance. Throughout this chapter, we will use the formula provided here.

MODELING IN THE REAL WORLD

Forecasting at Tupperware International

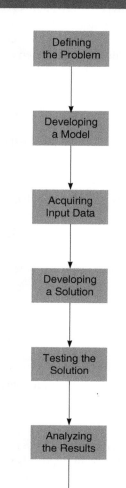

Defining the Problem

To drive production at each of Tupperware's 15 plants in the United States, Latin America, Africa, Europe, and Asia, the firm needs accurate forecasts of demand for its products.

Developing a Model

A variety of statistical models are used, including moving averages, exponential smoothing, and regression analysis. Qualitative analysis is also employed in the process.

Acquiring Input Data

At world headquarters in Orlando, Florida, huge databases are maintained that map the sales of each product, the test market results of each new product (since 20% of the firm's sales come from products less than 2 years old), and where each product falls in its own life cycle.

Developing a Solution

Each of Tupperware's 50 profit centers worldwide develops computerized monthly, quarterly, and 12-month sales projections. These are aggregated by region and then globally.

Testing the Solution

Reviews of these forecasts take place in sales, marketing, finance, and production departments.

Analyzing the Results

Participating managers analyze forecasts with Tupperware's version of a "jury of executive opinion."

Implementing the Results

Forecasts are used to schedule materials, equipment, and personnel at each plant.

Source: Interviews by the authors with Tupperware executives.

Besides the MAD and MSE, the **mean absolute percent error (MAPE)** is sometimes used. The MAPE is the average of the absolute values of the errors expressed as percentages of the actual values. This is computed as follows:

$$\text{MAPE} = \frac{\sum \left| \dfrac{\text{error}}{\text{actual}} \right|}{n} 100\% \tag{3}$$

Three common measures of error are MAD, MSE, and MAPE. Bias gives the average error and may be positive or negative.

There is another common term associated with error in forecasting. **Bias** is the average error and tells whether the forecast tends to be too high or too low and by how much. Thus, bias may be negative or positive. It is not a good measure of the actual size of the errors because the negative errors can cancel out the positive errors.

5   Time-Series Forecasting Models

A time series is based on a sequence of evenly spaced (weekly, monthly, quarterly, and so on) data points. Examples include weekly sales of HP personal computers, quarterly earnings reports of Microsoft Corporation, daily shipments of Eveready batteries, and annual U.S. consumer price indices. Forecasting time-series data implies that future values are predicted *only* from past values of that variable (such as we saw in Table 1) and that other variables, no matter how potentially valuable, are ignored.

Components of a Time Series

Four components of a time series are trend, seasonality, cycles, and random variations.

Analyzing time series means breaking down past data into components and then projecting them forward. A time series typically has four components:

1. *Trend* (*T*) is the gradual upward or downward movement of the data over time.
2. *Seasonality* (*S*) is a pattern of the demand fluctuation above or below the trend line that repeats at regular intervals.
3. *Cycles* (*C*) are patterns in annual data that occur every several years. They are usually tied into the business cycle.
4. *Random variations* (*R*) are "blips" in the data caused by chance and unusual situations; they follow no discernible pattern.

Figure 3 shows a time series and its components.

There are two general forms of time-series models in statistics. The first is a multiplicative model, which assumes that demand is the product of the four components. It is stated as follows:

$$\text{Demand} = T \times S \times C \times R$$

An additive model adds the components together to provide an estimate. Multiple regression is often used to develop additive models. This additive relationship is stated as follows:

$$\text{Demand} = T + S + C + R$$

There are other models that may be a combination of these. For example, one of the components (such as trend) might be additive while another (such as seasonality) could be multiplicative.

Understanding the components of a time series will help in selecting an appropriate forecasting technique to use. If all variations in a time series are due to random variations, with no trend, seasonal, or cyclical component, some type of averaging or smoothing model would be appropriate. The averaging techniques in this chapter are moving average, weighted moving average, and exponential smoothing. These methods will smooth out the forecasts and not be

FIGURE 3

Product Demand Charted over 4 Years, with Trend and Seasonality Indicated

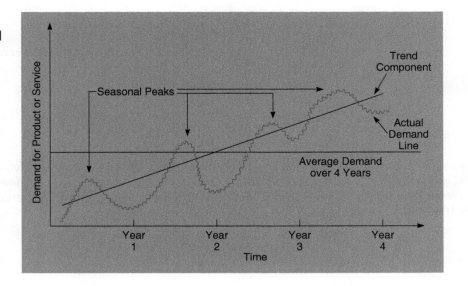

too heavily influenced by random variations. However, if there is a trend or seasonal pattern present in the data, then a technique which incorporates that particular component into the forecast should be used. Two such techniques are exponential smoothing with trend and trend projections. If there is a seasonal pattern present in the data, then a seasonal index may be developed and used with any of the averaging methods. If both trend and seasonal components are present, then a method such as the decomposition method should be used.

Moving Averages

Moving averages smooth out variations when forecasting demands are fairly steady.

Moving averages are useful if we can assume that market demands will stay fairly steady over time. For example, a four-month moving average is found simply by summing the demand during the past four months and dividing by 4. With each passing month, the most recent month's data are added to the sum of the previous three months' data, and the earliest month is dropped. This tends to smooth out short-term irregularities in the data series.

An *n*-period moving average forecast, which serves as an estimate of the next period's demand, is expressed as follows:

$$\text{Moving average forecast} = \frac{\text{Sum of demands in previous } n \text{ periods}}{n} \quad (4)$$

Mathematically, this is written as

$$F_{t+1} = \frac{Y_t + Y_{t-1} + \cdots + Y_{t-n+1}}{n} \quad (5)$$

where

$$F_{t+1} = \text{forecast for time period } t + 1$$
$$Y_t = \text{actual value in time period } t$$
$$n = \text{number of periods to average}$$

A 4-month moving average has $n = 4$; a 5-month moving average has $n = 5$.

WALLACE GARDEN SUPPLY EXAMPLE Storage shed sales at Wallace Garden Supply are shown in the middle column of Table 3. A 3-month moving average is indicated on the right. The forecast for the next January, using this technique, is 16. Were we simply asked to find a forecast for next January, we would only have to make this one calculation. The other forecasts are necessary only if we wish to compute the MAD or another measure of accuracy.

Weights can be used to put more emphasis on recent periods.

WEIGHTED MOVING AVERAGE A simple moving average gives the same weight $(1/n)$ to each of the past observations being used to develop the forecast. On the other hand, a **weighted moving average** allows different weights to be assigned to the previous observations. As the

TABLE 3
Wallace Garden Supply Shed Sales

MONTH	ACTUAL SHED SALES	3-MONTH MOVING AVERAGE
January	10	
February	12	
March	13	
April	16	(10 + 12 + 13)/3 = 11.67
May	19	(12 + 13 + 16)/3 = 13.67
June	23	(13 + 16 + 19)/3 = 16.00
July	26	(16 + 19 + 23)/3 = 19.33
August	30	(19 + 23 + 26)/3 = 22.67
September	28	(23 + 26 + 30)/3 = 26.33
October	18	(26 + 30 + 28)/3 = 28.00
November	16	(30 + 28 + 18)/3 = 25.33
December	14	(28 + 18 + 16)/3 = 20.67
January	—	(18 + 16 + 14)/3 = 16.00

weighted moving average method typically assigns greater weight to more recent observations, this forecast is more responsive to changes in the pattern of the data that occur. However, this is also a potential drawback to this method because the heavier weight would also respond just as quickly to random fluctuations.

A *weighted moving average* may be expressed as

$$F_{t+1} = \frac{\sum (\text{Weight in period } i)(\text{Actual value in period } i)}{\sum (\text{Weights})} \qquad (6)$$

Mathematically, this is

$$F_{t+1} = \frac{w_1 Y_t + w_2 Y_{t-1} + \cdots + w_n Y_{t-n+1}}{w_1 + w_2 + \cdots + w_n} \qquad (7)$$

where

$$w_i = \text{weight for } i\text{th observation}$$

Wallace Garden Supply decides to use a 3-month weighted moving average forecast with weights of 3 for the most recent observation, 2 for the next observation, and 1 for the most distant observation. This would be implemented as follows:

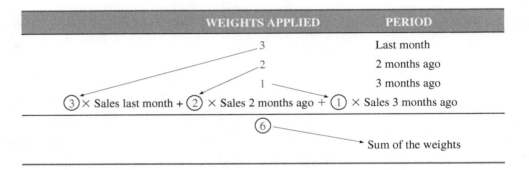

WEIGHTS APPLIED	PERIOD
3	Last month
2	2 months ago
1	3 months ago

(3) × Sales last month + (2) × Sales 2 months ago + (1) × Sales 3 months ago

(6) → Sum of the weights

The results of the Wallace Garden Supply weighted average forecast are shown in Table 4. In this particular forecasting situation, you can see that weighting the latest month more heavily provides a much more accurate projection, and calculating the MAD for each of these would verify this.

Choosing the weights obviously has an important impact on the forecasts. One way to choose weights is to try various combinations of weights, calculate the MAD for each, and select the set of weights that results in the lowest MAD. Some forecasting software has an option to search for the best set of weights, and forecasts using these weights are then provided. The best set of weights can also be found by using nonlinear programming, as will be seen in a later chapter.

Some software packages require that the weights add to 1, and this would simplify Equation 7 because the denominator would be 1. Forcing the weights to sum to 1 is easily achieved by dividing each of the weights by the sum of the weights. In the Wallace Garden Supply example in Table 4, the weights are 3, 2, and 1, which add to 6. These weights could be revised to the new weights 3/6, 2/6, and 1/6, which add to 1. Using these weights gives the same forecasts shown in Table 4.

Both simple and weighted moving averages are effective in smoothing out sudden fluctuations in the demand pattern in order to provide stable estimates. Moving averages do, however, have two problems. First, increasing the size of *n* (the number of periods averaged) does smooth out fluctuations better, but it makes the method less sensitive to *real* changes in the data should they occur. Second, moving averages cannot pick up trends very well. Because they are averages, they will always stay within past levels and will not predict a change to either a higher or a lower level.

Moving averages have two problems: the larger number of periods may smooth out real changes, and they don't pick up trend.

USING EXCEL AND EXCEL QM IN FORECASTING Excel and spreadsheets in general are frequently used in forecasting. Many forecasting techniques are supported by built-in Excel functions. You can also use Excel QM's forecasting module, which has several components. To access Excel

TABLE 4

Weighted Moving Average Forecast for Wallace Garden Supply

MONTH	ACTUAL SHED SALES	3-MONTH MOVING AVERAGE
January	10	
February	12	
March	13	
April	16	$[(3 \times 13) + (2 \times 12) + (10)]/6 = 12.17$
May	19	$[(3 \times 16) + (2 \times 13) + (12)]/6 = 14.33$
June	23	$[(3 \times 19) + (2 \times 16) + (13)]/6 = 17.00$
July	26	$[(3 \times 23) + (2 \times 19) + (16)]/6 = 20.5$
August	30	$[(3 \times 26) + (2 \times 23) + (19)]/6 = 23.83$
September	28	$[(3 \times 30) + (2 \times 26) + (23)]/6 = 27.5$
October	18	$[(3 \times 28) + (2 \times 30) + (26)]/6 = 28.33$
November	16	$[(3 \times 18) + (2 \times 28) + (30)]/6 = 23.33$
December	14	$[(3 \times 16) + (2 \times 18) + (28)]/6 = 18.67$
January	—	$[(3 \times 14) + (2 \times 16) + (18)]/6 = 15.33$

QM after it has been installed in Excel 2010 or Excel 2007, go to the *Add-Ins* tab and select *Excel QM* and then select *Forecasting*. If you click on a technique such as *Moving Average*, *Weighted Moving Average*, or *Exponential Smoothing*, an input window will open. To use Excel QM for the Wallace Garden Supply weighted moving average forecast, select *Forecasting—Weighted Moving Average*, as shown in Program 1A. Enter the number of past periods of data and the number of periods to be averaged, as shown in Program 1B. Click *OK* when finished, and a spreadsheet will be initialized. Simply enter the past observations and any parameters, such as the number of periods to be averaged, and the output will automatically appear because the formulas are automatically generated by Excel QM. Program 1C provides the results. To display the formulas in Excel, simply press Ctrl+ (grave accent). Pressing this again returns the display to the values instead of the formulas.

PROGRAM 1A

Selecting the Forecasting Module in Excel QM

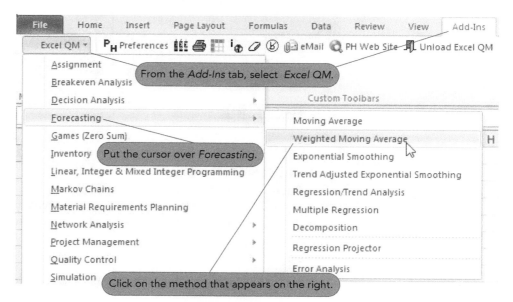

PROGRAM 1B

Initialization Screen for Weighted Moving Average

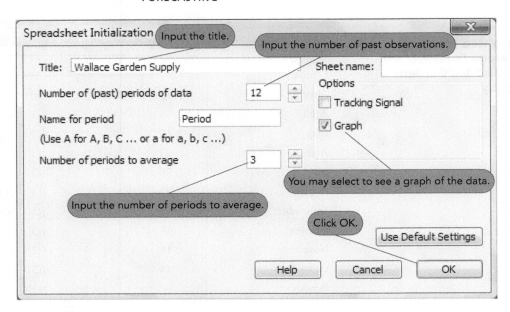

PROGRAM 1C

Weighted Moving Average in Excel QM for Wallace Garden Supply

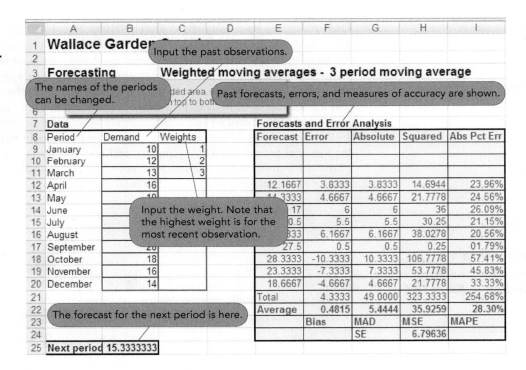

Exponential Smoothing

Exponential smoothing is a forecasting method that is easy to use and is handled efficiently by computers. Although it is a type of moving average technique, it involves little record keeping of past data. The basic exponential smoothing formula can be shown as follows:

$$\text{New forecast} = \text{Last period's forecast} + \alpha(\text{Last period's actual demand} - \text{Last period's forecast}) \qquad (8)$$

where α is a weight (or **smoothing constant**) that has a value between 0 and 1, inclusive.

Equation 8 can also be written mathematically as

$$F_{t+1} = F_t + \alpha(Y_t - F_t) \qquad (9)$$

where

F_{t+1} = new forecast (for time period $t + 1$)

F_t = previous forecast (for time period t)

α = smoothing constant $(0 \leq \alpha \leq 1)$

Y_t = previous period's actual demand

The smoothing constant, α, allows managers to assign weight to recent data.

The concept here is not complex. The latest estimate of demand is equal to the old estimate adjusted by a fraction of the error (last period's actual demand minus the old estimate).

The smoothing constant, α, can be changed to give more weight to recent data when the value is high or more weight to past data when it is low. For example, when $\alpha = 0.5$, it can be shown mathematically that the new forecast is based almost entirely on demand in the past three periods. When $\alpha = 0.1$, the forecast places little weight on any single period, even the most recent, and it takes many periods (about 19) of historic values into account.[*]

For example, in January, a demand for 142 of a certain car model for February was predicted by a dealer. Actual February demand was 153 autos. Using a smoothing constant of $\alpha = 0.20$, we can forecast the March demand using the exponential smoothing model. Substituting into the formula, we obtain

New forecast (for March demand) = $142 + 0.2(153 - 142)$

= 144.2

Thus, the demand forecast for the cars in March is 144.

Suppose that actual demand for the cars in March was 136. A forecast for the demand in April, using the exponential smoothing model with a constant of $\alpha = 0.20$, can be made:

New forecast (for April demand) = $144.2 + 0.2(136 - 144.2)$

= 142.6, or 143 autos

SELECTING THE SMOOTHING CONSTANT The exponential smoothing approach is easy to use and has been applied successfully by banks, manufacturing companies, wholesalers, and other organizations. The appropriate value of the smoothing constant, α, however, can make the difference between an accurate forecast and an inaccurate forecast. In picking a value for the smoothing constant, the objective is to obtain the most accurate forecast. Several values of the smoothing constant may be tried, and the one with the lowest MAD could be selected. This is analogous to how weights are selected for a weighted moving average forecast. Some forecasting software will automatically select the best smoothing constant. QM for Windows will display the MAD that would be obtained with values of α ranging from 0 to 1 in increments of 0.01.

PORT OF BALTIMORE EXAMPLE Let us apply this concept with a trial-and-error testing of two values of α in an example. The port of Baltimore has unloaded large quantities of grain from ships during the past eight quarters. The port's operations manager wants to test the use of exponential smoothing to see how well the technique works in predicting tonnage unloaded. He assumes that the forecast of grain unloaded in the first quarter was 175 tons. Two values of α are examined: $\alpha = 0.10$ and $\alpha = .50$. Table 5 shows the *detailed* calculations for $\alpha = 0.10$ only.

---

[*]The term *exponential smoothing* is used because the weight of any one period's demand in a forecast decreases exponentially over time. See an advanced forecasting book for algebraic proof.

TABLE 5

Port of Baltimore Exponential Smoothing Forecasts for α = 0.10 and α = 0.50

QUARTER	ACTUAL TONNAGE UNLOADED	FORECAST USING α = 0.10	FORECAST USING α = 0.50
1	180	175	175
2	168	$175.5 = 175.00 + 0.10(180 - 175)$	177.5
3	159	$174.75 = 175.50 + 0.10(168 - 175.50)$	172.75
4	175	$173.18 = 174.75 + 0.10(159 - 174.75)$	165.88
5	190	$173.36 = 173.18 + 0.10(175 - 173.18)$	170.44
6	205	$175.02 = 173.36 + 0.10(190 - 173.36)$	180.22
7	180	$178.02 = 175.02 + 0.10(205 - 175.02)$	192.61
8	182	$178.22 = 178.02 + 0.10(180 - 178.02)$	186.30
9	?	$178.60 = 178.22 + 0.10(182 - 178.22)$	184.15

To evaluate the accuracy of each smoothing constant, we can compute the absolute deviations and MADs (see Table 6). Based on this analysis, a smoothing constant of α = 0.10 is preferred to α = 0.50 because its MAD is smaller.

USING EXCEL QM FOR EXPONENTIAL SMOOTHING Program 2 illustrates how Excel QM handles exponential smoothing with the port of Baltimore example.

EXPONENTIAL SMOOTHING WITH TREND ADJUSTMENT The averaging or smoothing forecasting techniques are useful when a time series has only a random component, but these techniques fail to respond to trends. If there is trend present in the data, a forecasting model that explicitly incorporates this into the forecast should be used. One such technique is the exponential smoothing with trend model. The idea is to develop an exponential smoothing forecast and then adjust this for trend. Two smoothing constants, α and β, are used in this model, and both of these values must be between 0 and 1. The level of the forecast is adjusted by multiplying the first smoothing constant, α, by the most recent forecast error and adding it to the previous forecast. The trend is adjusted by multiplying the second smoothing constant, β, by the most recent error or excess amount in the trend. A higher value gives more weight to recent observations and thus responds more quickly to changes in the patterns.

Two smoothing constants are used.

As with simple exponential smoothing, the first time a forecast is developed, a previous forecast (F_t) must be given or estimated. If none is available, often the initial forecast is as-

TABLE 6

Absolute Deviations and MADs for the Port of Baltimore Example

QUARTER	ACTUAL TONNAGE UNLOADED	FORECAST WITH α = 0.10	ABSOLUTE DEVIATIONS FOR α = 0.10	FORECAST WITH α = 0.50	ABSOLUTE DEVIATIONS FOR α = 0.50
1	180	175	5	175	5
2	168	175.5	7.5	177.5	9.5
3	159	174.75	15.75	172.75	13.75
4	175	173.18	1.82	165.88	9.12
5	190	173.36	16.64	170.44	19.56
6	205	175.02	29.98	180.22	24.78
7	180	178.02	1.98	192.61	12.61
8	182	178.22	3.78	186.30	4.3
Sum of absolute deviations			82.45		98.63

$$\text{MAD} = \frac{\sum |\text{deviation}|}{n} = 10.31 \qquad \text{MAD} = 12.33$$

PROGRAM 2

Port of Baltimore Exponential Smoothing Example in Excel QM

	A	B	C	D	E	F	G	H
1	**Port of Baltimore**			If initial forecast is given, enter it here. If you do not want to include the error for this initial forecast, cells E10:H10.				
2								
3	**Forecasting**			**Exponential smoothing**				
4	Enter alpha (between 0 and 1), enter the past demands in the shaded column then enter a starting forecast. If the starting forecast is not in the first period then delete the error analysis for all rows above the starting forecast.							
5								
6								
7	Alpha		Enter the data and alpha.					
8	**Data**			**Forecasts and Error Analysis**				
9	Period	Demand		Forecast	Error	Absolut	Squared	Abs Pct E
10	Quarter 1	180		175	5	5	25	02.78%
11	Quarter 2	168		175.5	-7.5	7.5	56.25	04.46%
12	Quarter 3	159		174.75	-15.75	15.75	248.06	09.91%
13	Quarter 4	175		173.175	1.825	1.825	3.3306	01.04%
14	Quarter 5	190		173.358	16.643	16.643	276.97	08.76%
15	Quarter 6	205		175.022	29.978	29.978	898.7	14.62%
16	Quarter 7	180		178.02	1.9804	1.9804	3.9221	01.10%
17	Quarter 8	182		178.218	3.7824	3.7824	14.306	0.02078
18				**Total**	**35.959**	**82.459**	**1526.5**	**44.75%**
19	The forecast for quarter 9 is here.			**Average**	**4.4948**	**10.307**	**190.82**	**05.59%**
20					Bias	MAD	MSE	MAPE
21						SE	15.951	
22	**Next peri**	**178.596**						

sumed to be perfect. In addition, a previous trend (T_t) must be given or estimated. This is often estimated using other past data, if available, or by using subjective means, or by calculating the increase (or decrease) observed during the first few time periods of the data available. Without such an estimate available, the trend is sometimes assumed to be 0 initially, although this may lead to poor forecasts if the trend is large and β is small. Once these initial conditions have been set, the exponential smoothing forecast including trend (FIT_t) is developed using three steps:

Estimate or assume initial values for F_t *and* T_t

Step 1. Compute the smoothed forecast (F_{t+1}) for time period $t + 1$ using the equation

Smoothed forecast = Previous forecast including trend + α(Last error)

$$F_{t+1} = FIT_t + \alpha(Y_t - FIT_t) \tag{10}$$

Step 2. Update the trend (T_{t+1}) using the equation

Smoothed trend = Previous trend + β(Error or excess in trend)

$$T_{t+1} = T_t + \beta(F_{t+1} - FIT_t) \tag{11}$$

Step 3. Calculate the trend-adjusted exponential smoothing forecast (FIT_{t+1}) using the equation

Forecast including trend (FIT_{t+1}) = Smoothed forecast (F_{t+1}) + Smoothed trend (T_{t+1})

$$FIT_{t+1} = F_{t+1} + T_{t+1} \tag{12}$$

where

$$T_t = \text{smoothed trend for time period } t$$
$$F_t = \text{smoothed forecast for time period } t$$
$$FIT_t = \text{forecast including trend for time period } t$$
$$\alpha = \text{smoothing constant for forecasts}$$
$$\beta = \text{smoothing constant for trend}$$

TABLE 7

Midwestern Manufacturing's Demand

YEAR	ELECTRICAL GENERATORS SOLD
2004	74
2005	79
2006	80
2007	90
2008	105
2009	142
2010	122

Consider the case of Midwestern Manufacturing Company, which has a demand for electrical generators over the period 2004 to 2010 as shown in Table 7. To use the trend-adjusted exponential smoothing method, first set initial conditions (previous values for F and T) and choose α and β. Assuming that F_1 is perfect and T_1 is 0, and picking 0.3 and 0.4 for the smoothing constants, we have

$$F_1 = 74 \quad T_1 = 0 \quad \alpha = 0.3 \quad \beta = 0.4$$

This results in

$$FIT_1 = F_1 + T_1 = 74 + 0 = 74$$

Following the three steps to get the forecast for 2005 (time period 2), we have

Step 1. Compute F_{t+1} using the equation

$$F_{t+1} = FIT_t + \alpha(Y_t - FIT_t)$$
$$F_2 = FIT_1 + 0.3(Y_1 - FIT_1) = 74 + 0.3(74 - 74) = 74$$

Step 2. Update the trend (T_{t+1}) using the equation

$$T_{t+1} = T_t + \beta(F_{t+1} - FIT_t)$$
$$T_2 = T_1 + 0.4(F_2 - FIT_1) = 0 + 0.4(74 - 74) = 0$$

Step 3. Calculate the trend-adjusted exponential smoothing forecast (FIT_{t+1}) using the equation

$$FIT_2 = F_2 + T_2 = 74 + 0 = 74$$

For 2006 (time period 3) we have

Step 1.

$$F_3 = FIT_2 + 0.3(Y_2 - FIT_2) = 74 + 0.3(79 - 74) = 75.5$$

Step 2.

$$T_3 = T_2 + 0.4(F_3 - FIT_2) = 0 + 0.4(75.5 - 74) = 0.6$$

Step 3.

$$FIT_3 = F_3 + T_3 = 75.5 + 0.6 = 76.1$$

The other results are shown in Table 8. The forecast for 2011 would be about 131.35.

Using Excel QM for Trend-Adjusted Exponential Smoothing

Program 3 shows how Excel QM can be used for the exponential smoothing with trend forecasts.

TABLE 8 Midwestern Manufacturing Exponential Smoothing with Trend Forecasts

TIME (t)	DEMAND (Y_t)	$F_{t+1} = FIT_t + 0.3(Y_t - FIT_t)$	$T_{t+1} = T_t + 0.4(F_{t+1} - FIT_t)$	$FIT_{t+1} = F_{t+1} + T_{t+1}$
1	74	74	0	74
2	79	$74 = 74 + 0.3(74 - 74)$	$0 = 0 + 0.4(74 - 74)$	$74 = 74 + 0$
3	80	$75.5 = 74 + 0.3(79 - 74)$	$0.6 = 0 + 0.4(75.5 - 74)$	$76.1 = 75.5 + 0.6$
4	90	77.270 $= 76.1 + 0.3(80 - 76.1)$	1.068 $= 0.6 + 0.4(77.27 - 76.1)$	$78.338 = 77.270 + 1.068$
5	105	81.837 $= 78.338 + 0.3(90 - 78.338)$	2.468 $= 1.068 + 0.4(81.837 - 78.338)$	$84.305 = 81.837 + 2.468$
6	142	90.514 $= 84.305 + 0.3(105 - 84.305)$	4.952 $= 2.468 + 0.4(90.514 - 84.305)$	$95.466 = 90.514 + 4.952$
7	122	109.426 $= 95.466 + 0.3(142 - 95.466)$	10.536 $= 4.952 + 0.4(109.426 - 95.466)$	$119.962 = 109.426 + 10.536$
8		120.573 $= 119.962 + 0.3(122 - 119.962)$	10.780 $= 10.536 + 0.4(120.573 - 119.962)$	$131.353 = 120.573 + 10.780$

PROGRAM 3

Midwestern Manufacturing Trend-Adjusted Exponential Smoothing in Excel QM

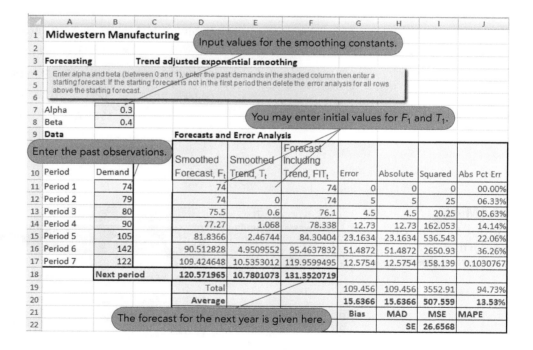

Trend Projections

A trend line is a regression equation with time as the independent variable.

Another method for forecasting time series with trend is called **trend projection**. This technique fits a trend line to a series of historical data points and then projects the line into the future for medium- to long-range forecasts. There are several mathematical trend equations that can be developed (e.g., exponential and quadratic), but in this section we look at linear (straight line) trends only. A trend line is simply a linear regression equation in which the independent variable (X) is the time period. The form of this is

$$\hat{Y} = b_0 + b_1 X$$

where

$\hat{Y}$ = predicted value

b_0 = intercept

b_1 = slope of the line

X = time period (i.e., $X = 1, 2, 3, \ldots, n$)

The **least squares** regression method may be applied to find the coefficients that minimize the sum of the squared errors, thereby also minimizing the mean squared error (MSE). In this section, we will rely on Excel and Excel QM to perform the calculations for coefficients.

MIDWESTERN MANUFACTURING COMPANY EXAMPLE Let us consider the case of Midwestern Manufacturing Company. That firm's demand for electrical generators over the period 2004–2010 was shown in Table 7. A trend line to predict demand (Y) based on the time period can be developed using a regression model. If we let 2004 be time period 1 ($X = 1$), then 2005 is time period 2 ($X = 2$), and so forth. The regression line can be developed using Excel 2010 by going to the *Data* tab and selecting *Data Analysis—Regression* and entering the information as shown in Program 4A. The results are shown in Program 4B. From this we get

$$\hat{Y} = 56.71 + 10.54X$$

To project demand in 2011, we first denote the year 2011 in our new coding system as $X = 8$:

$$(\text{sales in } 2011) = 56.71 + 10.54(8)$$

$$= 141.03, \text{ or } 141 \text{ generators}$$

We can estimate demand for 2012 by inserting $X = 9$ in the same equation:

$$(\text{sales in } 2012) = 56.71 + 10.54(9)$$

$$= 151.57, \text{ or } 152 \text{ generators}$$

PROGRAM 4A

Excel Input Screen for Midwestern Manufacturing Trend Line

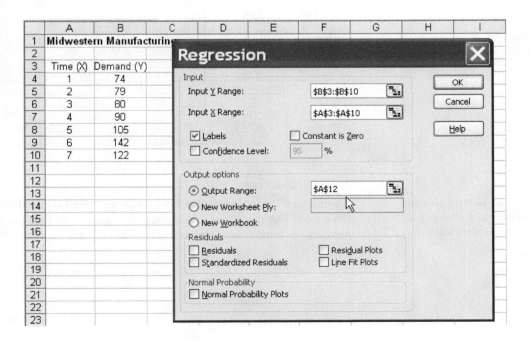

PROGRAM 4B

Excel Output for Midwestern Manufacturing Trend Line

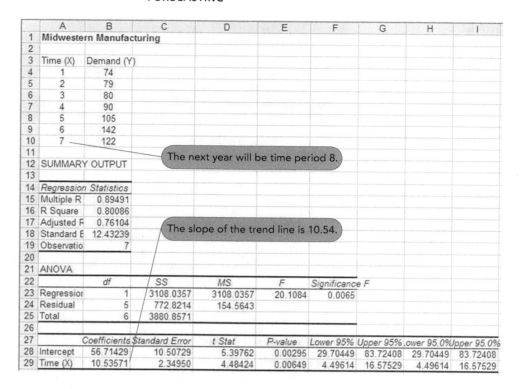

A plot of historical demand and the trend line is provided in Figure 4. In this case, we may wish to be cautious and try to understand the 2009–2010 swings in demand.

USING EXCEL QM IN TREND ANALYSIS Regression can also be performed in Excel QM. Go to the *Add-Ins* tab in Excel 2010 and select *Excel QM—Forecasting—Regression/Trend Analysis*. Enter the number of periods of data (7 in this example), enter a title and name for the time periods (e.g., week, month, year) if desired, and then click *OK*. When the initialized spreadsheet appears, enter the past data and the time periods, as shown in Program 5.

Seasonal Variations

Time-series forecasting such as that in the example of Midwestern Manufacturing involves looking at the *trend* of data over a series of time observations. Sometimes, however, recurring variations at certain seasons of the year make a *seasonal* adjustment in the trend line forecast

FIGURE 4

Electrical Generators and the Computed Trend Line

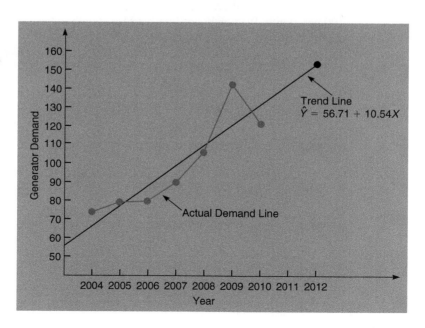

PROGRAM 5

Excel QM Trend Projection Model

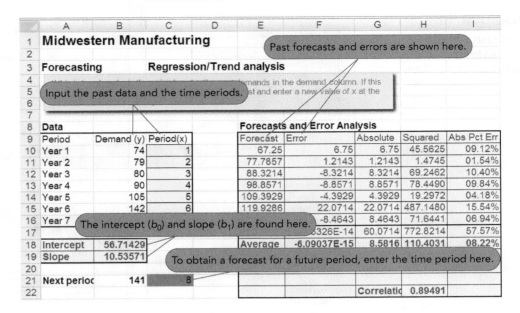

necessary. Demand for coal and fuel oil, for example, usually peaks during cold winter months. Demand for golf clubs or suntan lotion may be highest in summer. Analyzing data in monthly or quarterly terms usually makes it easy to spot seasonal patterns. A seasonal index is often used in multiplicative time series forecasting models to make an adjustment in the forecast when a seasonal component exists. An alternative is to use an additive model such as a regression model that will be introduced in a later section.

An average season has an index of 1.

A **seasonal index** indicates how a particular season (e.g., month or quarter) compares with an average season. When no trend is present, the index can be found by dividing the average value for a particular season by the average of all the data. Thus, an index of 1 means the season is average. For example, if the average sales in January were 120 and the average sales in all months were 200, the seasonal index for January would be $120/200 = 0.60$, so January is below average. The next example illustrates how to compute seasonal indices from historical data and to use these in forecasting future values.

Monthly sales of one brand of telephone answering machine at Eichler Supplies are shown in Table 9, for the two most recent years. The average demand in each month is computed, and these values are divided by the overall average (94) to find the seasonal index for each month. We then use the seasonal indices from Table 9 to adjust future forecasts. For example, suppose we expected the third year's annual demand for answering machines to be 1,200 units, which is 100 per month. We would not forecast each month to have a demand of 100, but we would adjust these based on the seasonal indices as follows:

Jan.	$\dfrac{1{,}200}{12} \times 0.957 = 96$		July	$\dfrac{1{,}200}{12} \times 1.117 = 112$
Feb.	$\dfrac{1{,}200}{12} \times 0.851 = 85$		Aug.	$\dfrac{1{,}200}{12} \times 1.064 = 106$
Mar.	$\dfrac{1{,}200}{12} \times 0.904 = 90$		Sept.	$\dfrac{1{,}200}{12} \times 0.957 = 96$
Apr.	$\dfrac{1{,}200}{12} \times 1.064 = 106$		Oct.	$\dfrac{1{,}200}{12} \times 0.851 = 85$
May	$\dfrac{1{,}200}{12} \times 1.309 = 131$		Nov.	$\dfrac{1{,}200}{12} \times 0.851 = 85$
June	$\dfrac{1{,}200}{12} \times 1.223 = 122$		Dec.	$\dfrac{1{,}200}{12} \times 0.851 = 85$

TABLE 9

Answering Machine Sales and Seasonal Indices

MONTH	SALES DEMAND YEAR 1	SALES DEMAND YEAR 2	AVERAGE 2-YEAR DEMAND	MONTHLY DEMAND[a]	AVERAGE SEASONAL INDEX[b]
January	80	100	90	94	0.957
February	85	75	80	94	0.851
March	80	90	85	94	0.904
April	110	90	100	94	1.064
May	115	131	123	94	1.309
June	120	110	115	94	1.223
July	100	110	105	94	1.117
August	110	90	100	94	1.064
September	85	95	90	94	0.957
October	75	85	80	94	0.851
November	85	75	80	94	0.851
December	80	80	80	94	0.851
		Total average demand = 1,128			

$$^a\text{Average monthly demand} = \frac{1,128}{12 \text{ months}} = 94 \qquad ^b\text{Seasonal index} = \frac{\text{Average 2 year demand}}{\text{Average monthly demand}}$$

Seasonal Variations with Trend

Centered moving averages are used to compute seasonal indices when there is trend.

When both trend and seasonal components are present in a time series, a change from one month to the next could be due to a trend, to a seasonal variation, or simply to random fluctuations. To help with this problem, the seasonal indices should be computed using a **centered moving average** (CMA) approach whenever trend is present. Using this approach prevents a variation due to trend from being incorrectly interpreted as a variation due to the season. Consider the following example.

Quarterly sales figures for Turner Industries are shown in Table 10. Notice that there is a definite trend as the total each year is increasing, and there is an increase for each quarter from one year to the next as well. The seasonal component is obvious as there is a definite drop from the fourth quarter of one year to the first quarter of the next. A similar pattern is observed in comparing the third quarters to the fourth quarters immediately following.

If a seasonal index for quarter 1 were computed using the overall average, the index would be too low and misleading, since this quarter has less trend than any of the others in the sample. If the first quarter of year 1 were omitted and replaced by the first quarter of year 4 (if it were available), the average for quarter 1 (and consequently the seasonal index for quarter 1) would be considerably higher. To derive an accurate seasonal index, we should use a CMA.

Consider quarter 3 of year 1 for the Turner Industries example. The actual sales in that quarter were 150. To determine the magnitude of the seasonal variation, we should compare this with an average quarter centered at that time period. Thus, we should have a total of four quarters (1 year of data) with an equal number of quarters before and after quarter 3 so the trend is averaged out. Thus, we need 1.5 quarters before quarter 3 and 1.5 quarters after it. To obtain the CMA,

TABLE 10

Quarterly Sales ($1,000,000s) for Turner Industries

QUARTER	YEAR 1	YEAR 2	YEAR 3	AVERAGE
1	108	116	123	115.67
2	125	134	142	133.67
3	150	159	168	159.00
4	141	152	165	152.67
Average	131.00	140.25	149.50	140.25

TABLE 11

Centered Moving Averages and Seasonal Ratios for Turner Industries

YEAR	QUARTER	SALES ($1,000,000s)	CMA	SEASONAL RATIO
1	1	108		
	2	125		
	3	150	132.000	1.136
	4	141	134.125	1.051
2	1	116	136.375	0.851
	2	134	138.875	0.965
	3	159	141.125	1.127
	4	152	143.000	1.063
3	1	123	145.125	0.848
	2	142	147.875	0.960
	3	168		
	4	165		

we take quarters 2, 3, and 4 of year 1, plus one-half of quarter 1 for year 1 and one-half of quarter 1 for year 2. The average will be

$$\text{CMA (quarter 3 of year 1)} = \frac{0.5(108) + 125 + 150 + 141 + 0.5(116)}{4} = 132.00$$

We compare the actual sales in this quarter to the CMA and we have the following seasonal ratio:

$$\text{Seasonal ratio} = \frac{\text{Sales in quarter 3}}{\text{CMA}} = \frac{150}{132.00} = 1.136$$

Thus, sales in quarter 3 of year 1 are about 13.6% higher than an average quarter at this time. All of the CMAs and the seasonal ratios are shown in Table 11.

Since there are two seasonal ratios for each quarter, we average these to get the seasonal index. Thus,

$$\text{Index for quarter 1} = I_1 = (0.851 + 0.848)/2 = 0.85$$
$$\text{Index for quarter 2} = I_2 = (0.965 + 0.960)/2 = 0.96$$
$$\text{Index for quarter 3} = I_3 = (1.136 + 1.127)/2 = 1.13$$
$$\text{Index for quarter 4} = I_4 = (1.051 + 1.063)/2 = 1.06$$

The sum of these indices should be the number of seasons (4) since an average season should have an index of 1. In this example, the sum is 4. If the sum were not 4, an adjustment would be made. We would multiply each index by 4 and divide this by the sum of the indices.

Steps Used to Compute Seasonal Indices Based on CMAs

1. Compute a CMA for each observation (where possible).
2. Compute seasonal ratio = Observation/CMA for that observation.
3. Average seasonal ratios to get seasonal indices.
4. If seasonal indices do not add to the number of seasons, multiply each index by (Number of seasons)/(Sum of the indices).

Figure 5 provides a scatterplot of the Turner Industries data and the CMAs. Notice that the plot of the CMAs is much smoother than the original data. A definite trend is apparent in the data.

FIGURE 5

Scatterplot of Turner Industries Sales and Centered Moving Average

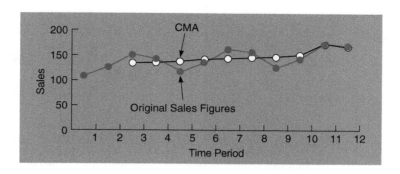

The Decomposition Method of Forecasting with Trend and Seasonal Components

The process of isolating linear trend and seasonal factors to develop more accurate forecasts is called **decomposition**. The first step is to compute seasonal indices for each season as we have done with the Turner Industries data. Then, the data are deseasonalized by dividing each number by its seasonal index, as shown in Table 12.

A trend line is then found using the **deseasonalized data**. Using computer software with this data, we have[*]

$$b_1 = 2.34$$
$$b_0 = 124.78$$

The trend equation is

$$\hat{Y} = 124.78 + 2.34X$$

where

$$X = \text{time}$$

This equation is used to develop the forecast based on trend, and the result is multiplied by the appropriate seasonal index to make a seasonal adjustment. For the Turner Industries data,

TABLE 12

Deseasonalized Data for Turner Industries

SALES ($1,000,000s)	SEASONAL INDEX	DESEASONALIZED SALES ($1,000,000s)
108	0.85	127.059
125	0.96	130.208
150	1.13	132.743
141	1.06	133.019
116	0.85	136.471
134	0.96	139.583
159	1.13	140.708
152	1.06	143.396
123	0.85	144.706
142	0.96	147.917
168	1.13	148.673
165	1.06	155.660

---

[*]If you do the calculations by hand, the numbers may differ slightly from these due to rounding.

the forecast for the first quarter of year 4 (time period $X = 13$ and seasonal index $I_1 = 0.85$) would be found as follows:

$$\hat{Y} = 124.78 + 2.34X$$
$$= 124.78 + 2.34(13)$$
$$= 155.2 \text{ (forecast before adjustment for seasonality)}$$

We multiply this by the seasonal index for quarter 1 and we get

$$\hat{Y} \times I_1 = 155.2 \times 0.85 = 131.92$$

Using this same procedure, we find the forecasts for quarters 2, 3, and 4 of the next year to be 151.24, 180.66, and 171.95, respectively.

Steps to Develop a Forecast Using the Decomposition Method

1. Compute seasonal indices using CMAs.
2. Deseasonalize the data by dividing each number by its seasonal index.
3. Find the equation of a trend line using the deseasonalized data.
4. Forecast for future periods using the trend line.
5. Multiply the trend line forecast by the appropriate seasonal index.

Most forecasting software, including Excel QM and QM for Windows, includes the decomposition method as one of the available techniques. This will automatically compute the CMAs, deseasonalize the data, develop the trend line, make the forecast using the trend equation, and adjust the final forecast for seasonality.

The following example provides another application of this process. The seasonal indices and trend line have already been computed using the decomposition process.

SAN DIEGO HOSPITAL EXAMPLE A San Diego hospital used 66 months of adult inpatient hospital days to reach the following equation:

$$\hat{Y} = 8{,}091 + 21.5X$$

where

$$\hat{Y} = \text{forecast patient days}$$
$$X = \text{time, in months}$$

Based on this model, the hospital forecasts patient days for the next month (period 67) to be

$$\text{Patient days} = 8{,}091 + (21.5)(67) = 9{,}532 \text{ (trend only)}$$

As well as this model recognized the slight upward trend line in the demand for inpatient services, it ignored the seasonality that the administration knew to be present. Table 13 provides seasonal indices based on the same 66 months. Such seasonal data, by the way, were found to be typical of hospitals nationwide. Note that January, March, July, and August seem to exhibit

TABLE 13

Seasonal Indices for Adult Inpatient Days at San Diego Hospital

MONTH	SEASONALITY INDEX	MONTH	SEASONALITY INDEX
January	1.0436	July	1.0302
February	0.9669	August	1.0405
March	1.0203	September	0.9653
April	1.0087	October	1.0048
May	0.9935	November	0.9598
June	0.9906	December	0.9805

Source: W. E. Sterk and E. G. Shryock. "Modern Methods Improve Hospital Forecasting," *Healthcare Financial Management* (March 1987): 97. Reprinted with permission of author.

significantly higher patient days on average, while February, September, November, and December experience lower patient days.

To correct the time-series extrapolation for seasonality, the hospital multiplied the monthly forecast by the appropriate seasonality index. Thus, for period 67, which was a January,

$$\text{Patient days} = (9{,}532)(1.0436) = 9{,}948 \text{ (trend and seasonal)}$$

Using this method, patient days were forecasted for January through June (periods 67 through 72) as 9,948, 9,236, 9,768, 9,678, 9,554, and 9,547. This study led to better forecasts as well as to more accurate forecast budgets.

USING EXCEL QM FOR DECOMPOSITION In Excel QM, to access the decomposition procedure, go to the *Add-Ins* tab and click *Excel QM—Forecasting—Decomposition*, and the initialization window will open. Input the relevant information, as illustrated in Program 6A, and the spreadsheet will be initialized for the size of problem specified. Enter the past periods of data, as shown in Program 6B, and the results will appear.

USING QM FOR WINDOWS FOR DECOMPOSITION QM for Windows can also be used for the decomposition method of forecasting. See Appendix 1 for details.

Using Regression with Trend and Seasonal Components

Multiple regression can be used to develop an additive decomposition model.

Multiple regression may be used to forecast with both trend and seasonal components present in a time series. One independent variable is time, and other independent variables are dummy variables to indicate the season. If we forecast quarterly data, there are four categories (quarters) so we would use three dummy variables. The basic model is an additive decomposition model and is expressed as follows:

$$\hat{Y} = a + b_1 X_1 + b_2 X_2 + b_3 X_3 + b_4 X_4$$

where

$$X_1 = \text{ time period}$$
$$X_2 = 1 \text{ if quarter 2}$$
$$\quad = 0 \text{ otherwise}$$
$$X_3 = 1 \text{ if quarter 3}$$
$$\quad = 0 \text{ otherwise}$$
$$X_4 = 1 \text{ if quarter 4}$$
$$\quad = 0 \text{ otherwise}$$

PROGRAM 6A

Initialization Screen for the Decomposition Method in Excel QM

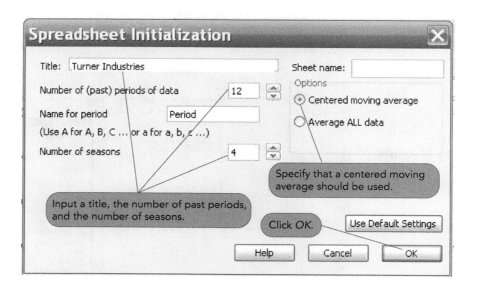

PROGRAM 6B

Turner Industries Forecast Using the Decomposition Method in Excel QM

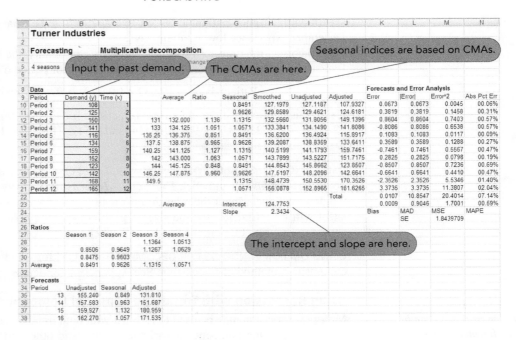

If $X_2 = X_3 = X_4 = 0$, then the quarter would be quarter 1. It is an arbitrary choice as to which of the quarters would not have a specific dummy variable associated with it. The forecasts will be the same regardless of which quarter does not have a specific dummy variable.

Program 7A provides the Excel input, and Program 7B provides the Excel output for the Turner Industries example. You can see how the data is input, and the regression equation (with coefficients rounded) is

$$\hat{Y} = 104.1 + 2.3X_1 + 15.7X_2 + 38.7X_3 + 30.1X_4$$

If this is used to forecast sales in the first quarter of the next year, we get

$$\hat{Y} = 104.1 + 2.3(13) + 15.7(0) + 38.7(0) + 30.1(0) = 134$$

For quarter 2 of the next year, we get

$$\hat{Y} = 104.1 + 2.3(14) + 15.7(1) + 38.7(0) + 30.1(0) = 152$$

Notice these are not the same values we obtained using the multiplicative decomposition method. We could compare the MAD or MSE for each method and choose the one that is better.

PROGRAM 7A

Excel Input for the Turner Industries Example Using Multiple Regression

	A	B	C	D	E	F	G
1	Year	Quarter	Sales	Time Peri	X2 Qtr 2	X3 Qtr 3	X4 Qtr 4
2	1	1	108	1	0	0	0
3		2	125	2	1	0	0
4		3	150	3	0	1	0
5		4	141	4	0	0	1
6	2	1	116	5	0	0	0
7		2	134	6	1	0	0
8		3	159	7	0	1	0
9		4	152	8	0	0	1
10	3	1	123	9	0	0	0
11		2	142	10	1	0	0
12		3	168	11	0	1	0
13		4	165	12	0	0	1

PROGRAM 7B

Excel Output for the Turner Industries Example Using Multiple Regression

	A	B	C	D	E	F	G	H	I
1	Year	Quarter	Sales	X1 Time Period	X2 Qtr 2	X3 Qtr 3	X4 Qtr4		
2	1	1	108	1	0	0	0		
3		2	125	2	1	0	0		
4		3	150	3	0	1	0		
5		4	141	4	0	0	1		
6	2	1	116	5	0	0	0		
7		2	134	6	1	0	0		
8		3	159	7	0	1	0		
9		4	152	8	0	0	1		
10	3	1	123	9	0	0	0		
11		2	142	10	1	0	0		
12		3	168	11	0	1	0		
13		4	165	12	0	0	1		
14									
15	SUMMARY OUTPUT								
16									
17	*Regression Statistics*								
18	Multiple R	0.99718							
19	R Square	0.99436							
20	Adjusted R	0.99114							
21	Standard E	1.83225							
22	Observation	12							
23									
24	ANOVA								
25		*df*	*SS*	*MS*	*F*	*Significance F*			
26	Regression	4	4144.75	1.0362E+03	3.0865E+02	6.0284E-08			
27	Residual	7	23.5	3.3571E+00					
28	Total	11	4168.25						
29									
30		*Coefficient*	*standard Err*	*t Stat*	*p-value*	*Lower 95%*	*Upper 95%*	*Lower 95.0%*	*Upper 95.0%*
31	Intercept	104.1042	1.3322	78.1449	0.0000	100.9540	107.2543	100.9540	107.2543
32	X1 Time Pe	2.3125	0.1619	14.2791	0.0000	1.9296	2.6954	1.9296	2.6954
33	X2 Qtr 2	15.6875	1.5048	10.4252	0.0000	12.1293	19.2457	12.1293	19.2457
34	X3 Qtr 3	38.7083	1.5307	25.2882	0.0000	35.0888	42.3278	35.0888	42.3278
35	X4 Qtr4	30.0625	1.5729	19.1123	0.0000	26.3431	33.7819	26.3431	33.7819

Quarter 1 is indicated by letting $X_2 = X_3 = X_4 = 0$.

IN ACTION **Forecasting at Disney World**

When the Disney chairman receives a daily report from his main theme parks in Orlando, Florida, the report contains only two numbers: the *forecast* of yesterday's attendance at the parks (Magic Kingdom, Epcot, Fort Wilderness, Hollywood Studios (formerly MGM Studios), Animal Kingdom, Typhoon Lagoon, and Blizzard Beach) and the actual attendance. An error close to zero (using MAPE as the measure) is expected. The chairman takes his forecasts very seriously.

The forecasting team at Disney World doesn't just do a daily prediction, however, and the chairman is not its only customer. It also provides daily, weekly, monthly, annual, and 5-year forecasts to the labor management, maintenance, operations, finance, and park scheduling departments. It uses judgmental models, econometric models, moving average models, and regression analysis. The team's annual forecast of total volume, conducted in 1999 for the year 2000, resulted in a MAPE of 0.

With 20% of Disney World's customers coming from outside the United States, its econometric model includes such variables as consumer confidence and the gross domestic product of seven countries. Disney also surveys one million people each year to examine their future travel plans and their experiences at the parks. This helps forecast not only attendance, but behavior at each ride (how long people will wait and how many times they will ride). Inputs to the monthly forecasting model include airline specials, speeches by the chair of the Federal reserve, and Wall Street trends. Disney even monitors 3,000 school districts inside and outside the United States for holiday/vacation schedules.

Source: Based on J. Newkirk and M. Haskell. "Forecasting in the Service Sector," presentation at the 12th Annual Meeting of the Production and Operations Management Society. April 1, 2001, Orlando, FL.

6   Monitoring and Controlling Forecasts

After a forecast has been completed, it is important that it not be forgotten. No manager wants to be reminded when his or her forecast is horribly inaccurate, but a firm needs to determine why the actual demand (or whatever variable is being examined) differed significantly from that projected.[*]

---

[*] If the forecaster is accurate, he or she usually makes sure that everyone is aware of his or her talents. Very seldom does one read articles in *Fortune, Forbes,* or the *Wall Street Journal,* however, about money managers who are consistently off by 25% in their stock market forecasts.

A tracking signal measures how well predictions fit actual data.

One way to monitor forecasts to ensure that they are performing well is to employ a **tracking signal**. A tracking signal is a measurement of how well the forecast is predicting actual values. As forecasts are updated every week, month, or quarter, the newly available demand data are compared to the forecast values.

The tracking signal is computed as the **running sum of the forecast errors (RSFE)** divided by the mean absolute deviation:

$$\text{Tracking signal} = \frac{\text{RSFE}}{\text{MAD}} \tag{13}$$

$$= \frac{\sum(\text{forecast error})}{\text{MAD}}$$

where

$$\text{MAD} = \frac{\sum|\text{forecast error}|}{n}$$

as seen earlier in Equation 1.

Positive tracking signals indicate that demand is greater than the forecast. Negative signals mean that demand is less than forecast. A good tracking signal—that is, one with a low RSFE—has about as much positive error as it has negative error. In other words, small deviations are okay, but the positive and negative deviations should balance so that the tracking signal centers closely around zero.

Setting tracking limits is a matter of setting reasonable values for upper and lower limits.

When tracking signals are calculated, they are compared with predetermined control limits. When a tracking signal exceeds an upper or lower limit, a signal is tripped. This means that there is a problem with the forecasting method, and management may want to reevaluate the way it forecasts demand. Figure 6 shows the graph of a tracking signal that is exceeding the range of acceptable variation. If the model being used is exponential smoothing, perhaps the smoothing constant needs to be readjusted.

How do firms decide what the upper and lower tracking limits should be? There is no single answer, but they try to find reasonable values—in other words, limits not so low as to be triggered with every small forecast error and not so high as to allow bad forecasts to be regularly overlooked. George Plossl and Oliver Wight, two inventory control experts, suggested using maximums of ±4 MADs for high-volume stock items and ±8 MADs for lower-volume items.[*]

Other forecasters suggest slightly lower ranges. One MAD is equivalent to approximately 0.8 standard deviation, so that ±2 MADs = 1.6 standard deviations, ±3 MADs = 2.4 standard deviations, and ±4 MADs = 3.2 standard deviations. This suggests that for a forecast to be "in

FIGURE 6
Plot of Tracking Signals

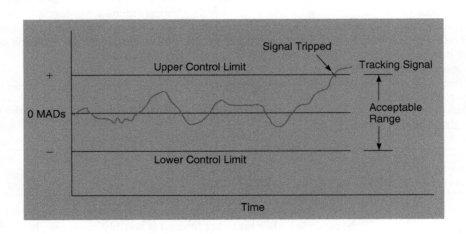

---

[*]See G. W. Plossl and O. W. Wight. *Production and Inventory Control.* Upper Saddle River, NJ: Prentice Hall, 1967.

control," 89% of the errors are expected to fall within ± 2 MADs, 98% within ± 3 MADs, or 99.9% within ± 4 MADs whenever the errors are approximately normally distributed.[*]

KIMBALL'S BAKERY EXAMPLE Here is an example that shows how the tracking signal and RSFE can be computed. Kimball's Bakery's quarterly sales of croissants (in thousands), as well as forecast demand and error computations, are in the following table. The objective is to compute the tracking signal and determine whether forecasts are performing adequately.

TIME PERIOD	FORECAST DEMAND	ACTUAL DEMAND	ERROR	RSFE	|FORECAST ERROR|	CUMULATIVE ERROR	MAD	TRACKING SIGNAL
1	100	90	−10	−10	10	10	10.0	−1
2	100	95	−5	−15	5	15	7.5	−2
3	100	115	+15	0	15	30	10.0	0
4	110	100	−10	−10	10	40	10.0	−1
5	110	125	+15	+5	15	55	11.0	+0.5
6	110	140	+30	+35	30	85	14.2	+2.5

In period 6, the calculations are

$$\text{MAD} = \frac{\sum |\text{forecast error}|}{n} = \frac{85}{6}$$
$$= 14.2$$

$$\text{Tracking signal} = \frac{\text{RSFE}}{\text{MAD}} = \frac{35}{14.2}$$
$$= 2.5 \text{ MADs}$$

This tracking signal is within acceptable limits. We see that it drifted from −2.0 MADs to +2.5 MADs.

Adaptive Smoothing

A lot of research has been published on the subject of adaptive forecasting. This refers to computer monitoring of tracking signals and self-adjustment if a signal passes its preset limit. In exponential smoothing, the α and β coefficients are first selected based on values that minimize error forecasts and are then adjusted accordingly whenever the computer notes an errant tracking signal. This is called **adaptive smoothing**.

Summary

Forecasts are a critical part of a manager's function. Demand forecasts drive the production, capacity, and scheduling systems in a firm and affect the financial, marketing, and personnel planning functions.

In this chapter we introduced three types of forecasting models: time series, causal, and qualitative. Moving averages, exponential smoothing, trend projection, and decomposition time-series models were developed. Regression and multiple regression models were recognized as causal models. Four qualitative models were briefly discussed. In addition, we explained the use of scatter diagrams and measures of forecasting accuracy. In future chapters you will see the usefulness of these techniques in determining values for the various decision-making models.

---

[*]To prove these three percentages to yourself, just set up a normal curve for ± 1.6 standard deviations (Z values). Using the normal table in Appendix A, you find that the area under that the curve is 0.89. This represents ± 2 MADs. Similarly, ± 3 MADs = 2.4 standard deviations encompasses 98% of the area, and so on for ± 4 MADs.

As we learned in this chapter, no forecasting method is perfect under all conditions. Even when management has found a satisfactory approach, it must still monitor and control its forecasts to make sure that errors do not get out of hand. Forecasting can often be a very challenging but rewarding part of managing.

Glossary

Adaptive Smoothing The process of automatically monitoring and adjusting the smoothing constants in an exponential smoothing model.

Bias A technique for determining the accuracy of a forecasting model by measuring the average error and its direction.

Causal Models Models that forecast using variables and factors in addition to time.

Centered Moving Average An average of the values centered at a particular point in time. This is used to compute seasonal indices when trend is present.

Decision-Making Group A group of experts in a Delphi technique that has the responsibility of making the forecast.

Decomposition A forecasting model that decomposes a time series into its seasonal and trend components.

Delphi A judgmental forecasting technique that uses decision makers, staff personnel, and respondents to determine a forecast.

Deseasonalized Data Time series data in which each value has been divided by its seasonal index to remove the effect of the seasonal component.

Deviation A term used in forecasting for error.

Error The difference between the actual value and the forecast value.

Exponential Smoothing A forecasting method that is a combination of the last forecast and the last observed value.

Holt's Method An exponential smoothing model that includes a trend component. This is also called a double exponential smoothing model or a second-order smoothing model.

Least Squares A procedure used in trend projection and regression analysis to minimize the squared distances between the estimated straight line and the observed values.

Mean Absolute Deviation (MAD) A technique for determining the accuracy of a forecasting model by taking the average of the absolute deviations.

Mean Absolute Percent Error (MAPE) A technique for determining the accuracy of a forecasting model by taking the average of the absolute errors as a percentage of the observed values.

Mean Squared Error (MSE) A technique for determining the accuracy of a forecasting model by taking the average of the squared error terms for a forecasting model.

Moving Average A forecasting technique that averages past values in computing the forecast.

Naïve Model A time-series forecasting model in which the forecast for next period is the actual value for the current period.

Qualitative Models Models that forecast using judgments, experience, and qualitative and subjective data.

Running Sum of Forecast Errors (RSFE) Used to develop a tracking signal for time-series forecasting models, this is a running total of the errors and may be positive or negative.

Scatter Diagrams Diagrams of the variable to be forecasted, plotted against another variable, such as time.

Seasonal Index An index number that indicates how a particular season compares with an average time period (with an index of 1 indicating an average season).

Smoothing Constant A value between 0 and 1 that is used in an exponential smoothing forecast.

Time-Series Models Models that forecast using only historical data.

Tracking Signal A measure of how well the forecast is predicting actual values.

Trend Projection The use of a trend line to forecast a time-series with trend present. A linear trend line is a regression line with time as the independent variable.

Weighted Moving Average A moving average forecasting method that places different weights on past values.

Key Equations

(1) $\text{MAD} = \dfrac{\sum |\text{forecast error}|}{n}$

A measure of overall forecast error called mean absolute deviation.

(2) $\text{MSE} = \dfrac{\sum (\text{error})^2}{n}$

A measure of forecast accuracy called mean squared error.

(3) $\text{MAPE} = \dfrac{\sum \left|\dfrac{\text{error}}{\text{actual}}\right|}{n} 100\%$

A measure of forecast accuracy called mean absolute percent error.

(4) $\text{Moving average forecast} = \dfrac{\text{Sum of demands in previous } n \text{ periods}}{n}$

An equation for computing a moving average forecast.

(5) $F_{t+1} = \dfrac{Y_t + Y_{t-1} + \cdots + Y_{t-n+1}}{n}$

A mathematical expression for a moving average forecast.

(6) $F_{t+1} = \dfrac{\Sigma(\text{Weight in period } i)(\text{Actual value in period } i)}{\Sigma(\text{Weights})}$

An equation for computing a weighted moving average forecast.

(7) $F_{t+1} = \dfrac{w_1 Y_t + w_2 Y_{t-1} + \cdots + w_n Y_{t-n+1}}{w_1 + w_2 + \cdots + w_n}$

A mathematical expression for a weighted moving average forecast.

(8) New forecast = Last period's forecast + α(Last period's actual demand − Last period's forecast)

An equation for computing an exponential smoothing forecast.

(9) $F_{t+1} = F_t + \alpha(Y_t - F_t)$

Equation 8 rewritten mathematically.

(10) $F_{t+1} = FIT_t + \alpha(Y_t - FIT_t)$

Equation to update the smoothed forecast (F_{t+1}) used in the trend adjusted exponential smoothing model.

(11) $T_{t+1} = T_t + \beta(F_{t+1} - FIT_t)$

Equation to update the smoothed trend value (T_{t+1}) used in the trend adjusted exponential smoothing model.

(12) $FIT_{t+1} = F_{t+1} + T_{t+1}$

Equation to develop forecast including trend (FIT) in the trend adjusted exponential smoothing model.

(13) $\text{Tracking signal} = \dfrac{\text{RSFE}}{\text{MAD}}$

$= \dfrac{\Sigma(\text{forecast error})}{\text{MAD}}$

An equation for monitoring forecasts with a tracking signal.

Solved Problems

Solved Problem 1

Demand for patient surgery at Washington General Hospital has increased steadily in the past few years, as seen in the following table:

YEAR	OUTPATIENT SURGERIES PERFORMED
1	45
2	50
3	52
4	56
5	58
6	—

The director of medical services predicted six years ago that demand in year 1 would be 42 surgeries. Using exponential smoothing with a weight of $\alpha = 0.20$, develop forecasts for years 2 through 6. What is the MAD?

Solution

YEAR	ACTUAL	FORECAST (SMOOTHED)	ERROR	|ERROR|
1	45	42	+3	3
2	50	$42.6 = 42 + 0.2(45 - 42)$	+7.4	7.4
3	52	$44.1 = 42.6 + 0.2(50 - 42.6)$	+7.9	7.9
4	56	$45.7 = 44.1 + 0.2(52 - 44.1)$	+10.3	10.3
5	58	$47.7 = 45.7 + 0.2(56 - 45.7)$	+10.3	10.3
6	—	$49.8 = 47.7 + 0.2(58 - 47.7)$	—	—

$$\text{MAD} = \dfrac{\Sigma|\text{errors}|}{n} = \dfrac{38.9}{5} = 7.78 \qquad\qquad 38.9$$

Solved Problem 2

Quarterly demand for Jaguar XJ8's at a New York auto dealership is forecast with the equation

$$\hat{Y} = 10 + 3X$$

where

X = time period (quarter): quarter 1 of last year = 0

quarter 2 of last year = 1

quarter 3 of last year = 2

quarter 4 of last year = 3

quarter 1 of this year = 4, and so on

and

$$\hat{Y} = \text{predicted quarterly demand}$$

The demand for luxury sedans is seasonal, and the indices for quarters 1, 2, 3, and 4 are 0.80, 1.00, 1.30, and 0.90, respectively. Using the trend equation, forecast the demand for each quarter of next year. Then adjust each forecast to adjust for seasonal (quarterly) variations.

Solution

Quarter 2 of this year is coded $X = 5$; quarter 3 of this year, $X = 6$; and quarter 4 of this year, $X = 7$. Hence, quarter 1 of next year is coded $X = 8$; quarter 2, $X = 9$; and so on.

$\hat{Y}$ (next year quarter 1) = 10 + (3)(8) = 34   Adjusted forecast = (0.80)(34) = 27.2

$\hat{Y}$ (next year quarter 2) = 10 + (3)(9) = 37   Adjusted forecast = (1.00)(37) = 37

$\hat{Y}$ (next year quarter 3) = 10 + (3)(10) = 40   Adjusted forecast = (1.30)(40) = 52

$\hat{Y}$ (next year quarter 4) = 10 + (3)(11) = 43   Adjusted forecast = (0.90)(43) = 38.7

Self-Test

- Before taking the self-test, refer to the learning objectives at the beginning of the chapter, the notes in the margins, and the glossary at the end of the chapter.
- Use the key at the end of the chapter to correct your answers.
- Restudy pages that correspond to any questions that you answered incorrectly or material you feel uncertain about.

1. Qualitative forecasting models include
   a. regression analysis.
   b. Delphi.
   c. time-series models.
   d. trend lines.
2. A forecasting model that only uses historical data for the variable being forecast is called a
   a. time-series model.
   b. causal model.
   c. Delphi model.
   d. variable model.
3. One example of a causal model is
   a. exponential smoothing.
   b. trend projections.
   c. moving averages.
   d. regression analysis.
4. Which of the following is a time series model?
   a. the Delphi model
   b. regression analysis
   c. exponential smoothing
   d. multiple regression
5. Which of the following is not a component of a time series?
   a. seasonality
   b. causal variations
   c. trend
   d. random variations
6. Which of the following may be negative?
   a. MAD
   b. bias
   c. MAPE
   d. MSE

7. When comparing several forecasting models to determine which one best fits a particular set of data, the model that should be selected is the one
   a. with the highest MSE.
   b. with the MAD closest to 1.
   c. with a bias of 0.
   d. with the lowest MAD.

8. In exponential smoothing, if you wish to give a significant weight to the most recent observations, then the smoothing constant should be
   a. close to 0.
   b. close to 1.
   c. close to 0.5.
   d. less than the error.

9. A trend equation is a regression equation in which
   a. there are multiple independent variables.
   b. the intercept and the slope are the same.
   c. the dependent variable is time.
   d. the independent variable is time.

10. Sales for a company are typically higher in the summer months than in the winter months. This variation would be called a
    a. trend.
    b. seasonal factor.
    c. random factor.
    d. cyclical factor.

11. A naïve forecast for monthly sales is equivalent to
    a. a one-month moving average model.
    b. an exponential smoothing model with $\alpha = 0$.
    c. a seasonal model in which the seasonal index is 1.
    d. none of the above.

12. If the seasonal index for January is 0.80, then
    a. January sales tend to be 80% higher than an average month.
    b. January sales tend to be 20% higher than an average month.
    c. January sales tend to be 80% lower than an average month.
    d. January sales tend to be 20% lower than an average month.

13. If both trend and seasonal components are present in a time-series, then the seasonal indices
    a. should be computed based on an overall average.
    b. should be computed based on CMAs.
    c. will all be greater than 1.
    d. should be ignored in developing the forecast.

14. Which of the following is used to alert the user of a forecasting model that a significant error occurred in one of the periods?
    a. a seasonal index
    b. a smoothing constant
    c. a tracking signal
    d. a regression coefficient

15. If the multiplicative decomposition model is used to forecast daily sales for a retail store, how many seasons will there be?
    a. 4
    b. 7
    c. 12
    d. 365

Discussion Questions and Problems

Discussion Questions

1 Describe briefly the steps used to develop a forecasting system.

2 What is a time-series forecasting model?

3 What is the difference between a causal model and a time-series model?

4 What is a qualitative forecasting model, and when is it appropriate?

5 What are some of the problems and drawbacks of the moving average forecasting model?

6 What effect does the value of the smoothing constant have on the weight given to the past forecast and the past observed value?

7 Describe briefly the Delphi technique.

8 What is MAD, and why is it important in the selection and use of forecasting models?

9 Explain how the number of season is determined when forecasting with a seasonal component.

10 A seasonal index may be less than one, equal to one, or greater than one. Explain what each of these values would mean.

11 Explain what would happen if the smoothing constant in an exponential smoothing model was equal to zero. Explain what would happen if the smoothing constant was equal to one.

12 Explain when a CMA (rather than an overall average) should be used in computing a seasonal index. Explain why this is necessary.

Problems

• 13 Develop a four-month moving average forecast for Wallace Garden Supply and compute the MAD.

Note: $\stackrel{Q}{=}$ means the problem may be solved with QM for Windows; ✖ means the problem may be solved with Excel QM; and ⚕ means the problem may be solved with QM for Windows and/or Excel QM.

A three-month moving average forecast was developed in the section on moving averages in Table 3.

• 14 Using MAD, determine whether the forecast in Problem 13 or the forecast in the section concerning Wallace Garden Supply is more accurate.

: 15 Data collected on the yearly demand for 50-pound bags of fertilizer at Wallace Garden Supply are shown in the following table. Develop a 3-year moving average to forecast sales. Then estimate demand again with a weighted moving average in which sales in the most recent year are given a weight of 2 and sales in the other 2 years are each given a weight of 1. Which method do you think is best?

YEAR	DEMAND FOR FERTILIZER (1,000S OF BAGS)
1	4
2	6
3	4
4	5
5	10
6	8
7	7
8	9
9	12
10	14
11	15

• 16 Develop a trend line for the demand for fertilizer in Problem 15, using any computer software.

: 17 In Problems 15 and 16, three different forecasts were developed for the demand for fertilizer. These three forecasts are a 3-year moving average, a weighted moving average, and a trend line. Which one would you use? Explain your answer.

: 18 Use exponential smoothing with a smoothing constant of 0.3 to forecast the demand for fertilizer given in Problem 15. Assume that last period's forecast for year 1 is 5,000 bags to begin the procedure. Would you prefer to use the exponential smoothing model or the weighted average model developed in Problem 15? Explain your answer.

: 19 Sales of Cool-Man air conditioners have grown steadily during the past 5 years:

YEAR	SALES
1	450
2	495
3	518
4	563
5	584
6	?

The sales manager had predicted, before the business started, that year 1's sales would be 410 air conditioners. Using exponential smoothing with a weight of $\alpha = 0.30$, develop forecasts for years 2 through 6.

• 20 Using smoothing constants of 0.6 and 0.9, develop forecasts for the sales of Cool-Man air conditioners (see Problem 19).

: 21 What effect did the smoothing constant have on the forecast for Cool-Man air conditioners? (See Problems 19 and 20.) Which smoothing constant gives the most accurate forecast?

• 22 Use a three-year moving average forecasting model to forecast the sales of Cool-Man air conditioners (see Problem 19).

• 23 Using the trend projection method, develop a forecasting model for the sales of Cool-Man air conditioners (see Problem 19).

• 24 Would you use exponential smoothing with a smoothing constant of 0.3, a 3-year moving average, or a trend to predict the sales of Cool-Man air conditioners? Refer to Problems 19, 22, and 23.

25 Sales of industrial vacuum cleaners at R. Lowenthal Supply Co. over the past 13 months are as follows:

SALES ($1,000s)	MONTH	SALES ($1,000s)	MONTH
11	January	14	August
14	February	17	September
16	March	12	October
10	April	14	November
15	May	16	December
17	June	11	January
11	July		

(a) Using a moving average with three periods, determine the demand for vacuum cleaners for next February.

(b) Using a weighted moving average with three periods, determine the demand for vacuum cleaners for February. Use 3, 2, and 1 for the weights of the most recent, second most recent, and third most recent periods, respectively. For example, if you were forecasting the demand for February, November would have a weight of 1, December would have a weight of 2, and January would have a weight of 3.

(c) Evaluate the accuracy of each of these methods.

(d) What other factors might R. Lowenthal consider in forecasting sales?

: 26   Passenger miles flown on Northeast Airlines, a commuter firm serving the Boston hub, are as follows for the past 12 weeks:

WEEK	ACTUAL PASSENGER MILES (1,000S)	WEEK	ACTUAL PASSENGER MILES (1,000S)
1	17	7	20
2	21	8	18
3	19	9	22
4	23	10	20
5	18	11	15
6	16	12	22

(a) Assuming an initial forecast for week 1 of 17,000 miles, use exponential smoothing to compute miles for weeks 2 through 12. Use $\alpha = 0.2$.

(b) What is the MAD for this model?

(c) Compute the RSFE and tracking signals. Are they within acceptable limits?

: 27   Emergency calls to Winter Park, Florida's 911 system, for the past 24 weeks are as follows:

WEEK	CALLS	WEEK	CALLS	WEEK	CALLS
1	50	9	35	17	55
2	35	10	20	18	40
3	25	11	15	19	35
4	40	12	40	20	60
5	45	13	55	21	75
6	35	14	35	22	50
7	20	15	25	23	40
8	30	16	55	24	65

(a) Compute the exponentially smoothed forecast of calls for each week. Assume an initial forecast of 50 calls in the first week and use $\alpha = 0.1$. What is the forecast for the 25th week?

(b) Reforecast each period using $\alpha = 0.6$.

(c) Actual calls during the 25th week were 85. Which smoothing constant provides a superior forecast?

: 28   Using the 911 call data in Problem 27, forecast calls for weeks 2 through 25 using $\alpha = 0.9$. Which is best? (Again, assume that actual calls in week 25 were 85 and use an initial forecast of 50 calls.)

: 29   Consulting income at Kate Walsh Associates for the period February–July has been as follows:

MONTH	INCOME ($1,000S)
February	70.0
March	68.5
April	64.8
May	71.7
June	71.3
July	72.8

Use exponential smoothing to forecast August's income. Assume that the initial forecast for February is $65,000. The smoothing constant selected is $\alpha = 0.1$.

: 30   Resolve Problem 29 with $\alpha = 0.3$. Using MAD, which smoothing constant provides a better forecast?

: 31   A major source of revenue in Texas is a state sales tax on certain types of goods and services. Data are compiled and the state comptroller uses them to project future revenues for the state budget. One particular category of goods is classified as Retail Trade. Four years of quarterly data (in $millions) for one particular area of southeast Texas follow:

QUARTER	YEAR 1	YEAR 2	YEAR 3	YEAR 4
1	218	225	234	250
2	247	254	265	283
3	243	255	264	289
4	292	299	327	356

(a) Compute seasonal indices for each quarter based on a CMA.

(b) Deseasonalize the data and develop a trend line on the deseasonalized data.

(c) Use the trend line to forecast the sales for each quarter of year 5.

(d) Use the seasonal indices to adjust the forecasts found in part (c) to obtain the final forecasts.

: 32   Using the data in Problem 31, develop a multiple regression model to predict sales (both trend and seasonal components), using dummy variables to incorporate the seasonal factor into the model. Use this model to predict sales for each quarter of the next year. Comment on the accuracy of this model.

: 33   Trevor Harty, an avid mountain biker, always wanted to start a business selling top-of-the-line mountain bikes and other outdoor supplies. A little over 6 years ago, he and a silent partner opened a store called Hale and Harty Trail Bikes and Supplies. Growth was rapid in the first 2 years, but since that time, growth in sales has slowed a bit, as expected. The quarterly sales (in $1,000s) for the past 4 years are shown in the table below:

	YEAR 1	YEAR 2	YEAR 3	YEAR 4
QUARTER 1	274	282	282	296
QUARTER 2	172	178	182	210
QUARTER 3	130	136	134	158
QUARTER 4	162	168	170	182

(a) Develop a trend line using the data in the table. Use this to forecast sales for each quarter of year 5. What does the slope of this line indicate?

(b) Use the multiplicative decomposition model to incorporate both trend and seasonal components into the forecast. What does the slope of this line indicate?

(c) Compare the slope of the trend line in part *a* to the slope in the trend line for the decomposition model that was based on the deseasonalized sales figures. Discuss why these are so different and explain which one is best to use.

: 34 The unemployment rates in the United States during a 10-year period are given in the following table. Use exponential smoothing to find the best forecast for next year. Use smoothing constants of 0.2, 0.4, 0.6, and 0.8. Which one had the lowest MAD?

YEAR	1	2	3	4	5	6	7	8	9	10
Unemployment rate (%)	7.2	7.0	6.2	5.5	5.3	5.5	6.7	7.4	6.8	6.1

• 35 Management of Davis's Department Store has used time-series extrapolation to forecast retail sales for the next four quarters. The sales estimates are $100,000, $120,000, $140,000, and $160,000 for the respective quarters before adjusting for seasonality. Seasonal indices for the four quarters have been found to be 1.30, 0.90, 0.70, and 1.10, respectively. Compute a seasonalized or adjusted sales forecast.

: 36 In the past, Judy Holmes's tire dealership sold an average of 1,000 radials each year. In the past two years, 200 and 250, respectively, were sold in fall, 350 and 300 in winter, 150 and 165 in spring, and 300 and 285 in summer. With a major expansion planned, Judy projects sales next year to increase to 1,200 radials. What will the demand be each season?

: 37 The following table provides the Dow Jones Industrial Average (DJIA) opening index value on the first working day of 1991–2010:

Develop a trend line and use it to predict the opening DJIA index value for years 2011, 2012, and 2013. Find the MSE for this model.

YEAR	DJIA	YEAR 2	DJIA
2010	10,431	2000	11,502
2009	8,772	1999	9,213
2008	13,262	1998	7,908
2007	12,460	1997	6,448
2006	10,718	1996	5,117
2005	10,784	1995	3,834
2004	10,453	1994	3,754
2003	8,342	1993	3,301
2002	10,022	1992	3,169
2001	10,791	1991	2,634

: 38 Using the DJIA data in Problem 37, use exponential smooth with trend adjustment to forecast the opening DJIA value for 2011. Use $\alpha = 0.8$ and $\beta = 0.2$. Compare the MSE for this technique with the MSE for the trend line.

: 39 Refer to the DJIA data in Problem 37.
(a) Use an exponential smoothing model with a smoothing constant of 0.4 to predict the opening DJIA index value for 2011. Find the MSE for this.
(b) Use QM for Windows or Excel and find the smoothing constant that would provide the lowest MSE.

: 40 The following table gives the average monthly exchange rate between the U.S. dollar and the euro for 2009. It shows that 1 euro was equivalent to 1.324 U.S. dollars in January 2009. Develop a trend line that could be used to predict the exchange rate for 2010. Use this model to predict the exchange rate for January 2010 and February 2010.

MONTH	EXCHANGE RATE
January	1.324
February	1.278
March	1.305
April	1.320
May	1.363
June	1.402
July	1.409
August	1.427
September	1.456
October	1.482
November	1.491
December	1.461

: 41 For the data in Problem 40, develop an exponential smoothing model with a smoothing constant of 0.3. Using the MSE, compare this with the model in Problem 40.

Internet Homework Problems

See our Internet home page, at **www.pearsonhighered.com/render**, for additional homework problems, Problems 42 to 50.

Case Study

Forecasting Attendance at SWU Football Games

Southwestern University (SWU), a large state college in Stephenville, Texas, 30 miles southwest of the Dallas/Fort Worth metroplex, enrolls close to 20,000 students. In a typical town–gown relationship, the school is a dominant force in the small city, with more students during fall and spring than permanent residents.

A longtime football powerhouse, SWU is a member of the Big Eleven conference and is usually in the top 20 in college football rankings. To bolster its chances of reaching the elusive and long-desired number-one ranking, in 2005 SWU hired the legendary Bo Pitterno as its head coach. Although the number-one ranking remained out of reach, attendance at the five Saturday home games each year increased. Prior to Pitterno's arrival, attendance generally averaged 25,000 to 29,000 per game. Season ticket sales bumped up by 10,000 just with the announcement of the new coach's arrival. Stephenville and SWU were ready to move to the big time!

The immediate issue facing SWU, however, was not NCAA ranking. It was capacity. The existing SWU stadium, built in 1953, has seating for 54,000 fans. The following table indicates attendance at each game for the past six years.

One of Pitterno's demands upon joining SWU had been a stadium expansion, or possibly even a new stadium. With attendance increasing, SWU administrators began to face the issue head-on. Pitterno had wanted dormitories solely for his athletes in the stadium as an additional feature of any expansion.

SWU's president, Dr. Marty Starr, decided it was time for his vice president of development to forecast when the existing stadium would "max out." He also sought a revenue projection, assuming an average ticket price of $20 in 2011 and a 5% increase each year in future prices.

Discussion Questions

1. Develop a forecasting model, justify its selection over other techniques, and project attendance through 2012.
2. What revenues are to be expected in 2011 and 2012?
3. Discuss the school's options.

Southwestern University Football Game Attendance, 2005–2010

GAME	2005 ATTENDEES	OPPONENT	2006 ATTENDEES	OPPONENT	2007 ATTENDEES	OPPONENT
1	34,200	Baylor	36,100	Oklahoma	35,900	TCU
2*	39,800	Texas	40,200	Nebraska	46,500	Texas Tech
3	38,200	LSU	39,100	UCLA	43,100	Alaska
4**	26,900	Arkansas	25,300	Nevada	27,900	Arizona
5	35,100	USC	36,200	Ohio State	39,200	Rice

GAME	2008 ATTENDEES	OPPONENT	2009 ATTENDEES	OPPONENT	2010 ATTENDEES	OPPONENT
1	41,900	Arkansas	42,500	Indiana	46,900	LSU
2*	46,100	Missouri	48,200	North Texas	50,100	Texas
3	43,900	Florida	44,200	Texas A&M	45,900	Prairie View A&M
4**	30,100	Miami	33,900	Southern	36,300	Montana
5	40,500	Duke	47,800	Oklahoma	49,900	Arizona State

*Homecoming games

**During the fourth week of each season, Stephenville hosted a hugely popular southwestern crafts festival. This event brought tens of thousands of tourists to the town, especially on weekends, and had an obvious negative impact on game attendance.

Source: J. Heizer and B. Render. *Operations Management*, 6th ed. Upper Saddle River, NJ: Prentice Hall, 2001, p. 126.

Case Study

Forecasting Monthly Sales

For years The Glass Slipper restaurant has operated in a resort community near a popular ski area of New Mexico. The restaurant is busiest during the first 3 months of the year, when the ski slopes are crowded and tourists flock to the area.

When James and Deena Weltee built The Glass Slipper, they had a vision of the ultimate dining experience. As the view of surrounding mountains was breathtaking, a high priority was placed on having large windows and providing a spectacular view from anywhere inside the restaurant. Special attention was also given to the lighting, colors, and overall ambiance, resulting in a truly magnificent experience for all who came to enjoy gourmet dining. Since its opening, The Glass Slipper has developed and maintained a reputation as one of the "must visit" places in that region of New Mexico.

While James loves to ski and truly appreciates the mountains and all that they have to offer, he also shares Deena's dream of retiring to a tropical paradise and enjoying a more relaxed lifestyle on the beach. After some careful analysis of their financial condition, they knew that retirement was many years away. Nevertheless, they were hatching a plan to bring them closer to their dream. They decided to sell The Glass Slipper and open a bed and breakfast on a beautiful beach in Mexico. While this would mean that work was still in their future, they could wake up in the morning to the sight of the palm trees blowing in the wind and the waves lapping at the shore. They also knew that hiring the right manager would allow James and Deena the time to begin a semi-retirement in a corner of paradise.

To make this happen, James and Deena would have to sell The Glass Slipper for the right price. The price of the business would be based on the value of the property and equipment, as well as projections of future income. A forecast of sales for the next year is needed to help in the determination of the value of the restaurant. Monthly sales for each of the past 3 years are provided in Table 14.

Discussion Questions

1. Prepare a graph of the data. On this same graph, plot a 12-month moving average forecast. Discuss any apparent trend and seasonal patterns.
2. Use regression to develop a trend line that could be used to forecast monthly sales for the next year. Is the slope of this line consistent with what you observed in question 1? If not, discuss a possible explanation.
3. Use the multiplicative decomposition model on these data. Use this model to forecast sales for each month of the next year. Discuss why the slope of the trend equation with this model is so different from that of the trend equation in question 2.

TABLE 14
Monthly Revenue (in $1,000s)

MONTH	2008	2009	2010
January	438	444	450
February	420	425	438
March	414	423	434
April	318	331	338
May	306	318	331
June	240	245	254
July	240	255	264
August	216	223	231
September	198	210	224
October	225	233	243
November	270	278	289
December	315	322	335

Internet Case Study

See our Internet home page, at **www.pearsonhighered.com/render**, for the additional case study on Akron Zoological Park. This case involves forecasting attendance at Akron's zoo.

Bibliography

Berenson, Mark L., David M. Levine, and Timothy C. Kriehbiel. *Business Statistics: Concepts and Applications*, 10th ed. Upper Saddle River, NJ: Prentice Hall, 2006.

Billah, Baki, Maxwell L. King Ralph D. Snyder, and Anne B. Koehler. "Exponential Smoothing Model Selection for Forecasting," *International Journal of Forecasting* 22, 2, (April–June 2006): 239–247.

Black, Ken. *Business Statistics: For Contemporary Decision Making*, 6th ed. John Wiley & Sons, Inc., 2009.

Diebold, F. X. *Elements of Forecasting*, 2nd ed. Cincinnati: South-Western College Publishing, 2001.

Gardner, Everette Jr. "Exponential Smoothing: The State of the Art—Part II," *International Journal of Forecasting* 22, 4 (October 2006): 637–666.

Granger, Clive W., and J. M. Hashem Pesaran. "Economic and Statistical Measures of Forecast Accuracy," *Journal of Forecasting*, 19, 7 (December 2000): 537–560.

Hanke, J. E., and D. W. Wichern. *Business Forecasting*, 9th ed. Upper Saddle River, NJ: Prentice Hall, 2009.

Heizer, J., and B. Render. *Operations Management,* 9th ed. Upper Saddle River, NJ: Prentice Hall, 2008.

Hyndman, Rob J. "The Interaction Between Trend and Seasonality," *International Journal of Forecasting* 20, 4 (October–December 2004): 561–563.

Hyndman, Rob J., and Anne B. Koehler. "Another Look at Measures of Forecast Accuracy," *International Journal of Forecasting* 22, 4 (October 2006): 679–688.

Li, X. "An Intelligent Business Forecaster for Strategic Business Planning," *Journal of Forecasting* 18, 3 (May 1999): 181–205.

Meade, Nigel. "Evidence for the Selection of Forecasting Methods," *Journal of Forecasting* 19, 6 (November 2000): 515–535.

Snyder, Ralph D., and Roland G. Shami. "Exponential Smoothing of Seasonal Data: A Comparison," *Journal of Forecasting* 20, 3 (April 2001): 197–202.

Yurkiewicz, J. "Forecasting Software Survey," *OR/MS Today* 35, 3 (August 2008): 54–63.

Appendix 1 Forecasting with QM for Windows

In this section, we look at our other forecasting software package, QM for Windows. QM for Windows can project moving averages (both simple and weighted), do simple and trend-adjusted exponential smoothing, handle least squares trend projection, solve regression problems, and use the decomposition method.

To develop forecasts in QM for Windows, select *Module* on the toolbar and select *Forecasting*. Then either click the new document icon or click *File—New—Time Series Analysis* to enter a new time series problem. Specify the number of past observations and enter a title, if desired.

To illustrate QM for Windows, we will use the Port of Baltimore data from Table 5. The number of past observations was eight in that example. When you enter those data, the screen shown in Program 8A opens and allows for data input. Once the data is entered, click the arrow

PROGRAM 8A

QM for Windows Forecasting Methods

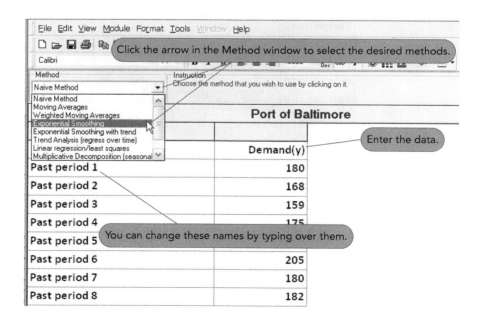

on the message box to see all the options and select the one desired. In selecting exponential smoothing for this example, a box appears where α (alpha) may be entered and a column where any previous forecasts (if available) may be entered, as shown in Program 8B. With other forecasting methods, other types of input boxes may appear. Click the *Solve* button, and the *Forecasting Results* screen appears, as shown in Program 8C. If you want to try a different value for α, click Edit to return to the input screen, where you can change α. Note that you can enter an initial forecast if desired, but the error analysis will begin with the first forecast generated by the computer. Any forecasts entered by the user are ignored in the error analysis.

Notice that additional output, including detailed results of the procedure and a graph, are available from the *Window* option in the toolbar once the problem has been solved. With exponential smoothing, one output is called *Errors as a function of alpha*. This will display the MAD and MSE for all values of α from 0 to 1, in increments of 0.01. You can simply scroll down this screen to find the value for α that minimizes the MAD or MSE.

For another example, we will use the decomposition method on the Turner Industries example from Table 10. Enter a time-series problem with 12 past periods of data and select *Multiplicative Decomposition* under *Method*. When this is done, additional input is needed, so indicate that there are four seasons, select *Centered Moving Average* as the basis for smoothing, and specify that the seasonal factors should not be rescaled, as shown in Program 9. This output screen provides both the unadjusted forecasts found using the trend equation on the deseasonalized data and the final or adjusted forecasts, which are found by multiplying the unadjusted forecast by the seasonal factor or index. Additional details can be seen by selecting *Details and Error Analysis* under *Window*.

PROGRAM 8B

Exponential Smoothing in the Port of Baltimore Example with QM for Windows

PROGRAM 8C

Exponential Smoothing in the Port of Baltimore Output with QM for Windows

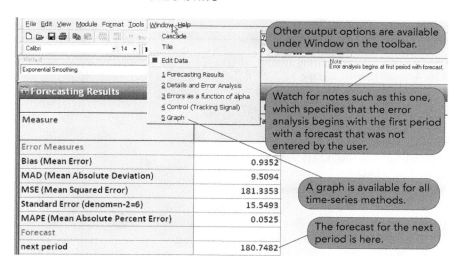

PROGRAM 9

QM for Windows Decomposition Output for the Turner Industries Example

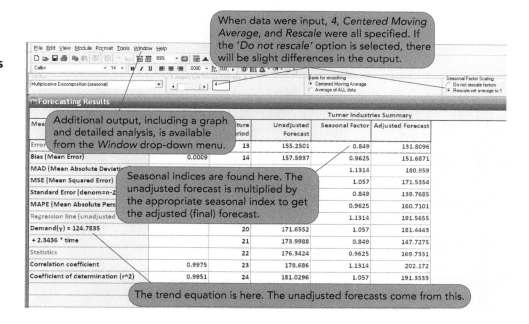

Solutions to Selected Problems

14 MAD = 6.48 for 3-month moving average; MAD = 7.78 for 4-month moving average

16 $Y = 2.22 + 1.05X$

18 Forecast for year 12 is 11.789; MAD = 2.437

20 Forecasts for year 6 are 565.6 and 581.4

22 Forecast for year 6 is 555

24 MAD = 5.6 for trend line; MAD = 74.56 for exponential smoothing; MAD = 67 for moving average

26 (b) MAD = 2.60; RSFE = 5.11 at week 10

28 MAD = 14.48

30 MAD = 3.34

34 $F_{11} = 6.26$; MAD = 0.58 for $\alpha = 0.8$ is lowest.

36 270, 390, 189, 351

Solutions to Self-Tests

1.	b
2.	a
3.	d
4.	c
5.	b
6.	b
7.	d
8.	b
9.	d
10.	b
11.	a
12.	d
13.	b
14.	c
15.	b

Inventory Control Models

LEARNING OBJECTIVES

After completing this chapter, students will be able to:

1. Understand the importance of inventory control.
2. Use inventory control models to determine how much to order or produce and when to order or produce.
3. Understand inventory models that allow quantity discounts.
4. Understand the use of safety stock with known and unknown stockout costs.
5. Understand the importance of ABC inventory analysis.
6. Use Excel to analyze a variety of inventory control models.

CHAPTER OUTLINE

Summary • Glossary • Solved Problems • Discussion Questions and Problems • Case Study: Sturdivant Sound Systems • Case Study: Martin-Pullin Bicycle Corporation • Internet Case Studies

1 Introduction

Inventory is one of the most expensive and important assets of many companies, representing as much as 50% of total invested capital. Managers have long recognized that good inventory control is crucial. On one hand, a firm can try to reduce costs by reducing on-hand inventory levels. On the other hand, customers become dissatisfied when frequent inventory outages, called **stockouts**, occur. Thus, companies must make the balance between low and high inventory levels. As you would expect, cost minimization is the major factor in obtaining this delicate balance.

Inventory **is any stored resource that is used to satisfy a current or future need.**

Inventory is any stored resource that is used to satisfy a current or future need. Raw materials, work-in-process, and finished goods are examples of inventory. Inventory levels for finished goods, such as clothes dryers, are a direct function of market demand. By using this demand information, it is possible to determine how much raw materials (e.g., sheet metal, paint, and electric motors in the case of clothes dryers) and work-in-process are needed to produce the finished product.

Every organization has some type of inventory planning and control system. A bank has methods to control its inventory of cash. A hospital has methods to control blood supplies and other important items. State and federal governments, schools, and virtually every manufacturing and production organization are concerned with inventory planning and control. Studying how organizations control their inventory is equivalent to studying how they achieve their objectives by supplying goods and services to their customers. Inventory is the common thread that ties all the functions and departments of the organization together.

Figure 1 illustrates the basic components of an inventory planning and control system. The *planning* phase involves primarily what inventory is to be stocked and how it is to be acquired (whether it is to be manufactured or purchased). This information is then used in *forecasting* demand for the inventory and in *controlling* inventory levels. The feedback loop in Figure 1 provides a way of revising the plan and forecast based on experiences and observation.

Through inventory planning, an organization determines what goods and/or services are to be produced. In cases of physical products, the organization must also determine whether to produce these goods or to purchase them from another manufacturer. When this has been determined, the next step is to forecast the demand. Many mathematical techniques can be used in forecasting demand for a particular product. The emphasis in this chapter is on inventory control—that is, how to maintain adequate inventory levels within an organization to support a production or procurement plan that will satisfy the forecasted demand.

In this chapter, we discuss several different inventory control models that are commonly used in practice. For each model, we provide examples of how they are analyzed. Although we show the equations needed to compute the relevant parameters for each model, we use Excel worksheets (included on this text's Companion Website) to actually calculate these values.

2 Importance of Inventory Control

There are five main uses of inventory.

Inventory control serves several important functions and adds a great deal of flexibility to the operation of a firm. Five main uses of inventory are as follows:

1. The decoupling function
2. Storing resources

FIGURE 1
Inventory Planning and Control

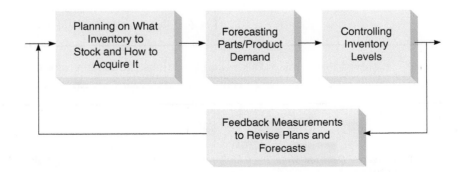

3. Irregular supply and demand
4. Quantity discounts
5. Avoiding stockouts and shortages

Decoupling Function

Inventory can act as a buffer.

One of the major functions of inventory is to decouple manufacturing processes within the organization. If a company did not store inventory, there could be many delays and inefficiencies. For example, when one manufacturing activity has to be completed before a second activity can be started, it could stop the entire process. However, stored inventory between processes could act as a buffer.

Storing Resources

Resources can be stored in work-in-process.

Agricultural and seafood products often have definite seasons over which they can be harvested or caught, but the demand for these products is somewhat constant during the year. In these and similar cases, inventory can be used to store these resources.

In a manufacturing process, raw materials can be stored by themselves, as work-in-process, or as finished products. Thus, if your company makes lawn mowers, you might obtain lawn mower tires from another manufacturer. If you have 400 finished lawn mowers and 300 tires in inventory, you actually have 1,900 tires stored in inventory. Three hundred tires are stored by themselves, and 1,600 (= 4 tires per lawn mower × 400 lawn mowers) tires are stored on the finished lawn mowers. In the same sense, labor can be stored in inventory. If you have 500 subassemblies and it takes 50 hours of labor to produce each assembly, you actually have 25,000 labor hours stored in inventory in the subassemblies. In general, any resource, physical or otherwise, can be stored in inventory.

Irregular Supply and Demand

Inventory helps when there is irregular supply or demand.

When the supply or demand for an inventory item is irregular, storing certain amounts in inventory can be important. If the greatest demand for Diet-Delight beverage is during the summer, the Diet-Delight company will have to make sure there is enough supply to meet this irregular demand. This might require that the company produce more of the soft drink in the winter than is actually needed in order to meet the winter demand. The inventory levels of Diet-Delight will gradually build up over the winter, but this inventory will be needed in the summer. The same is true for irregular *supplies*.

Quantity Discounts

Purchasing in large quantities may lower unit costs.

Another use of inventory is to take advantage of quantity discounts. Many suppliers offer discounts for large orders. For example, an electric jigsaw might normally cost $10 per unit. If you order 300 or more saws at one time, your supplier may lower the cost to $8.75. Purchasing in larger quantities can substantially reduce the cost of products. There are, however, some disadvantages of buying in larger quantities. You will have higher storage costs and higher costs due to spoilage, damaged stock, theft, insurance, and so on. Furthermore, if you invest in more inventory, you will have less cash to invest elsewhere.

Avoiding Stockouts and Shortages

Inventory can help avoid stockouts.

Another important function of inventory is to avoid shortages or stockouts. If a company is repeatedly out of stock, customers are likely to go elsewhere to satisfy their needs. Lost goodwill can be an expensive price to pay for not having the right item at the right time.

3 Inventory Control Decisions

Even though there are literally millions of different types of products manufactured in our society, there are only two fundamental decisions that you have to make when controlling inventory:

1. How much to order
2. When to order

TABLE 1
Inventory Cost Factors

ORDERING COST FACTORS	CARRYING COST FACTORS
Developing and sending purchase orders	Cost of capital
Processing and inspecting incoming inventory	Taxes
Bill paying	Insurance
Inventory inquiries	Spoilage
Utilities, phone bills, and so on for the purchasing department	Theft
Salaries and wages for purchasing department employees	Obsolescence
Supplies such as forms and paper for the purchasing department	Salaries and wages for warehouse employees
	Utilities and building costs for the warehouse
	Supplies such as forms and papers for the warehouse

The purpose of all inventory models is to minimize inventory costs.

The purpose of all inventory models is to determine how much to order and when to order. As you know, inventory fulfills many important functions in an organization. But as the inventory levels go up to provide these functions, the cost of storing and holding inventory also increases. Thus, we must reach a fine balance in establishing inventory levels. A major objective in controlling inventory is to minimize total inventory costs. Some of the most significant inventory costs are as follows:

Components of total cost.

1. Cost of the items
2. Cost of ordering
3. Cost of carrying, or holding, inventory
4. Cost of stockouts
5. Cost of safety stock, the additional inventory that may be held to help avoid stockouts

The inventory models discussed in the first part of this chapter assume that demand and the time it takes to receive an order are known and constant, and that no quantity discounts are given. When this is the case, the most significant costs are the cost of placing an order and the cost of holding inventory items over a period of time. Table 1 provides a list of important factors that make up these costs. Later in this chapter we discuss several more sophisticated inventory models.

4 Economic Order Quantity: Determining How Much to Order

The **economic order quantity (EOQ)** model is one of the oldest and most commonly known inventory control techniques. Research on its use dates back to a 1915 publication by Ford W. Harris. This model is still used by a large number of organizations today. This technique is relatively easy to use, but it makes a number of assumptions. Some of the more important assumptions follow:

Assumptions of the EOQ model.

1. Demand is known and constant.
2. The **lead time**—that is, the time between the placement of the order and the receipt of the order—is known and constant.
3. The receipt of inventory is instantaneous. In other words, the inventory from an order arrives in one batch, at one point in time.
4. Quantity discounts are not possible.
5. The only variable costs are the cost of placing an order, **ordering cost**, and the cost of holding or storing inventory over time, **carrying, or holding, cost**.
6. If orders are placed at the right time, stockouts and shortages can be avoided completely.

The inventory usage curve has a sawtooth shape in the EOQ model.

With these assumptions, inventory usage has a sawtooth shape, as in Figure 2. Here, Q represents the amount that is ordered. If this amount is 500 units, all 500 units arrive at one time

IN ACTION | Optimizing Inventory at Procter & Gamble

Procter & Gamble (P&G) is a world leader in consumer products with annual sales of over $76 billion. Managing inventory in such a large and complex organization requires making effective use of the right people, organizational structure, and tools. P&G's logistics planning personnel coordinate material flow, capacity, inventory, and logistics for the firm's extensive supply chain network, which comprises 145 P&G-owned manufacturing facilities, 300 contract manufacturers, and 6,900 unique product-category market combinations. Each supply chain requires effective management based on the latest available information, communication, and planning tools to handle complex challenges and trade-offs on issues such as production batch sizes, order policies, replenishment timing, new-product introductions, and assortment management.

Through the effective use of inventory optimization models, P&G has reduced its total inventory investment significantly. Spreadsheet-based inventory models that locally optimize different portions of the supply chain drive nearly 60 percent of P&G's business. For more complex supply chain networks (which drive about 30 percent of P&G's business), advanced multi-stage models yield additional average inventory reductions of 7 percent. P&G estimates that the use of these tools was instrumental in driving $1.5 billion in cash savings in 2009, while maintaining or increasing service levels.

Source: Based on I. Farasyn et al. "Inventory Optimization at Procter & Gamble: Achieving Real Benefits Through User Adoption of Inventory Tools," *Interfaces* 41, 1 (January–February 2011): 66–78.

when an order is received. Thus, the inventory level jumps from 0 to 500 units. In general, the inventory level increases from 0 to Q units when an order arrives.

Because demand is constant over time, inventory drops at a uniform rate over time. (Refer to the sloped line in Figure 2.) Another order is placed such that when the inventory level reaches 0, the new order is received and the inventory level again jumps to Q units, represented by the vertical lines. This process continues indefinitely over time.

Ordering and Inventory Costs

The objective of most inventory models is to minimize the **total cost**. With the assumptions just given, the significant costs are the ordering cost and the inventory carrying cost. All other costs, such as the cost of the inventory itself, are constant. Thus, if we minimize the sum of the ordering and carrying costs, we also minimize the total cost.

The objective of the simple EOQ model is to minimize ordering and carrying costs.

To help visualize this, Figure 3 graphs total cost as a function of the order quantity, Q. As the value of Q increases, the total number of orders placed per year decreases. Hence, the total ordering cost decreases. However, as the value of Q increases, the carrying cost increases because the firm has to maintain larger average inventories.

The optimal order size, Q^*, is the quantity that minimizes the total cost. Note in Figure 3 that Q^* occurs at the point where the ordering cost curve and the carrying cost curve intersect. This is not by chance. With this particular type of cost function, the optimal quantity always occurs at a point where the ordering cost is equal to the carrying cost.

FIGURE 2
Inventory Usage over Time

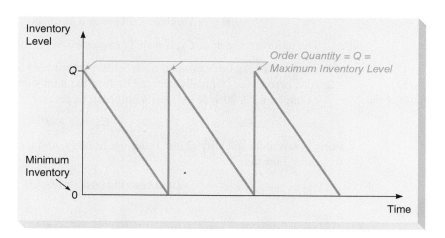

FIGURE 3
Total Cost as a Function of Order Quantity

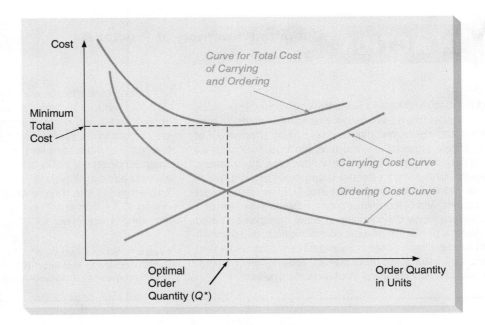

The average inventory level is one-half the maximum level.

Now that we have a better understanding of inventory costs, let us see how we can determine the value of Q^* that minimizes the total cost. In determining the *annual* carrying cost, it is convenient to use the **average inventory**. Referring to Figure 2, we see that the on-hand inventory ranges from a high of Q units to a low of zero units, with a uniform rate of decrease between these levels. Thus, the average inventory can be calculated as the average of the minimum and maximum inventory levels. That is,

$$\text{Average inventory level} = (0 + Q)/2 = Q/2 \qquad (1)$$

We multiply this average inventory by a factor called the *annual inventory carrying cost per unit* to determine the annual inventory cost.

Finding the Economic Order Quantity

We pointed out that the optimal order quantity, Q^*, is the point that minimizes the total cost, where total cost is the sum of ordering cost and carrying cost. We also indicated graphically that the optimal order quantity was at the point where the ordering cost was equal to the carrying cost. Let us now define the following parameters:

$Q^* = $ Optimal order quantity (i.e., the EOQ)

$D \quad = $ Annual demand, in units, for the inventory item

$C_o \quad = $ Ordering cost per order

$C_h \quad = $ Carrying or holding cost per unit per year

$P \quad = $ Purchase cost per unit of the inventory item

The unit carrying cost, C_h, is usually expressed in one of two ways, as follows:

1. As a fixed cost. For example, C_h is $0.50 per unit per year.
2. As a percentage (typically denoted by I) of the item's unit **purchase cost** or price. For example, C_h is 20% of the item's unit cost. In general,

I is the annual carrying cost expressed as a percentage of the unit cost of the item.

$$C_h = I \times P \qquad (2)$$

For a given order quantity Q, the ordering, holding, and total costs can be computed using the following formulas:[1]

$$\text{Total ordering cost} = (D/Q) \times C_o \qquad (3)$$

---

[1] See a recent operations management textbook such as J. Heizer and B. Render. *Operations Management*, 10th ed. Upper Saddle River, NJ: Prentice Hall, 2011, for more details of these formulas (and other formulas in this chapter).

$$\text{Total carrying cost} = (Q/2) \times C_h \qquad (4)$$

$$\text{Total cost} = \text{Total ordering cost} + \text{Total carrying cost} + \text{Total purchase cost}$$

$$= (D/Q) \times C_o \qquad + (Q/2) \times C_h \qquad + P \times D \qquad (5)$$

Observe that the total purchase cost (i.e., $P \times D$) does not depend on the value of Q. This is so because regardless of how many orders we place each year, or how many units we order each time, we will still incur the same annual total purchase cost.

The presence of Q in the denominator of the first term makes Equation 5 a *nonlinear* equation with respect to Q. Nevertheless, because the total ordering cost is equal to the total carrying cost at the optimal value of Q, we can set the terms in Equations 3 and 4 equal to each other and calculate the EOQ as

Total cost is a **nonlinear** *function of Q.*

We determine **Q*** *by setting ordering cost equal to carrying cost.*

$$Q^* = \sqrt{(2DC_o/C_h)} \qquad (6)$$

Sumco Pump Company Example

Let us now apply these formulas to the case of Sumco, a company that buys pump housings from a manufacturer and distributes to retailers. Sumco would like to reduce its inventory cost by determining the optimal number of pump housings to obtain per order. The annual demand is 1,000 units, the ordering cost is $10 per order, and the carrying cost is $0.50 per unit per year. Each pump housing has a purchase cost of $5. How many housings should Sumco order each time? To answer these and other questions, we use the ExcelModules program.

Using ExcelModules for Inventory Model Computations

Excel Notes

- The Companion Website for this text, at www.pearsonhighered.com/balakrishnan, contains a set of Excel worksheets, bundled together in a software package called ExcelModules. Appendix B describes the procedure for installing and running this program, and it gives a brief description of its contents.
- The Companion Website also provides the Excel file for each sample problem discussed here. The relevant file name is shown in the margin next to each example.
- For clarity, all worksheets for inventory models in ExcelModules are color coded as follows:
  - *Input cells*, where we enter the problem data, are shaded yellow.
  - *Output cells*, which show results, are shaded green.

We use Excel worksheets to do all inventory model computations.

When we run the ExcelModules program, we see a new tab titled ExcelModules in Excel's Ribbon. We select this tab and then click the Modules icon followed by the Inventory Models menu. The choices shown in Screenshot 1A are displayed. From these choices, we select the appropriate model.

When we select any of the inventory models in ExcelModules, we are first presented with a window that allows us to specify several options. Some of these options are common for all models, whereas others are specific to the inventory model selected. For example, Screenshot 1B shows the options window that appears when we select the Economic Order Quantity (EOQ) model. The options here include the following:

1. *Title.* The default value is Problem Title.
2. *Graph.* Checking this box results in a graph of ordering, carrying, and total costs versus order quantity.
3. *Holding cost.* This is either a fixed amount or a percentage of unit purchase cost.
4. *Reorder Point.* Checking this box results in the calculation of the reorder point, for a given lead time between placement of the order and receipt of the order. We discuss the reorder point in section 5. This option is available only for the EOQ model.

USING EXCELMODULES FOR THE EOQ MODEL Screenshot 2A shows the options we select for the Sumco Pump Company example.

When we click OK on this screen, we get the worksheet shown in Screenshot 2B. We now enter the values for the annual demand, D, ordering cost, C_o, carrying cost, C_h, and unit purchase cost, P, in cells B6 to B9, respectively.

File: 12-2.xls, sheet: 12-2B

SCREENSHOT 1A Inventory Models Menu in ExcelModules

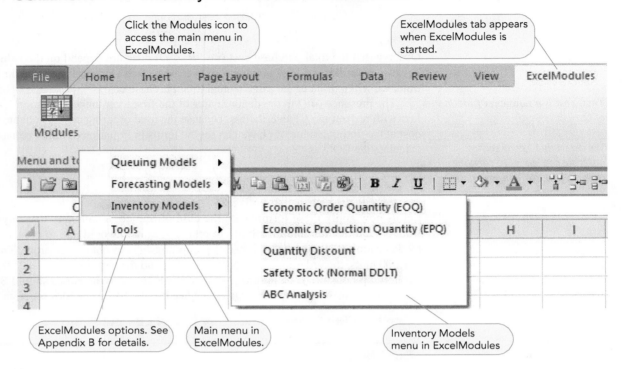

Click the Modules icon to access the main menu in ExcelModules.

ExcelModules tab appears when ExcelModules is started.

ExcelModules options. See Appendix B for details.

Main menu in ExcelModules.

Inventory Models menu in ExcelModules

SCREENSHOT 1B Sample Options Window for Inventory Models in ExcelModules

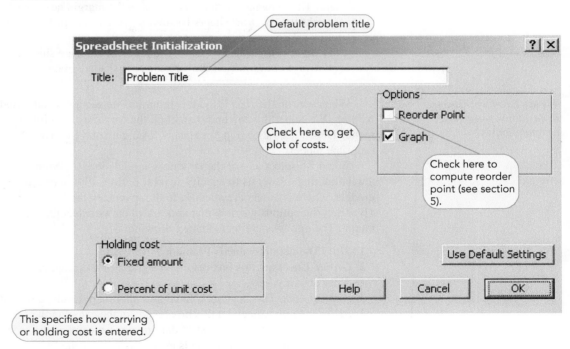

Default problem title

Check here to get plot of costs.

Check here to compute reorder point (see section 5).

This specifies how carrying or holding cost is entered.

SCREENSHOT 2A   Options Window for EOQ Model in ExcelModules

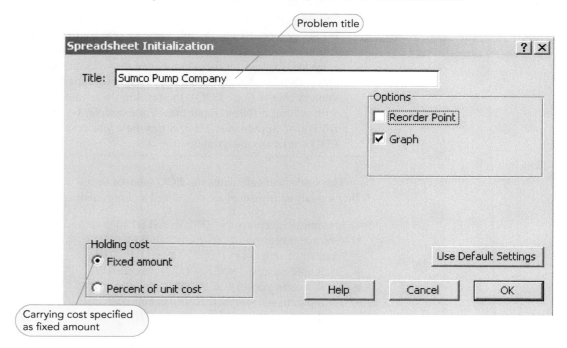

Problem title

Spreadsheet Initialization   ? X

Title: Sumco Pump Company

┌Options────────────────┐
│   ☐ Reorder Point   │
│   ☑ Graph   │
└───────────────────────┘

┌Holding cost──────────┐
│ ⦿ Fixed amount   │   Use Default Settings
│ ○ Percent of unit cost│
└──────────────────────┘   Help   Cancel   OK

Carrying cost specified
as fixed amount

SCREENSHOT 2B   EOQ Model for Sumco Pump

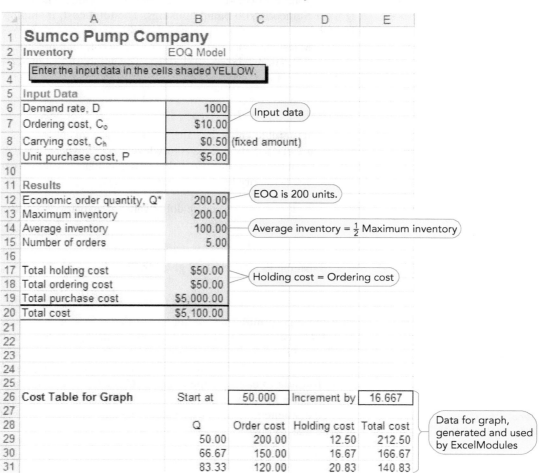

	A	B	C	D	E
1	**Sumco Pump Company**				
2	Inventory	EOQ Model			
3	Enter the input data in the cells shaded YELLOW.				
4					
5	Input Data				
6	Demand rate, D	1000			
7	Ordering cost, C_o	$10.00			
8	Carrying cost, C_h	$0.50	(fixed amount)		
9	Unit purchase cost, P	$5.00			
10					
11	Results				
12	Economic order quantity, Q^*	200.00			
13	Maximum inventory	200.00			
14	Average inventory	100.00			
15	Number of orders	5.00			
16					
17	Total holding cost	$50.00			
18	Total ordering cost	$50.00			
19	Total purchase cost	$5,000.00			
20	Total cost	$5,100.00			
21					
22					
23					
24					
25					
26	Cost Table for Graph	Start at	50.000	Increment by	16.667
27					
28		Q	Order cost	Holding cost	Total cost
29		50.00	200.00	12.50	212.50
30		66.67	150.00	16.67	166.67
31		83.33	120.00	20.83	140.83

Input data

EOQ is 200 units.

Average inventory = $\frac{1}{2}$ Maximum inventory

Holding cost = Ordering cost

Data for graph, generated and used by ExcelModules

Excel Notes

- The worksheets in ExcelModules contain formulas to compute the results for different inventory models. The default value of zero for the input data causes the results of these formulas to initially appear as #N/A, #VALUE!, or #DIV/0!. However, as soon as we enter valid values for these input data, the worksheets display the formula results.
- Once ExcelModules has been used to create the Excel worksheet for a particular inventory model (e.g., EOQ), the resulting worksheet can be used to compute the results with several different input data. For example, we can enter different input data in cells B6:B9 of Screenshot 2B and compute the results without having to create a new EOQ worksheet each time.

The worksheet calculates the EOQ (shown in cell B12 of Screenshot 2B). In addition, the following output measures are calculated and reported:

- Maximum inventory $(= Q^*)$, in cell B13
- Average inventory $(= Q^{*/2})$, in cell B14
- Number of orders $(= D/Q^*)$, in cell B15
- Total holding cost $(= C_h \times Q^{*/2})$, in cell B17
- Total ordering cost $(= C_o \times D/Q^*)$, in cell B18
- Total purchase cost $(= P \times D)$, in cell B19
- Total cost $(= C_h \times Q^{*/2} + C_o \times D/Q^* + P \times D)$, in cell B20

As you might expect, the total ordering cost of $50 is equal to the total carrying cost. (Refer to Figure 3.) You may wish to try different values for the order quantity Q, such as 100 or 300 pump housings. (Plug in these values one at a time in cell B12.) You will find that the total cost (in cell B20) has the lowest value when Q is 200 units. That is, the EOQ, Q^*, for Sumco is 200 pump housings. The total cost, including the purchase cost of $5,000, is $5,100.

If requested, a plot of the total ordering cost, total holding cost and total cost for different values of Q is drawn by ExcelModules. The graph, shown in Screenshot 2C, is drawn on a separate worksheet.

Purchase Cost of Inventory Items

We can calculate the average inventory value in dollar terms.

It is often useful to know the value of the average inventory level in dollar terms. We know from Equation 1 that the average inventory level is $Q/2$, where Q is the order quantity. If we order Q^* (the EOQ) units each time, the value of the average inventory can be computed by multiplying the average inventory by the unit purchase cost, P. That is,

$$\text{Average dollar value of inventory} = P \times (Q^*/2) \tag{7}$$

Calculating the Ordering and Carrying Costs for a Given Value of Q

Recall that the EOQ formula is given by Equation 6 as

$$Q^* = \sqrt{(2DC_0/C_h)}$$

In using this formula, we assumed that the values of the ordering cost C_o and carrying cost C_h are *known* constants. In some situations, however, these costs may be difficult to estimate precisely. For example, if the firm orders several items from a supplier simultaneously, it may be difficult to identify the ordering cost separately for each item. In such cases, we can use the EOQ formula to compute the value of C_o or C_h that would make a given order quantity the optimal order quantity.

For a given Q, we compute a C_o or C_h that makes Q optimal.

To compute these C_o or C_h values, we can manipulate the EOQ formula algebraically and rewrite it as follows:

$$C_o = Q^2 \times C_h/(2D) \tag{8}$$

File: 12-2.xls, sheet: 12-2C

SCREENSHOT 2C Plot of Costs versus Order Quantity for Sumco Pump

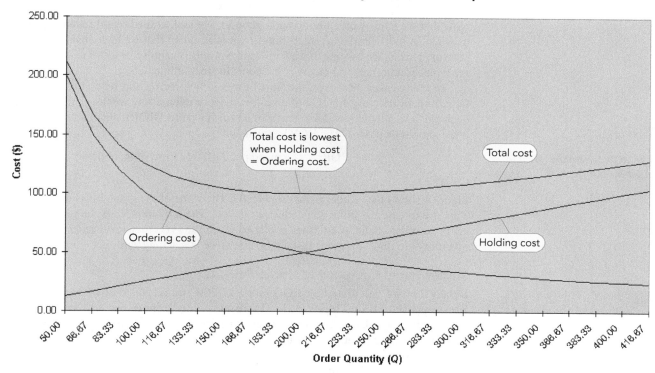

and

$$C_h = 2DC_o/Q^2 \qquad (9)$$

where Q is the given order quantity. We illustrate the use of these formulas in Solved Problem 1 at the end of this chapter.

Sensitivity of the EOQ Formula

If any of the input data values change, the EOQ also changes.

The EOQ formula in Equation 6 assumes that all input data are known with certainty. What happens if one of the input values is incorrect? If any of the values used in the formula changes, the optimal value of Q^* also changes. Determining the magnitude and effect of these changes on Q^* is called *sensitivity analysis*. This type of analysis is important in practice because the input values for the EOQ model are usually *estimated* and hence subject to error or change.

Let us use the Sumco example again to illustrate this issue. Suppose the ordering cost, C_o, is actually $15, instead of $10. Let us assume that the annual demand for pump housings is still the same, namely, $D = 1,000$ units, and that the carrying cost, C_h, is $0.50 per unit per year.

Due to the nonlinear formula for EOQ, changes in Q* are less severe than changes in input data values.

If we use these new values in the EOQ worksheet (as in Screenshot 2B), the revised EOQ turns out to be 245 units. (See if you can verify this for yourself.) That is, when the ordering cost increases by 50% (from $10 to $15), the optimal order quantity increases only by 22.5% (from 200 to 245). This is because the EOQ formula involves a square root and is, therefore, *nonlinear*.

We observe a similar occurrence when the carrying cost, C_h, changes. Let us suppose that Sumco's annual carrying cost is $0.80 per unit, instead of $0.50. Let us also assume that the annual demand is still 1,000 units, and the ordering cost is $10 per order. Using the EOQ worksheet in ExcelModules, we can calculate the revised EOQ as 158 units. That is, when the carrying cost increases by 60% (from $0.50 to $0.80), the EOQ decreases by only 21%. Note that the order quantity decreases here because a higher carrying cost makes holding inventory more expensive.

5   Reorder Point: Determining When to Order

Now that we have decided how much to order, we look at the second inventory question: when to order. In most simple inventory models, it is assumed that we have **instantaneous inventory receipt**. That is, we assume that a firm waits until its inventory level for a particular item reaches zero, places an order, and receives the items in stock immediately.

In many cases, however, the time between the placing and receipt of an order, called the *lead time*, or delivery time, is often a few days or even a few weeks. Thus, the when to order decision is usually expressed in terms of a **reorder point (ROP)**, the inventory level at which an order should be placed. The ROP is given as

*The **ROP** determines when to order inventory.*

$$\text{ROP} = (\text{Demand per day}) \times (\text{Lead time, in days}) \qquad (10)$$
$$= d \times L$$

Figure 4 shows the reorder point graphically. The slope of the graph is the daily inventory usage. This is expressed in units demanded per day, *d*. The *lead time*, *L*, is the time that it takes to receive an order. Thus, if an order is placed when the inventory level reaches the ROP, the new inventory arrives at the same instant the inventory is reaching zero. Let's look at an example.

Sumco Pump Company Example Revisited

Recall that we calculated an EOQ value of 200 and a total cost of $5,100 for Sumco (see Screenshot 2B). These calculations were based on an annual demand of 1,000 units, an ordering cost of $10 per order, an annual carrying cost of $0.50 per unit, and a purchase cost of $5 per pump housing.

Now let us assume that there is a lead time of 3 business days between the time Sumco places an order and the time the order is received. Further, let us assume there are 250 business days in a year.

To compute the ROP, we need to know the demand rate per period.

To calculate the ROP, we must first determine the daily demand rate, *d*. In Sumco's case, because there are 250 business days in a year and the annual demand is 1,000, the daily demand rate is 4 (=1,000/250) pump housings.

File: 12-3.xls

USING EXCELMODULES TO COMPUTE THE ROP We can include the ROP computation in the EOQ worksheet provided in ExcelModules. To do so for Sumco's problem, we once again choose the choice titled Economic Order Quantity (EOQ) from the Inventory Models menu in ExcelModules (refer to Screenshot 1A). The only change in the options window (see Screenshot 2A) is that we now check the box labeled Reorder Point.

FIGURE 4
Reorder Point (ROP) Curve

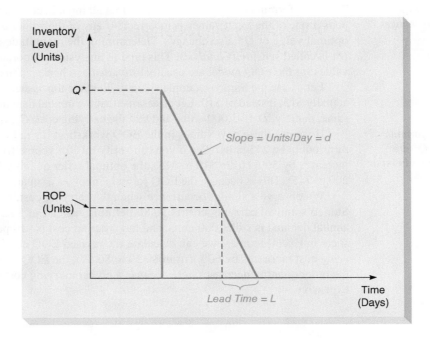

SCREENSHOT 3
EOQ Model with ROP for Sumco Pump

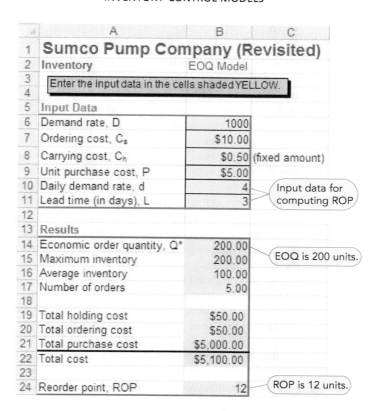

	A	B	C
1	**Sumco Pump Company (Revisited)**		
2	Inventory	EOQ Model	
3	Enter the input data in the cells shaded YELLOW.		
4			
5	Input Data		
6	Demand rate, D	1000	
7	Ordering cost, C_s	$10.00	
8	Carrying cost, C_h	$0.50	(fixed amount)
9	Unit purchase cost, P	$5.00	
10	Daily demand rate, d	4	Input data for computing ROP
11	Lead time (in days), L	3	
12			
13	Results		
14	Economic order quantity, Q*	200.00	EOQ is 200 units.
15	Maximum inventory	200.00	
16	Average inventory	100.00	
17	Number of orders	5.00	
18			
19	Total holding cost	$50.00	
20	Total ordering cost	$50.00	
21	Total purchase cost	$5,000.00	
22	Total cost	$5,100.00	
23			
24	Reorder point, ROP	12	ROP is 12 units.

The worksheet shown in Screenshot 3 is now displayed. We enter the input data as before (see Screenshot 2B). Note the additional input entries for the daily demand rate in cell B10 and the lead time in cell B11. In addition to all the computations shown in Screenshot 2B, the worksheet now calculates and reports the ROP of 12 units (shown in cell B24).

Hence, when the inventory stock of pump housings drops to 12, an order should be placed. The order will arrive three days later, just as the firm's stock is depleted to zero. It should be mentioned that this calculation assumes that all the assumptions listed earlier for EOQ are valid. When demand is not known with complete certainty, these calculations must be modified. This is discussed later in this chapter.

IN ACTION | Dell Uses Inventory Optimization Models in Its Supply Chain

Dell was the leader in global market share in the computer-systems industry during the early 2000s. It was also the fastest-growing company in this industry, competing in multiple market segments. Dell was founded on the concept of selling computer systems directly to customers without a retail middleman, thereby reducing delays and costs due to the elimination of this stage in the supply chain. Dell's superior financial performance during this period can be attributed in large measure to its successful implementation of this direct-sales model.

In the rapidly evolving computer systems industry, holding inventory is a huge liability. It is common for components to lose 0.5 to 2.0 percent of their value each week, rendering a supply chain filled with old technology obsolete in a short time. Within Dell, the focus was on speeding components and products through its supply chain, while carrying very little inventory.

Dell's management was, however, keen that its suppliers also hold just the right inventory to ensure a high level of customer service while reducing total costs. Working with a team from the University of Michigan, Dell identified a sustainable process and decision-support tools for determining optimal levels of component inventory at different stages of the supply chain to support the final assembly process.

The tools allowed Dell to change how inventory was being pulled from supplier logistics centers into Dell's assembly facilities, resulting in a more linear, predictable product pull for suppliers. The direct benefit for Dell is that there is more robustness in supply continuity and suppliers are better able to handle unexpected demand variations.

Source: Based on R. Kapuscinski et al. "Inventory Decisions in Dell's Supply Chain," *Interfaces* 34, 3 (May–June 2004): 191–205.

6 Economic Production Quantity: Determining How Much to Produce

In the EOQ model, we assumed that the receipt of inventory is instantaneous. In other words, the entire order arrives in one batch, at a single point in time. In many cases, however, a firm may build up its inventory gradually over a period of time. For example, a firm may receive shipments from its supplier uniformly over a period of time. Or, a firm may be producing at a rate of p per day *and* simultaneously selling at a rate of d per day (where $p > d$). Figure 5 shows inventory levels as a function of time in these situations. Clearly, the EOQ model is no longer applicable here, and we need a new model to calculate the optimal order (or production) quantity. Because this model is especially suited to the production environment, it is also commonly known as the *production lot size* model or the **economic production quantity (EPQ) model**. We refer to this model as the EPQ model in the remainder of this chapter.

The EPQ model eliminates the instantaneous receipt assumption.

In a production process, instead of having an ordering cost, there will be a **setup cost**. This is the cost of setting up the production facility to manufacture the desired product. It normally includes the salaries and wages of employees who are responsible for setting up the equipment, engineering and design costs of making the setup, and the costs of paperwork, supplies, utilities, and so on. The carrying cost per unit is composed of the same factors as the traditional EOQ model, although the equation to compute the annual carrying cost changes.

In determining the annual carrying cost for the EPQ model, it is again convenient to use the *average* on-hand inventory. Referring to Figure 5, we can show that the maximum on-hand inventory is $Q \times (1 - d/p)$ units, where d is the daily demand rate and p is the daily production rate. The minimum on-hand inventory is again zero units, and the inventory decreases at a uniform rate between the maximum and minimum levels. Thus, the average inventory can be calculated as the average of the minimum and maximum inventory levels. That is,

This is the formula for average inventory in the EPQ model.

$$\text{Average inventory level} = [0 + Q \times (1 - d/p)]/2 = Q \times (1 - d/p)/2 \tag{11}$$

Analogous to the EOQ model, it turns out that the optimal order quantity in the EPQ model also occurs when the total setup cost equals the total carrying cost. We should note, however, that making the total setup cost equal to the total carrying cost does not always guarantee optimal solutions for models more complex than the EPQ model.

Finding the Economic Production Quantity

Let us first define the following additional parameters:

$$Q^* = \text{Optimal order or production quantity (i.e., the EPQ)}$$
$$C_s = \text{Setup cost per setup}$$

For a given order quantity, Q, the setup, holding, and total costs can now be computed using the following formulas:

$$\text{Total setup cost} = (D/Q) \times C_s \tag{12}$$

$$\text{Total carrying cost} = [Q(1 - d/p)/2] \times C_h \tag{13}$$

FIGURE 5
Inventory Control and the Production Process

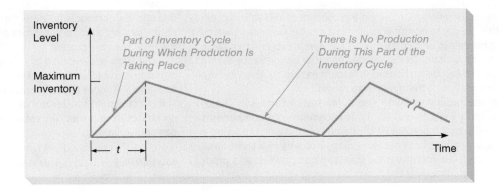

$$\text{Total cost} = \text{Total setup cost} + \text{Total carrying cost} + \text{Total production cost}$$
$$= (D/Q) \times C_s + [Q(1 - d/p)/2] \times C_h + P \times D \tag{14}$$

As in the EOQ model, the total production (or purchase, if the item is purchased) cost does not depend on the value of Q. Further, the presence of Q in the denominator of the first term makes the total cost function nonlinear. Nevertheless, because the total setup cost should equal the total ordering cost at the optimal value of Q, we can set the terms in Equations 12 and 13 equal to each other and calculate the EPQ as

$$Q^* = \sqrt{2DC_s/[C_h(1 - d/p)]} \tag{15}$$

Brown Manufacturing Example

Brown Manufacturing produces mini-sized refrigeration packs in batches. The firm's estimated demand for the year is 10,000 units. Because Brown operates for 167 business days each year, this annual demand translates to a daily demand rate of about 60 units per day. It costs about $100 to set up the manufacturing process, and the carrying cost is about $0.50 per unit per year. When the production process has been set up, 80 refrigeration packs can be manufactured daily. Each pack costs $5 to produce. How many packs should Brown produce in each batch? As discussed next, we determine this value, as well as values for the associated costs, by using ExcelModules.

File: 12-4.xls, sheet: 12-4A

USING EXCELMODULES FOR THE EPQ MODEL We select the choice titled Economic Production Quantity (EPQ) from the Inventory Models menu in ExcelModules (refer to Screenshot 1A). The options for this procedure are similar to those for the EOQ model (see Screenshot 2A). The only change is that the ROP option is not available here. After we enter the title and other options for this problem, we get the worksheet shown in Screenshot 4A. We now enter the values for the annual demand, D, setup cost, C_s, carrying cost, C_h, daily production rate, p, daily demand rate, d, and unit production (or purchase) cost, P, in cells B7 to B12, respectively.

The worksheet calculates and reports the EPQ (shown in cell B15), as well as the following output measures:

- Maximum inventory ($= Q^*[1 - d/p]$), in cell B16
- Average inventory ($= Q^*[1 - d/p]/2$), in cell B17
- Number of setups ($= D/Q^*$), in cell B18
- Total holding cost ($= C_h \times Q^*[1 - d/p]/2$), in cell B20
- Total setup cost ($= C_s \times D/Q^*$), in cell B21
- Total purchase cost ($= P \times D$), in cell B22
- Total cost ($= C_h \times Q^*[1 - d/p]/2 + C_s \times D/Q^* + P \times D$), in cell B23

Here again, as you might expect, the total setup cost is equal to the total carrying cost ($250 each). You may wish to try different values for Q, such as 3,000 or 5,000 pumps. (Plug these values, one at a time, into cell B15.) You will find that the minimum total cost occurs when Q is 4,000 units. That is, the EPQ, Q^*, for Brown is 4,000 units. The total cost, including the production cost of $50,000, is $50,500.

If requested, a plot of the total setup cost, holding cost, and total cost for different values of Q is drawn by ExcelModules. This graph, shown in Screenshot 4B, is drawn on a separate worksheet.

File: 12-4.xls, sheet: 12-4B

Length of the Production Cycle

Referring to Figure 5, we see that the inventory buildup occurs over a period t during which Brown is both producing and selling refrigeration packs. We refer to this period t as the *production cycle*. In Brown's case, if $Q^* = 4,000$ units and we know that 80 units can be produced daily, the length of each production cycle will be $Q^*/p = 4,000/80 = 50$ days. Thus, when Brown decides to produce refrigeration packs, the equipment will be set up to manufacture the units for a 50-day time span.

SCREENSHOT 4A EPQ Model for Brown Manufacturing

	A	B	C	D	E
1	**Brown Manufacturing**				
2	Inventory	Economic Production Quantity Model			
3	Enter the data in the cells shaded YELLOW. You may have to do some				
4	work to compute the daily production and demand rates.				
5					
6	Input Data				
7	Demand rate, D	10000			
8	Setup cost, C_s	$100.00			
9	Carrying cost, C_h	$0.50	(fixed amount)		
10	Daily production rate, p	80			
11	Daily demand rate, d	60		Carrying cost is specified	
12	Unit purchase cost, P	$5.00		as a fixed amount.	
13					
14	Results				
15	Economic production quantity, Q^*	4000.00	EPQ is 4,000 units.		
16	Maximum inventory	1000.00			
17	Average inventory	500.00			
18	Number of setups	2.50			
19					
20	Total holding cost	$250.00	Holding cost = Setup cost		
21	Total setup cost	$250.00			
22	Total production cost	$50,000.00			
23	Total cost, TC	$50,500.00			
24					
25					
26	**Cost Table for Graph**	Start at	1000.00	Increment by	333.33
27					
28		Q	Setup cost	Holding cost	Total cost
29		1000.00	1000.00	62.50	1062.50
30		1333.33	750.00	83.33	833.33
31		1666.67	600.00	104.17	704.17

Data for graph, generated and used by ExcelModules

SCREENSHOT 4B Plot of Costs versus Order Quantity for Brown Manufacturing

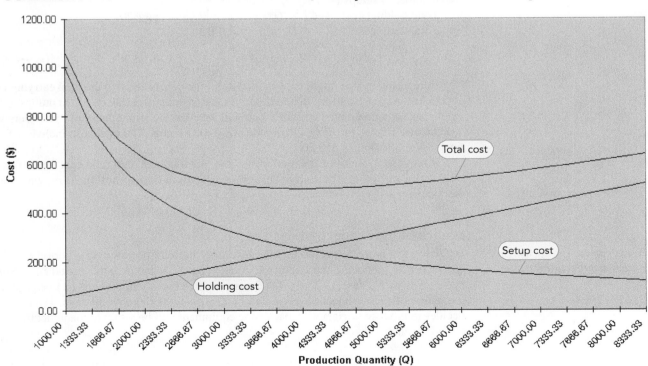

7 Quantity Discount Models

To increase sales, many companies offer quantity discounts to their customers. A **quantity discount** is simply a decreased unit cost for an item when it is purchased in larger quantities. It is not uncommon to have a discount schedule with several discounts for large orders. A typical quantity discount schedule is shown in Table 2.

A discount is a reduced price for an item when it is purchased in large quantities.

As can be seen in Table 2, the normal cost for the item in this example is $5. When 1,000 to 1,999 units are ordered at one time, the cost per unit drops to $4.80, and when the quantity ordered at one time is 2,000 units or more, the cost is $4.75 per unit. As always, management must decide when and how much to order. But with quantity discounts, how does a manager make these decisions?

As with other inventory models discussed so far, the overall objective is to minimize the total cost. Because the unit cost for the third discount in Table 2 is lowest, you might be tempted to order 2,000 units or more to take advantage of this discount. Placing an order for that many units, however, might not minimize the total inventory cost. As the discount quantity goes up, the item cost goes down, but the carrying cost increases because the order sizes are large. Thus, the major trade-off when considering quantity discounts is between the reduced item cost and the increased carrying cost.

Recall that we computed the total cost (including the total purchase cost) for the EOQ model as follows (see Equation 5):

$$\text{Total cost} = \text{Total ordering cost} + \text{Total carrying cost} + \text{Total purchase cost}$$
$$= (D/Q) \times C_o \qquad + (Q/2) \times C_h \qquad + P \times D$$

Next, we illustrate the four-step process to determine the quantity that minimizes the total cost. However, we use a worksheet included in ExcelModules to actually compute the optimal order quantity and associated costs in our example.

Four Steps to Analyze Quantity Discount Models

We calculate Q* values for each discount.

1. For each discount price, calculate a Q^* value, using the EOQ formula (see Equation 6). In quantity discount EOQ models, the unit carrying cost, C_h, is typically expressed as a percentage (I) of the unit purchase cost (P). That is, $C_h = I \times P$, as discussed in Equation 2. As a result, the value of Q^* will be different for each discounted price.

Next, we adjust the Q* values.

2. For any discount level, if the Q^* computed in step 1 is too low to qualify for the discount, adjust Q^* upward to the *lowest* quantity that qualifies for the discount. For example, if Q^* for discount 2 in Table 2 turns out to be 500 units, adjust this value up to 1,000 units. The reason for this step is illustrated in Figure 6.

The total cost curve is broken into parts.

As seen in Figure 6, the total cost curve for the discounts shown in Table 2 is broken into three different curves. There are separate cost curves for the first ($0 \leq Q \leq 999$), second ($1,000 \leq Q \leq 1,999$), and third ($Q \geq 2,000$) discounts. Look at the total cost curve for discount 2. The Q^* for discount 2 is less than the allowable discount range of 1,000 to 1,999 units. However, the total cost at 1,000 units (which is the minimum quantity needed to get this discount) is still less than the lowest total cost for discount 1. Thus, step 2 is needed to ensure that we do not discard any discount level that may indeed produce the minimum total cost. Note that an order quantity computed in step 1 that is *greater* than the range that would qualify it for a discount may be discarded.

Next, we compute total cost.

3. Using the total cost equation (Equation 5), compute a total cost for every Q^* determined in steps 1 and 2. If a Q^* had to be adjusted upward because it was below the allowable quantity range, be sure to use the adjusted Q^* value.

We select the Q* with the lowest total cost.

4. Select the Q^* that has the lowest total cost, as computed in step 3. It will be the order quantity that minimizes the total cost.

TABLE 2
Quantity Discount Schedule

DISCOUNT NUMBER	DISCOUNT QUANTITY	DISCOUNT	DISCOUNT COST
1	0 to 999	0%	$5.00
2	1,000 to 1,999	4%	$4.80
3	2,000 and over	5%	$4.75

FIGURE 6
Total Cost Curve for the
Quantity Discount Model

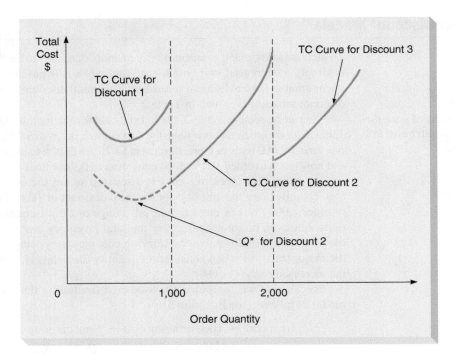

Brass Department Store Example

This is an example of the quantity discount model.

Brass Department Store stocks toy cars. Recently, the store was given a quantity discount schedule for the cars, as shown in Table 2. Thus, the normal cost for the cars is $5. For orders between 1,000 and 1,999 units, the unit cost is $4.80, and for orders of 2,000 or more units, the unit cost is $4.75. Furthermore, the ordering cost is $49 per order, the annual demand is 5,000 race cars, and the inventory carrying charge as a percentage of cost, I, is 20%, or 0.2. What order quantity will minimize the total cost? We use the ExcelModules program to answer this question.

USING EXCELMODULES FOR THE QUANTITY DISCOUNT MODEL We select the choice titled Quantity Discount from the Inventory Models menu in ExcelModules (refer back to Screenshot 1A). The window shown in Screenshot 5A is displayed. The option entries in this window are similar to those for the EOQ model (see Screenshot 2A).

SCREENSHOT 5A
Options Window for
Quantity Discount Model
in ExcelModules

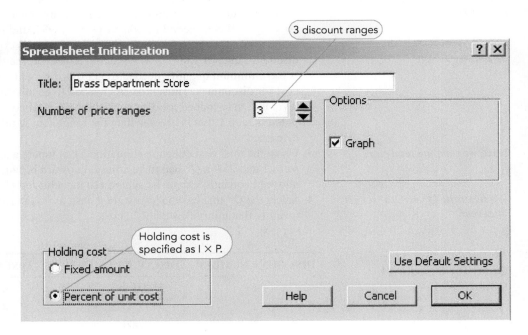

The only additional choice is the box labeled Number of price ranges. The specific entries for Brass Department Store's problem are shown in Screenshot 5A.

File: 12-5.xls, sheet: 12-5B

When we click OK on this screen, we get the worksheet shown in Screenshot 5B. We now enter the values for the annual demand, D, ordering cost, C_o, and holding cost percentage, I, in cells B7 to B9, respectively. Note that I is entered as a percentage value (e.g., enter 20 for the Brass Department Store example). Then, for each of the three discount ranges, we enter the minimum quantity needed to get the discount and the discounted unit price, P. These entries are shown in cells B12:D13 of Screenshot 5B.

The worksheet works through the four-step process and reports the following output measures for each discount range:

- EOQ value (shown in cells B17:D17), computed using Equation 6
- Adjusted EOQ value (shown in cells B18:D18), as discussed in step 2 of the four-step process
- Total holding cost, total ordering cost, total purchase cost, and overall total cost, shown in cells B20:D23

File: 12-5.xls, sheet: 12-5C

In the Brass Department Store example, observe that the Q^* values for discounts 2 and 3 are too low to be eligible for the discounted prices. They are, therefore, adjusted upward to 1,000 and 2,000, respectively. With these adjusted Q^* values, we find that the lowest total cost of $24,725 results when we use an order quantity of 1,000 units.

If requested, ExcelModules will also draw a plot of the total cost for different values of Q. This graph, shown in Screenshot 5C, is drawn on a separate worksheet.

SCREENSHOT 5B Quantity Discount Model for Brass Department Store

	A	B	C	D	E	F	G
1	**Brass Department Store**						
2	Inventory	Quantity Discount Model					
3	Enter the data in the cells shaded YELLOW. The minimum quantity is the minimum						
4	amount that needs to be ordered in order to get the price for that range.						
5							
6	Input Data						
7	Demand rate, D	5000					
8	Ordering cost, C_o	49		20% is entered as 20 here.			
9	Carrying cost %, I	20.00%	(percentage)				
10							
11		Range 1	Range 2	Range 3			
12	Minimum quantity	0	1000	2000			
13	Unit purchase cost, P	$5.00	$4.80	$4.75			
14							
15	Results						
16		Range 1	Range 2	Range 3			
17	Economic order quantity, Q*	700.00	714.43	718.18	Q* for each price range		
18	Adjusted order quantity	700.00	1000.00	2000.00	Adjusted Q* value		
19							
20	Total holding cost	350.00	480.00	950.00			
21	Total ordering cost	350.00	245.00	122.50			
22	Total purchase cost	25,000.00	24,000.00	23,750.00			
23	Total cost	25,700.00	24,725.00	24,822.50			
24				Lowest cost option			
25							
26	Cost Table for Graph	Start at	525.00	Increment by	86.00		
27		Q	Unit cost	Setup cost	Holding cost	Total unit cost	Total Cost
28		1	525.00	5.00	466.67	262.50	25000.00	25729.17
29	Data for graph, generated and used by ExcelModules	2	611.00	5.00	400.98	305.50	25000.00	25706.48
30		3	697.00	5.00	351.51	348.50	25000.00	25700.01
31		4	783.00	5.00	312.90	391.50	25000.00	25704.40

SCREENSHOT 5C   Plot of Total Cost versus Order Quantity for Brass Department Store

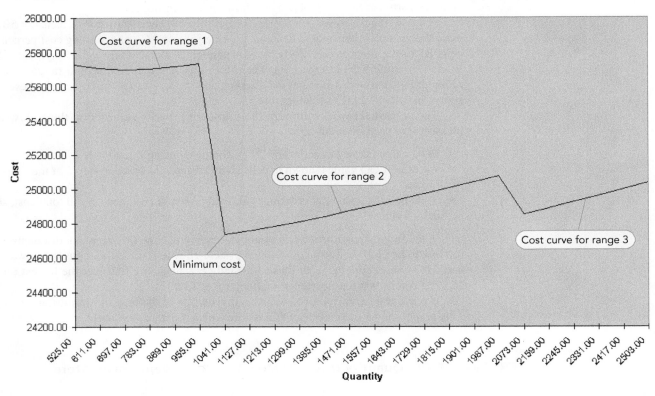

8   Use of Safety Stock

Safety stock *helps in avoiding stockouts. It is extra stock kept on hand.*

Safety stock is additional stock that is kept on hand.[2] If, for example, the safety stock for an item is 50 units, you are carrying an average of 50 units more of inventory during the year. When demand is unusually high, you dip into the safety stock instead of encountering a stockout. Thus, the main purpose of safety stock is to avoid stockouts when the demand is higher than expected. Its use is shown in Figure 7. Note that although stockouts can often be avoided by using safety stock, there is still a chance that they may occur. The demand may be so high that all the safety stock is used up, and thus there is still a stockout.

One of the best ways of maintaining a safety stock level is to use the ROP. This can be accomplished by adding the number of units of safety stock as a buffer to the reorder point. Recall from Equation 10 that

$$ROP = d \times L$$

where d is the daily demand rate and L is the order lead time. With the inclusion of safety stock (SS), the reorder point becomes

Safety stock is included in the ROP.

$$ROP = d \times L + SS \tag{16}$$

How to determine the correct amount of safety stock is the only remaining question. The answer to this question depends on whether we know the cost of a stockout. We discuss both of these situations next.

Safety Stock with Known Stockout Costs

When the EOQ is fixed and the ROP is used to place orders, the only time a stockout can occur is during the lead time. Recall that the lead time is the time between when an order is placed

---

[2] Safety stock is used only when demand is uncertain, and models under uncertainty are generally much harder to deal with than models under certainty.

FIGURE 7
Use of Safety Stock

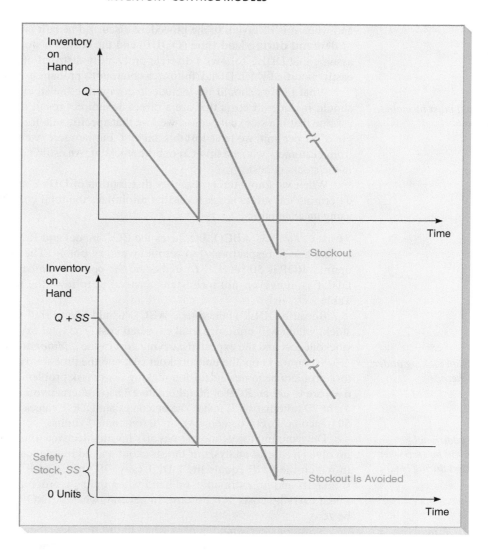

<table>
</table>

IN ACTION   3M Uses Inventory Models to Reduce Inventory Costs

3M, a diverse company that manufactures tens of thousands of products, has operations in 60 countries with annual sales of over $16 billion. Supply-chain structures at 3M vary as much as its product offerings. While many of 3M's products are made entirely within individual facilities, others are manufactured and distributed using multiple steps across several facilities. 3M's finished-goods inventory just in the United States exceeds $400 million and therefore reducing inventory-related costs in the supply chain is of vital importance.

Historically, most 3M supply chains have used ad hoc inventory-control policies that do not account for differences in factors such as set-up costs, demand and supply variability, lead time, or site- or product-specific issues. As a result, lot sizes, safety stocks, and service levels can often be severely misestimated. To address these limitations, 3M extended the classical reorder-point/order-quantity

approach to develop an integrated inventory-management system that determines optimal lot sizes and safety stocks based on the characteristics of each individual stock-keeping-unit (SKU) in the supply chains.

Between 2003 and 2004, the new system was implemented at just 22 of 3M's supply chains, which varied from a few dozen SKUs to over 10,000 SKUs. The system reduced inventory by over $17 million and annual operating expenses by over $1.4 million, leading 3M to implement it at several other of its supply chains. Although this initiative began as a grassroots effort, 3M's management has fully embraced it and made it the standard for managing inventory.

Source: Based on D. M. Strike and A. Benjaafar. "Practice Abstracts: Optimizing Inventory Management at 3M," *Interfaces* 34, 2 (March–April 2004): 113–116.

and when it is received. In the procedure discussed here, it is necessary to know the probability of **demand during lead time (DDLT)** and the cost of a stockout. In the following pages, we assume that DDLT follows a discrete probability distribution. This approach, however, can be easily modified when DDLT follows a continuous probability distribution.

What factors should we include in computing the stockout cost per unit? In general, we should include all costs that are a direct or indirect result of a stockout. For example, let us assume that if a stockout occurs, we lose that specific sale forever. Thus, if there is a profit margin of $1 per unit, we have lost this amount. Furthermore, we may end up losing future business from customers who are upset about the stockout. An estimate of this cost must also be included in the stockout cost.

Loss of goodwill must be included in stockout costs.

When we know the probability distribution of DDLT and the cost of a stockout, we can determine the safety stock level that minimizes the total cost. We illustrate this computation using an example.

ABCO EXAMPLE ABCO, Inc., uses the EOQ model and ROP analysis (which we saw in sections 4 and 5, respectively) to set its inventory policy. The company has determined that its optimal ROP is 50 ($= d \times L$) units, and the optimal number of orders per year is 6. ABCO's DDLT is, however, not a constant. Instead, it follows the probability distribution shown in Table 3.[3]

Because DDLT is uncertain, ABCO would like to find the revised ROP, including safety stock, which will minimize total expected cost. The total expected cost is the sum of expected stockout cost and the expected carrying cost of the *additional* inventory.

We use a decision making under risk approach here.

When we know the unit stockout cost and the probability distribution of DDLT, the inventory problem becomes a decision making under risk problem. For ABCO, the decision alternatives are to use an ROP of 30 (alternative 1), 40 (alternative 2), 50 (alternative 3), 60 (alternative 4), or 70 (alternative 5) units. The outcomes are DDLT values of 30 (outcome 1), 40 (outcome 2), 50 (outcome 3), 60 (outcome 4), or 70 (outcome 5) units.

Stockout and additional carrying costs will be zero when ROP = demand during lead time.

Determining the economic payoffs for any decision alternative and outcome combination involves a careful analysis of the stockout and additional carrying costs. Consider a situation in which the ROP equals the DDLT (say, 30 units each). This means that there will be no stockouts and no extra units on hand when the new order arrives. Thus, stockouts and additional carrying costs will be zero. In general, when the ROP equals the DDLT, total cost will be zero.

If ROP > DDLT, total cost = total stockout cost.

Now consider what happens when the ROP is less than the DDLT. For example, say that ROP is 30 units and DDLT is 40 units. In this case we will be 10 units short. The cost of this stockout situation is $2,400 ($=10$ units short $\times$ $40 per stockout $\times$ 6 orders per year). Note that we have to multiply the stockout cost per unit and the number of units short by the number of orders per year (6, in this case) to determine annual expected stockout cost. Likewise, if the ROP is 30 units and the DDLT is 50 units, the stockout cost will be $4,800 ($= 20 \times$ 40×6), and so on. In general, when the ROP is less than the DDLT, the total cost is equal to the total stockout cost.

TABLE 3
Probability of Demand during Lead Time for ABCO, Inc.

NUMBER OF UNITS	PROBABILITY
30	0.2
40	0.2
ROP → 50	0.3
60	0.2
70	0.1
	1.0

[3] Note that we have assumed that we already know the values of Q^* and ROP. If this is not true, the values of Q^*, ROP, and safety stock would have to be determined simultaneously. This requires a more complex solution.

If ROP > DDLT, total cost = total additional inventory carrying cost.

File: 12-6.xls, sheets: 12-6A and 12-6B

Finally, consider what happens when the ROP exceeds the DDLT. For example, say that ROP is 70 units and DDLT is 60 units. In this case, we will have 10 additional units on hand when the new inventory is received. If this situation continues during the year, we will have 10 additional units on hand, on average. The additional carrying cost is $50 (= 10 additional units × $5 carrying cost per unit per year). Likewise, if the DDLT is 50 units, we will have 20 additional units on hand when the new inventory arrives, and the additional carrying cost will be $100 (= 20 × $5). In general, when the ROP is greater than the DDLT, total cost will be equal to the total additional carrying cost.

Using the procedures described previously, we can easily set up a spreadsheet to compute the total cost for every alternative and state of nature combination. The formula view for this spreadsheet is shown in Screenshot 6A.

The results of the analysis are shown in Screenshot 6B. The expected monetary values (EMV) in column G show that the best reorder point for ABCO is 70 units, with an expected total cost of $110. Recall that ABCO had determined its optimal ROP to be 50 units if DDLT was a constant. Hence, the results in Screenshot 6B imply that due to the uncertain nature of DDLT, ABCO should carry a safety stock of 20 (= 70 − 50) units.

SCREENSHOT 6A Formula View of Safety Stock Computation for ABCO, Inc.

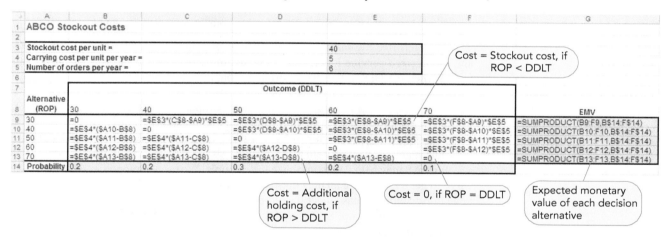

**SCREENSHOT 6B
Safety Stock
Computation for
ABCO, Inc.**

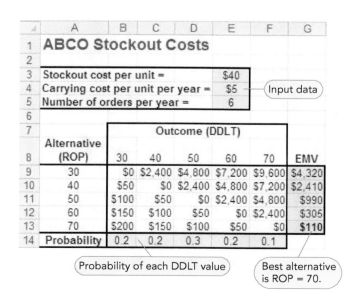

Safety Stock with Unknown Stockout Costs

Determining stockout costs may be difficult or impossible.

When stockout costs are not available or if they are not relevant, the preceding type of analysis cannot be used. Actually, there are many situations in which stockout costs are unknown or extremely difficult to determine. For example, let's assume that you run a small bicycle shop that sells mopeds and bicycles with a one-year service warranty. Any adjustments made within the year are done at no charge to the customer. If the customer comes in for maintenance under the warranty, and you do not have the necessary part, what is the stockout cost? It cannot be lost profit because the maintenance is done free of charge. Thus, the major stockout cost is the loss of goodwill. The customer may not buy another bicycle from your shop if you have a poor service record. In this situation, it could be very difficult to determine the stockout cost. In other cases, a stockout cost may simply not apply. What is the stockout cost for life-saving drugs in a hospital? The drugs may cost only $10 per bottle. Is the stockout cost $10? Is it $100 or $10,000? Perhaps the stockout cost should be $1 million. What is the cost when a life may be lost as a result of not having the drug?

In such cases, an alternative approach to determining safety stock levels is to use a service level. In general, a **service level** is the percentage of the time that you will have the item in stock. In other words, the probability of having a stockout is 1 minus the service level. That is,

$$\text{Service level} = 1 - \text{Probability of a stockout}$$

or

$$\text{Probability of a stockout} = 1 - \text{Service level} \tag{17}$$

To determine the safety stock level, it is only necessary to know the probability of DDLT and the *desired* service level. Here is an example of how the safety stock level can be determined when the DDLT follows a normal probability distribution.

An alternative to determining safety stock is to use service level and the normal distribution.

HINSDALE COMPANY EXAMPLE Hinsdale Company carries an item whose DDLT follows a normal distribution, with a mean of 350 units and a standard deviation of 10 units. Hinsdale wants to follow a policy that results in a service level of 95%. How much safety stock should Hinsdale maintain for this item?

We find the Z value for the desired service level.

Figure 8 may help you to visualize the example. We use the properties of a standardized normal curve to get a Z value for an area under the normal curve of $0.95 = (1 - 0.05)$. Using the normal table in Appendix: Areas Under the Normal Standard Curve, we find this Z value to be 1.645.

As shown in Figure 8, Z is equal to $(X - \mu)/\sigma$, or SS/σ. Hence, SS is equal to $Z \times \sigma$. That is, Hinsdale's safety stock for a service level of 95% is $(1.645 \times 10) = 16.45$ units

FIGURE 8
Safety Stock and the Normal Distribution

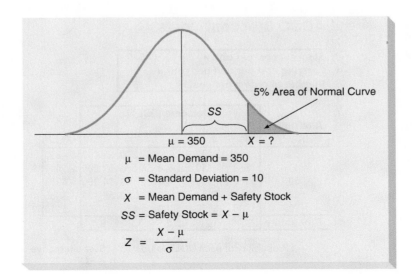

5% Area of Normal Curve

SS

$\mu = 350$ $X = ?$

μ = Mean Demand = 350

σ = Standard Deviation = 10

X = Mean Demand + Safety Stock

SS = Safety Stock = $X - \mu$

$Z = \dfrac{X - \mu}{\sigma}$

(which can be rounded off to 17 units, if necessary). We can calculate the safety stocks for different service levels in a similar fashion.

A safety stock level is determined for each service level.

Let's assume that Hinsdale has a carrying cost of $1 per unit per year. What is the carrying cost for service levels that range from 90% to 99.99%? To compute this cost, we first compute the safety stock for each service level (as discussed earlier) and then multiply the safety stock by the unit carrying cost. The Z value, safety stock, and total carrying cost for different service levels for Hinsdale are summarized in Table 4. A graph of the total carrying cost as a function of the service level is given in Figure 9.

The relationship between service level and carrying cost is nonlinear.

Note from Figure 9 that the relationship between service level and carrying cost is nonlinear. As the service level increases, the carrying cost increases at an increasing rate. Indeed,

TABLE 4
Cost of Different Service Levels

SERVICE LEVEL	Z VALUE FROM NORMAL CURVE TABLE	SAFETY STOCK (UNITS)	CARRYING COST
90%	1.28	12.8	$12.80
91%	1.34	13.4	$13.40
92%	1.41	14.1	$14.10
93%	1.48	14.8	$14.80
94%	1.55	15.5	$15.50
95%	1.65	16.5	$16.50
96%	1.75	17.5	$17.50
97%	1.88	18.8	$18.80
98%	2.05	20.5	$20.50
99%	2.33	23.3	$23.20
99.99%	3.72	37.2	$37.20

FIGURE 9
Service Level versus Annual Carrying Costs

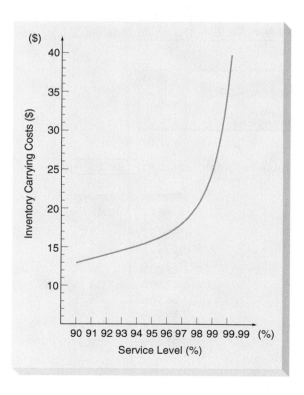

at very high service levels, the carrying cost becomes very large. Therefore, as you are setting service levels, you should be aware of the additional carrying cost that you will encounter. Although Figure 9 was developed for a specific case, the general shape of the curve is the same for all service-level problems.

USING EXCELMODULES TO COMPUTE THE SAFETY STOCK We select the choice titled Safety Stock (Normal DDLT) from the Inventory Models menu in ExcelModules (refer to Screenshot 1A). The options for this procedure include the problem title and a box to specify whether we want a graph of carrying cost versus service level. After we specify these options, we get the worksheet shown in Screenshot 7A. We now enter values for the mean DDLT (μ), standard deviation of DDLT (σ), service level desired, and carrying cost, C_h, in cells B6 to B9, respectively.

The worksheet calculates and displays the following output measures:

- Safety stock, SS ($= Z \times \sigma$), in cell B12
- Reorder point ($= \mu + Z \times \sigma$), in cell B13
- Safety stock carrying *cost* ($= C_h \times Z \times \sigma$), in cell B15

If requested, ExcelModules will draw a plot of the safety stock carrying cost for different values of the service level. This graph, shown in Screenshot 7B, is drawn on a separate worksheet. As expected, the shape of this graph is the same as that shown in Figure 9.

File: 12-7.xls, sheets: 12-7A and 12-7B

SCREENSHOT 7A
Safety Stock (Normal DDLT) Model for Hinsdale

	A	B	C	D	E
1	**Hinsdale Company**				
2	Inventory	Safety Stock (Normal DDLT)			
3	Enter the input data in the cells shaded				
4					
5	Input Data				
6	Mean DDLT, μ	350			
7	Std deviation of DDLT, σ	10			
8	Service level desired	95.00%	(percentage)		
9	Carrying cost, C$_h$	$1.00			
10			95% is entered as 95 here.		
11	Results				
12	Safety stock, SS	16.45			
13	Reorder point, ROP	366.45	ROP = μ + SS		
14					
15	SS carrying cost	$16.45			
16					
17					
18	**Cost Table for Graph**	Start at	89.00%	Increment by	1.00%
19					
20		Service level	SS carrying cost		
21		89.00%	12.27		
22		90.00%	12.82		
23		91.00%	13.41		
24		92.00%	14.05		
25		93.00%	14.76		
26		94.00%	15.55		
27		95.00%	16.45		
28		96.00%	17.51		
29		97.00%	18.81		

Data for graph, generated and used by ExcelModules

SCREENSHOT 7B Plot of Safety Stock Cost versus Service Level for Hinsdale

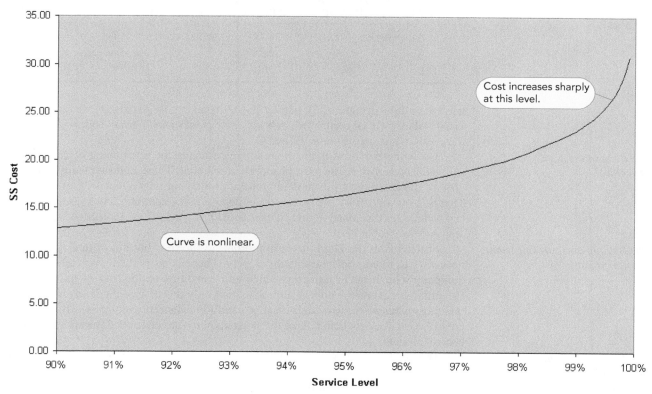

IN ACTION

Inventory Modeling at the San Miguel Corporation in the Philippines

In a typical manufacturing firm, inventories comprise a big part of assets. At the San Miguel Corporation (SMC), which produces and distributes more than 300 products to every corner of the Philippine archipelago, raw material accounts for about 10% of total assets. The significant amount of money tied up in inventory encouraged the company's Operations Research Department to develop a series of cost-minimizing inventory models.

One major SMC product, ice cream, uses dairy and cheese curd imported from Australia, New Zealand, and Europe. The normal mode of delivery is sea, and delivery frequencies are limited by supplier schedules. Stockouts, however, are avoidable through airfreight expediting. SMC's inventory model for ice cream

balances ordering, carrying, and stockout costs while considering delivery frequency constraints and minimum order quantities. Results showed that current safety stocks of 30–51 days could be cut in half for dairy and cheese curd. Even with the increased use of expensive airfreight, SMC saved $170,000 per year through the new policy.

Another SMC product, beer, consists of three major ingredients: malt, hops, and chemicals. Because these ingredients are characterized by low expediting costs and high unit costs, inventory modeling pointed to optimal policies that reduced safety stock levels, saving another $180,000 per year.

Source: Based on E. Del Rosario. "Logistical Nightmare," *OR/MS Today* (April 1999): 44–45. Reprinted with permission.

9 ABC Analysis

So far, we have shown how to develop inventory policies using quantitative decision models. There are, however, some very practical issues, such as **ABC analysis**, that should be incorporated into inventory decisions. ABC analysis recognizes the fact that some inventory items are more important than others. The purpose of this analysis is to divide all of a company's inventory

TABLE 5
Summary of ABC
Analysis

INVENTORY GROUP	DOLLAR USAGE	INVENTORY ITEMS	ARE QUANTITATIVE INVENTORY CONTROL TECHNIQUES USED?
A	70%	10%	Yes
B	20%	20%	In some cases
C	10%	70%	No

items into three groups: A, B, and C. Then, depending on the group, we decide how the inventory levels should be controlled. A brief description of each group follows, with general guidelines as to which items are A, B, and C.

The items in the A group are critical.

The inventory items in the A group are critical to the functioning of the company. As a result, their inventory levels must be closely monitored. These items typically make up more than 70% of the company's business in monetary value but only about 10% of all inventory items. That is, a few inventory items are very important to the company. As a result, the inventory control techniques discussed in this chapter should be used where appropriate for every item in the A group (see Table 5).

The B group items are important but not critical.

The items in the B group are important to the firm but not critical. Thus, it may not be necessary to monitor all these items closely. These items typically represent about 20% of the company's business in monetary value and constitute about 20% of the items in inventory. Quantitative inventory models should be used only on some of the B items. The cost of implementing and using these models must be carefully balanced with the benefits of better inventory control. Usually, less than half of the B group items are controlled through the use of inventory control models.

The C group items are not as important as the others in terms of annual dollar value.

The items in the C group are not as important to the operation of the company. These items typically represent only about 10% of the company's business in monetary value but may constitute 70% of the items in inventory. Group C could include inexpensive items such as bolts, washers, screws, and so on. They are usually not controlled using inventory control models because the cost of implementing and using such models would far exceed the value gained.

We illustrate the use of ABC analysis using the example of Silicon Chips, Inc.

Silicon Chips, Inc., Example

Silicon Chips, Inc., maker of super-fast DRAM chips, has organized its 10 inventory items on an annual dollar-volume basis. Table 6 shows the items (identified by item number and part number), their annual demands, and unit costs. How should the company classify these items into groups A, B, and C? As discussed next, we use the worksheet provided in ExcelModules to answer this question.

USING EXCELMODULES FOR ABC ANALYSIS We select the choice titled ABC Analysis from the Inventory Models menu in ExcelModules (refer to Screenshot 1A). The options for this procedure include the problem title and boxes to specify the number and names of the items we want to classify. After we specify these options for the Silicon Chips example,

File: 12-8.xls

TABLE 6
Inventory Data for
Silicon Chips, Inc.

ITEM NUMBER	PART NUMBER	ANNUAL VOLUME (UNITS)	UNIT COST
Item 1	01036	100	$ 8.50
Item 2	01307	1,200	$ 0.42
Item 3	10286	1,000	$ 90.00
Item 4	10500	1,000	$ 12.50
Item 5	10572	250	$ 0.60
Item 6	10867	350	$ 42.86
Item 7	11526	500	$154.00
Item 8	12572	600	$ 14.17
Item 9	12760	1,550	$ 17.00
Item 10	14075	2,000	$ 0.60

SCREENSHOT 8   ABC Analysis for Silicon Chips, Inc.

Click this button *after* entering all input data.

	A	B	C	D	E	F	G	H
1	**Silicon Chips, Inc.**							
2	Inventory	ABC Analysis						
3	Analyze			Enter the volume and the costs into the data table. Then click the **Analyze** button.				
4								
5	Input Data							
6		Volume	Unit cost		Dollar volume	% Dollar volume	Cumulative $-vol %	
7	Item 1	100	$8.50		$850.00	0.37%	0.37%	
8	Item 2	1200	$0.42		$504.00	0.22%	0.58%	
9	Item 3	1000	$90.00		$90,000.00	38.78%	39.37%	
10	Item 4	1000	$12.50		$12,500.00	5.39%	44.75%	
11	Item 5	250	$0.60		$150.00	0.06%	44.82%	
12	Item 6	350	$42.86		$15,001.00	6.46%	51.28%	
13	Item 7	500	$154.00		$77,000.00	33.18%	84.46%	
14	Item 8	600	$14.17		$8,502.00	3.66%	88.13%	
15	Item 9	1550	$17.00		$26,350.00	11.35%	99.48%	
16	Item 10	2000	$0.60		$1,200.00	0.52%	100.00%	
17		Input data			Total	$232,057.00		
18								
19	ABC Analysis: Items sorted in descending order by dollar volume							
20		Volume	Unit cost		Dollar volume	% Dollar volume	Cumulative $-vol %	
21	Item 3	1000.000	90.000	A	$90,000.00	38.78%	38.78%	2 items
22	Item 7	500.000	154.000		$77,000.00	33.18%	71.97%	
23	Item 9	1550.000	17.000	B	$26,350.00	11.35%	83.32%	3 items
24	Item 6	350.000	42.860		$15,001.00	6.46%	89.78%	
25	Item 4	1000.000	12.500		$12,500.00	5.39%	95.17%	
26	Item 8	600.000	14.170		$8,502.00	3.66%	98.83%	
27	Item 10	2000.000	0.600	C	$1,200.00	0.52%	99.35%	5 items
28	Item 1	100.000	8.500		$850.00	0.37%	99.72%	
29	Item 2	1200.000	0.420		$504.00	0.22%	99.94%	
30	Item 5	250.000	0.600		$150.00	0.06%	100.00%	
31					Total	$232,057.00		

Items are sorted in descending order of percentage $ volume.

Sorted values of percentage $ volume

Items are sorted in descending order of percentage dollar volume.

we get the worksheet shown in Screenshot 8. We now enter the volume and unit cost for each item in cells B7:C16 of this worksheet.

When we enter the input data, the worksheet computes the dollar volume and percentage dollar volume (based on total dollar volume) for each item. These values are shown in cells E7:F16 of Screenshot 8. After entering the data for *all* items, we click the Analyze button. The worksheet now sorts the items, in descending order of percentage dollar volume. These values are shown in descending order in cells F21:F30 of Screenshot 8.

The sorted results for the Silicon Chips, Inc., problem are shown in cells A21:C30 of Screenshot 8. Items 3 and 7, which constitute only 20% ($= 2/10$) of the total number of items, account for 71.97% of the total dollar volume of all items. These two items should therefore be classified as group A items.

Items 9, 6, and 4, which constitute 30% ($= 3/10$) of the total number of items, account for 23.20% ($= 95.17 - 71.97$) of the total dollar volume of all items. These three items should therefore be classified as group B items.

IN ACTION Inventory Modeling at Teradyne

Teradyne, a huge manufacturer of electronic testing equipment for semiconductor plants worldwide, asked the Wharton School of Business to evaluate its global inventory parts system. Teradyne's system is complex because it stocks over 10,000 parts with a wide variety of prices (from a few dollars to $10,000) because its customers are dispersed all over the world, and because customers demand immediate response when a part is needed.

The professors selected two basic inventory models they felt could be used to improve the current inventory system effectively. An important consideration in using basic inventory models is their simplicity, which improved the professors' communication with Teradyne executives. In the field of modeling, it is very important for managers who depend on the models to thoroughly understand the underlying processes and a model's limitations.

Input data to the inventory models included actual planned inventory levels, holding costs, observed demand rates, and estimated lead times. The outputs included service levels and a prediction of the expected number of late part shipments. The first inventory model showed that Teradyne could reduce late shipments by over 90% with just a 3% increase in inventory investment. The second model showed that the company could reduce inventory by 37% while improving customer service levels by 4%.

Source: Based on M. A. Cohen, Y. Zheng, and Y. Wang. "Identifying Opportunities for Improving Teradyne's Service Parts Logistics System," *Interfaces* 29, 4 (July–August 1999): 1–18.

The remaining items constitute 50% ($= 5/10$) of the total number of items. However, they account for only 4.83% ($= 100 - 95.17$) of the total dollar volume of all items. These five items should therefore be classified as group C items.

Summary

This chapter presents several inventory models and discusses how we can use ExcelModules to analyze these models. The focus of all models is to answer the same two primary questions in inventory planning: (1) how much to order and (2) when to order. The basic EOQ inventory model makes a number of assumptions: (1) known and constant demand and lead times, (2) instantaneous receipt of inventory, (3) no quantity discounts, (4) no stockouts or shortages, and (5) the only variable costs are ordering costs and carrying costs. If these assumptions are valid, the EOQ inventory model provides optimal solutions.

If these assumptions do not hold, more complex models are needed. For such cases, the economic production quantity and quantity discount models are necessary. We also discuss the computation of safety stocks when demand during lead time is unknown for two cases: (1) Cost of stockout is known and (2) Cost of stockout is unknown. Finally, we present ABC analysis to determine how inventory items should be classified based on their importance and value. For all models discussed in this chapter, we show how Excel worksheets can be used to perform the computations.

Glossary

ABC Analysis An analysis that divides inventory into three groups: Group A is more important than group B, which is more important than group C.

Average Inventory The average inventory on hand. Computed as (Maximum inventory + Minimum inventory)/2.

Carrying Cost The cost of holding one unit of an item in inventory for one period (typically a year). Also called *holding cost*.

Demand during Lead Time (DDLT) The demand for an item during the lead time, between order placement and order receipt.

Economic Order Quantity (EOQ) The amount of inventory ordered that will minimize the total inventory cost. It is also called the optimal order quantity, or Q^*.

Economic Production Quantity (EPQ) Model An inventory model in which the instantaneous receipt assumption has been eliminated. The inventory build-up, therefore, occurs over a period of time.

Instantaneous Inventory Receipt A system in which inventory is received or obtained at one point in time and not over a period of time.

Lead Time The time it takes to receive an order after it is placed.

Ordering Cost The cost of placing an order.

Purchase Cost The cost of purchasing one unit of an inventory item.

Quantity Discount The cost per unit when large orders of an inventory item are placed.

Reorder Point (ROP)   The number of units on hand when an order for more inventory is placed.

Safety Stock   Extra inventory that is used to help avoid stockouts.

Service Level   The chance, expressed as a percentage, that there will not be a stockout. Service level $= 1 -$ Probability of a stockout.

Setup Cost   The cost to set up the manufacturing or production process.

Stockout   A situation that occurs when there is no inventory on hand.

Total Cost   The sum of the total ordering, total carrying, and total purchasing costs.

Solved Problems

Solved Problem 1

Patterson Electronics supplies microcomputer circuitry to a company that incorporates microprocessors into refrigerators and other home appliances. Currently, Patterson orders a particular component in batches of 300 units from one of its suppliers. The annual demand for this component is 2,000.

    a. If the carrying cost is estimated at $1 per unit per year, what would the ordering cost have to be to make the order quantity optimal?

    b. If the ordering cost is estimated to be $50 per order, what would the carrying cost have to be to make the order quantity optimal?

Solution

    a. Recall from Equation 8 that the ordering cost can be computed as

$$C_o = Q^2 \times C_h/(2D)$$

In Patterson's case, $D = 2,000$, $Q = 300$, and $C_h = \$1$. Substituting these values, we get an ordering cost, C_o, of $22.50 per order.

    b. Recall from Equation 9 that the carrying cost can be computed as

$$C_h = 2DC_o/Q^2$$

In Patterson's case, $D = 2,000$, $Q = 300$, and $C_o = \$50$. Substituting these values, we get a carrying cost, C_h, of $2.22 per unit per year.

Solved Problem 2

Flemming Accessories produces paper slicers used in offices and in art stores. The minislicer has been one of its most popular items: Annual demand is 6,750 units. Kristen Flemming, owner of the firm, produces the minislicers in batches. On average, Kristen can manufacture 125 minislicers per day. Demand for these slicers during the production process is 30 per day. The setup cost for the equipment necessary to produce the minislicers is $150. Carrying costs are $1 per minislicer per year. How many minislicers should Kristen manufacture in each batch? Assume that minislicers cost $10 each to produce.

Solution

File: 12-9.xls

To solve this problem, we select the choice titled Economic Production Quantity (EPQ) from the Inventory Models menu in ExcelModules. The input entries, as well as the resulting computations, are shown in Screenshot 9.

    The results show that Flemming Accessories has an EPQ of 1,632 units. The annual total setup and carrying costs are $620.28 each. The annual total cost, including the cost of production, is $68,740.56.

SCREENS HOT 9
EPQ Model for Flemming Accessories

	A	B	C	D
1	**Solved Problem 2**			
2	Inventory	Economic Production Quantity Model		
3	Enter the data in the cells shaded YELLOW. You may have to do some			
4	work to compute the daily production and demand rates.			
5				
6	Input Data			
7	Demand rate, D	6750		
8	Setup cost, C_s	$150.00	Input data	
9	Carrying cost, C_h	$1.00	(fixed amount)	
10	Daily production rate, p	125		
11	Daily demand rate, d	30		
12	Unit purchase cost, P	$10.00		
13				
14	Results			
15	Economic production quantity, Q*	1632.32	EPQ is 1632 units.	
16	Maximum inventory	1240.56		
17	Average inventory	620.28		
18	Number of setups	4.14		
19				
20	Total holding cost	$620.28		
21	Total setup cost	$620.28		
22	Total production cost	$67,500.00		
23	Total cost, TC	$68,740.56	Total cost is $68,740.56.	

Solved Problem 3

File: 12-10.xls

Dorsey Distributors has an annual demand for a metal detector of 1,400. The cost of a typical detector to Dorsey is $400. Carrying cost is estimated to be 20% of the unit cost, and the ordering cost is $25 per order. If Dorsey orders in quantities of 300 or more, it can get a 5% discount on the cost of the detectors. Should Dorsey take the quantity discount?

Solution

To solve this problem, we select the choice titled Quantity Discount option from the Inventory Models menu in ExcelModules. There are two discount levels in this case. The input en-

SCREENSHOT 10
Quantity Discount Model for Dorsey Distributors

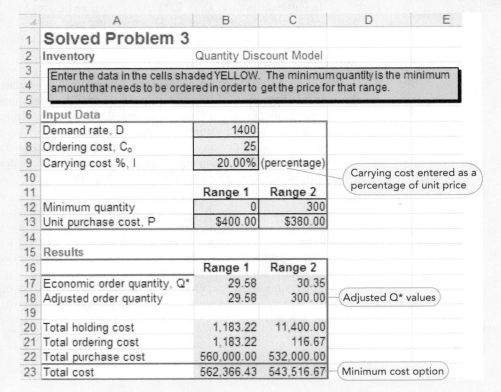

	A	B	C	D	E
1	**Solved Problem 3**				
2	Inventory	Quantity Discount Model			
3	Enter the data in the cells shaded YELLOW. The minimum quantity is the minimum				
4	amount that needs to be ordered in order to get the price for that range.				
5					
6	Input Data				
7	Demand rate, D	1400			
8	Ordering cost, C_o	25			
9	Carrying cost %, I	20.00%	(percentage)	Carrying cost entered as a percentage of unit price	
10					
11		Range 1	Range 2		
12	Minimum quantity	0	300		
13	Unit purchase cost, P	$400.00	$380.00		
14					
15	Results				
16		Range 1	Range 2		
17	Economic order quantity, Q*	29.58	30.35		
18	Adjusted order quantity	29.58	300.00	Adjusted Q* values	
19					
20	Total holding cost	1,183.22	11,400.00		
21	Total ordering cost	1,183.22	116.67		
22	Total purchase cost	560,000.00	532,000.00		
23	Total cost	562,366.43	543,516.67	Minimum cost option	

tries and the resulting computations are shown in Screenshot 10. The results show that Dorsey should order 300 units each time, at a discounted unit cost of $380. The annual total ordering cost is $116.67, and the annual total carrying cost is $11,400. The annual total cost, including the total purchase cost, is $543,516.57.

Discussion Questions and Problems

Discussion Questions

1 Why is inventory an important consideration for managers?

2 What is the purpose of inventory control?

3 Why wouldn't a company always store large quantities of inventory to eliminate shortages and stockouts?

4 Describe the major decisions that must be made in inventory control.

5 What are some of the assumptions made in using the EOQ?

6 Discuss the major inventory costs that are used in determining the EOQ.

7 What is the ROP? How is it determined?

8 What is the purpose of sensitivity analysis?

9 What assumptions are made in the EPQ model?

10 What happens to the EPQ model when the daily production rate becomes very large?

11 In the quantity discount model, why is the carrying cost expressed as a percentage of the unit cost, I, instead of the cost per unit per year, C_h?

12 Briefly describe what is involved in solving a quantity discount model.

13 Discuss the methods that are used in determining safety stock when the stockout cost is known and when the stockout cost is unknown.

14 Briefly describe what is meant by ABC analysis. What is the purpose of this inventory technique?

Problems

15 Shakina Harris, who works in her brother's hardware store, is in charge of purchasing. Shakina has determined that the annual demand for #6 screws is 150,000 and is fairly constant over the 200 days that the store is open each year. She estimates that it costs $30 every time an order is placed. This cost includes her wages, the cost of the forms used in placing the order, and so on. Furthermore, she estimates that the cost of carrying one screw in inventory for a year is 0.6 cents.

(a) How many #6 screws should Shakina order at a time?

(b) It takes 8 working days for an order of #6 screws to arrive once the order has been placed.

Because the demand is fairly constant, Shakina believes that she can avoid stockouts completely if she orders the screws only when necessary. What is the ROP?

(c) Shakina's brother believes that she is placing too many orders for screws each year. He believes that orders should be placed only twice per year. If Shakina follows her brother's policy, how much more would this cost every year over the ordering policy that she developed in part (a)? If only two orders are placed each year, what effect would this have on the ROP?

(d) Shakina now believes that her estimate of an ordering cost of $30 per order is too low. Although she does not know the exact cost, she believes that it could be as high as $60 per order. How would the optimal order quantity in part (a) change if the ordering cost were $40, $50, or $60?

16 Neha Shah is the purchasing agent for a firm that sells industrial valves and fluid control devices. One of the most popular valves is the KA1, which has an annual demand of 6,000 units. The cost of each valve is $120, and the inventory carrying cost is estimated to be 8% of the cost of each valve. Neha has made a study of the costs involved in placing an order for any of the valves that the firm stocks, and she has concluded that the average ordering cost is $45 per order. Furthermore, it takes about two weeks for an order to arrive from the supplier, and during this time the demand per week for KA1 valves is approximately 120. Compute the EOQ, ROP, optimal number of orders per year, and total annual cost for KA1 valves.

17 Keith Smart has been in the building business for most of his life. Keith's biggest competitor is Delta Birch. Through many years of experience, Keith knows that the ordering cost for an order of plywood is $150 and that the carrying cost is 25% of the unit cost. Both Keith and Delta receive plywood in loads that cost $600 per load. Furthermore, Keith and Delta use the same supplier of plywood, and Keith was able to find out that Delta orders in quantities of 300 loads at a time. Ken also knows that 300 loads is the EOQ for Delta. What is Delta's annual demand, in loads of plywood?

18 Shoes R Us is a local shoe store located in Camden. Annual demand for a popular sandal is 1,000 pairs

of sandals, and Gary Cole, the owner of Shoes R Us, has been in the habit of ordering 200 pairs of sandals at a time. Gary estimates that the ordering cost is $20 per order. The cost of a pair of sandals is $10.

(a) For Gary's ordering policy to be correct, what would the carrying cost have to be as a percentage of the unit cost?

(b) If the carrying cost were 20% of the unit cost, what would be the optimal order quantity?

19 Annual demand for the Dobbs model airplane kit is 80,000 units. Albert Dobbs, president of Dobbs' Terrific Toys, controls one of the largest toy companies in Nevada. He estimates that the ordering cost is $40 per order. The carrying cost is $7 per unit per year. It takes 25 days between the time that Albert places an order for the model airplane kit and the time when they are received at his warehouse. During this time, the daily demand is estimated to be 450 units.

(a) Compute the EOQ, ROP, and optimal number of orders per year.

(b) Albert Dobbs now believes that the carrying cost may be as high as $14 per unit per year. Furthermore, Albert estimates that the lead time may be 35 days instead of 25 days. Redo part (a), using these revised estimates.

20 Floral Beauty, Inc., is a large floral arrangements store located in Eastwood Mall. Bridal Lilies, which are a specially created bunch of lilies for bridal bouquets, cost Floral Beauty $17 each. There is an annual demand for 24,000 Bridal Lilies. The manager of Floral Beauty has determined that the ordering cost is $120 per order, and the carrying cost, as a percentage of the unit cost, is 18%. Floral Beauty is now considering a new supplier of Bridal Lilies. Each lily would cost only $16.50, but to get this discount, Floral Beauty would have to buy shipments of 3,000 Bridal Lilies at a time. Should Floral Beauty use the new supplier and take this discount for quantity buying?

21 Cameron Boats, a supplier of boating equipment, sells 5,000 WM-4 diesel engines every year. These engines are shipped to Cameron in a shipping container of 100 cubic feet, and Cameron Boats keeps the warehouse full of these WM-4 motors. The warehouse can hold 5,000 cubic feet of boating supplies. Cameron estimates that the ordering cost is $400 per order and that the carrying cost is $100 per motor per year. Cameron Boats is considering the possibility of expanding the warehouse for the WM-4 motors. How much should Cameron Boats expand, and how much would it be worth it for the company to make the expansion?

22 Tarbutton Lawn Distributors is a wholesale organization that supplies retail stores with lawn care and household products. One building is used to store FirstClass lawn mowers. The building is 50 feet wide by 40 feet deep by 8 feet high. Andrea Dormer, manager of the warehouse, estimates that only 90% of the warehouse can be used to store the FirstClass lawn mowers. The remaining 10% is used for walkways and a small office. Each FirstClass lawn mower comes in a box that is 5 feet by 4 feet by 2 feet high. The annual demand for these lawn mowers is 48,000, and the ordering cost for Tarbutton Lawn Distributors is $75 per order. It is estimated that it costs Tarbutton Lawn $45 per lawn mower per year for storage. Tarbutton Lawn Distributors is thinking about increasing the size of the warehouse. The company can do this only by making the warehouse deeper. At the present time, the warehouse is 40 feet deep. How many feet of depth should be added on to the warehouse if they wish to minimize the total annual costs? How much should the company be willing to pay for this addition? Remember that only 90% of the total space can be used to store FirstClass lawn mowers.

23 Morgan Arthur has spent the past few weeks determining inventory costs for Armstrong, a toy manufacturer located near Cincinnati, Ohio. She knows that annual demand will be 30,000 units per year and that carrying cost will be $1.50 per unit per year. Ordering cost, on the other hand, can vary from $45 per order to $50 per order. During the past 450 working days, Morgan has observed the following frequency distribution for the ordering cost:

ORDERING COST	FREQUENCY
$45	85
$46	95
$47	90
$48	80
$49	55
$50	45

Morgan's boss would like Morgan to determine an EOQ value for each possible ordering cost and to determine an EOQ value for the expected ordering cost.

24 Blaine Abrams is the owner of a small company that produces electric scissors used to cut fabric. The annual demand is for 75,000 scissors, and Blaine produces the scissors in batches. On average, Blaine can produce 1,000 pairs of scissors per day during the production process. Demand for scissors has been about 250 pairs of scissors per day. The cost to set up the production process is $800, and it costs Blaine $0.90 to carry 1 pair of

scissors for one year. How many scissors should Blaine produce in each batch?

25 Carter Cohen, inventory control manager for Raydex, receives wheel bearings from Wheel & Gears, a small producer of metal parts. Unfortunately, Wheel & Gears can produce only 5,000 wheel bearings per day. Raydex receives 100,000 wheel bearings from Wheel & Gears each year. Because Raydex operates 200 working days each year, the average daily demand of wheel bearings by Raydex is 500. The ordering cost for Raydex is $400 per order, and the carrying cost is $6 per wheel bearing per year. How many wheel bearings should Raydex order from Wheel & Gears at one time? Wheel & Gears has agreed to ship the maximum number of wheel bearings that it produces each day to Raydex when an order has been received.

26 Chandler Manufacturing has a demand for 1,000 pumps each year. The cost of a pump is $50. It costs Chandler Manufacturing $40 to place an order, and the carrying cost is 25% of the unit cost. If pumps are ordered in quantities of 200, Chandler Manufacturing can get a 3% discount on the cost of the pumps. Should Chandler Manufacturing order 200 pumps at a time and take the 3% discount?

27 Arms of Steel is an organization that sells weight training sets. The carrying cost for the AS1 model is $5 per set per year. To meet demand, Arms of Steel orders large quantities of AS1 seven times a year. The stockout cost for AS1 is estimated to be $50 per set. Over the past several years, Arms of Steel has observed the following demand during the lead time for AS1:

DEMAND DURING LEAD TIME	PROBABILITY
40	0.1
50	0.2
60	0.2
70	0.2
80	0.2
90	0.1

The reorder point for AS1 is 60 units. What level of safety stock should be maintained for the AS1 model?

28 Victoria Blunt is in charge of maintaining hospital supplies at Mercy Hospital. During the past year, the mean lead time demand for bandage BX-5 was 600. Furthermore, the standard deviation for BX-5 was 70. Ms. Blunt would like to maintain a 95% service level.

(a) What safety stock level do you recommend for BX-5?

(b) Victoria has just been severely chastised for her inventory policy. Dwight Seymour, her boss, believes that the service level should be 99%. Compute the safety stock levels for a 99% service level.

(c) Victoria knows that the carrying cost of BX-5 is $0.50 per unit per year. Compute the carrying cost associated with 95% and 99% service levels.

29 Finn simply does not have time to analyze all the items in his company's inventory. As a young manager, he has more important things to do. The following is a table of six items in inventory, along with the unit cost and the demand, in units:

IDENTIFICATION CODE	UNIT COST	DEMAND (UNITS)
U1	$ 2.00	1,110
V2	$ 5.40	1,110
W3	$ 2.08	961
X4	$74.54	1,104
Y5	$ 5.84	1,200
Z6	$ 1.12	896

Which item(s) should be carefully controlled using a quantitative inventory technique, and what item(s) should not be closely controlled?

30 The demand for barbeque grills has been fairly large in the past several years, and Estate Supplies, Inc., usually orders new barbeque grills five times a year. It is estimated that the ordering cost is $60 per order. The carrying cost is $10 per grill per year. Furthermore, Estate Supplies, Inc., has estimated that the stockout cost is $50 per unit. The reorder point is 650 units. Although the demand each year is high, it varies considerably. The demand during the lead time is as follows (see Table for Problem 30 at the top of the next page).

The lead time is 12 working days. How much safety stock should Estate Supplies, Inc., maintain?

31 Omar Haaris receives 5,000 tripods annually from Top-Grade Suppliers to meet his annual demand. Omar runs a large photographic outlet, and the tripods are used primarily with 35mm cameras. The ordering cost is $15 per order, and the carrying cost is $0.50 per unit per year. Weekly demand is 100 tripods.

(a) What is the optimal order quantity?

(b) Top-Grade is offering a new shipping option. When an order is placed, Top-Grade will ship one-third of the order every week for three weeks instead of shipping the entire order at one time. What is the order quantity if Omar

Table for Problem 30

DEMAND DURING LEAD TIME	PROBABILITY
600	0.25
650	0.23
700	0.12
750	0.10
800	0.08
850	0.05
900	0.05
950	0.04
1,000	0.03
1,050	0.03
1,100	0.02

chooses to use this option? To simplify your calculations, assume that the average inventory is equal to one-half of the maximum inventory level for Top-Grade's new option.

(c) Suppose Top-Grade Suppliers offers to ship one-fifth of the order every week for five weeks. What is the order quantity under this option? Make the same assumption as in part (b).

(d) Calculate the total cost for each option. What do you recommend?

32 Amco Convenience Store purchases 500 hammers a year for its inventory from its supplier, who offers pricing at quantity discounts. The quantities and pricing from this supplier are shown in the following table:

ORDER QUANTITY	UNIT PRICE
0–149	$12.00
150–349	$11.50
350–599	$10.50
600 or more	$ 9.80

The cost for Amco to place an order is $60, and the cost to store a hammer in inventory for a year is $2. What quantity should Amco order?

33 Asbury Products offers the following discount schedule for its 4- by 8-foot sheets of good-quality plywood:

ORDER QUANTITY	UNIT PRICE
99 sheets or less	$18.00
100 to 500 sheets	$17.70
More than 500 sheets	$17.45

Home Sweet Home Company orders plywood from Asbury Products. Home Sweet Home has an ordering cost of $55. The carrying cost is 25%, and the annual demand is 1,000 sheets. What do you recommend?

34 Tropic Citrus Products produces orange juice, grapefruit juice, and other citrus-related items. Tropic obtains fruit concentrate from a cooperative in Orlando that consists of approximately 50 citrus growers. The cooperative will sell a minimum of 100 cans of fruit concentrate to citrus processors such as Tropic. The cost per can is $9.90.

Last year, a cooperative developed an incentive bonus program (IBP) to give an incentive to its large customers to buy in quantity. Here is how it works: If 200 cans of concentrate are purchased, 10 cans of free concentrate are included in the deal. In addition, the names of the companies purchasing the concentrate are added to a drawing for a new personal computer. The personal computer has a value of about $3,000, and currently about 1,000 companies are eligible for this drawing. At 300 cans of concentrate, the cooperative will give away 30 free cans and will also place the company name in the drawing for the personal computer. When the quantity goes up to 400 cans of concentrate, 40 cans of concentrate will be given away free with the order. In addition, the company is also placed in a drawing for the personal computer and a free trip for two. The value of the trip for two is approximately $5,000. About 800 companies are expected to qualify and to be in the running for this trip.

Tropic estimates that its annual demand for fruit concentrate is 1,000 cans. In addition, the ordering cost is estimated to be $10.00, and the carrying cost is estimated to be 10%, or about $1.00 per unit. The firm is intrigued with the IBP. If the company decides that it will keep the trip or the computer if they are won, what should it do?

35 Lindsay Hawkes sells discs that contain 25 software packages that perform a variety of financial functions typically used by business students. Depending on the quantity ordered, Lindsay offers the following price discounts:

ORDER QUANTITY	PRICE
1 to 600	$10.00
601 to 1,100	$ 9.92
1,101 to 1,550	$ 9.86
1,551 and up	$ 9.80

The annual demand is 3,000 units on average. Lindsay's setup cost to produce the discs is $350. She estimates holding costs to be 10% of the price, or about $1 per unit per year. What is the optimal number of discs to produce at a time?

36 Demand during lead time for one brand of TV is normally distributed with a mean of 56 TVs and a standard deviation of 18 TVs. What safety stock should be carried for a 95% service level? What is the appropriate ROP?

37 Based on available information, lead time demand for CD-ROM drives averages 250 units (normally distributed), with a standard deviation of 25 drives. Management wants a 98% service level. How many drives should be carried as safety stock? What is the appropriate ROP?— Excel QM

38 A product is delivered to Monica's company once a year. The ROP, without safety stock, is 300 units. Carrying cost is $25 per unit per year, and the cost of a stockout is $80 per unit per year. Given the following demand probabilities during the reorder period, how much safety stock should be carried?

DEMAND DURING REORDER PERIOD	PROBABILITY
100	0.3
200	0.1
300	0.3
400	0.2
500	0.1

39 Barb's company has compiled the following data on a small set of products:

ITEM	ANNUAL DEMAND	UNIT COST
1	410	$ 0.75
2	330	$ 17.00
3	300	$ 3.00
4	200	$ 0.90
5	240	$110.00
6	625	$ 0.75
7	85	$ 25.00
8	75	$ 2.00
9	100	$125.00
10	125	$ 1.50

Perform an ABC analysis on her data.

40 The Century One Store has 10 items in inventory, as shown in the following table. The manager wants to divide these items into ABC classifications. What would you recommend?

ITEM	ANNUAL DEMAND	UNIT COST
A	1,750	$ 10
B	300	$1,500
C	500	$ 500
D	6,000	$ 10
E	1,000	$ 20
F	1,500	$ 45
G	4,000	$ 12
H	600	$ 20
I	3,000	$ 50
J	2,500	$ 5

41 Lea Ash opens a new cosmetics store. There are numerous items in inventory, and Lea knows that there are costs associated with inventory. Lea wants to classify the items according to dollars invested in them. The following table provides information about the 10 items that she carries:

ITEM NUMBER	UNIT COST	DEMAND (UNITS)
A	$4	1,500
B	$1	1,500
C	$3	700
D	$1	1,200
E	$8	200
F	$6	500
G	$2	1,000
H	$7	800
I	$8	1,200
J	$4	800

Use ABC analysis to classify these items into categories A, B, and C.

42 The following table shows the inventory data for the six items stocked by Apex Enterprises:

Lynn Robinson, Apex's inventory manager, does not feel that all the items can be controlled. What ordered quantities do you recommend for which inventory product(s)?

ITEM CODE	UNIT COST	ANNUAL DEMAND (UNITS)	ORDERING COST	CARRYING COST AS A PERCENTAGE OF UNIT COST
1	$150.00	560	$40	15
2	$ 4.10	490	$40	17
3	$ 2.25	500	$50	15
4	$ 10.60	600	$40	20
5	$ 4.00	540	$35	16
6	$ 11.00	450	$30	25

Case Study

Sturdivant Sound Systems

Sturdivant Sound Systems manufactures and sells stereo and CD sound systems in both console and component styles. All parts of the sound systems, with the exception of speakers, are produced in the Rochester, New York, plant. Speakers used in the assembly of Sturdivant's systems are purchased from Morris Electronics of Concord, New Hampshire.

Jason Pierce, purchasing agent for Sturdivant Sound Systems, submits a purchase requisition for the speakers once every four weeks. The company's annual requirements total 5,000 units (20 per working day), and the cost per unit is $60. (Sturdivant does not purchase in greater quantities because Morris Electronics, the supplier, does not offer quantity discounts.) Rarely does a shortage of speakers occur because Morris promises delivery within 1 week following receipt of a purchase requisition. (Total time between date of order and date of receipt is 10 days.)

Associated with the purchase of each shipment are procurement costs. These costs, which amount to $20 per order, include the costs of preparing the requisition, inspecting and storing the delivered goods, updating inventory records, and issuing a voucher and a check for payment. In addition to procurement costs, Sturdivant Sound Systems incurs inventory carrying costs, which include costs of insurance, storage, handling, taxes, and so on. These costs equal $6 per unit per year.

Beginning in August of this year, management of Sturdivant Sound Systems will embark on a companywide cost control program in an attempt to improve its profits. One of the areas to be scrutinized closely for possible cost savings is inventory procurement.

Discussion Questions

1. Compute the optimal order quantity.
2. Determine the appropriate ROP (in units).
3. Compute the cost savings that the company will realize if it implements the optimal inventory procurement decision.
4. Should procurement costs be considered a linear function of the number of orders?

Source: Jerry Kinard, Western Carolina University, and Brian Kinard, University of North Carolina–Wilmington.

Case Study

Martin-Pullin Bicycle Corporation

Martin-Pullin Bicycle Corporation (MPBC), located in Dallas, is a wholesale distributor of bicycles and bicycle parts. Formed in 1981 by cousins Ray Martin and Jim Pullin, the firm's primary retail outlets are located within a 400-mile radius of the distribution center. These retail outlets receive the order from Martin-Pullin within two days after notifying the distribution center, provided that the stock is available. However, if an order is not fulfilled by the company, no backorder is placed; the retailers arrange to get their shipment from other distributors, and MPBC loses that amount of business.

The company distributes a wide variety of bicycles. The most popular model, and the major source of revenue to the company, is the AirWing. MPBC receives all the models from a single manufacturer overseas, and shipment takes as long as four weeks from the time an order is placed. With the cost of communication, paperwork, and customs clearance included, MPBC estimates that each time an order is placed, it incurs a cost of $65. The purchase price paid by MPBC, per bicycle, is roughly 60% of the suggested retail price for all the styles available, and the inventory carrying cost is 1% per month (12% per year) of the purchase price paid by MPBC. The retail price (paid by the customers) for the AirWing is $170 per bicycle.

MPBC is interested in making the inventory plan for 2012. The firm wants to maintain a 95% service level with its customers to minimize the losses on the lost orders. The data collected for the past two years are summarized in the following table:

A forecast for AirWing model sales in the upcoming year 2012 has been developed and will be used to make an inventory plan for MPBC.

Discussion Questions

1. Develop an inventory plan to help MPBC.
2. Discuss ROPs and total costs.
3. How can you address demand that is not at the level of the planning horizon?

Source: "Martin-Pullin Bicycle Corporation" by Professor Kala Chand Seal, Loyola Marymount University. Copyright © Kala Chand Seal. Reprinted with permission.

MONTH	2010	2011	FORECAST FOR 2012
January	6	7	8
February	12	14	15
March	24	27	31
April	46	53	59
May	75	86	97
June	47	54	60
July	30	34	39
August	18	21	24
September	13	15	16
October	12	13	15
November	22	25	28
December	38	42	47
Total	343	391	439

 Internet Case Studies

See the Companion Website for this text, at www.pearsonhighered.com/balakrishnan, for additional case studies.

Project Management

The companion website for this text is www.pearsonhighered.com/balakrishnan.

1   Introduction

Every organization at one time or another will take on a large and complex project. For example, when Microsoft Corporation sets out to develop a major new operating system (e.g., Windows 7), a program costing hundreds of millions of dollars, and has hundreds of programmers working on millions of lines of code, immense stakes ride on the project being delivered properly and on time. Likewise, whenever STX Europe AS, a leading builder of cruise and offshore vessels headquartered in Oslo, Noway undertakes the construction of a cruise ship, this large, expensive project requires the coordination of tens of thousands of steps. Companies in almost every industry worry about how to manage similar large-scale complicated projects effectively.[1]

Project management techniques can be used to manage large, complex projects.

Scheduling large projects is a difficult challenge for most managers, especially when the stakes are high. There are numerous press reports of firms that have incurred millions of dollars in cost overruns in their projects for various reasons; one prominent recent example is Boeing's Dreamliner project. Unnecessary delays have occurred in many projects due to poor scheduling, and companies have gone bankrupt due to poor controls. How can such problems be solved? The answers lie in a popular decision modeling approach known as **project management**.

Phases in Project Management

A *project* can be defined as a series of related tasks (or activities) directed toward a major well-defined output. A project can consist of thousands of specific activities, each with its own set of requirements of time, money, and other resources, such as labor, raw materials, and machinery. Regardless of the scope and nature of the project, the management of large projects involves the three phases discussed in the following sections (see Figure 1). Each phase addresses specific questions regarding the project.

There are three phases in managing large projects.

Project planning is the first phase.

PROJECT PLANNING Project planning is the first phase of project management and involves considering issues such as goal setting, defining the project, and team organization. Specific questions that are considered in this phase include the following:

1. What is the goal or objective of the project?
2. What are the various activities (or tasks) that constitute the project?
3. How are these activities linked? That is, what are the precedence relationships between the activities?
4. What is the time required for each activity?
5. What other resources (e.g., labor, raw materials, machinery) are required for each activity?

Project scheduling is the second phase.

PROJECT SCHEDULING The second phase of project management involves developing the specific time schedule for each activity and assigning people, money, and supplies to specific activities. The questions addressed in this phase should be considered soon after the project has been planned but *before* it is actually started. These questions include the following:

1. When will the entire project be completed?
2. What is the schedule (start and finish time) for each activity?
3. What are the critical activities in the project? That is, what activities will delay the entire project if they are late?
4. What are the noncritical activities in the project? That is, what activities can run late without delaying the completion time of the entire project?
5. By how much can a noncritical activity be delayed without affecting the completion time of the entire project?
6. If we take the variability in activity times into consideration, what is the probability that a project will be completed by a specific deadline?

Gantt charts are useful for project scheduling.

One popular project scheduling approach is to use a **Gantt chart**. Gantt charts are low-cost means of helping managers make sure that (1) all activities are planned for, (2) their order of

---

[1] Portions of sections 1 and 2 have been adapted from J. Heizer and B. Render. *Operations Management*, Tenth Edition, © 2011. Adapted by permission of Pearson Eduction, Inc., Upper Saddle River, NJ.

FIGURE 1
Project Planning, Scheduling, and Controlling

Source: Adapted from J. Heizer and B. Render. *Operations Management*, Eighth Edition, © 2006. Reprinted by permission of Pearson Education, Inc., Upper Saddle River, NJ.

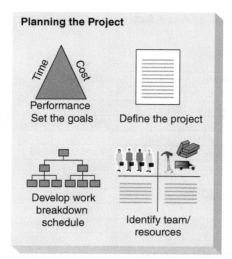

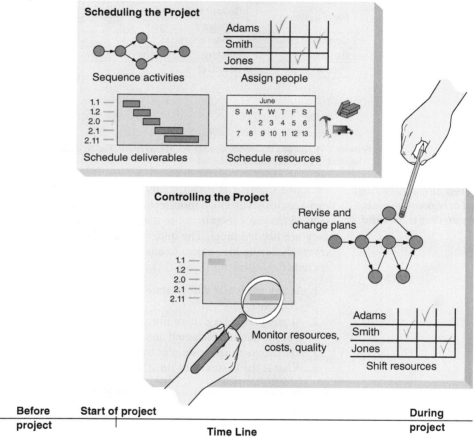

performance is accounted for, (3) the activity time schedules are recorded, and (4) the overall project time is developed. Gantt charts are easy to construct and understand, and they permit managers to plan and track the progress of each activity. For example, Figure 2 shows the Gantt chart for a routine servicing of a Delta jetliner during a 60-minute layover. Horizontal bars are drawn for each project activity along a time line.

For large projects, Gantt charts are used mainly to provide project summaries.

On simple projects, Gantt charts such as the one in Figure 2 can be used alone. Gantt charts, though, do not adequately illustrate the interrelationships between the activities and the resources. For this reason, on most large projects, Gantt charts are used mainly to provide summaries of a project's status. Projects are planned and scheduled using other network-based approaches, as discussed in subsequent sections.

FIGURE 2   Gantt Chart of Service Activities for a Commercial Aircraft During a Layover

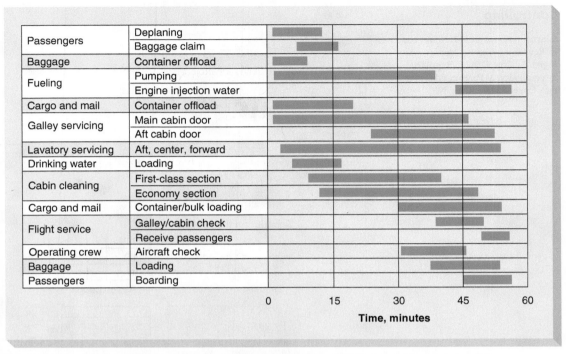

Source: J. Heizer and B. Render. *Operations Management*, Eighth Edition, © 2006. Adapted by permission of Pearson Education, Inc., Upper Saddle River, NJ.

Projects must be monitored and controlled at regular intervals. Project controlling is the third phase.

PROJECT CONTROLLING Like the control of any other management system, the control of large projects involves close monitoring of schedules, resources, and budgets. Control also means using a feedback loop to revise the project plan and having the ability to shift resources to where they are needed most. The questions addressed in this phase should be considered at regular intervals during the project to ensure that it meets all time and cost schedules. These questions include the following:

1. At any particular date or time, is the project on schedule, behind schedule, or ahead of schedule?
2. At any particular date or time, is the money spent on the project equal to, less than, or greater than the budgeted amount?
3. Are there enough resources available to finish the project on time?
4. What is the best way to finish the project in a shorter amount of time and at the least cost?

In this chapter, we investigate how project management techniques can be used to answer all these questions.

Use of Software Packages in Project Management

Software packages automate many of the routine calculations in project management.

In recent times, managing large and complex projects has become considerably easier due to the availability and capabilities of specialized project management software packages. These programs typically have simple interfaces for entering the project data, and they automate many of the routine calculations required for effective project management. In addition, they are capable of efficiently presenting the status of a project, using comprehensive graphs and tables. Some of these programs are Microsoft Project (by Microsoft Corp.), Primavera Project Planner (by Primavera Systems, Inc.), Turboproject (by OfficeWork Software), and Prochain Project Management (by Prochain Solutions, Inc.).

These programs produce a broad variety of reports, including (1) detailed cost breakdowns for each task, (2) total program labor curves, (3) cost distribution tables, (4) functional cost and hour summaries, (5) raw material expenditure forecasts, (6) variance reports, (7) time analysis reports, and (8) work status reports.

Excel is not a convenient software tool to use for project management.

Although it is possible to set up spreadsheets to perform many of the routine calculations involved, Excel is not the ideal choice for such tasks. So, in this chapter, we illustrate how Microsoft Project can be used to plan, schedule, and monitor projects.

There are, however, some issues that Microsoft Project does not handle. One such issue is question 4 posed in the section "Project Controlling" (What is the best way to finish the project in a shorter amount of time and at the least cost?) We can best answer this question by setting up and solving the problem as a linear programming (LP) model. For this question, we describe using Excel's Solver to solve the LP model.

2 Project Networks

Once a project's mission or goal has been clearly specified, the first issues we need to address deal with *project planning*. That is, we need to identify the activities that constitute the project, the precedence relationships between those activities, and the time and other resources required for each **activity**.

Identifying Activities

A project can be subdivided into several activities.

Almost any large project can be subdivided into a series of smaller activities or tasks. Identifying the activities involved in a project and the precedence relationships that may exist between these activities is the responsibility of the project team. In subdividing a project into various activities, however, the project team must be careful to ensure the following:

- Each activity has clearly identifiable starting and ending points. In other words, we should be able to recognize when an activity has started and when it has ended. For example, if the project goal is to build a house, an activity may be to lay the foundation. It is possible to clearly recognize when we start this activity and when we finish this activity.
- Each activity is clearly distinguishable from every other activity. That is, we should be able to associate every action we take and every dollar we spend with a specific (and unique) activity. For example, while building a house, we need to be able to recognize which actions and expenses are associated with laying the foundation.

An activity in a project may be a project of its own.

The number of activities in a project depends on the nature and scope of the project. It also depends on the level of detail with which the project manager wants to monitor and control the project. In a typical project, it is common for each activity in the project to be a project of its own. That is, a project may actually be a master project that, in turn, consists of several miniprojects. In practice, it is convenient to develop a work breakdown structure to identify the activities in a project.

A work breakdown structure details the activities in a project.

WORK BREAKDOWN STRUCTURE A **work breakdown structure (WBS)** defines a project by dividing it into its major subcomponents, which are then subdivided into more detailed subcomponents, and so on. Gross requirements for people, supplies, and equipment are also estimated in this planning phase. The WBS typically decreases in size from top to bottom and is indented like this:

Level	
1	Project
2	Major tasks in the project
3	Subtasks in major tasks
4	Activities to be completed

This hierarchical framework can be illustrated with the development of Microsoft's next operating system, internally code-named Windows 8. As we see in Figure 3, the project, creating a new operating system, is labeled 1.0. The first step is to identify the major tasks in the project (level 2). Two examples would be development of graphical user interfaces (GUIs) (1.1) and creating compatibility with previous versions of Windows (1.2). The major subtasks for 1.2 would be creating a team to handle compatibility with Windows 7 (1.21), Windows Vista

FIGURE 3
Work Breakdown Structure

Source: Adapted from J. Heizer and B. Render. *Operations Management*, Eighth Edition, © 2006. Reprinted by permission of Pearson Education, Inc., Upper Saddle River, NJ.

Level	Level ID Number	Activity
1	1.0	Develop/launch Windows 8 operating system
2	1.1	Development of GUIs
2	1.2	Ensure compatibility with earlier Windows versions
3	1.21	Compatibility with Windows 7
3	1.22	Compatibility with Windows Vista
3	1.23	Compatibility with Windows XP
4	1.231	Ability to import files

(1.22), Windows XP (1.23), and so on. Then each major subtask is broken down into level 4 activities that need to be done, such as importing files created in the previous version (1.231), saving files to work with the previous version (1.232), etc. There are usually many level 4 activities.

Identifying Activity Times and Other Resources

Activity times need to be estimated.

Once the activities of a project have been identified, the time required and other resources (e.g., money, labor, raw materials) for each activity are determined. In practice, identifying this input data is a complicated task involving a fair amount of expertise and competence on the project leader's part. For example, many individuals automatically present inflated time estimates, especially if their job is on the line if they fail to complete the activity on time. The project leader has to be able to recognize these types of issues and adjust the time estimates accordingly.

Project Management Techniques: PERT and CPM

PERT and CPM are two popular project management techniques.

When the questions in the project planning phase have been addressed, we move on to the project scheduling phase. The **program evaluation and review technique (PERT)** and the **critical path method (CPM)** are two popular decision modeling procedures that help managers answer the questions in the scheduling phase, even for large and complex projects. They were developed because there was a critical need for a better way to manage projects (see the *History* box).

Although some people still view PERT and CPM as separate techniques and refer to them by their original names, the two are similar in basic approach. The growing practice, therefore, is to refer to PERT and CPM simply as *project management* techniques.

HISTORY | How PERT and CPM Started

Managers have been planning, scheduling, monitoring, and controlling large-scale projects for hundreds of years, but it has only been in the past 50 years that decision modeling techniques have been applied to major projects. One of the earliest techniques was the *Gantt chart*. This type of chart shows the start and finish times of one or more activities, as shown in the accompanying chart.

In 1958, the Special Projects Office of the U.S. Navy developed the program evaluation and review technique (PERT) to plan and control the Polaris missile program. This project involved the coordination of thousands of contractors. Today, PERT is still used to monitor countless government contract schedules. At about the same time (1957), the critical path method (CPM) was developed by J. E. Kelly of Remington Rand and M. R. Walker of du Pont. Originally, CPM was used to assist in the building and maintenance of chemical plants at du Pont.

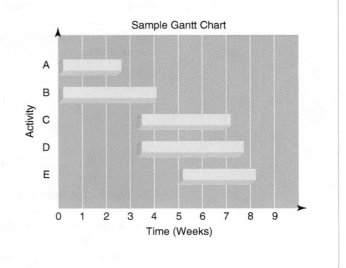

PERT is a probabilistic technique, whereas CPM is a deterministic technique.

PERT VERSUS CPM The primary difference between PERT and CPM is in the way the time needed for each activity in a project is estimated. In PERT, each activity has three time estimates that are combined to determine the expected activity completion time and its variance. PERT is considered a *probabilistic* technique; it allows us to find the probability that the entire project will be completed by a specific due date.

In contrast, CPM is a *deterministic* approach. It estimates the completion time of each activity using a single time estimate. This estimate, called the *standard* or *normal* time, is the time we estimate it will take under typical conditions to complete the activity. In some cases, CPM also associates a second time estimate with each activity. This estimate, called the *crash time*, is the shortest time it would take to finish an activity if additional funds and resources were allocated to the activity.

As noted previously, identifying these time estimates is a complicated task in most real-world projects. In our discussions in this chapter, however, we will assume that the time estimates (a single time estimate in CPM and three time estimates in PERT) are available for each activity.

Project Management Example: General Foundry, Inc.

General Foundry, Inc., a metal works plant in Milwaukee, has long tried to avoid the expense of installing air pollution control equipment. The local environmental protection agency has recently given the foundry 16 weeks to install a complex air filter system on its main smokestack. General Foundry has been warned that it may be forced to close unless the device is installed in the allotted period. Lester Harky, the managing partner, wants to make sure that installation of the filtering system progresses smoothly and on time.

Activities in the General Foundry project

General Foundry has identified the eight activities that need to be performed in order for the project to be completed. When the project begins, two activities can be simultaneously started: building the internal components for the device (activity A) and making the modifications necessary for the floor and roof (activity B). The construction of the collection stack (activity C) can begin when the internal components are completed. Pouring the concrete floor and installing the frame (activity D) can be started as soon as the internal components are completed and the roof and floor have been modified.

After the collection stack has been constructed, two activities can begin: building the high-temperature burner (activity E) and installing the pollution control system (activity F). The air pollution device can be installed (activity G) after the concrete floor has been poured, the frame has been installed, and the high-temperature burner has been built. Finally, after the control system and pollution device have been installed, the system can be inspected and tested (activity H).

All these activities and precedence relationships seem rather confusing and complex when they are presented in a descriptive form, as here. It is therefore convenient to list all the activity information in a table, as shown in Table 1. We see in the table that activity A is listed as an **immediate predecessor** of activity C. Likewise, both activities D and E must be performed prior to starting activity G.

It is enough to list only the immediate predecessors for each activity.

Note that it is enough to list just the immediate predecessors for each activity. For example, in Table 1, because activity A precedes activity C and activity C precedes activity E, the fact that activity A precedes activity E is *implicit*. This relationship need not be explicitly shown in the activity precedence relationships.

Networks consist of nodes that are connected by arcs.

When a project has many activities with fairly complicated precedence relationships, it is difficult for an individual to comprehend the complexity of the project from just the tabular information. In such cases, a visual representation of the project, using a project network, is

TABLE 1
Activities and Their Immediate Predecessors for General Foundry

ACTIVITY	DESCRIPTION	IMMEDIATE PREDECESSORS
A	Build internal components	—
B	Modify roof and floor	—
C	Construct collection stack	A
D	Pour concrete and install frame	A, B
E	Build high-temperature burner	C
F	Install pollution control system	C
G	Install air pollution device	D, E
H	Inspect and test	F, G

FIGURE 4
Beginning AON Network for General Foundry

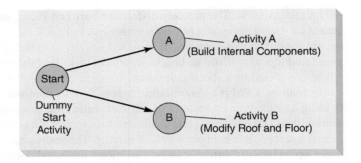

convenient and useful. A **project network** is a diagram of all the activities and the precedence relationships that exist between these activities in a project. We now illustrate how to construct a project network for General Foundry, Inc.

Drawing the Project Network

There are two types of project networks—AON and AOA.

A network consists of nodes (or points) and arcs (or lines) that connect the nodes together. There are two approaches to drawing a project network: **activity on node (AON) network** and **activity on arc (AOA) network**. In the AON approach, we denote each activity with a node. Arcs represent precedence relationships between activities. In contrast, in the AOA approach, we represent each activity with an arc. Each node represents an **event**, such as the start or finish of an activity.

Although both approaches are popular in practice, many of the project management software packages, including Microsoft Project, use AON networks. For this reason, we focus only on AON networks in this chapter. For details on AOA project networks, we refer you to a project management text.

Nodes denote activities in an AON network.

AON NETWORK FOR GENERAL FOUNDRY In the General Foundry example, two activities (A and B) do not have any predecessors. We draw separate nodes for each of these activities, as shown in Figure 4. Although not required, it is usually convenient to have a unique starting activity for a project. We have therefore included a **dummy activity** called Start in Figure 4. This dummy activity does not really exist and takes up zero time and resources. Activity Start is an immediate predecessor for both activities A and B, and it serves as the unique starting activity for the entire project.

Arcs denote precedence relationships in an AON network.

We now show the precedence relationships by using arcs (shown with arrow symbols: →). For example, an arrow from activity Start to activity A indicates that Start is a predecessor for activity A. In a similar fashion, we draw an arrow from Start to B.

Next, we add a new node for activity C. Because activity A precedes activity C, we draw an arc from node A to node C (see Figure 5). Likewise, we first draw a node to represent activity D. Then, because activities A and B both precede activity D, we draw arcs from A to D and from B to D (see Figure 5).

We proceed in this fashion, adding a separate node for each activity and a separate arc for each precedence relationship that exists. The complete AON project network for the General Foundry project example is shown in Figure 6.

FIGURE 5
Intermediate AON Network for General Foundry

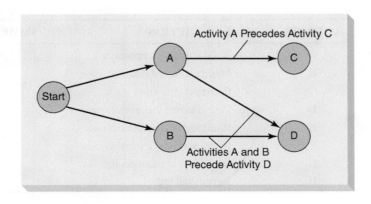

FIGURE 6 Complete AON Network for General Foundry

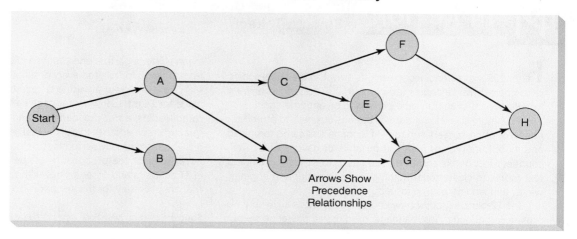

Drawing a project network properly takes some time and experience. When we first draw a project network, it is not unusual that we place our nodes (activities) in the network in such a fashion that the arcs (precedence relationships) are not simple straight lines. That is, the arcs could be intersecting each other and even facing in opposite directions. For example, if we switched the locations of the nodes for activities E and F in Figure 6, the arcs from F to H and E to G would intersect. Although such a project network is perfectly valid, it is good practice to have a well-drawn network. One rule that we especially recommend is to place the nodes in such a fashion that all arrows point in the same direction. To achieve this, we suggest that you first draw a rough draft version of the network to make sure all the relationships are shown. Then you can redraw the network to make appropriate changes in the location of the nodes.

It is convenient, but not required, to have unique starting and ending activities in a project.

As with the unique starting node, it is convenient to have the project network finish with a unique ending node. In the General Foundry example, it turns out that a unique activity, H, is the last activity in the project. We therefore automatically have a unique ending node here. However, in situations where a project has multiple ending activities, we include a dummy ending activity. This is an activity that does not exist and takes up zero time or resources. This dummy activity has all the multiple ending activities in the project as immediate predecessors. We illustrate this type of situation in Solved Problem 2 at the end of this chapter.

3 Determining the Project Schedule

Look back at Figure 6 for a moment to see General Foundry's completed AON project network. Once this project network has been drawn to show all the activities and their precedence relationships, the next step is to determine the project schedule. That is, we need to identify the planned starting and ending times for each activity.

Critical path analysis helps determine the project schedule.

Let us assume that General Foundry estimates the **activity time** required for each activity, in weeks, as shown in Table 2. The table indicates that the total time for all eight of General Foundry's activities is 25 weeks. However, because several activities can take place simultaneously, it is clear that the total project completion time may be much less than 25 weeks. To find out just how long the project will take, we perform **critical path analysis** for the network.

The critical path is the longest path in the network.

The **critical path** is the *longest* time path through the network. To find the critical path, we calculate two distinct starting and ending times for each activity. These are defined as follows:

Earliest start time (EST)	=	the earliest time at which an activity can start, assuming all predecessors have been completed
Earliest finish time (EFT)	=	the earliest time at which an activity can be finished
Latest start time (LST)	=	the latest time at which an activity can start so as to not delay the completion time of the entire project
Latest finish time (LFT)	=	the latest time by which an activity has to finish so as to not delay the completion time of the entire project

IN ACTION **Delta's Ground Crew Orchestrates a Smooth Takeoff**

Flight 199's three engines screech its arrival as the wide-bodied jet lumbers down Orlando's taxiway with 200 passengers arriving from San Juan. In an hour, the plane is to be airborne again.

But before this jet can depart, there is business to attend to: hundreds of passengers and tons of luggage and cargo to unload and load; hundreds of meals, thousands of gallons of jet fuel, countless soft drinks and bottles of liquor to restock; cabin and rest rooms to clean; toilet holding tanks to drain; and engines, wings, and landing gear to inspect.

The 12-person ground crew knows that a miscue anywhere—a broken cargo loader, lost baggage, misdirected passengers—can

mean a late departure and trigger a chain reaction of headaches from Orlando to Dallas to every destination of a connecting flight.

Like a pit crew awaiting a race car, trained crews are in place for Flight 199 with baggage carts and tractors, hydraulic cargo loaders, a truck to load food and drinks, another to lift the cleanup crew, another to put fuel on, and a fourth to take water off. The team usually performs so smoothly that most passengers never suspect the proportions of the effort. Gantt charts and PERT aid Delta and other airlines with the staffing and scheduling that are necessary for this symphony to perform.

Source: Based on *New York Times* (January 21, 1998): C1, C20.

TABLE 2
Time Estimates for General Foundry

ACTIVITY	DESCRIPTION	TIME (WEEKS)
A	Build internal components	2
B	Modify roof and floor	3
C	Construct collection stack	2
D	Pour concrete and install frame	4
E	Build high-temperature burner	4
F	Install pollution control system	3
G	Install air pollution device	5
H	Inspect and test	2
	Total time (weeks)	25

We use a two-pass procedure to find the project schedule.

We use a two-pass process, consisting of a forward pass and a backward pass, to determine these time schedules for each activity. The earliest times (EST and EFT) are determined during the **forward pass**. The latest times (LST and LFT) are determined during the **backward pass**.

Forward Pass

The forward pass identifies all the earliest times.

To clearly show the activity schedules on a project network, we use the notation shown in Figure 7. The EST of an activity is shown in the top-left corner of the node denoting that activity.

FIGURE 7
Notation Used in Nodes for Forward and Backward Passes

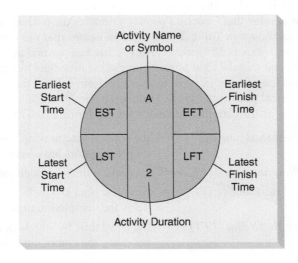

FIGURE 8   Earliest Start Times and Earliest Finish Times for General Foundry

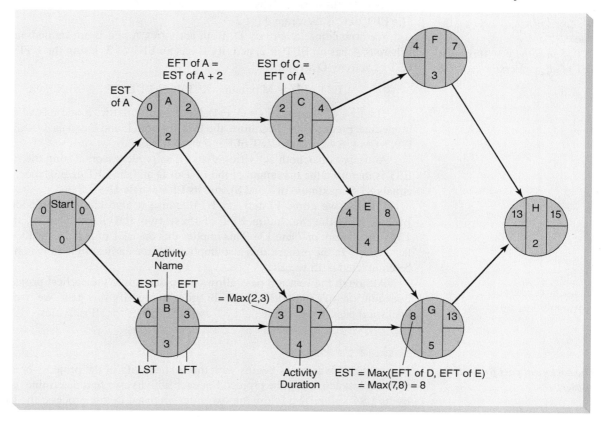

The EFT is shown in the top-right corner. The latest times, LST and LFT, are shown in the bottom-left and bottom-right corners, respectively.

All predecessor activities must be completed before an activity can begin.

Maximum ∅
Sum

EST RULE   Before an activity can start, *all* its immediate predecessors must be finished:

- If an activity has only a single immediate predecessor, its EST equals the EFT of the predecessor.
- If an activity has multiple immediate predecessors, its EST is the maximum of all EFT values of its predecessors.

That is,

$$\text{EST} = \text{Maximum \{EFT value of all immediate predecessors\}} \tag{1}$$

EFT RULE   The EFT of an activity is the sum of its EST and its activity time. That is,

$$\text{EFT} = \text{EST} + \text{Activity time} \tag{2}$$

Figure 8 shows the complete project network for General Foundry's project, along with the EST and EFT values for all activities. We next describe how these values have been calculated.

Because activity Start has no predecessors, we begin by setting its EST to 0. That is, activity Start can begin at the *end* of week 0, which is the same as the beginning of week 1.[2] If activity Start has an EST of 0, its EFT is also 0 because its activity time is 0.

Next, we consider activities A and B, both of which have only Start as an immediate predecessor. Using the EST rule, the EST for both activities A and B equals zero, which is the EFT

---

[2] In writing all earliest and latest times, we need to be consistent. For example, if we specify that the EST value of activity *i* is week 4, do we mean the *beginning* of week 4 or the *end* of week 4? Note that if the value refers to the *beginning* of week 4, it means that week 4 is also available for performing activity *i*. In our discussions, *all* earliest and latest time values correspond to the *end* of a period. That is, if we specify that the EST of activity *i* is week 4, it means that activity *i* starts work only at the beginning of week 5.

EFT = EST + Activity time

of activity Start. Now, using the EFT rule, the EFT for A is 2 (= 0 + 2), and the EFT for B is 3 (= 0 + 3). Because activity A precedes activity C, the EST of C equals the EFT of A (= 2). The EFT of C is therefore 4 (= 2 + 2).

We now come to activity D. Both activities A and B are immediate predecessors for D. Whereas A has an EFT of 2, activity B has an EFT of 3. Using the EST rule, we compute the EST of activity D as follows:

EST of an activity = Maximum EFT of all predecessor activities

$$\text{EST of D} = \text{Maximum (EFT of A, EFT of B)} = \text{Maximum (2, 3)} = 3$$

The EFT of D equals 7 (= 3 + 4). Next, both activities E and F have activity C as their only immediate predecessor. Therefore, the EST for both E and F equals 4 (= EFT of C). The EFT of E is 8 (= 4 + 4), and the EFT of F is 7 (= 4 + 3).

Activity G has both activities D and E as predecessors. Using the EST rule, we know its EST is therefore the maximum of the EFT of D and the EFT of E. Hence, the EST of activity G equals 8 (= maximum of 7 and 8), and its EFT equals 13 (= 8 + 5).

Finally, we come to activity H. Because it also has two predecessors, F and G, the EST of H is the maximum EFT of these two activities. That is, the EST of H equals 13 (= maximum of 7 and 13). This implies that the EFT of H is 15 (= 13 + 2). Because H is the last activity in the project, this also implies that the earliest time in which the entire project can be completed is 15 weeks.

Although the forward pass allows us to determine the earliest project completion time, it does not identify the critical path. In order to identify this path, we need to now conduct the backward pass to determine the LST and LFT values for all activities.

Backward Pass

The backward pass finds all the latest times.

Just as the forward pass begins with the first activity in the project, the backward pass begins with the last activity in the project. For each activity, we first determine its LFT value, followed by its LST value. The following two rules are used in this process: the LFT rule and the LST rule.

LFT RULE This rule is again based on the fact that before an activity can start, all its immediate predecessors must be finished:

- If an activity is an immediate predecessor for just a single activity, its LFT equals the LST of the activity that immediately follows it.
- If an activity is an immediate predecessor to more than one activity, its LFT is the minimum of all LST values of all activities that immediately follow it. That is,

$$\text{LFT} = \text{Minimum \{LST of all immediate following activities\}} \tag{3}$$

LST RULE The LST of an activity is the difference between its LFT and its activity time. That is,

$$\text{LST} = \text{LFT} - \text{Activity time} \tag{4}$$

LST = LFT − Activity time

Figure 9 shows the complete project network for General Foundry's project, along with LST and LFT values for all activities. Next, we analyze how these values were calculated.

We begin by assigning an LFT value of 15 weeks for activity H. That is, we specify that the LFT for the entire project is the same as its EFT. Using the LST rule, we calculate that the LST of activity H is equal to 13 (= 15 − 2).

Because activity H is the lone succeeding activity for both activities F and G, the LFT for both F and G equals 13. This implies that the LST of G is 8 (= 13 − 5), and the LST of F is 10 (= 13 − 3).

Proceeding in this fashion, we find that the LFT of E is 8 (= LST of G), and its LST is 4 (= 8 − 4). Likewise, the LFT of D is 8 (= LST of G), and its LST is 4 (= 8 − 4).

LFT of an activity = Minimum LST of all activities that follow

We now consider activity C, which is an immediate predecessor to two activities: E and F. Using the LFT rule, we compute the LFT of activity C as follows:

$$\text{LFT of C} = \text{Minimum (LST of E, LST of F)} = \text{Minimum (4, 10)} = 4$$

The LST of C is computed as 2 (= 4 − 2). Next, we compute the LFT of B as 4 (= LST of D) and its LST as 1 (= 4 − 3).

FIGURE 9 Latest Start Times and Latest Finish Times for General Foundry

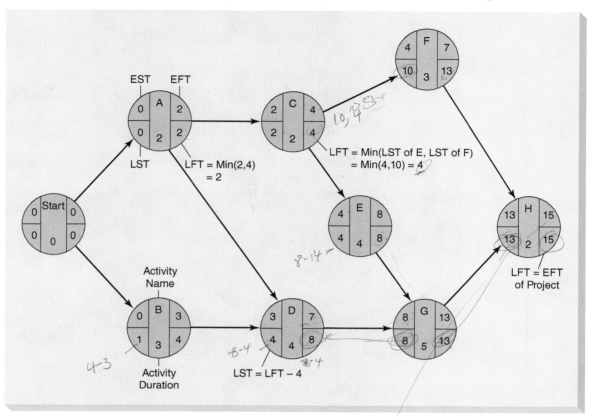

We now consider activity A. We compute its LFT as 2 (= Minimum of LST of C and LST of D). Hence, the LST of activity A is 0 (= 2 − 2). Finally, both the LFT and LST of activity Start are equal to 0.

Calculating Slack Time and Identifying the Critical Path(s)

Slack time *is free time for an activity.*

After we have computed the earliest and latest times for all activities, it is a simple matter to find the amount of **slack time**, or free time, that each activity has. *Slack* is the length of time an activity can be delayed without delaying the entire project. Mathematically,

$$\text{Slack} = \text{LST} - \text{EST or Slack} = \text{LFT} - \text{EFT} \qquad (5)$$

Table 3 summarizes the EST, EFT, LST, LFT, and slack time for all of General Foundry's activities. Activity B, for example, has 1 week of slack time because its LST is 1 and its EST is 0

TABLE 3 General Foundry's Project Schedule and Slack Times

ACTIVITY	EST	EFT	LST	LFT	SLACK, LST−EST	ON CRITICAL PATH?
A	0	2	0	2	0	Yes
B	0	3	1	4	1	No
C	2	4	2	4	0	Yes
D	3	7	4	8	1	No
E	4	8	4	8	0	Yes
F	4	7	10	13	6	No
G	8	13	8	13	0	Yes
H	13	15	13	15	0	Yes

FIGURE 10   Critical Path and Slack Times for General Foundry

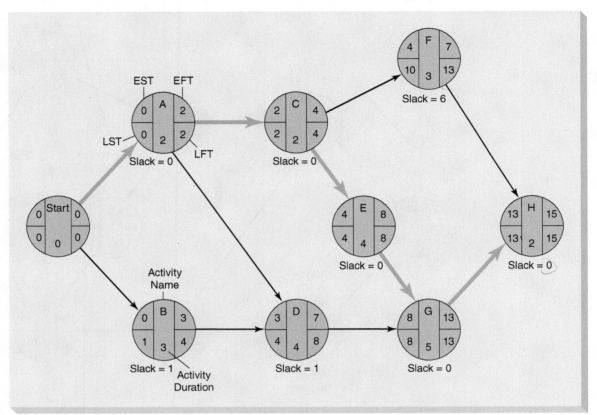

(alternatively, its LFT is 4 and its EFT is 3). This means that activity B can be delayed by up to 1 week, and the whole project can still finish in 15 weeks.

Critical activities have no slack time.

On the other hand, activities A, C, E, G, and H have *no* slack time. This means that none of them can be delayed without delaying the entire project. This also means that if Harky wants to reduce the total project time, he will have to reduce the length of one of these activities. These activities are called *critical activities* and are said to be on the *critical path*. The critical path is a

The critical path is the longest path through the network.

continuous path through the project network that

- Starts at the first activity in the project (Start in our example)
- Terminates at the last activity in the project (H in our example)
- Includes only critical activities (i.e., activities with no slack time)

General Foundry's critical path, Start-A-C-E-G-H, is shown in the network in Figure 10. The total project completion time of 15 weeks corresponds to the longest path in the network.

A project can have multiple critical paths.

MULTIPLE CRITICAL PATHS   In General Foundry's case, there is just a single critical path. Can a project have multiple critical paths? The answer is yes. For example, in General Foundry's case, what if the time required for activity B were estimated as 4 weeks instead of 3 weeks? Due to this change, the earliest and latest times for activities B and D would have to be revised, as shown in Figure 11.

Note that in addition to the original critical path (Start-A-C-E-G-H), there is now a second critical path (Start-B-D-G-H). Delaying an activity on either critical path will delay the completion of the entire project.

Total Slack Time versus Free Slack Time

Let us now refer to the project network in Figure 10. Consider activities B and D, which have slacks of 1 week each. Does it mean that we can delay *each* activity by 1 week and still complete the project in 15 weeks? The answer is no, as discussed next.

FIGURE 11   Modified Network with Multiple Critical Paths for General Foundry

Total slack time is shared among more than one activity.

Let's assume that activity B is delayed by 1 week. It has used up its slack of 1 week and now has an EFT of 4. This implies that activity D now has an EST of 4 and an EFT of 8. Note that these are also its LST and LFT values, respectively. That is, activity D also has no slack time now. Essentially, the slack of 1 week that activities B and D had was *shared* between them. Delaying either activity by 1 week causes not only that activity but also the other activity to lose its slack. This type of a slack time is referred to as *total slack*. Typically, when two or more non-critical activities appear successively in a path, they share total slack.

IN ACTION   Project Management and Software Development

Although computers have revolutionized how companies conduct business and allowed some organizations to achieve a long-term competitive advantage in the marketplace, the software that controls these computers is often more expensive than intended and takes longer to develop than expected. In some cases, large software projects are never fully completed. The London Stock Exchange, for example, had an ambitious software project called TAURUS that was intended to improve computer operations at the exchange. The TAURUS project, which cost hundreds of millions of dollars, was never completed. After numerous delays and cost overruns, the project was finally halted. The FLORIDA system, an ambitious software development project for the Department of Health and Rehabilitative Services for the state of Florida, was also delayed, cost more than expected, and didn't operate

as everyone had hoped. Although not all software development projects are delayed or over budget, it has been estimated that more than half of all software projects cost more than 189% of their original projections.

To control large software projects, many companies are now using project management techniques. Ryder Systems, Inc., American Express Financial Advisors, and United Air Lines have all created project management departments for their software and information systems projects. These departments have the authority to monitor large software projects and make changes to deadlines, budgets, and resources used to complete software development efforts.

Source: Based on J. King. "Tough Love Reins in IS Projects," *Computerworld* (June 19, 1995): 1–2.

Free slack time is associated with a single activity.

In contrast, consider the slack time of 6 weeks in activity F. Delaying this activity decreases only its slack time and does not affect the slack time of any other activity. This type of a slack time is referred to as *free slack*. Typically, if a noncritical activity has critical activities on either side of it in a path, its slack time is free slack.

4 Variability in Activity Times

Activity times are subject to variability.

In identifying all earliest and latest times so far, and the associated critical path(s), we have adopted the CPM approach of assuming that all activity times are known and fixed constants. That is, there is no variability in activity times. However, in practice, it is likely that activity completion times vary depending on various factors.

For example, building internal components (activity A) for General Foundry is estimated to finish in 2 weeks. Clearly, factors such as late arrival of raw materials, absence of key personnel, and so on, could delay this activity. Suppose activity A actually ends up taking 3 weeks. Because activity A is on the critical path, the entire project will now be delayed by 1 week, to 16 weeks. If we had anticipated completion of this project in 15 weeks, we would obviously miss our deadline.

Although some activities may be relatively less prone to delays, others could be extremely susceptible to delays. For example, activity B (modify roof and floor) could be heavily dependent on weather conditions. A spell of bad weather could significantly affect its completion time.

There are three approaches to studying the impact of variability in activity times.

The preceding discussion implies that we cannot ignore the impact of variability in activity times when deciding the schedule for a project. In general, there are three approaches that we can use to analyze the impact of variability in activity times on the completion time of the project:

- The first approach is to provide for variability by building in "buffers" to activity times. For example, if we know based on past experience that a specific activity has exceeded its time estimate by 20% on several occasions, we can build in a 20% time buffer for this activity by inflating its time estimate by 20%. There are, of course, a few obvious drawbacks to this approach. For example, if every activity has inflated time estimates due to these buffers, the entire project duration will be artificially large. Incidentally, practicing project managers will tell you that providing time buffers is not practical because the people concerned with the activity will just proceed more slowly than planned on the activity because they know that the buffer exists (i.e., the duration will stretch to fit the allotted time).
- The second approach, known as PERT analysis, employs a probability-based analysis of the project completion time. A primary advantage of this approach is that it is fairly easy to understand and implement. However, the drawback is that we have to make certain assumptions regarding the probability distributions of activity times. We discuss this approach in detail in this section.
- The third approach uses computer simulation. This approach, while typically being the most difficult approach from an implementation point of view, is also likely to be the most comprehensive in terms of its capabilities and analysis.

PERT Analysis

PERT uses three time estimates for each activity.

Recall that in our study so far, we have estimated the duration for each activity by using a single time estimate (such as 2 weeks for activity A in General Foundry's project). In practice, such durations may be difficult to estimate for many activities. For example, think about the difficulty you would have if someone asked you to estimate exactly how long your next assignment in this course will take to complete. (Remember, your estimate must be guaranteed to be sufficient and should not include any unnecessary buffers.) To correct for this difficulty, in PERT analysis we base the duration of each activity on three separate time estimates:

Optimistic time (a) = The time an activity will take, assuming favorable conditions (i.e., everything goes as planned). In estimating this value, there should be only a small probability (say, 1/100) that the activity time will be *a* or lower.

Most likely time (m) = The most realistic estimate of the time required to complete an activity.

Pessimistic time (b) = The time an activity will take, assuming unfavorable conditions (i.e., nothing goes as planned). In estimating this value, there should also be only a small probability that the activity time will be *b* or higher.

The beta probability distribution is often used to describe activity times.

How do we use these three time estimates? It turns out that a probability distribution, known as the **beta probability distribution**, is very appropriate for approximating the distribution of activity times. As shown in Figure 12, one way to characterize the beta distribution is to use three parameters—which, in the case of activity durations, correspond to the optimistic, most likely, and pessimistic time estimates we have already defined for each activity.

By using these three parameters for each activity, we can compute its expected activity time and variance. To find the **expected activity time (*t*)**, the beta distribution weights the three time estimates as follows:

$$t = (a + 4m + b)/6 \qquad (6)$$

The expected activity time is used in the project network to compute all earliest and latest times.

That is, the most likely time (*m*) is given four times the weight of the optimistic time (*a*) and pessimistic time (*b*). It is important to note that this expected activity time, *t*, computed using Equation 6 for each activity, is used in the project network to compute all earliest and latest times.

To compute the **variance of activity completion time**, we use this formula:[3]

$$\text{Variance} = \left[(b - a)/6 \right]^2 \qquad (7)$$

The standard deviation of activity completion time is the square root of the variance. Hence,

$$\text{Standard deviation} = \sqrt{\text{Variance}} = (b - a)/6 \qquad (8)$$

FIGURE 12   Beta Probability Distribution with Three Time Estimates

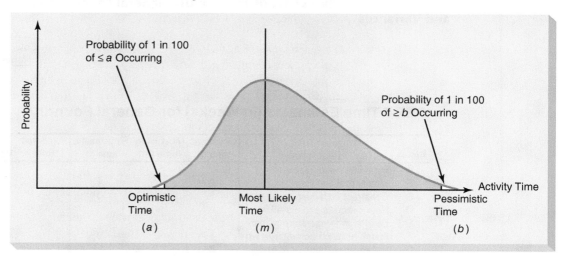

_____

[3]This formula is based on the statistical concept that from one end of the beta distribution to the other is 6 standard deviations (± 3 standard deviations from the mean). Because $(b - a)$ is 6 standard deviations, the variance is $[(b - a)/6]^2$.

Excel Note

The Companion Website for this text, at www.pearsonhighered.com/balakrishnan, contains the Excel file for each sample problem discussed here. The relevant file name is shown in the margin next to each example.

File: 7-1.xls

For General Foundry's project, let us assume that Lester Harky has estimated the optimistic, most likely, and pessimistic times for each activity, as shown in columns C, D, and E, respectively, in Screenshot 1. Note that some activities (e.g., A, B) have relatively small variability, while others (e.g., F, G) have a large spread between their pessimistic and optimistic time estimates. On occasion, it is possible for an activity to have no variability at all (i.e., the activity's a, m, and b time estimates are all the same).

Using these estimates in Equations 6 through 8, we compute the expected time, variance, and standard deviation for each activity. These values are shown in columns F, G, and H, respectively, of Screenshot 1. Note that the expected times shown in column F are, in fact, the activity times we used in our earlier computation and identification of the critical path. Hence, the earliest and latest times we computed before (see Table 3) are valid for the PERT analysis of General Foundry's project.

Probability of Project Completion

The critical path analysis helped us determine that General Foundry's expected project completion time is 15 weeks. Lester Harky knows, however, that there is significant variation in the time estimates for several activities. Variation in activities that are on the critical path can affect the overall project completion time, possibly delaying it. This is one occurrence that worries Harky considerably.

We compute the project variance by summing variances of only those activities that are on the critical path.

PERT uses the variance of critical path activities to help determine the variance of the overall project. Project variance is computed by summing variances of critical activities:

$$\text{Project variance} = \sum (\text{Variances of activities on critical path}) \qquad (9)$$

From Screenshot 1 we know that the variance of activity A is 0.11, variance of activity C is 0.11, variance of activity E is 1.00, variance of activity G is 1.78, and variance of activity H is 0.11. Hence, the total project variance and project standard deviation may be computed as

$$\text{Project variance } (\sigma_P^2) = 0.11 + 0.11 + 1.00 + 1.78 + 0.11 = 3.11$$

SCREENSHOT 1 Excel Layout to Compute General Foundry's Expected Times and Variances

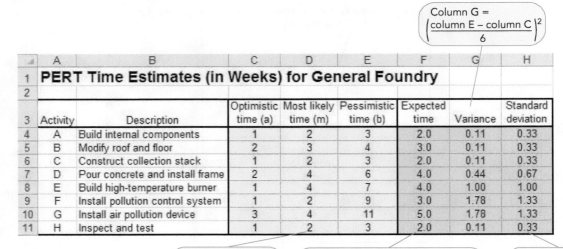

	A	B	C	D	E	F	G	H
1	**PERT Time Estimates (in Weeks) for General Foundry**							
2								
3	Activity	Description	Optimistic time (a)	Most likely time (m)	Pessimistic time (b)	Expected time	Variance	Standard deviation
4	A	Build internal components	1	2	3	2.0	0.11	0.33
5	B	Modify roof and floor	2	3	4	3.0	0.11	0.33
6	C	Construct collection stack	1	2	3	2.0	0.11	0.33
7	D	Pour concrete and install frame	2	4	6	4.0	0.44	0.67
8	E	Build high-temperature burner	1	4	7	4.0	1.00	1.00
9	F	Install pollution control system	1	2	9	3.0	1.78	1.33
10	G	Install air pollution device	3	4	11	5.0	1.78	1.33
11	H	Inspect and test	1	2	3	2.0	0.11	0.33

Column G = $\left(\dfrac{\text{column E} - \text{column C}}{6}\right)^2$

Three time estimates for each activity

Column F = $\dfrac{\text{column C} + 4 \times \text{column D} + \text{column E}}{6}$

=SQRT (column G)

FIGURE 13
Probability Distribution for Project Completion Times

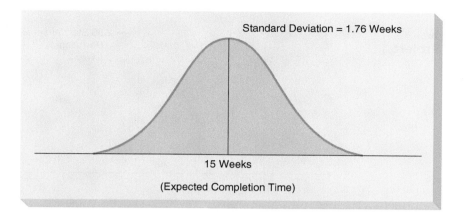

Standard Deviation = 1.76 Weeks

15 Weeks
(Expected Completion Time)

which implies

$$\text{Project standard deviation}(\sigma_p) = \sqrt{\text{Project variance}} = \sqrt{3.11} = 1.76$$

PERT now makes two assumptions: (1) Total project completion times follow a normal probability distribution, and (2) activity times are statistically independent. With these assumptions, the bell-shaped normal curve shown in Figure 13 can be used to represent project completion dates. This normal curve implies that there is a 50% chance that the project completion time will be less than 15 weeks and a 50% chance that it will exceed 15 weeks. That is, instead of viewing the computed project completion time as a guaranteed estimate (as we did earlier, when using the CPM approach), the PERT analysis views it as just the expected completion time, with only a 50% probability of completion within that time.

How can this information be used to help answer questions regarding the probability of finishing the project at different times? For example, what is the probability that Harky will finish this project on or before the 16-week deadline imposed by the environmental agency? To find this probability, Harky needs to determine the appropriate area under the normal curve. The standard normal equation can be applied as follows:

$$Z = (\text{Target completion time} - \text{Expected completion time})/\sigma_P$$
$$= (16 \text{ weeks} - 15 \text{ weeks})/1.76 \text{ weeks} = 0.57 \qquad (10)$$

where Z is the number of standard deviations the target completion time lies from the expected completion time.

Now we compute the probability of project completion.

Referring to the normal probability table in Appendix Areas Under the Standard Normal Curve, we find a probability of 0.7157. Thus, there is a 71.57% chance that the pollution control equipment can be put in place in 16 weeks or less. This is shown in Figure 14.

FIGURE 14
Probability of General Foundry Meeting the 16-Week Deadline

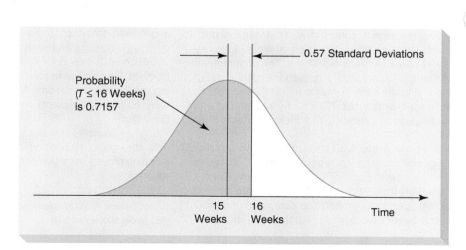

0.57 Standard Deviations

Probability
(T ≤ 16 Weeks)
is 0.7157

15
Weeks

16
Weeks

Time

FIGURE 15
Z **Value for 99%**
Probability of Project
Completion

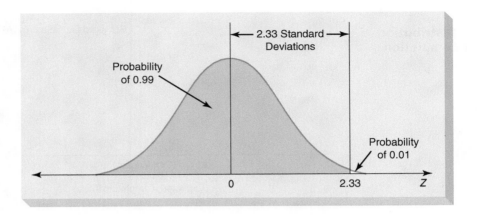

Determining Project Completion Time for a Given Probability

Lester Harky is extremely worried that there is only a 71.57% chance that the pollution control equipment can be put in place in 16 weeks or less. He thinks that it may be possible for him to plead with the environmental agency for more time. However, before he approaches the agency, he wants to arm himself with sufficient information about the project. Specifically, he wants to find the target completion time by which he has a 99% chance of completing the project. He hopes to use his analysis to convince the agency to agree to this extended deadline.

Clearly, this target completion time would be greater than 16 weeks. However, what is the exact value of this new deadline? To answer this question, we again use the assumption that General Foundry's project completion time follows a normal probability distribution, with a mean of 15 weeks and a standard deviation of 1.76 weeks.

For Harky to find the target completion time under which the project has a 99% chance of completion, he needs to determine the *Z* value that corresponds to 99%, as shown in Figure 15.

Now we compute the due date for a given probability.

Referring again to the normal probability table in Appendix Areas Under the Standard Normal Curve, we identify a *Z* value of 2.33 as being closest to the probability of 0.99. That is, Harky's target completion time should be 2.33 standard deviations above the expected

---

 **IN ACTION**   **Project Management Provides**
a Competitive Advantage for Bechtel

Now in its second century, the San Francisco–based Bechtel Group is the world's premier manager of massive construction and engineering projects. Known for billion-dollar projects, Bechtel is famous for its construction feats on the Hoover Dam, the Ted Williams Tunnel project, and the rebuilding of Kuwait's oil and gas infrastructure after the invasion by Iraq.

Even for Bechtel, whose competitive advantage is project management, restoring the 650 blazing oil wells lit by Iraqi sabotage in 1990 was a logistical nightmare. The panorama of destruction in Kuwait was breathtaking, with fire roaring out of the ground from virtually every compass point. Kuwait had no water, electricity, food, or facilities. The country was littered with unexploded mines, bombs, grenades, and shells, and lakes of oil covered its roads.

In Phase 1 of the project, Bechtel devised an unprecedented emergency program to regain control of Kuwait's oil fields and to halt destruction of the environment. Phase 2 focused on rehabilitation. With a major global procurement program, Bechtel specialists tapped the company's network of suppliers and buyers worldwide. At the port of Dubai,

550 miles southeast of Kuwait, the firm established a central transshipment point and deployed 125,000 tons of equipment and supplies. Creating a workforce of 16,000, Bechtel mobilized 742 airplanes and ships and more than 5,800 bulldozers, ambulances, and other pieces of operating equipment from 40 countries on five continents.

Now, more than two decades later, the fires are long out, and Kuwait continues to ship oil. Bechtel's more recent projects include (1) building and running a rail line between London and the Channel Tunnel ($7.4 billion); (2) developing an oil pipeline from the Caspian Sea region to Russia ($850 million); (3) expanding the Miami International Airport ($2 billion); and (4) building liquefied natural gas plants on the island of Trinidad, West Indies ($1 billion).

When countries seek out firms to manage these massive projects, they go to Bechtel, which, again and again, through outstanding project management, has demonstrated its competitive advantage.

Source: Adapted from J. Heizer and B. Render. *Operations Management*, Eighth Edition, © 2006. Reprinted by permission of Pearson Education, Inc., Upper Saddle River, NJ.

completion time. Starting with the standard normal equation (see Equation 10), we can solve for the target completion time and rewrite the equation as

$$\text{Target completion time} = \text{Expected completion time} + Z \times \sigma p$$
$$= 15 + 2.33 \times 1.76 = 19.1 \text{ weeks} \qquad (11)$$

Hence, if Harky can get the environmental agency to give him a new target completion time of 19.1 weeks (or more), he can be 99% sure of finishing the project on time.

Variability in Completion Time of Noncritical Paths

Noncritical paths with large variances should be closely monitored.

In our discussion so far, we have focused exclusively on the variability in completion times of activities on the critical path. This seems logical because these activities are, by definition, the more important activities in a project network. However, when there is variability in activity times, it is important that we also investigate the variability in the completion times of activities on *noncritical* paths.

Consider, for example, activity D in General Foundry's project. Recall from Table 3 that this is a noncritical activity, with a slack time of 1 week. We have therefore not considered the variability in D's time in computing the probabilities of project completion times. We observe, however, that D has a variance of 0.44 (see Screenshot 1). In fact, the pessimistic completion time for D is 6 weeks. This means that if D ends up taking its pessimistic time to finish, the project will not finish in 15 weeks, even though D is not a critical activity.

For this reason, when we find probabilities of project completion times, it may be necessary for us to not focus only on the critical path(s). We may need to also compute these probabilities for noncritical paths, especially those that have relatively large variances. It is possible for a noncritical path to have a smaller probability of completion within a due date compared with the critical path. In fact, a different critical path can evolve because of the probabilistic situation.

5   Managing Project Costs and Other Resources

The techniques discussed so far are very good for planning, scheduling, and monitoring a project with respect to time. We have not, however, considered another very important factor—project *cost*. In this section, we begin by investigating how costs can be planned and scheduled. Then we see how costs can be monitored and controlled.

Planning and Scheduling Project Costs: Budgeting Process

The budgeting process determines the budget per period of the project.

The overall approach in the budgeting process of a project is to determine how much is to be spent every week or month. This is accomplished as follows:

Three Steps of the Budgeting Process

1. Identify all costs associated with each of the activities. Then add these costs together to get one estimated cost or budget for each activity. When dealing with a large project, several activities may be combined into larger work packages. A work package is simply a logical collection of activities. Because the General Foundry project is quite small, each activity can be a work package.

2. Identify when and how the budgeted cost for an activity will actually be spent. In practice, this would be specific to the activity in question. For example, in some cases the entire cost may be spent at the start of the activity. In others, the expense may occur only after the activity has been completed.

   In our discussion here, we assume that the cost of each activity is spent at a linear rate over time. Thus, if the budgeted cost for a given activity is $48,000, and the activity's expected time is 4 weeks, the budgeted cost per week is $12,000 (=$48,000/4 weeks).

3. Using the earliest and latest start and finish times for each activity, find out how much money should be spent during each period of the project to finish it by the target completion time.

TABLE 4
Activity Costs for General Foundry

ACTIVITY	EXPECTED TIME (t)	EST	LST	TOTAL BUDGETED COST	BUDGETED COST PER WEEK
A	2	0	0	$22,000	$11,000
B	3	0	1	$30,000	$10,000
C	2	2	2	$26,000	$13,000
D	4	3	4	$48,000	$12,000
E	4	4	4	$56,000	$14,000
F	3	4	10	$30,000	$10,000
G	5	8	8	$80,000	$16,000
H	2	13	13	$16,000	$8,000
				Total $308,000	

BUDGETING FOR GENERAL FOUNDRY Let us apply the three-step budgeting process to the General Foundry problem. Lester Harky has carefully computed the costs associated with each of his eight activities. Assuming that the cost of each activity is spent at a linear rate over time, he has also divided the total budget for each activity by the activity's expected time to determine the weekly budget for the activity. The budget for activity A, for example, is $22,000 (see Table 4). Because its expected time (t) is 2 weeks, $11,000 is spent each week to complete the activity. Table 4 also provides two pieces of data we found earlier: the EST and LST for each activity.

Looking at the total of the budgeted activity costs, we see that the entire project will cost $308,000. Finding the weekly budget will help Harky determine how the project is progressing on a week-to-week basis.

We can form a weekly budget using EST values.

The weekly budget for the project is developed from the data in Table 4. The EST for activity A is 0. Because A takes 2 weeks to complete, its weekly budget of $11,000 should be spent in weeks 1 and 2. For activity B, the EST is 0, the expected completion time is 3 weeks, and the budgeted cost per week is $10,000. Hence, $10,000 should be spent for activity B in each of weeks 1, 2, and 3. Using the EST, we can find the exact weeks during which the budget for each activity should be spent. These weekly amounts can be summed for all activities to arrive at the weekly budget for the entire project. For example, a total of $21,000 each should be spent during weeks 1 and 2. These weekly totals can then be added to determine the total amount that should be spent to date (total to date). All these computations are shown in Table 5.

TABLE 5 Budgeted Costs (in Thousands) for General Foundry, Using Earliest Start Times

ACTIVITY	1	2	3	4	5	6	7	8	9	10	11	12	13	14	15	TOTAL
A	$11	$11														$22
B	$10	$10	$10													$30
C			$13	$13												$26
D				$12	$12	$12	$12									$48
E					$14	$14	$14	$14								$56
F					$10	$10	$10									$30
G									$16	$16	$16	$16	$16			$80
H														$8	$8	$16
																$308
Total per week	$21	$21	$23	$25	$36	$36	$36	$14	$16	$16	$16	$16	$16	$8	$8	
Total to date	$21	$42	$65	$90	$126	$162	$198	$212	$228	$244	$260	$276	$292	$300	$308	

TABLE 6 Budgeted Costs (in Thousands) for General Foundry, Using Latest Start Times

ACTIVITY	WEEK															TOTAL
	1	2	3	4	5	6	7	8	9	10	11	12	13	14	15	
A	$11	$11														$622
B		$10	$10	$10												$630
C			$13	$13												$626
D					$12	$12	$12	$12								$648
E					$614	$614	$614	$614								$656
F											$10	$10	$10			$630
G									$16	$16	$16	$16	$16			$680
H														$8	$8	$616
																$308
Total per week	$11	$21	$23	$23	$26	$26	$26	$26	$16	$16	$26	$26	$26	$8	$8	
Total to date	$11	$32	$55	$78	$104	$130	$156	$182	$198	$214	$240	$266	$292	$300	$308	

We can also form a weekly budget using LST values.

The activities along the critical path must spend their budgets at the times shown in Table 5. The activities that are *not* on the critical path, however, can be started at a later date. This concept is embodied in the LST for each activity. Thus, if LST values are used, another budget can be obtained. This budget will delay the expenditure of funds until the last possible moment. The procedures for computing the budget when LST is used are the same as when EST is used. The results of the new computations are shown in Table 6.

Compare the budgets given in Tables 5 and 6. The amount that should be spent to date (total to date) for the budget in Table 5 reveals the earliest possible time that funds can be expended. In contrast, the budget in Table 6 uses fewer financial resources in the first few weeks because it was prepared using LST values. That is, the budget in Table 6 shows the latest possible time that funds can be expended and have the project still finish on time. Therefore, Lester Harky can use any budget between these feasible ranges and still complete the air pollution project on time. These two tables form feasible budget ranges.

The two tables form feasible budget ranges.

This concept is illustrated in Figure 16, which plots the total-to-date budgets for EST and LST.

Monitoring and Controlling Project Costs

We can track costs to see if the project is on budget

Budget charts like the ones shown in Figure 16 are typically developed before the project is started. Then, as the project is being completed, funds expended should be monitored and controlled. The purpose of monitoring and controlling project costs is to ensure that the project is progressing on schedule and that cost overruns are kept to a minimum. The status of the entire project should be checked periodically.

Lester Harky wants to know how his air pollution project is going. It is now the end of the sixth week of the 15-week project. Activities A, B, and C have been fully completed. These activities incurred costs of $20,000, $36,000, and $26,000, respectively. Activity D is only 10% complete, and so far the cost expended on it has been $6,000. Activity E is 20% complete, with an incurred cost of $20,000. Activity F is 20% complete, with an incurred cost of $4,000. Activities G and H have not been started. Is the air pollution project on schedule? What is the value of work completed? Are there any cost overruns?

We compute the value of work completed for each activity.

One way to measure the value of the work completed (or the cost-to-date) for an activity is to multiply its total budgeted cost by the percentage of completion for that activity.[4]

---

[4] The percentage of completion for each activity can be measured in many ways. For example, we might use the ratio of labor hours expended to total labor hours estimated.

FIGURE 16
Budget Ranges for General Foundry

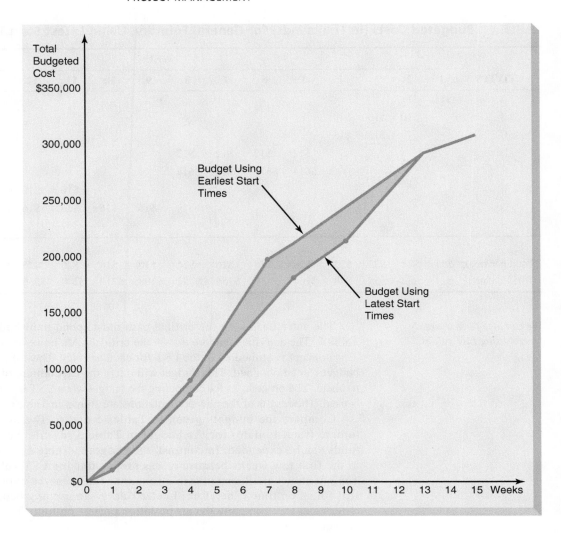

That is,

$$\text{Value of work completed} = \text{Percentage of work completed} \times \text{Total activity budget} \quad (12)$$

To determine the cost difference (i.e., the amount of overrun or underrun) for an activity, the value of work completed is subtracted from the actual cost. Hence,

$$\text{Cost difference} = \text{Actual cost} - \text{Value of work completed} \quad (13)$$

If a cost difference is negative, it implies that there is a cost underrun. In contrast, if the number is positive, there has been a cost overrun.

Table 7 summarizes this information for General Foundry's project. The second column shows the total budgeted cost (from Table 4), and the third column contains the percentage of completion for each activity. Using these data, and the actual cost expended for each activity, we can compute the value of work completed and the cost difference for every activity.

We compute cost underruns and overruns.

Activity D, for example, has a value of work completed of $4,800 (=$48,000 × 10%). The actual cost is $6,000, implying that there is a cost overrun of $1,200. The cost difference for all activities can be added to determine the total project overrun or underrun. In General Foundry's case, we can see from Table 7 that there is a $12,000 cost overrun at the end of the sixth week. The total value of work completed so far is only $100,000, and the actual cost of the project to date is $112,000.

How do these costs compare with the budgeted costs for week 6? If Harky had decided to use the budget for ESTs (see Table 5), we can see that $162,000 should have been spent. Thus, the project is behind schedule, and there are cost overruns. Harky

TABLE 7   Monitoring and Controlling Budgeted Costs for General Foundry

ACTIVITY	TOTAL BUDGETED COST	PERCENTAGE COMPLETED	VALUE OF WORK COMPLETED	ACTUAL COST	ACTIVITY DIFFERENCE
A	$22,000	100	$ 22,000	$ 20,000	–$ 2,000
B	$30,000	100	$ 30,000	$ 36,000	$ 6,000
C	$26,000	100	$ 26,000	$ 26,000	$ 0
D	$48,000	10	$ 4,800	$ 6,000	$ 1,200
E	$56,000	20	$ 11,200	$ 20,000	$ 8,800
F	$30,000	20	$ 6,000	$ 4,000	–$ 2,000
G	$80,000	0	$ 0	$ 0	$ 0
H	$16,000	0	$ 0	$ 0	$ 0
		Total	$100,000	$112,000	$12,000 Overrun

needs to move faster on this project to finish on time. He must also control future costs carefully to try to eliminate the current cost overrun of $12,000. To monitor and control costs, the budgeted amount, the value of work completed, and the actual costs should be computed periodically.

Managing Other Resources

Other resources can also be planned for and monitored.

So far, we have focused on monitoring and controlling costs. Although this is clearly an important issue, there may be other resources (e.g., labor, machinery, materials) that also need to be carefully planned for and monitored in order for a project to finish on schedule. For example, activity E (build high-temperature burner) may need some specialized equipment in order to be performed. Likewise, installation of the air pollution device (activity G) may require a specialist to be present. It is therefore important that we be aware of such resource requirements and ensure that the right resources are available at the right time.

Just as we constructed a weekly budget using activity schedules and costs (see Tables 5 and 6), we can construct weekly requirement charts for any resource. Assume that Lester Harky has estimated the support staff requirement for each of the eight activities in the project, as shown in Table 8. For example, during each week that activity A is in progress, Harky needs four support staffers to be available.

Table 9 shows the weekly support staff needed for General Foundry's project using EST values. A graph that plots the total resource (such as labor) needed per period (*Y*-axis) versus time (*X*-axis) is called a **resource loading chart**. Figure 17 shows the support staff loading chart for General Foundry's project.

**TABLE 8
Support Staff
Requirements for
General Foundry**

ACTIVITY	DESCRIPTION	SUPPORT STAFF NEEDED PER WEEK
A	Build internal components	4
B	Modify roof and floor	5
C	Construct collection stack	6
D	Pour concrete and install frame	4
E	Build high-temperature burner	3
F	Install pollution control system	4
G	Install air pollution device	7
H	Inspect and test	2

TABLE 9 Support Staff Requirements for General Foundry, Using Earliest Start Times

ACTIVITY	WEEK															TOTAL
	1	2	3	4	5	6	7	8	9	10	11	12	13	14	15	
A	4	4														8
B	5	5	5													15
C			6	6												12
D				4	4	4	4									16
E					3	3	3	3								12
F					4	4	4									12
G									7	7	7	7	7			35
H														2	2	4
																114
Total per week	9	9	11	10	11	11	11	3	7	7	7	7	7	2	2	
Total to date	9	18	29	39	50	61	72	75	82	89	96	103	110	112	114	

FIGURE 17
Support Staff Loading Chart for General Foundry

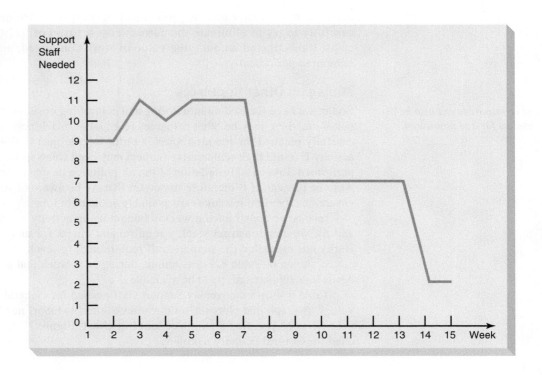

6 Project Crashing 30

Reducing a project's duration is called **crashing.**

While managing a project, it is not uncommon for a project manager to be faced with either (or both) of the following situations: (1) The project is behind schedule, and (2) the scheduled project completion time has been moved forward. In either situation, some or all of the remaining activities need to be speeded up in order to finish the project by the desired due date. The process of shortening the duration of a project in the least expensive manner possible is called **crashing**.

As noted earlier, in section 2, CPM is a deterministic technique in which each activity has two estimates of time. The first is the *standard* or *normal* time that we used in our computation of earliest and latest times. Associated with this standard time is the *standard* or *normal cost* of the activity, which we used in section 5 to schedule and monitor the cost of the project.

IN ACTION Costing Projects at Nortel

Many companies, including Nortel, a large telecommunications company, are benefiting from project management. With more than 20,000 active projects, worth a total of more than $2 billion, effectively managing projects at Nortel has been challenging. Getting the needed input data, including times and costs, can be difficult.

Like most other companies, Nortel used standard accounting practices to monitor and control costs. This typically involves allocating costs to each department. Most projects, however, span multiple departments. This can make it very difficult to get timely cost information. Project managers often get project cost data later than they want it. Because the cost data are allocated to departments, the data are often not detailed enough to help manage projects and get an accurate picture of true project costs.

To get more accurate cost data for project management, Nortel adopted an activity-based costing (ABC) method that is often used in manufacturing operations. In addition to standard cost data, each project activity was coded with a project identification number and a regional research development location number. This greatly improved the ability of project managers to control costs. Because some of the month-end costing processes were simplified, the approach also lowered project costs in most cases. Project managers also were able to get more detailed costing information. Because the cost data were coded for each project, getting timely feedback was also possible. In this case, getting good input data reduced project costs, reduced the time needed to get critical project feedback, and made project management more accurate.

Source: Based on C. Dorey. "The ABCs of R&D at Nortel," *CMA Magazine* (March 1998): 19–23.

Crash time *is the shortest duration of an activity.*

The second time is the *crash time*, which is defined as the shortest duration required to complete an activity. Associated with this crash time is the *crash cost* of the activity. Usually, we can shorten an activity by adding extra resources (e.g., equipment, people) to it. Hence, it is logical for the crash cost of an activity to be higher than its standard cost.

The amount of time by which an activity can be shortened (i.e., the difference between its standard time and crash time) depends on the activity in question. We may not be able to shorten some activities at all. For example, if a casting needs to be heat-treated in a furnace for 48 hours, adding more resources does not help shorten the time. In contrast, we may be able to shorten some activities significantly (e.g., we may be able to frame a house in 3 days instead of 10 days by using three times as many workers).

We want to find the cheapest way of crashing a project to the desired due date.

Likewise, the cost of crashing (or shortening) an activity depends on the nature of the activity. Managers are usually interested in speeding up a project at the least additional cost. Hence, in choosing which activities to crash, and by how much, we need to ensure that all the following occur:

- The amount by which an activity is crashed is, in fact, permissible.
- Taken together, the shortened activity durations will enable us to finish the project by the due date.
- The total cost of crashing is as small as possible.

In the following pages, we first illustrate how to crash a small project using simple calculations that can even be performed by hand. Then, we describe an LP-based approach that can be used to determine the optimal crashing scheme for projects of any size.

Crashing General Foundry's Project (Hand Calculations)

Suppose that General Foundry has been given only 13 weeks (instead of 16 weeks) to install the new pollution control equipment or face a court-ordered shutdown. As you recall, the length of Lester Harky's critical path was 15 weeks. Which activities should Harky crash, and by how much, in order to meet this 13-week due date? Naturally, Harky is interested in speeding up the project by 2 weeks, at the least additional cost.

Crashing a project using hand calculations involves four steps, as follows:

Four Steps of Project Crashing

1. Compute the crash cost per week (or other time period) for all activities in the network. If crash costs are assumed to be linear over time, the following formula can be used:

$$\text{Crash cost per period} = \frac{(\text{Crash cost} - \text{Standard cost})}{(\text{Standard time} - \text{Crash time})} \quad (14)$$

2. Using the current activity times, find the critical path(s) in the project network. Identify the critical activities.

3. If there is only one critical path, select the activity on this critical path that (a) can still be crashed and (b) has the smallest crash cost per period. Crash this activity by one period.

 If there is more than one critical path, select one activity from each critical path such that (a) each selected activity can still be crashed, and (b) total crash cost per period of all selected activities is the smallest. Crash each activity by one period. Note that a single activity may be common to more than one critical path.

4. Update all activity times. If the desired due date has been reached, stop. If not, return to step 2.

General Foundry's standard and crash times and standard and crash costs are shown in Table 10. Note, for example, that activity B's standard time is 3 weeks (the estimate used in computing the current critical path), and its crash time is 1 week. This means that activity B can be shortened by up to 2 weeks if extra resources are provided. The cost of these additional resources is $4,000 (= Difference between the crash cost of $34,000 and the standard cost of $30,000). If we assume that the crashing cost is linear over time (i.e., the cost is the same each week), activity B's crash cost per week is $2,000 (= $4,000/2 weeks).

This assumes that crash costs are linear over time.

This calculation is shown in Figure 18. Crash costs for all other activities can be computed in a similar fashion.

TABLE 10
Standard and Crash Times and Costs for General Foundry

ACTIVITY	TIME (WEEKS)		COST		CRASH COST PER WEEK
	STANDARD	CRASH	STANDARD	CRASH	
A	2	1	$22,000	$22,750	$750
B	3	1	$30,000	$34,000	$2,000
C	2	1	$26,000	$27,000	$1,000
D	4	3	$48,000	$49,000	$1,000
E	4	2	$56,000	$58,000	$1,000
F	3	2	$30,000	$30,500	$500
G	5	2	$80,000	$84,500	$1,500
H	2	1	$16,000	$19,000	$3,000

FIGURE 18
Standard and Crash Times and Costs for Activity B

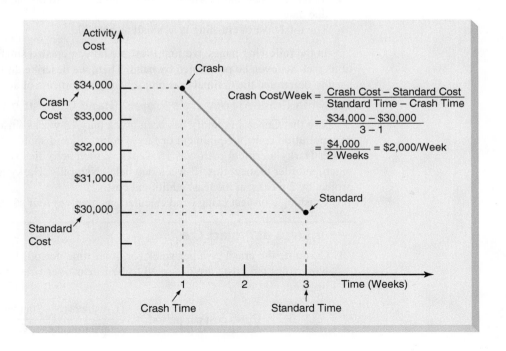

264

FIGURE 19 Critical Path and Slack Times for General Foundry

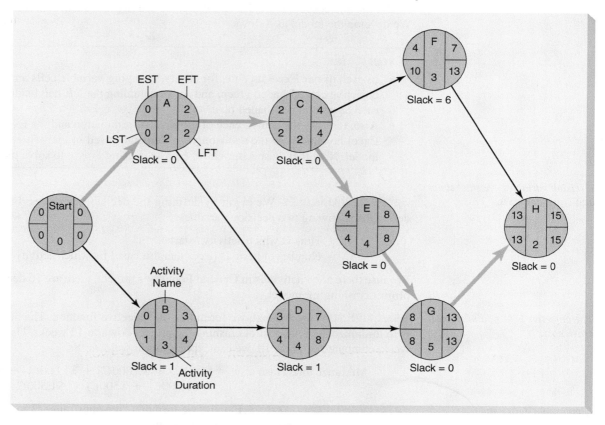

Steps 2, 3, and 4 of the project crashing process can now be applied to reduce General Foundry's project completion time at a minimum cost. For your convenience, we show the project network for General Foundry again in Figure 19.

The current critical path (using standard times) is Start-A-C-E-G-H, in which Start is a dummy starting activity. Of these critical activities, activity A has the lowest crash cost per week, at $750. Harky should therefore crash activity A by 1 week to reduce the project completion time to 14 weeks. The cost is an additional $750. Note that activity A cannot be crashed any further because it has reached its crash limit of 1 week.

There are now two critical paths.

At this stage, the original path Start-A-C-E-G-H remains critical, with a completion time of 14 weeks. However, a new path Start-B-D-G-H is also critical now, with a completion time of 14 weeks. Hence, any further crashing must be done to both critical paths.

On each of these critical paths, we need to identify one activity that can still be crashed. We also want the total cost of crashing an activity on each path to be the smallest. We might be tempted to simply pick the activities with the smallest crash cost per period in each path. If we do this, we would select activity C from the first path and activity D from the second path. The total crash cost would then be $2,000 (=$1,000 + $1,000).

Crashing activities common to more than one critical path may be cheapest.

But we spot that activity G is common to both paths. That is, by crashing activity G, we will simultaneously reduce the completion time of both paths. Even though the $1,500 crash cost for activity G is higher than that for activities C or D, we would still prefer crashing G because the total cost is now only $1,500 (compared with the $2,000 if we crash C and D).

Hence, to crash the project down to 13 weeks, Lester Harky should crash activity A by 1 week and activity G by 1 week. The total additional cost is $2,250(=$750 + $1,500).

Crashing General Foundry's Project Using Linear Programming

Although the preceding crashing procedure is simple for projects involving just a few activities, it can become extremely cumbersome to use for larger projects. Linear programming (LP) is an excellent technique for determining the optimal (i.e., least expensive) way to crash even larger projects. Let us examine how this technique may be used here.

The data needed for General Foundry's project crashing LP model are the standard and crash time and cost data (see Table 10) and the activity precedence information (see Figure 19). We develop the model as follows.

Excel Notes

- In each of our Excel layouts, for clarity, changing variable cells are shaded yellow, the objective cell is shaded green, and cells containing the left-hand-side (LHS) formula for each constraint are shaded blue.
- Also, to make the equivalence of the written formulation and the Excel layout clear, our Excel layouts show the decision variable names used in the written formulation of the model. Note that these names have no role in using Solver to solve the model.

Decision variables are start times and crash amounts.

DECISION VARIABLES We begin by defining the decision variables. For each activity i, we define the following two decision variables:

T_i = Time at which activity i starts
C_i = Number of periods (weeks, in this case) by which activity i is crashed

Because there are 8 activities in General Foundry's project, there are 16 decision variables in the project crashing LP model.

The objective is to minimize total crash cost.

OBJECTIVE FUNCTION Next, we formulate the objective function. The objective function here is to minimize the total cost of crashing the project down to 13 weeks. Using the crash cost per week, computed in Table 10, we can express this as follows:

$$\text{Minimize total crash cost} = \$750C_A + \$2,000C_B + \$1,000C_C + \$1,000C_D$$
$$+ \$1,000C_E + \$500C_F + \$1,500C_G + \$3,000C_H$$

Constraints define the precedence relationships.

PRECEDENCE CONSTRAINTS Finally, we formulate the constraints. The first set of constraints in this LP model enforces the precedence relationships between activities (shown in the project network in Figure 19). We write one constraint for each precedence relationship (i.e., arc) in the project network. In writing these constraints, we must remember that the duration of each activity may be reduced by a crash amount (C_i). For example, consider the precedence relationship between activities A and C. Activity A starts at time T_A, and its duration is $(2 - C_A)$ weeks. Hence, activity A finishes at time $(T_A + 2 - C_A)$. This implies that the earliest start time of activity C (i.e., T_C) can be *no earlier* than $(T_A + 2 - C_A)$. We can express this mathematically as

$$T_C \geq T_A + (2 - C_A) \quad (\text{precedence A} \rightarrow \text{C})$$

In a similar fashion, we can express all other activity precedence relationships as follows:

$$T_D \geq T_A + (2 - C_A) \quad (\text{precedence A} \rightarrow \text{D})$$
$$T_D \geq T_B + (3 - C_B) \quad (\text{precedence B} \rightarrow \text{D})$$
$$T_E \geq T_C + (2 - C_C) \quad (\text{precedence C} \rightarrow \text{E})$$
$$T_F \geq T_C + (2 - C_C) \quad (\text{precedence C} \rightarrow \text{F})$$
$$T_G \geq T_D + (4 - C_D) \quad (\text{precedence D} \rightarrow \text{G})$$
$$T_G \geq T_E + (4 - C_E) \quad (\text{precedence E} \rightarrow \text{G})$$
$$T_H \geq T_F + (3 - C_F) \quad (\text{precedence F} \rightarrow \text{H})$$
$$T_H \geq T_G + (5 - C_G) \quad (\text{precedence G} \rightarrow \text{H})$$

Each activity can be crashed by only a finite amount.

CRASH TIME LIMIT CONSTRAINTS We need a second set of constraints to restrict the number of periods by which each activity can be crashed. Using the crash time limits given in Table 10, we can write these constraints as

$$C_A \leq 1 \quad C_B \leq 2 \quad C_C \leq 1 \quad C_D \leq 1$$
$$C_E \leq 2 \quad C_F \leq 1 \quad C_G \leq 3 \quad C_H \leq 1$$

The constraint specifies the project due date

PROJECT COMPLETION CONSTRAINT Finally, we specify that the project must be completed in 13 weeks or less. Activity H, the last activity in the project, starts at time T_H. The standard time for H is 2 weeks, and C_H denotes the number of weeks by which its duration can be crashed. Hence, the actual duration of activity H is $(2 - C_H)$, and its completion time is $(T_H + 2 - C_H)$. We write this constraint, and the nonnegativity constraints, as

$$T_H + 2 - C_H \le 13$$

$$\text{All } T_i \text{ and } C_i \ge 0$$

File: 7-2.xls, sheet: 7-2A

EXCEL SOLUTION Screenshot 2A shows the formula view of the Excel layout for General Foundry's project crashing LP model. This layout follows the same structure and logic for all LP models. That is, we have modeled all parameters (solution value, objective coefficients, and constraint coefficients) associated with a decision variable in a separate column of the worksheet. We have then computed the objective function and LHS formulas for all constraints, using Excel's SUMPRODUCT function. In implementing this model on Excel, we have algebraically modified each constraint so that all variables are in the LHS of the equation, and only a constant appears on the right-hand side (RHS). For example, the precedence relationship between activities A and C has been modified from $\left[T_C \ge T_A + (2 - C_A) \right]$ to $\left[T_C - T_A + C_A \ge 2 \right]$.

File: 7-2.xls, sheet: 7-2B

Solver entries are objective cell, changing variable cells, and constraints.

INTERPRETING THE RESULTS The Solver entries and solution for this LP model are shown in Screenshot 2B. The results show that the General Foundry project can be crashed to 13 weeks, at a cost of $2,250 (cell R6). To do so, activities A (cell J5) and G (cell P5) should be crashed by 1 week each. As expected, this is the same as the result we obtained earlier, using hand calculations. Cells B5:I5 show the revised starting times for activities A through H, respectively.

Using Linear Programming to Determine Earliest and Latest Starting Times

It turns out that we can make minor modifications to the project crashing LP model presented earlier to compute the EST and LST for each activity in a project. However, because the two-pass procedure we discussed in section 3 is rather straightforward, LP is seldom used in

SCREENSHOT 2A Formula View of Excel Layout for Project Crashing at General Foundry

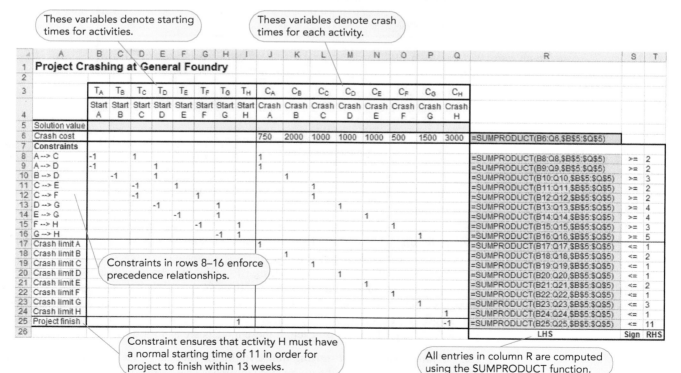

SCREENSHOT 2B   Solver Entries for Project Crashing at General Foundry

(Activity start times)   *(Crash values)*   *(Total crash cost)*

	T_A	T_B	T_C	T_D	T_E	T_F	T_G	T_H	C_A	C_B	C_C	C_D	C_E	C_F	C_G	C_H			
	Start A	Start B	Start C	Start D	Start E	Start F	Start G	Start H	Crash A	Crash B	Crash C	Crash D	Crash E	Crash F	Crash G	Crash H			
Solution value	0.0	0.0	1.0	3.0	3.0	8.0	7.0	11.0	1.0	0.0	0.0	0.0	0.0	0.0	1.0	0.0			
Crash cost									\$750	\$2,000	\$1,000	\$1,000	\$1,000	\$500	\$1,500	\$3,000	\$2,250		
Constraints																			
A --> C	-1		1						1								2	>=	2
A --> D	-1			1					1								4	>=	2
B --> D		-1		1						1							3	>=	3
C --> E			-1		1						1						2	>=	2
C --> F			-1			1					1						7	>=	2
D --> G				-1			1					1					4	>=	4
E --> G					-1		1						1				4	>=	4
F --> H						-1		1						1			3	>=	3
G --> H							-1	1							1		5	>=	5
Crash limit A									1								1	<=	1
Crash limit B										1							0	<=	2
Crash limit C											1						0	<=	1
Crash limit D												1					0	<=	1
Crash limit E													1				0	<=	2
Crash limit F														1			0	<=	1
Crash limit G															1		1	<=	3
Crash limit H																1	0	<=	1
Project finish								1								-1	11	<=	11
																	LHS	Sign	RHS

Solver Parameters   [×]

Se_t Objective: $R$6

To: ○ Max   ◉ Mi_n   ○ _Value Of: [0]

_By Changing Variable Cells:

$B$5:$Q$5

Su_bject to the Constraints:

$R$17:$R$25 <= $T$17:$T$25
$R$8:$R$16 >= $T$8:$T$16

[Add]

(Precedence constraints)   *(Crash limit constraints and project deadline constraint)*   *(Make sure that the nonnegativity constraints have been enforced and Simplex LP has been selected as the solving method)*

practice for this purpose. For this reason, we do not discuss these LP models in detail here and just briefly illustrate their construction.

We first modify the project crashing LP model by removing the project completion constraint and setting all crashing decision variables (C_i) to zero. All precedence constraints in this model remain as is. Then, we solve two LP models in sequence: the first to identify the earliest times and the second to identify the latest times. The additional modifications needed to the project crashing LP model for each of these models are as follows:

- **LP model for earliest starting times.** In this LP model, we set the objective function to minimize the sum of all activity starting times. That is, the objective is

$$\text{Minimize sum of activity times} = T_A + T_B + \cdots + T_H$$

- **LP model for latest starting times.** In this LP model, we set the objective function to maximize the sum of all activity starting times. That is, the objective is

$$\text{Maximize sum of activity times} = T_A + T_B + \cdots + T_H$$

However, we need to ensure that the entire project finishes at its earliest completion time (as computed by the LP model for the EST). Hence, we add a constraint regarding the starting time of the *last activity* in the project. For example, in General Foundry's project, we set the LST of activity H at 13 weeks (i.e., $T_H = 13$).

7 Using Microsoft Project to Manage Projects

The analyses discussed so far in this chapter are effective for managing small projects. However, for managing large, complex projects, using specialized project management software is preferred. In this section, we provide a brief introduction to a popular example of such specialized software, Microsoft Project 2010.

We should note that at this introductory level, our intent is not to describe the full capabilities of Microsoft Project. Rather, we illustrate how it can be used to perform some of the basic calculations in managing projects. We leave it to you to explore the advanced capabilities and functions of Microsoft Project (or any other project management software) in greater detail, either on your own or as part of an elective course in project management.

Microsoft Project is useful for project scheduling and control.

Microsoft Project is extremely useful in drawing project networks (section 2), identifying the project schedule (section 3), and managing project costs and other resources (section 5). It does not, however, perform PERT probability calculations (section 4) or have an LP-based procedure built in for project crashing (section 6).

File: 7-3.mpp

First, we define a new project.

Creating a Project Schedule Using Microsoft Project

Let us consider the General Foundry project again. Recall from section 2 that this project has eight activities. The first step is to define the activities and their precedence relationships. To do so, we start Microsoft Project, click File | New, and select the blank project template. We can now select the Project Information menu command (found within the Project tab) to obtain the window shown in Screenshot 3A and enter summary information such as the project start date. Note that dates are referred to by actual calendar dates rather than as day 0, day 1, and so on. For example, we have specified July 1 as our project starting date in Screenshot 3A (dates can be shown using several different formats, including showing the year, too, if desired). Microsoft Project automatically updates the project finish date once we have entered all the project information. In Screenshot 3A, we have specified the current date as August 12.

ENTERING ACTIVITY INFORMATION After entering the summary information, we use the window shown in Screenshot 3B to enter all activity information. For each activity (or task, as Microsoft Project calls it), we enter its name and duration. Microsoft Project identifies tasks by numbers (e.g., 1, 2) rather than letters. Hence, for convenience, we have shown both the letter (e.g., A, B) and the description of the activity in the Task Name column in Screenshot 3B. By default, the duration is measured in days. To specify weeks, we include the letter *w* after the duration of each activity. For example, we enter the duration of activity A as 2*w*.

Next, we enter the activity information.

Durations

Activity	Time (weeks)
A	2
B	3
C	2
D	4
E	4
F	3
G	5
H	2

The schedule automatically takes into account nonworking days.

As we enter the activities and durations, the software automatically inserts start and finish dates. Note that all activities have the same start date (i.e., July 1) because we have not yet defined the precedence relationships. Also, as shown in Screenshot 3B, if the Gantt Chart option is selected in the View menu, a horizontal bar corresponding to the duration of each activity appears on the right pane of the window.

Observe that Saturdays and Sundays are automatically grayed out in the Gantt chart to reflect the fact that these are nonworking days. In most project management software, we can link the entire project to a master calendar (or, alternatively, link each activity to its own specific calendar). Additional nonworking days can be defined using these calendars. For example, we have used the Change Working Time menu command (found within the Project tab) to specify Monday, July 4, as a nonworking day in Screenshot 3B. (Note that this day is also grayed out in the Gantt chart.) This automatically extends all activity completion times by one day. Because activity A starts on Friday, July 1, and takes 2 weeks (i.e., 10 working days), its finish time is now Friday, July 15 (rather than Thursday, July 14).

SCREENSHOT 3A Project Summary Information in Microsoft Project

Specify current data, if necessary (will automatically show today's date). Used for tracking project status.

Date can be formatted to show year also, if desired.

Specify project start date.

Specify master calendar that project should follow.

This date will be automatically updated after the project data has been entered.

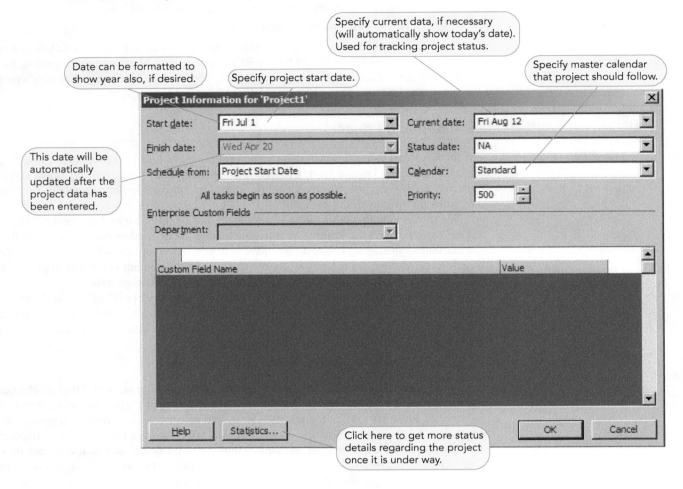

Click here to get more status details regarding the project once it is under way.

SCREENSHOT 3B Activity Entry in Microsoft Project for General Foundry

Change the layout by selecting *Layout* (found within the *Format* tab).

We either of these options to adjust the scale of the Gantt chart.

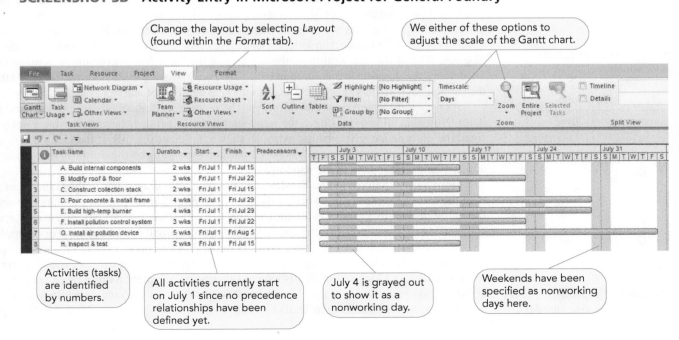

Activities (tasks) are identified by numbers.

All activities currently start on July 1 since no precedence relationships have been defined yet.

July 4 is grayed out to show it as a nonworking day.

Weekends have been specified as nonworking days here.

SCREENSHOT 3C Defining Links between Activities in Microsoft Project

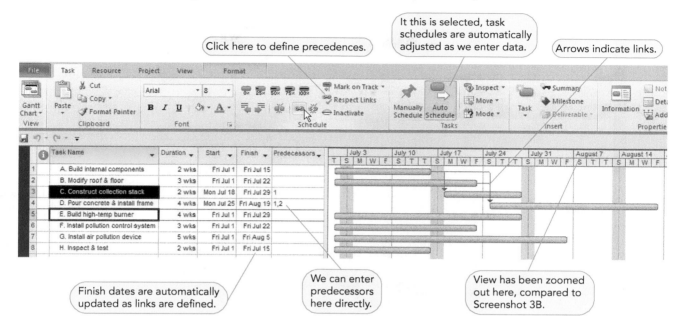

DEFINING PRECEDENCE RELATIONSHIPS The next step is to define precedence relationships (or links) between the activities. There are two ways of specifying these links. The first is to enter the relevant activity numbers (e.g., 1, 2) in the Predecessor column, as shown in Screenshot 3C for activities C and D. The other approach uses the Link icon. For example, to specify the precedence relationship between activities C and E, we click activity C first, hold down the Control (Ctrl) key, and then click activity E. We then click the Link icon (found within the Task tab), as shown in Screenshot 3C. As soon as we define a link, the bars in the Gantt chart are repositioned to reflect the new start and finish times for the linked activities if the Auto Schedule mode is enabled (as in Screenshot 3C). Further, the link itself is shown as an arrow extending from the predecessor activity.

VIEWING THE PROJECT SCHEDULE When all links have been defined, the complete project schedule can be viewed as a Gantt chart, as shown in Screenshot 3D. We can also select Network Diagram (found within the View tab) to view the schedule as a project network (shown

Precedences	
Activity	*Predecessors*
A	—
B	—
C	A
D	A, B
E	C
F	C
G	D, E
H	F, G

SCREENSHOT 3D Gantt Chart in Microsoft Project for General Foundry

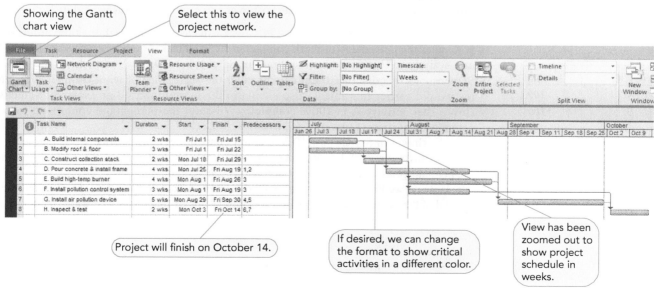

SCREENSHOT 3E Project Network in Microsoft Project for General Foundry

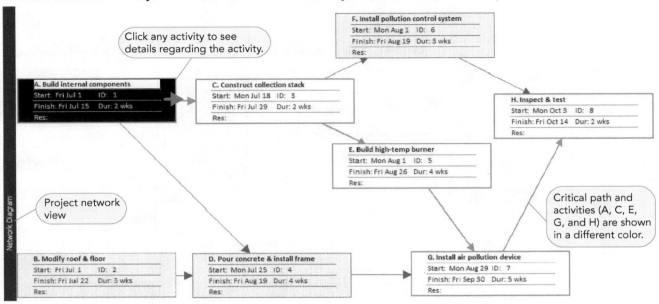

The project can be viewed either as a Gantt chart or as a network.

in Screenshot 3E). The critical path is shown in red on the screen in the network diagram. We can click any of the activities in the project network to view details of the activities. Likewise, we can easily add or remove activities and/or links from the project network. Each time we do so, Microsoft Project automatically updates all start dates, all finish dates, and the critical path(s). If desired, we can manually change the layout of the network (e.g., reposition activities) by changing the options in Format | Layout.

Screenshots 3D and 3E show that if General Foundry's project starts July 1, it can be finished on October 14. The start and finish dates for all activities are also clearly identified. This schedule takes into account the nonworking days on all weekends and on July 4. These screenshots illustrate how the use of specialized project management software can greatly simplify the scheduling procedures discussed in sections 2 and 3.

The biggest benefit of using software is to track a project.

File: 7-4.mpp

Tracking Progress and Managing Costs Using Microsoft Project

Perhaps the biggest advantage of using specialized software to manage projects is that it can track the progress of the project. In this regard, Microsoft Project has many features available to track individual activities in terms of time, cost, resource usage, and so on. In this section, we first illustrate how we can track the progress of a project in terms of time. We then introduce project costs so that we can compute cost overruns or underruns (as we did in Table 7).

TRACKING THE TIME STATUS OF A PROJECT An easy way to track the time progress of tasks is to enter the percentage of work completed for each task. One way to do so is to double-click any activity in the Task Name column in Screenshot 3D. A window like the one shown in Screenshot 4A is displayed. Let us now enter the percentage of work completed for each task (as we did earlier in Table 7; also shown in the margin note). For example, Screenshot 4A shows that activity A is 100% complete. We enter the percentage completed for all other activities in a similar fashion.

As shown in Screenshot 4B, the Gantt chart immediately reflects this updated information by drawing a thick line within each activity's bar. The length of this line is proportional to the percentage of that activity's work that has been completed.

How do we know if we are on schedule? Let us assume that today is Friday, August 12 (i.e., the end of the sixth week in the project schedule).[5] Notice that there is a vertical dashed line shown

Percentage Completed

Activity	Completed
A	100
B	100
C	100
D	10
E	20
F	20
G	0
H	0

---

[5] Remember that the nonworking day on July 4 has moved all schedules forward by one day.

SCREENSHOT 4A   Updating Activity Progress in Microsoft Project

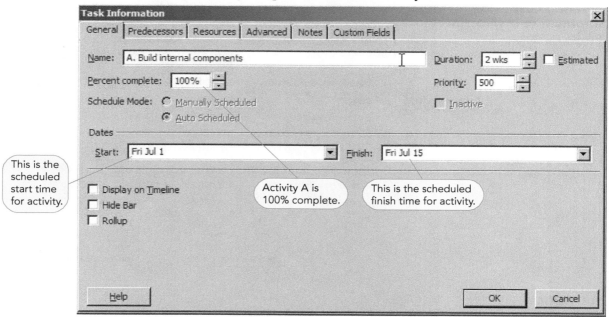

SCREENSHOT 4B   Tracking Project Progress in Microsoft Project

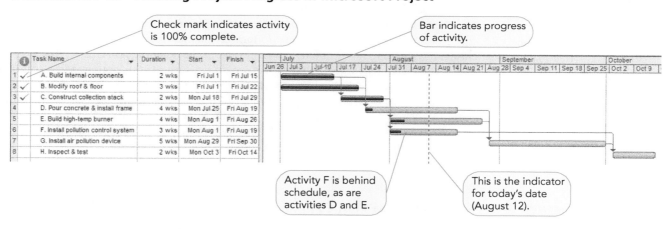

on the Gantt chart corresponding to today's date. Microsoft Project will automatically move this line to correspond with the current date. If the project is on schedule, we should see all bars to the *left* of today's line indicate that they have been completed. For example, Screenshot 4B shows that activities A, B, and C are on schedule. In contrast, activities D, E, and F appear to be behind schedule. These activities need to be investigated further to determine the reason for the delay. This type of easy *visual* information is what makes project management software so useful in practice.

TRACKING THE COST STATUS OF A PROJECT   Just as we tracked a project's progress with regard to time, we can track its current status with regard to budget. There are several ways to define the cost of an activity. If the total cost consists of both fixed and variable costs, we need to define the resources used in the project, the unit costs of those resources, and the level of usage for each resource by each activity. We can even specify how resources should be charged to an activity (e.g., prorated basis, full billing upon completion). Microsoft Project uses this information to first calculate the variable cost of each activity based on its level of resource usage. This is then added to the fixed costs to find the total cost for each activity.

In the case of General Foundry's project, because we have not specified the fixed and variable costs separately, an alternate way to enter activity costs is to click Tables | Cost (found within the View tab). The window shown in Screenshot 4C is displayed. We enter the budgeted cost

We define the costs for each activity.

Budgeted Cost

Activity	Budget
A	$22,000
B	$30,000
C	$26,000
D	$48,000
E	$56,000
F	$30,000
G	$80,000
H	$16,000

SCREENSHOT 4C
Entering Cost Information in Microsoft Project

> Establish baseline by clicking Set Baseline (found within the Project tab).

	Task Name	Fixed Cost	Fixed Cost Accrual	Total Cost	Baseline
1	A. Build internal components	$22,000.00	Prorated	$22,000.00	$22,000.00
2	B. Modify roof & floor	$30,000.00	Prorated	$30,000.00	$30,000.00
3	C. Construct collection stack	$26,000.00	Prorated	$26,000.00	$26,000.00
4	D. Pour concrete & install frame	$48,000.00	Prorated	$48,000.00	$48,000.00
5	E. Build high-temp burner	$56,000.00	Prorated	$56,000.00	$56,000.00
6	F. Install pollution control system	$30,000.00	Prorated	$30,000.00	$30,000.00
7	G. Install air pollution device	$80,000.00	Prorated	$80,000.00	$80,000.00
8	H. Inspect & test	$16,000.00	Prorated	$16,000.00	$16,000.00

> In this case, we have entered the activity costs as fixed costs.

> Total cost = Fixed cost since no variable costs have been defined.

We compute the variances in activity budgets.

Actual Cost

Activity	Cost
A	$20,000
B	$36,000
C	$26,000
D	$ 6,000
E	$20,000
F	$ 4,000
G	$ 0
H	$ 0

for each activity (see Table 7) in the Fixed Cost column. Microsoft Project automatically copies these values to the Total Cost column. We can now use these total costs to establish the Baseline Cost (or budgeted cost) by clicking Set Baseline (found within the Project tab). This information is also shown in Screenshot 4C.

Once we have entered this cost information, how do we compare our current expenses with the budget? To do so, we first need to turn off the automatic calculation option in Microsoft Project by clicking File | Options | Schedule and unchecking the box labeled Actual costs are always calculated by Project. Note that if we do not turn off this option, Microsoft Project assumes that all activities are always working as per the budget.

We now enter the actual costs (from Table 7; also shown in the margin note) in the column titled Actual, as shown in Screenshot 4D. Microsoft Project calculates the budget overrun or underrun associated with each activity and shows it in the column titled Variance. As expected, these are the same values we computed manually in Table 7.

SCREENSHOT 4D   Checking Budget Status in Microsoft Project

> Budgeted costs

	Task Name	Fixed Cost	Fixed Cost Accrual	Total Cost	Baseline	Variance	Actual	Remaining
1	A. Build internal components	$20,000.00	Prorated	$20,000.00	$22,000.00	($2,000.00)	$20,000.00	$0.00
2	B. Modify roof & floor	$30,000.00	Prorated	$36,000.00	$30,000.00	$6,000.00	$36,000.00	$0.00
3	C. Construct collection stack	$26,000.00	Prorated	$26,000.00	$26,000.00	$0.00	$26,000.00	$0.00
4	D. Pour concrete & install frame	$48,000.00	Prorated	$49,200.00	$48,000.00	$1,200.00	$6,000.00	$43,200.00
5	E. Build high-temp burner	$56,000.00	Prorated	$64,800.00	$56,000.00	$8,800.00	$20,000.00	$44,800.00
6	F. Install pollution control system	$28,000.00	Prorated	$28,000.00	$30,000.00	($2,000.00)	$5,600.00	$22,400.00
7	G. Install air pollution device	$80,000.00	Prorated	$80,000.00	$80,000.00	$0.00	$0.00	$80,000.00
8	H. Inspect & test	$16,000.00	Prorated	$16,000.00	$16,000.00	$0.00	$0.00	$16,000.00

> Total cost values are changed to reflect variances.

> Cost overruns and underruns. (Negative values indicate underruns.)

> Current expenses. You must turn off automatic calculations in order to enter information here.

As noted earlier, our intent here is to provide just a brief introduction to Microsoft Project. This software (and other specialized project management software) has several other features and capabilities that we have not discussed here. For example, we can use it to associate individual resources with specific activities and establish a separate calendar for each resource. The time schedule of the activity will then be determined based not only on its duration and predecessors but also on the resource calendars. Likewise, we can track each resource and identify possible conflicts (e.g., the same resource being required by two different activities at the same time). Once again, we encourage you to try these procedures on your own to understand the full capabilities of specialized project management software.

Summary

This chapter presents the fundamentals of project management techniques. We discuss two techniques, PERT and CPM, both of which are excellent for controlling large and complex projects.

We first show how to express projects using project networks. Using a two-pass procedure, we can then identify the project schedule and the critical path(s). PERT is probabilistic and allows three time estimates for each activity; these estimates are used to compute the project's expected completion time and variance. We show how to use these parameters to find the probability that the project will be completed by a given date.

We discuss how project management techniques can also be used to plan, schedule, monitor, and control project costs. Using these techniques, we show how to determine whether a project is on schedule at any point in time and whether there are cost overruns or underruns.

Next, we discuss how to crash projects by reducing their completion time through additional resource expenditures. We also illustrate how LP can be used to find the least-cost approach to crashing large projects.

Finally, we provide a brief introduction to Microsoft Project, one of several popular project management software packages.

Glossary

Activity A job or task that consumes time and is a key subpart of a total project.

Activity on Arc (AOA) Network A project network in which arcs denote activities and nodes denote events.

Activity on Node (AON) Network A project network in which nodes denote activities and arcs denote precedence relationships.

Activity Time The duration of an activity.

Backward Pass A procedure that moves from the end of the network to the beginning of the network and is used in determining an activity's LFT and LST.

Beta Probability Distribution A probability distribution that is often used in PERT to compute expected activity completion times and variances.

Crashing The process of reducing the total time it takes to complete a project by expending additional funds.

Critical Path A series of activities that have zero slack. It is the longest time path through the network. A delay for any activity that is on the critical path will delay the completion of the entire project.

Critical Path Analysis An analysis that determines the total project completion time, the critical path for the project, slack, EST, EFT, LST, and LFT for every activity.

Critical Path Method (CPM) A deterministic network technique that is similar to PERT but uses only one time estimate. CPM is used for monitoring budgets and project crashing.

Dummy Activity A fictitious activity that consumes no time and is inserted into an AOA project network to display the proper precedence relationships between activities.

Earliest Finish Time (EFT) The earliest time that an activity can be finished without violation of precedence requirements.

Earliest Start Time (EST) The earliest time that an activity can start without violation of precedence requirements.

Event A point in time that marks the beginning or ending of an activity. It is used in AOA networks.

Expected Activity Time (t) The average time it should take to complete an activity. Expected time $= (a + 4m + b)/6$.

Forward Pass A procedure that moves from the beginning of a network to the end of the network. It is used in determining an activity's EST and EFT.

Gantt Chart An alternative to project networks for showing a project schedule.

Immediate Predecessor An activity that must be completed before another activity can be started.

Latest Finish Time (LFT) The latest time that an activity can be finished without delaying the entire project.

Latest Start Time (LST) The latest time that an activity can be started without delaying the entire project.

Most Likely Time (m) The amount of time that you would expect it would take to complete an activity. Used in PERT.

Optimistic Time (*a*)   The shortest amount of time that could be required to complete an activity. Used in PERT.

Pessimistic Time (*b*)   The greatest amount of time that could be required to complete an activity. Used in PERT.

Program Evaluation and Review Technique (PERT)   A probabilistic modeling procedure that allows three time estimates for each activity in a project.

Project Management   A decision modeling approach that allows managers to plan, schedule, and control projects.

Project Network   A graphical display of a project that shows activities and precedence relationships.

Resource Loading Chart   A graph that plots the resource needed per period versus time.

Slack Time   The amount of time that an activity can be delayed without delaying the entire project. Slack = LST − EST or LFT − EFT.

Variance of Activity Completion Time   A measure of dispersion of the activity completion time. Variance = $[(b − a)/6]^2$.

Work Breakdown Structure (WBS)   A plan that details the activities in a project.

Solved Problems

Solved Problem 1

To complete the wing assembly for an experimental aircraft, Scott DeWitte has laid out the seven major activities involved. These activities have been labeled A through G in the following table, which also shows their estimated times (in weeks) and immediate predecessors:

ACTIVITY	*a*	*m*	*b*	IMMEDIATE PREDECESSORS
A	1	2	3	—
B	2	3	4	—
C	4	5	6	A
D	8	9	10	B
E	2	5	8	C, D
F	4	5	6	D
G	1	2	3	E

Determine the expected time and variance for each activity.

Solution

For each activity, the expected time and variance can be computed using the formulas presented in Equations 6 and 7, respectively. The results are summarized in the following table:

ACTIVITY	EXPECTED TIME (WEEKS)	VARIANCE
A	2	0.111
B	3	0.111
C	5	0.111
D	9	0.111
E	5	1.000
F	5	0.111
G	2	0.111

Solved Problem 2

Referring to Solved Problem 1, Scott would now like to determine the critical path for the entire wing assembly project as well as the expected completion time for the total project. In addition, he would like to determine the probability that the project will finish in 21 weeks or less.

FIGURE 20 Critical Path for Solved Problem 2

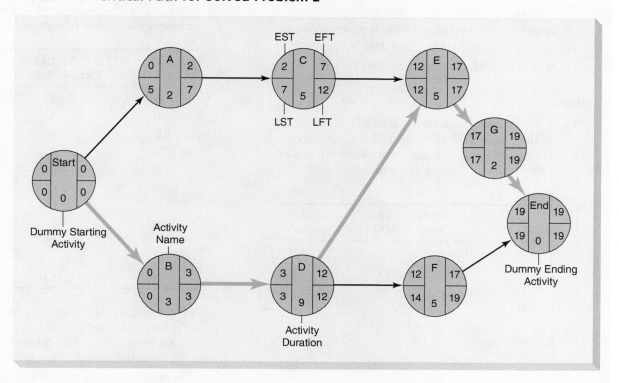

Solution

The AON network for Scott DeWitte's project is shown in Figure 20. Note that this project has multiple activities (A and B) with no immediate predecessors and multiple activities (F and G) with no successors. Hence, in addition to a dummy unique starting activity (Start), we have included a dummy unique finishing activity (End) for the project.

Figure 20 shows the earliest and latest times for all activities. The activities along the critical path are B, D, E, and G. These activities have zero slack. The expected project completion time is 19 weeks. The sum of the variances of the critical activities is 1.333, which implies that the standard deviation of the project completion time is 1.155 weeks. Hence,

$$P(\text{Completion time} \le 21 \text{ weeks}) = P(Z \le (21 - 19)/1.155) = P(Z \le 1.73)$$
$$= 0.9582$$

Discussion Questions and Problems

Discussion Questions

1 What are some of the questions that can be answered with project management?

2 What are the major differences between PERT and CPM?

3 What is an activity? What is an immediate predecessor?

4 Describe how expected activity times and variances can be computed in a PERT analysis.

5 Briefly discuss what is meant by critical path analysis. What are critical path activities, and why are they important?

6 What are the EST and LST? How are they computed?

7 Describe the meaning of slack and discuss how it can be determined.

8 How can we determine the probability that a project will be completed by a certain date? What assumptions are made in this computation?

9 Briefly describe how project budgets can be monitored.

10 What is crashing, and how is it done by hand?

11 Why is LP useful in project crashing?

Problems

12 A certification program consists of a series of activities that must be accomplished in a certain order. The activities, their immediate predecessors, and estimated durations appear in the following table.

ACTIVITY	IMMEDIATE PREDECESSORS	TIME (DAYS)
A	—	2
B	—	5
C	—	1
D	B	10
E	A, D	3
F	C	6
G	E, F	8

(a) Develop a project network for the certification program.

(b) Determine the EST, EFT, LST, LFT, and slack for each activity. Also determine the total program completion time and the critical path(s).

13 A local political campaign must coordinate a number of necessary activities to be prepared for an upcoming election. The following table describes the relationships between these activities that need to be completed, as well as estimated times.

ACTIVITY	IMMEDIATE PREDECESSORS	TIME (WEEKS)
A	—	4
B	—	6
C	A	3
D	A	4
E	B, C	8
F	B	7
G	D, E	2
H	F	1

(a) Develop a project network for this problem.

(b) Determine the EST, EFT, LST, LFT, and slack for each activity. Also determine the total project completion time and the critical path(s).

14 The Pickett Marketing Firm is developing a new Web-based media campaign for a client. The following table describes the relationships between the activities that need to be completed.

ACTIVITY	IMMEDIATE PREDECESSORS	TIME (DAYS)
A	—	4
B	A	6
C	B	12
D	B	11
E	D	9
F	D	8
G	D	10
H	C	5
I	C	7
J	E, F, G	4
K	H, I	9

(a) Develop a project network for this problem.

(b) Determine the EST, EFT, LST, LFT, and slack for each activity. Also determine the total project completion time and the critical path(s).

15 The activities required to design a prototype of an experimental machine are listed in the following table, along with their immediate predecessors and estimated durations.

ACTIVITY	IMMEDIATE PREDECESSORS	TIME (DAYS)
A	—	5
B	—	4
C	A	2
D	A	1
E	B	5
F	B	7
G	C, E	9
H	D, F	6

(a) Develop a project network for this problem.

(b) Determine the EST, EFT, LST, LFT, and slack for each activity. Also determine the total project completion time and the critical path(s).

16 An office complex is to be renovated. Before the job can be completed, various tradespeople and skilled workers must install their materials. The table at the top of the next page describes the relationships between the activities that need to be completed.

(a) Develop a project network for this problem.

(b) Determine the EST, EFT, LST, LFT, and slack for each activity. Also determine the total project completion time and the critical path(s).

ACTIVITY	IMMEDIATE PREDECESSORS	TIME (DAYS)
A1	—	5
A2	A1	6
A3	A1	2
A4	A1	9
A5	A2	9
A6	A3, A4	3
A7	A4	7
A8	A4	4
A9	A5, A6, A7	6
A10	A8	5

17 An electrical contractor is examining the amount of time his crews take to complete wiring jobs. Some crews seem to take longer than others. For an upcoming job, a list of activities and their optimistic, most likely, and pessimistic completion times are given in the following table.

ACTIVITY	DAYS			IMMEDIATE PREDECESSORS
	a	m	b	
A	3	6	9	—
B	2	4	6	—
C	1	2	3	—
D	6	7	8	C
E	2	4	6	B, D
F	6	10	14	A, E
G	1	2	6	A, E
H	3	6	9	F
I	10	11	12	G
J	14	16	21	G
K	2	8	11	H, I

(a) Develop a project network for this problem.
(b) Determine the expected duration and variance for each activity.
(c) Determine the EST, EFT, LST, LFT, and slack for each activity. Also determine the total project completion time and critical path(s) for installing electrical wiring and equipment.
(d) What is the probability that this job will finish in 38 days or less?

18 A plant engineering group needs to set up an assembly line to produce a new product. The table in the next column describes the relationships between the activities that need to be completed for this product to be manufactured.
(a) Develop a project network for this problem.
(b) Determine the expected duration and variance for each activity.

(c) Determine the EST, EFT, LST, LFT, and slack for each activity. Also determine the total project completion time and the critical path(s).
(d) Determine the probability that the project will be completed in less than 34 days.
(e) Determine the probability that the project will take more than 29 days.

ACTIVITY	DAYS			IMMEDIATE PREDECESSORS
	a	m	b	
A	3	6	6	—
B	5	8	11	A
C	5	6	10	A
D	1	2	6	B, C
E	7	11	15	D
F	7	9	14	D
G	6	8	10	D
H	3	4	8	F, G
I	3	5	7	E, F, H

19 A plant is acquiring new production machinery. Before the machinery can be fully functional, a number of activities must be performed, including roughing out for power, placing the machinery, installing the equipment that will feed product to the machinery, etc. The activities, their precedence relationships, and their durations are shown in the following table.

ACTIVITY	DAYS			IMMEDIATE PREDECESSORS
	a	m	b	
A	8	10	12	—
B	6	7	8	—
C	3	3	6	—
D	10	20	30	A
E	6	7	8	C
F	9	10	11	B, D, E
G	6	7	11	B, D, E
H	14	15	16	F
I	10	11	12	F
J	6	7	8	G, H
K	4	7	10	I, J
L	1	2	6	G, H

(a) Determine the expected times and variances for each activity.
(b) Construct a project network for this problem.
(c) Determine the EST, EFT, LST, LFT, and slack for each activity. Also determine the critical path and project completion time.
(d) What is the probability that the project will be finished in 70 days?
(e) What is the probability that the project will need at least 75 days?

20 A series of activities must be completed in a coordinated fashion to complete a landscaping overhaul. The following table shows the activities; their optimistic, most likely, and pessimistic durations; and their immediate predecessors.

ACTIVITY	DAYS			IMMEDIATE PREDECESSORS
	a	*m*	*b*	
A	4	8	12	—
B	4	10	13	A
C	7	14	18	B
D	9	16	20	B
E	6	9	12	B
F	2	4	6	D, E
G	4	7	13	C, F
H	3	5	7	G
I	2	3	4	G, H

$t = (a + 4m + b)/6$

$\Rightarrow = [(b - a)/6]$

(a) Determine the expected times and variances for each activity.
(b) Construct a project network for this problem.
(c) Determine the EST, EFT, LST, LFT, and slack for each activity. Also determine the critical path and project completion time.
(d) What is the probability that the project will be finished in less than 57 days?
(e) What is the probability that the project will need at least 50 days?

21 LeBron Woods is responsible for developing a leadership training program for his organization. The following table describes the relationships between the activities that need to be completed.

ACTIVITY	DAYS			IMMEDIATE PREDECESSORS
	a	*m*	*b*	
A	3	7	14	—
B	5	10	15	—
C	3	5	10	A, B
D	5	12	13	C
E	2	5	8	C
F	2	5	14	E
G	5	8	11	F
H	6	10	14	D
I	3	4	8	F, H
J	4	7	10	G, I

(a) Determine the expected times and variances for each activity.
(b) Construct a project network for this problem.
(c) Determine the EST, EFT, LST, LFT, and slack for each activity. Also determine the critical path and project completion time.

(d) What is the probability that the project will be finished in less than 49 days?
(e) What is the probability that the project will need at least 54 days?

22 The expected project completion time for the construction of a pleasure yacht is 21 months, and the project variance is 6. What is the probability that the project will $\sqrt{6}$
(a) require at least 17 months?
(b) be completed within 20 months?
(c) require at least 23 months?
(d) be completed within 25 months?

23 The Coogan Construction Company has determined that the expected completion time for its most popular model home follows the normal probability distribution with a mean of 25 weeks and a standard deviation of 4 weeks.
(a) What is the probability that the next home will be completed within 30 weeks?
(b) What is the probability that the next home will be completed within 22 weeks?
(c) Find the number of weeks within which Coogan is 99% sure the next home will be completed.
(d) Find the number of weeks within which Coogan is 85% sure the next home will be completed.

24 The General Foundry air pollution project discussed in this chapter has progressed over the past several weeks, and it is now the end of week 8. Lester Harky would like to know the value of the work completed, the amount of any cost overruns or underruns for the project, and the extent to which the project is ahead of schedule or behind schedule by developing a table like the one in Table 7. The current project status is shown in the following table.

ACTIVITY	PERCENTAGE COMPLETED	ACTUAL COST
A	100	$20,000
B	100	$36,000
C	100	$26,000
D	100	$44,000
E	55	$29,000
F	55	$12,000
G	10	$5,000
H	13	$1,800

25 Fred Ridgeway has been given the responsibility of managing a training and development program. He knows the EST and LST (both in months), and the total costs for each activity. This information is given in the table at the top of the next page.
(a) Using ESTs, determine Fred's total monthly budget.
(b) Using LSTs, determine Fred's total monthly budget.

ACTIVITY	EST	LST	t	TOTAL COST
A	0	0	6	$10,000
B	1	4	2	$14,000
C	3	3	7	$ 5,000
D	4	9	3	$ 6,000
E	6	6	10	$14,000
F	14	15	11	$13,000
G	12	18	2	$ 4,000
H	14	14	11	$ 6,000
I	18	21	6	$18,000
J	18	19	4	$12,000
K	22	22	14	$10,000
L	22	23	8	$16,000
M	18	24	6	$18,000

26 Fred Ridgeway's project (see Problem 25) has progressed over the past several months, and it is now the end of month 16. Fred would like to know the current status of the project with regard to schedule and budget by developing an appropriate table. The relevant data are shown in the following table.

ACTIVITY	PERCENTAGE COMPLETED	ACTUAL COST
A	100	$13,000
B	100	$12,000
C	100	$6,000
D	100	$6,000
E	60	$9,000
F	10	$800
G	80	$3,600
H	15	$375

Assume that activities not shown in the table have not yet started and have incurred no cost to date. All activities follow their earliest time schedules.

27 Susan Roger needs to coordinate the opening of a new office for her company in the city of Denver. The activity time and relationships for this project, as well as the total budgeted cost for each activity, are shown in the following table.

ACTIVITY	IMMEDIATE PREDECESSORS	TIME (WEEKS)	TOTAL COST
A	—	2	$2,200
B	A	3	$5,100
C	A	4	$6,000
D	B, C	2	$3,600
E	C	3	$2,700
F	D, E	3	$1,800

(a) Develop a weekly budget for this project, using the earliest start times.
(b) Develop a weekly budget for this project, using the latest start times.

28 Susan Roger's project (see Problem 27) has progressed over the past several weeks, and it is now the end of week 8. Susan would like to know the current status of the project with regard to schedule and budget by developing an appropriate table. Assume that all activities follow their earliest time schedules. The relevant data are shown in the following table.

ACTIVITY	PERCENTAGE COMPLETED	ACTUAL COST
A	100	$1,900
B	100	$5,300
C	100	$6,150
D	40	$1,800
E	60	$1,755
F	0	$ 0

29 General Foundry's project crashing data are shown in Table 10. Crash this project by hand to 10 weeks. What are the final times for each activity after crashing, and what is the total cost associated with reducing the duration of this project from 15 to 10 weeks?

30 Bowman Builders manufactures steel storage sheds for commercial use. Joe Bowman, president of Bowman Builders, is contemplating producing sheds for home use. The activities necessary to build an experimental model and related data are given in the table on the next page. The project completion time using standard times is 14 weeks.

Set up and solve an LP model using Excel to crash this project to 10 weeks. How much does it cost to reduce the duration of this project from 14 to 10 weeks?

31 The table on the next page describes the various activities of a construction project in a chemical plant.
(a) Set up and solve an LP model using Excel to crash this project to 22 days. What is the total crashing cost?
(b) Assuming each activity can only be crashed in whole days, what is the earliest completion of this project? What is the total associated crash cost?

32 A new order filling system needs to be installed as soon as possible. The table on the next page lists the project's activities and their predecessors. Also provided is the cost information to reduce the standard activity times.

Set up and solve an LP model using Excel to crash this project to 24 days. What is the total crashing cost?

Table for Problem 30

ACTIVITY	IMMEDIATE PREDECESSORS	STANDARD TIME (WEEKS)	STANDARD COST	CRASH TIME (WEEKS)	CRASH COST
A	—	3	$1,000	2	$1,600
B	—	2	$2,000	1	$2,700
C	—	1	$300	1	$300
D	A	7	$1,300	3	$1,600
E	B	6	$850	3	$1,000
F	C	2	$4,000	1	$5,000
G	D, E	4	$1,500	2	$2,000

Table for Problem 31

ACTIVITY	IMMEDIATE PREDECESSORS	STANDARD TIME (DAYS)	STANDARD COST	CRASH TIME (DAYS)	CRASH COST
A	—	4	$2,000	2	$2,600
B	A	6	$3,500	5	$4,300
C	A	8	$3,300	6	$3,900
D	B	5	$1,200	4	$1,800
E	C, D	3	$1,700	2	$2,200
F	E	7	$2,200	5	$3,600
G	E	5	$ 900	4	$1,550
H	F, G	4	$1,200	3	$1,700

Table for Problem 32

ACTIVITY	IMMEDIATE PREDECESSORS	STANDARD TIME (DAYS)	STANDARD COST	CRASH TIME (DAYS)	CRASH COST
A	—	7	$2,000	5	$ 3,500
B	A	10	$3,000	8	$ 4,700
C	A	8	$3,400	7	$ 3,700
D	C	6	$1,600	4	$ 2,600
E	C	7	$1,900	4	$ 4,000
F	D, E	5	$1,200	3	$ 2,800
G	B, C	11	$8,200	8	$10,900
H	F, G	4	$2,600	3	$ 3,800

33 Software Development Specialists (SDS) is involved with developing software for customers in the banking industry. SDS breaks a large programming project into teams that perform the necessary steps. Team A is responsible for going from general systems design all the way through to actual systems testing. This involves 18 separate activities. Team B is then responsible for the final installation.

To determine cost and time factors, optimistic, most likely, and pessimistic time estimates have been made for all of the 18 activities involved for team A.

The first step that this team performs is general systems design. The optimistic, most likely, and pessimistic times are 3, 4, and 5 weeks. Following this, a number of activities can begin. Activity 2 is involved with procedures design. Optimistic, most likely, and pessimistic times for completing this activity are 4, 5, and 12 weeks. Activity 3 is developing detailed report designs. Optimistic, most likely, and pessimistic time estimates are 6, 8, and 10 weeks. Activity 4, detailed forms design, has optimistic, most likely, and pessimistic time estimates of 2, 5, and 5 weeks.

Activities 5 and 6 involve writing detailed program specifications and developing file specifications. The three time estimates for activity 5 are 6, 7, and 8 weeks, and the three time estimates for activity 6 are 3, 4, and 5 weeks. Activity 7 involves specifying system test data. Before this is done, activity 6, involving file specifications, must be completed. The time estimates for activity 7 are 2, 3, and 7 weeks. Activity 8 involves reviewing forms. Before activity 8 can be conducted, detailed forms design must be completed. The time estimates for activity 8 are 3, 3, and 9 weeks. The next activity, activity 9, is reviewing the detailed report design. This requires that the detailed report design, activity 3, be completed first. The time estimates for activity 9 are 1, 3, and 5 weeks, respectively.

Activity 10 involves reviewing procedures design. Time estimates are 1, 2, and 9 weeks. Of course, procedures design must be done before activity 10 can be started. Activity 11 involves the system design checkpoint review. A number of activities must be completed before this is done. These activities include reviewing the forms, reviewing the detailed report design, reviewing the procedures design, writing detailed program specs, and specifying system test data. The optimistic, most likely, and pessimistic time estimates for activity 11 are 3, 4, and 5 weeks. Performing program logic design is activity 12. This can be started only after the system design checkpoint review is completed. The time estimates for activity 12 are 4, 5, and 6 weeks.

Activity 13, coding the programs, is done only after the program logic design is completed. The time estimates for this activity are 6, 10, and 14 weeks. Activity 14 is involved in developing test programs. Activity 13 is the immediate predecessor. Time estimates for activity 14 are 3, 4, and 11 weeks. Developing a system test plan is activity 15. A number of activities must be completed before activity 15 can be started. These activities include specifying system test data, writing detailed program specifications, and reviewing procedure designs, the detailed report design, and forms. The time estimates for activity 15 are 3, 4, and 5 weeks.

Activity 16, creating system test data, has time estimates of 2, 4, and 6 weeks. Activity 15 must be done before activity 16 can be started. Activity 17 is reviewing program test results. The immediate predecessor to activity 17 is to test the programs (activity 14). The three time estimates for activity 17 are 2, 3, and 4 weeks. The final activity is conducting system tests. This is activity 18. Before activity 18 can be started, activities 16 and 17 must be complete. The three time estimates for conducting these system tests are 2, 6, and 7 weeks.

How long will it take for team A to complete its programming assignment?

34 Bradshaw Construction is involved in constructing municipal buildings and other structures that are used primarily by city and state municipalities. The construction process involves developing legal documents, drafting feasibility studies, obtaining bond ratings, and so forth. Recently, Bradshaw was given a request to submit a proposal for the construction of a municipal building. The first step is to develop legal documents and to perform all steps necessary before the construction contract is signed. This requires more than 20 separate activities that must be completed. These activities, their immediate predecessors, and optimistic (a), most likely (m), and pessimistic (b) time estimates are given in the table on the next page.

Determine the total project completion time for this preliminary step, the critical path, and slack time for all activities involved.

35 Getting a degree from a college or university can be a long and difficult task. Certain courses must be completed before other courses may be taken. Develop a network diagram in which every activity is a particular course that you must take for your degree program. The immediate predecessors will be course prerequisites. Don't forget to include all university, college, and departmental course requirements. Then try to group these courses into semesters or quarters for your particular school. How long do you think it will take you to graduate? Which courses, if not taken in the proper sequence, could delay your graduation?

36 Dream Team Productions is in the final design phases of its new film, *Killer Worms*, to be released next summer. Market Wise, the firm hired to coordinate the release of *Killer Worms* toys, has identified 16 activities to be completed before the release of the film. These activities, their immediate predecessors, and optimistic (a), most likely (m), and pessimistic (b) time estimates are given in the table on the next page.

(a) How many weeks in advance of the film release should Market Wise start its marketing campaign? What are the critical paths?

(b) If activities I and J were not necessary, what impact would this have on the critical path and the number of weeks needed to complete the marketing campaign?

37 Sager Products has been in the business of manufacturing and marketing toys for toddlers for the past two decades. Jim Sager, president of the firm, is considering the development of a new manufacturing line to allow it to produce high-quality plastic toys at reasonable prices. The development process is long and complex. Jim estimates that there are five phases involved and multiple activities for each phase.

Phase 1 of the development process involves the completion of four activities. These activities have no immediate predecessors. Activity A has an optimistic completion time of 2 weeks, a most likely completion time of 3 weeks, and a pessimistic

Table for Problem 34

ACTIVITY	WEEKS			DESCRIPTION OF ACTIVITY	IMMEDIATE PREDECESSORS
	a	m	b		
1	1	4	7	Draft legal documents	—
2	2	3	4	Prepare financial statements	—
3	3	4	5	Draft history	—
4	7	8	9	Draft demand portion of feasibility study	—
5	4	4	7	Review and approval of legal documents	1
6	1	2	6	Review and approval of history	3
7	4	5	6	Review feasibility study	4
8	1	2	6	Draft final financial portion of feasibility study	7
9	3	4	5	Draft facts relevant to the bond transaction	5
10	1	1	4	Review and approve financial statements	2
11	18	20	22	Receive firm price of project	—
12	1	2	3	Review and complete financial portion of feasibility study	8
13	1	1	4	Complete draft statement	6, 9, 10, 11, 12
14	0.25	0.50	0.75	Send all materials to bond rating services	13
15	0.20	0.30	0.40	Print statement and distributed it to all interested parties	14
16	1	1	4	Make presentation to bond rating services	14
17	1	2	3	Receive bond rating	16
18	3	5	7	Market bonds	15, 17
19	0.10	0.20	0.30	Execute purchase contract	18
20	0.10	0.15	0.50	Authorize and complete final statement	19
21	2	3	7	Purchase contract	19
22	0.20	0.50	0.80	Make bond proceeds available	20
23	0	0.20	0.40	Sign construction contract	21, 22

Table for Problem 36

ACTIVITY	IMMEDIATE PREDECESSORS	WEEKS		
		a	m	b
A	—	1	2	6
B	—	3	3.5	4
C	—	10	12	14
D	—	4	5	9
E	—	2	4	6
F	A	6	7	8
G	B	2	4	6
H	C	5	7	9
I	C	9	10	14
J	C	2	4	6
K	D	2	4	6
L	E	2	4	6
M	F, G, H	5	6	7
N	J, K, L	1	1.5	2
O	I, M	5	7	9
P	N	5	7	9

completion time of 4 weeks. Activity B has estimated values of 5, 6, and 10 weeks for these three completion times. Similarly, activity C has estimated completion times of 1, 1, and 4 weeks; and activity D has expected completion times of 8, 9, and 13 weeks.

Phase 2 involves six separate activities. Activity E has activity A as an immediate predecessor. Time estimates are 1, 1, and 4 weeks. Activity F and activity G both have activity B as their immediate predecessor. For activity F, the time estimates are 3, 4, and 5 weeks. For activity G, the time estimates are 1, 3, and 5 weeks. The only immediate predecessor for activity H is activity C. All three time estimates for activity H are 5 weeks. Activity D must be performed before activity I and activity J can be started. Activity I has estimated completion times of 9, 10, and 11 weeks. Activity J has estimated completion times of 1, 2, and 6 weeks.

Phase 3 is the most difficult and complex of the entire development project. It also consists of six separate activities. Activity K has time estimates of 2, 3, and 4 weeks. The immediate predecessor for this activity is activity E. The immediate predecessor for activity L is activity F. The time estimates for activity L are 3, 4, and 8 weeks. Activity M has 2, 2, and 5 weeks for the estimates of the optimistic, probable, and pessimistic times. The immediate predecessor for activity M is activity G. Activities N and O both have activity I as their immediate predecessor. Activity N has 8, 9, and 10 weeks for its three time estimates. Activity O has 1, 1, and 4 weeks as its time estimates. Finally, activity P has time estimates of 4, 4, and 10 weeks. Activity J is the only immediate predecessor.

Phase 4 involves five activities. Activity Q requires activity K to be completed before it can be started. All three time estimates for activity Q are 6 weeks. Activity R requires that both activity L and activity M be completed first. The three time estimates for activity R are 1, 2, and 3 weeks. Activity S requires activity N to be completed first. Its time estimates are 6, 6, and 9 weeks. Activity T requires that activity O be completed. The time estimates for activity T are 3, 4, and 5 weeks. The final activity for phase 4 is activity U. The time estimates for this activity are 1, 2, and 3 weeks. Activity P must be completed before activity U can be started.

Phase 5 is the final phase of the development project. It consists of only two activities. Activity V requires that activity Q and activity R be completed before it can be started. Time estimates for this activity are 9, 10, and 11 weeks. Activity W is the final activity of the process. It requires three activities to be completed before it can be started: activities S, T, and U. The estimated completion times for activity W are 2, 3, and 7 weeks.

(a) Given this information, determine the expected completion time for the entire process. Also determine which activities are along the critical path.
(b) Jim hopes that the total project will take less than 40 weeks. Is this likely to occur?
(c) Jim has just determined that activities D and I have already been completed and that they do not need to be part of the project. What is the impact of this change on the project completion time and the critical path?

Case Study

Haygood Brothers Construction Company

George and Harry Haygood are building contractors who specialize in the construction of private home dwellings, storage warehouses, and small businesses (less than 20,000 sq. ft. of floor space). Both George and Harry entered a carpenter union's apprenticeship program in the early 1990s and, upon completion of the apprenticeship, became skilled craftsmen in 1996. Before going into business for themselves, they worked for several local building contractors in the Detroit area.

Typically, Haygood Brothers submits competitive bids for the construction of proposed dwellings. Whenever its bids are accepted, various aspects of the construction (e.g., electrical wiring, plumbing, brick laying, painting) are subcontracted. George and Harry, however, perform all carpentry work. In addition, they plan and schedule all construction operations, frequently arrange interim financing, and supervise all construction activities.

The philosophy under which Haygood Brothers has always operated can be simply stated: "Time is money." Delays in construction increase the costs of interim financing and postpone the initiation of their building projects. Consequently, Haygood Brothers deals with all bottlenecks promptly and avoids all delays whenever possible. To minimize the time consumed in a construction project, Haygood Brothers uses PERT.

First, all construction activities and events are itemized and properly arranged (in parallel and sequential combinations) in a network. Then time estimates for each activity are made, the expected time for completing each activity is determined, and the critical (longest) path is calculated. Finally, earliest times, latest times, and slack values are computed. Having made these calculations, George and Harry can place their resources in the critical areas to minimize the time of completing the project.

TABLE 11
**Project Data for
Haygood Brothers
Construction Co.**

		DAYS		
ACTIVITY	IMMEDIATE PREDECESSORS	a	m	b
A	—	4	5	6
B	A	2	5	8
C	B	5	7	9
D	B	4	5	6
E	C	2	4	6
F	E	3	5	9
G	E	4	5	6
H	E	3	4	7
I	E	5	7	9
J	D, I	10	11	12
K	F, G, H, J	4	6	8
L	F, G, H, J	7	8	9
M	L	4	5	10
N	K	5	7	9
O	N	5	6	7
P	M, O	2	3	4

The following are the activities that constitute an upcoming project (home dwelling) for Haygood Brothers:

1. Arrange financing (A)
2. Let subcontracts (B)
3. Set and pour foundations (C)
4. Plumbing (D)
5. Framing (E)
6. Roofing (F)
7. Electrical wiring (G)
8. Installation of windows and doors (H)
9. Ductwork and insulation (including heating and cooling units) (I)
10. Sheetrock, paneling, and paper hanging (J)
11. Installation of cabinets (K)
12. Bricking (L)
13. Outside trim (M)
14. Inside trim (including fixtures) (N)
15. Painting (O)
16. Flooring (P)

The immediate predecessors and optimistic (a), most likely (m), and pessimistic (b) time estimates are shown in Table 11.

Discussion Questions

1. What is the time length of the critical path? What is the significance of the critical path?
2. Compute the amount of time that the completion of each activity can be delayed without affecting the overall project.
3. The project was begun August 1. What is the probability that the project can be completed by September 30? (*Note:* Scheduled completion time = 60 days.)

Source: Jerry Kinard, Western Carolina University, and Brian Kinard, University of North Carolina - Wilmington.

Case Study

Family Planning Research Center of Nigeria

Dr. Adinombe Watage, deputy director of the Family Planning Research Center in Nigeria's Over-the-River Province, was assigned the task of organizing and training five teams of field workers to perform educational and outreach activities as part of a large project to demonstrate acceptance of a new method of birth control. These workers already had training in family planning education but must receive specific training regarding the new method of contraception. Two types of materials must also be prepared: (1) those for use in training the workers and (2) those for distribution in the field. Training faculty must be brought in, and arrangements must be made for transportation and accommodations for the participants.

Dr. Watage first called a meeting of this office staff. Together they identified the activities that must be carried out, their necessary sequences, and the time they would require. Their results are displayed in Table 12.

Louis Odaga, the chief clerk, noted that the project had to be completed in 60 days. Whipping out his solar-powered calculator, he added up the time needed. It came to 94 days. "An

TABLE 12
Project Data for Family Planning Research Center

ACTIVITY	IMMEDIATE PREDECESSORS	TIME (DAYS)	STAFFING NEEDED
A. Identify faculty and their schedules	—	5	2
B. Arrange transport to base	—	7	3
C. Identify and collect training materials	—	5	2
D. Arrange accommodations	A	3	1
E. Identify team	A	7	4
F. Bring in team	B, E	2	1
G. Transport faculty to base	A, B	3	2
H. Print program material	C	10	6
I. Have program material delivered	H	7	3
J. Conduct training program	D, F, G, I	15	0
K. Perform fieldwork training	J	30	0

TABLE 13
Cost Data for Family Planning Research Center

ACTIVITY	STANDARD TIME	STANDARD COST	CRASH TIME	CRASH COST
A. Identify faculty and their schedules	5	$ 400	2	$ 700
B. Arrange transport to base	7	$ 1,000	4	$ 1,450
C. Identify and collect training materials	5	$ 400	3	$ 500
D. Arrange accommodations	3	$ 2,500	1	$ 3,000
E. Identify team	7	$ 400	4	$ 850
F. Bring in team	2	$ 1,000	1	$ 2,000
G. Transport faculty to base	3	$ 1,500	2	$ 2,000
H. Print program material	10	$ 3,000	5	$ 4,000
I. Have program material delivered	7	$ 200	2	$ 600
J. Conduct training program	15	$ 5,000	10	$ 7,000
K. Perform fieldwork training	30	$10,000	20	$14,000

impossible task, then," he noted. "No," Dr. Watage replied, "some of these tasks can go forward in parallel." "Be careful, though," warned Mr. Oglagadu, the chief nurse, "There aren't that many of us to go around. There are only 10 of us in this office."

"I can check whether we have enough heads and hands once I have tentatively scheduled the activities," Dr. Watage responded. "If the schedule is too tight, I have permission from the Pathminder Fund to spend some funds to speed it up, just so long as I can prove that it can be done at the least cost necessary. Can you help me prove that? Here are the costs for the activities with the elapsed time that we planned and the costs and times if we shorten them to an absolute minimum." Those data are given in Table 13.

Discussion Questions

1. Some of the tasks in this project can be done in parallel. Prepare a diagram showing the required network of tasks and define the critical path. What is the length of the project without crashing?
2. At this point, can the project be done given the personnel constraint of 10 persons?
3. If the critical path is longer than 60 days, what is the least amount that Dr. Watage can spend and still achieve this schedule objective? Assume that crash costs are linear over time.

Source: "Family Planning Research Center of Nigeria" by Curtis P. McLaughlin. © 1992 by the Kenan-Flagler Business School, University of North Carolina at Chapel Hill, NC. 27599-3490. All rights reserved. Used with permission.

Internet Case Studies

See the Companion Website for this text, at www.pearsonhighered.com/balakrishnan, for additional case studies.

13 Critical path = A–C–E–G, Project length = 17 weeks.

15 Critical path B–E–G, Project length = 18 days.

17 (c) Critical path = C–D–E–F–H–K, Project length = 36.5 days. (d) 0.7352.

19 (c) Critical path = A–D–F–H–J–K, Project length = 69 days. (d) 0.6097. (e) 0.0473.

21 (c) Critical path = B–C–D–H–I–J, Project length = 48 days. (d) 0.6279. (e) 0.0251.

23 (a) 0.8944. (b) 0.2266. (c) 34.31 weeks. (d) 29.15 weeks.

25 (a) *EST totals for months* 1–36: $1,667, $8,667, $8,667, $2,381, $4,381, $4,381, $4,114, $2,114, $2,114, $2,114, $1,400, $1,400, $3,400, $3,400, $3,127, $3,127, $1,727, $1,727, $10,727, $10,727, $10,727, $10,727, $10,442, $10,442, $4,442, $2,714, $2,714, $2,714, $2,714, $2,714, $714, $714, $714, $714, $714, and $714. (b) *LST totals for months* 1–36: $1,667, $1,667, $1,667, $2,381, $9,381, $9,381, $2,114, $2,114, $2,114, $4,114, $3,400, $3,400, $1,400, $1,400, $1,945, $3,127, $1,727, $1,727, $3,727, $6,727, $4,727, $7,727, $8,442, $7,442, $10,442, $9,896, $8,714, $5,714, $5,714, $5,714, $2,714, $714, $714, $714, $714, and $714.

27 (a) *EST totals for weeks* 1–12: $1,100, $1,100, $3,200, $3,200, $3,200, $1,500, $2,700, $2,700, $900, $600, $600, and $600. (b) *LST totals for weeks* 1–12: $1,100, $1,100, $1,500, $1,500, $3,200, $3,200, $2,600, $2,700, $2,700, $600, $600, and $600.

29 Total crash cost = $7,250. New durations for A = 1, C = 1, D = 3, and G = 2.

31 (a) Crash A by 2, D by 1, E by 1, F by 2, and H by 1. Total crash cost = $3,600. (b) Possible to crash project to 21 days. Total cost = $4,400.

33 Critical path = 1–3–9–11–12–13–14–17–18. Completion time = 47.5 weeks.

35 Answer will vary based on student. First list all courses including electives to get a degree. Then list all prerequisites for every course. Develop network diagram. Potential difficulties include incorporating min/max number of courses to take during a given semester, and scheduling electives.

37 (a) Critical path = D–I–N–S–W. Project length = 38.5 weeks. (b) Probability = 0.8642. (c) Critical path = B–F–L–R–V. Project length = 27 weeks.

Network Models

After completing this chapter, students will be able to:

1. Connect all points of a network while minimizing total distance using the minimal-spanning tree technique.
2. Determine the maximum flow through a network using the maximal-flow technique and linear programming.
3. Find the shortest path through a network using the shortest-route technique and linear programming.
4. Understand the important role of software in solving network models.

CHAPTER OUTLINE

1   Introduction
2   Minimal-Spanning Tree Problem

3   Maximal-Flow Problem
4   Shortest-Route Problem

Summary • Glossary • Solved Problems • Self-Test • Discussion Questions and Problems • Internet Homework Problems • Case Study: Binder's Beverage • Case Study: Southwestern University Traffic Problems • Internet Case Study • Bibliography

From Chapter 11 of *Quantitative Analysis for Management,* 11/e. Barry Render. Ralph M. Stair, Jr. Michael E. Hanna. Copyright © 2012 by Pearson Education. All rights reserved.

1 Introduction

Three network models are covered in this chapter.

Networks are used to model a wide variety of problems. The transportation, transshipment, and assignment problems model as networks. Linear programming was used for solving them, and other techniques were presented as well. In this chapter, the following network problems will be presented: the minimal-spanning tree problem, the maximal-flow problem, and the shortest-route problem. Special techniques for solving these will be presented, and when appropriate, a linear programming formulation will be provided. The *minimal-spanning tree technique* determines the path through the network that connects all the points while minimizing total distance. When the points represent houses in a subdivision, the minimal-spanning tree technique can be used to determine the best way to connect all of the houses to electrical power, water systems, and so on, in a way that minimizes the total distance or length of power lines or water pipes. The *maximal-flow technique* finds the maximum flow of any quantity or substance through a network. This technique can determine, for example, the maximum number of vehicles (cars, trucks, and so forth) that can go through a network of roads from one location to another. Finally, the *shortest-route technique* can find the shortest path through a network. For example, this technique can find the shortest route from one city to another through a network of roads.

All of the examples used to describe the various network techniques in this chapter are small and simple compared to real problems. This is done to make it easier for you to understand the techniques. In many cases, these smaller network problems can be solved by inspection or intuition. For larger problems, however, finding a solution can be very difficult and requires the use of these powerful network techniques. Larger problems may require hundreds, or even thousands, of iterations. To computerize these techniques, it is necessary to use the systematic approach we present.

The circles in the networks are called nodes. *The lines connecting them are called* arcs.

You will see several types of networks in this chapter. Although they represent many different things, some terminology is common to all of them. The points on the network are referred to as **nodes**. Typically these are presented as circles, although sometimes squares or rectangles are used for the nodes. The lines connecting the nodes are called **arcs**.

2 Minimal-Spanning Tree Problem

This minimal-spanning tree technique connects nodes at a minimum distance.

The minimal-spanning tree technique involves connecting all the points of a network together while minimizing the distance between them. It has been applied, for example, by telephone companies to connect a number of phones together while minimizing the total length of telephone cable.

Let us consider the Lauderdale Construction Company, which is currently developing a luxurious housing project in Panama City Beach, Florida. Melvin Lauderdale, owner and president of Lauderdale Construction, must determine the least expensive way to provide water and power to each house. The network of houses is shown in Figure 1.

As seen in Figure 1, there are eight houses on the gulf. The distance between each house in hundreds of feet is shown on the network. The distance between houses 1 and 2, for example, is 300 feet. (The number 3 is between nodes 1 and 2.) Now, the minimal-spanning tree technique is used to determine the minimal distance that can be used to connect all of the nodes. The approach is outlined as follows:

There are four steps for the minimal-spanning tree problem.

Steps for the Minimal-Spanning Tree Technique

1. Select any node in the network.
2. Connect this node to the nearest node that minimizes the total distance.
3. Considering all of the nodes that are now connected, find and connect the nearest node that is not connected. If there is a tie for the nearest node, select one arbitrarily. A tie suggests there may be more than one optimal solution.
4. Repeat the third step until all nodes are connected.

FIGURE 1

Network for Lauderdale Construction

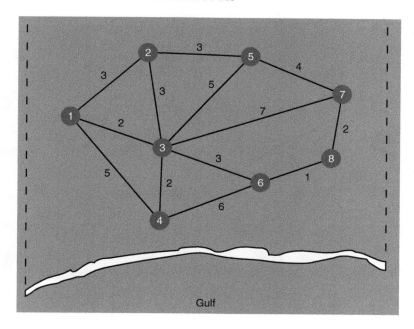

Gulf

Step 1: We select node 1.
Step 2: We connect node 1 to node 3.

Step 3: We connect the next nearest node.

Step 4: We repeat the process.

Now, we solve the network in Figure 1 for Melvin Lauderdale. We start by arbitrarily selecting node 1. Since the nearest node is the third node at a distance of 2 (200 feet), we connect node 1 to node 3. This is shown in Figure 2.

Considering nodes 1 and 3, we look for the next-nearest node. This is node 4, which is the closest to node 3. The distance is 2 (200 feet). Again, we connect these nodes (see Figure 3, part (a)).

We continue, looking for the nearest unconnected node to nodes 1, 3, and 4. This is node 2 or node 6, both at a distance of 3 from node 3. We will pick node 2 and connect it to node 3 (see Figure 3, part (b)).

We continue the process. There is another tie for the next iteration with a minimum distance of 3 (node 2–node 5 and node 3–node 6). You should note that we do not consider node 1–node 2 with a distance of 3 because both nodes 1 and 2 are already connected. We arbitrarily select

FIGURE 2

First Iteration for Lauderdale Construction

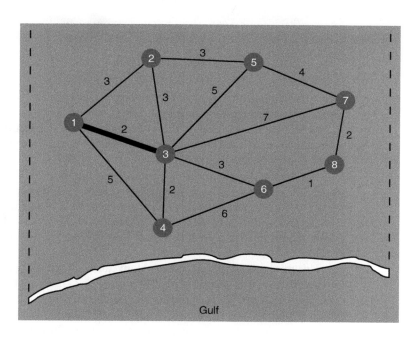

Gulf

FIGURE 3   Second and Third Iterations

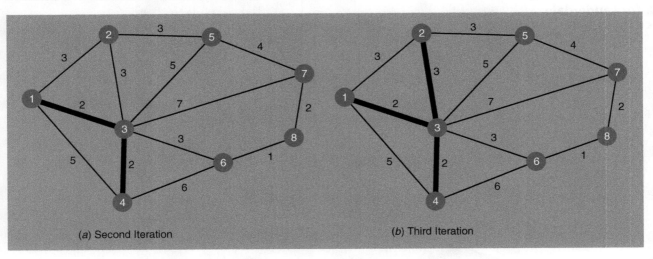

(a) Second Iteration

(b) Third Iteration

FIGURE 4   Fourth and Fifth Iterations

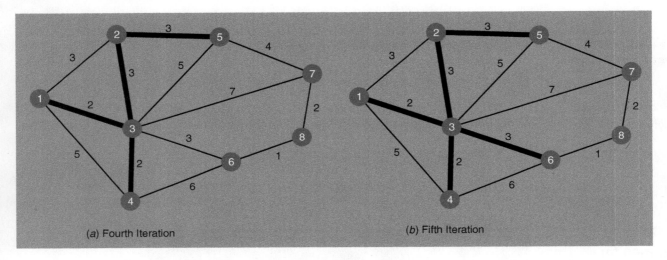

(a) Fourth Iteration

(b) Fifth Iteration

node 5 and connect it to node 2 (see Figure 4, part (a)). The next nearest node is node 6, and we connect it to node 3 (see Figure 4, part (b)).

At this stage, we have only two unconnected nodes left. Node 8 is the nearest to node 6, with a distance of 1 and we connect it (see Figure 5, part (a)). Then the remaining node 7 is connected to node 8 (see Figure 5, part (b)).

The final solution can be seen in the seventh and final iteration (see Figure 5, part (b)). Nodes 1, 2, 4, and 6 are all connected to node 3. Node 2 is connected to node 5. Node 6 is connected to node 8, and node 8 is connected to node 7. All of the nodes are now connected. The total distance is found by adding the distances for the arcs used in the spanning tree. In this example, the distance is $2 + 2 + 3 + 3 + 3 + 1 + 2 = 16$ (or 1,600 feet). This is summarized in Table 1.

This **minimal-spanning tree problem** can be solved using QM for Windows. Select *Networks* for the Module drop-down menu. Then click *File—New* and select *Minimal Spanning Tree* as the type of network. In the screen that appears, enter the number of arcs and click OK. The input screen will allow you to enter the starting node, ending node, and cost (distance) for each arc. These are reproduced in the output screen shown in Program 1. Notice that multiple optimal solutions exist, as stated in the output.

FIGURE 5 Sixth and Seventh (Final) Iterations

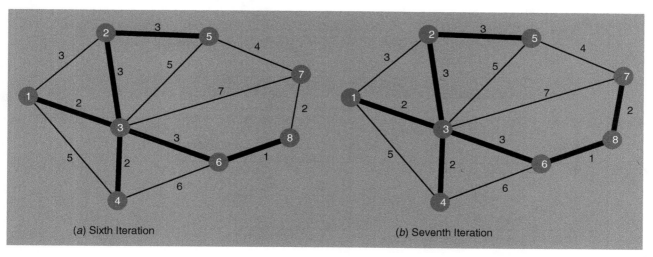

(a) Sixth Iteration   (b) Seventh Iteration

TABLE 1 Summary of Steps in Lauderdale Construction Minimal-Spanning Tree Problem

STEP	CONNECTED NODES	UNCONNECTED NODES	CLOSEST UNCONNECTED NODE	ARC SELECTED	ARC LENGTH	TOTAL DISTANCE
1	1	2, 3, 4, 5, 6, 7, 8	3	1–3	2	2
2	1, 3	2, 4, 5, 6, 7, 8	4	3–4	2	4
3	1, 3, 4	2, 5, 6, 7, 8	2 or 6	2–3	3	7
4	1, 2, 3, 4	5, 6, 7, 8	5 or 6	2–5	3	10
5	1, 2, 3, 4, 5	6, 7, 8	6	3–6	3	13
6	1, 2, 3, 4, 5, 6	7, 8	8	6–8	1	14
7	1, 2, 3, 4, 5, 6, 8	7	7	7–8	2	16

3 Maximal-Flow Problem

The maximal-flow technique finds the most that can flow through a network.

The **maximal-flow problem** involves determining the maximum amount of material that can flow from one point (the **source**) to another (the **sink**) in a network. Examples of this type of problem include determining the maximum number of cars that can flow through a highway system, the maximum amount of a liquid that can flow through a series of pipes, and the maximum amount of data that can flow through a computer network.

To find the maximal flow from the source or start of a network to the sink or finish of that network, two common methods are used: the maximal-flow technique and linear programming. We will begin by presenting an example and demonstrating the first of these methods.

Maximal-Flow Technique

Waukesha, a small town in Wisconsin, is in the process of developing a road system for the downtown area. Bill Blackstone, one of the city planners, would like to determine the maximum number of cars that can flow through the town from west to east. The road network is shown in Figure 6.

PROGRAM 1 **QM for Windows Solution for Lauderdale Construction Company Minimal Spanning Tree Problem**

Networks Results

Lauderdale Construction Company Solution					
Branch name	Start node	End node	Cost	Include	Cost
Branch 1	1	2	3	Y	3
Branch 2	1	3	2	Y	2
Branch 3	1	4	5		
Branch 4	2	3	3		
Branch 5	2	5	3	Y	3
Branch 6	3	4	2	Y	2
Branch 7	3	5	5		
Branch 8	3	6	3	Y	3
Branch 9	3	7	7		
Branch 10	4	6	6		
Branch 11	5	7	4		
Branch 12	6	8	1	Y	1
Branch 13	7	8	2	Y	2
Total					16

The streets are indicated by their respective nodes. Look at the street between nodes 1 and 2. The numbers by the nodes indicate the maximum number of cars (in hundreds of cars per hour) that can flow *from* the various nodes. The number 3 by node 1 indicates that 300 cars per hour can flow *from* node 1 to node 2. Look at the numbers 1, 1, and 2 by node 2. These numbers indicate

FIGURE 6

Road Network for Waukesha

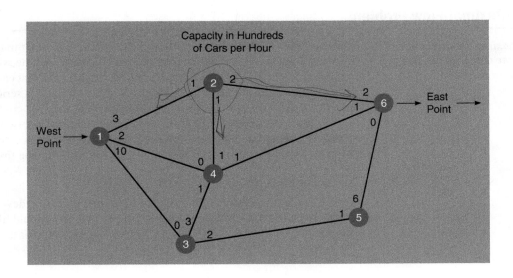

Spanning Tree Analysis of a Telecommunications Network

Network models have been used to solve a variety of problems for many different companies. In telecommunications, there is always a need to connect computer systems and devices together in an efficient and effective manner. Digital Equipment Corporation (DEC) for example, was concerned about how computer systems and devices were connected to a local area network (LAN) using a technology called Ethernet. The DECnet routing department was responsible for this and other network and telecommunications solutions.

Because of a number of technical difficulties, it was important to have an effective way to transport packets of information throughout the LAN. The solution was to use a spanning tree algorithm. The success of this approach can be seen in a poem written by one of the developers:

"I think I shall never see a graph more lovely than a tree.
A tree whose critical property is loop-free connectivity.
A tree that must be sure to span, so packets can reach every LAN.

First the route must be selected, by ID it is elected.
Least-cost paths from the root are traced.
In the tree these paths are placed.
A mesh is made for folks by me, then bridges find a spanning tree."

Source: Based on Radia Perlman, et al. "Spanning the LAN," *Data Communications* (October 21, 1997): 68–70.

Traffic can flow in both directions.

the maximum flow *from* node 2 to nodes 1, 4, and 6, respectively. As you can see, the maximum flow from node 2 back to node 1 is 100 cars per hour (1). One hundred cars per hour (1) can flow from node 2 to node 4, and 200 cars (2) can flow to node 6. Note that traffic can flow in both directions down a street. A zero (0) means no flow or a one-way street.

The maximal-flow technique is not difficult. It involves the following steps:

The four maximal-flow technique steps.

Four Steps of the Maximal-Flow Technique

1. Pick any path from the start (source) to the finish (sink) with some flow. If no path with flow exists, then the optimal solution has been found.
2. Find the arc on this path with the smallest flow capacity available. Call this capacity *C*. This represents the maximum additional capacity that can be allocated to this route.
3. For each node on this path, decrease the flow capacity in the direction of flow by the amount *C*. For each node on this path, increase the flow capacity in the reverse direction by the amount *C*.
4. Repeat these steps until an increase in flow is no longer possible.

We start by arbitrarily picking a path and adjusting the flow.

We start by arbitrarily picking the path 1–2–6, which is at the top of the network. What is the maximum flow from west to east? It is 2 because only 2 units (200 cars) can flow from node 2 to node 6. Now we adjust the flow capacities (see Figure 7). As you can see, we subtracted the maximum flow of 2 along the path 1–2–6 in the direction of the flow (west to east) and added 2 to the path in the direction against the flow (east to west). The result is the new path in Figure 7.

It is important to note that the new path in Figure 7 reflects the new relative capacity at this stage. The flow number by any node represents two factors. One factor is the flow that can come *from* that node. The second factor is flow that can be *reduced* coming *into* the node. First consider the flow from west to east. Look at the path that goes from node 1 to node 2. The number 1 by node 1 tells us that 100 cars can flow *from* node 1 to node 2. Looking at the path from node 2 to node 6, we can see that the number 0 by node 2 tells us that 0 cars can flow *from* node 2 to node 6. Now consider the flow from east to west shown in the new path in Figure 7. First, consider the path from node 6 to node 2. The number 4 by node 6 tells us the total by which we can either reduce the flow from node 2 to node 6 or increase the flow from node 6 to node 2 (or some combination of these flows into and out of node 6), depending on the current status of the flows. Since we have indicated that there would currently only be 2 units (200 cars) flowing from node 2 to node 6, the maximum we could reduce this is 2, leaving us with the capacity to also allow a

FIGURE 7

Capacity Adjustment for Path 1–2–6 Iteration 1

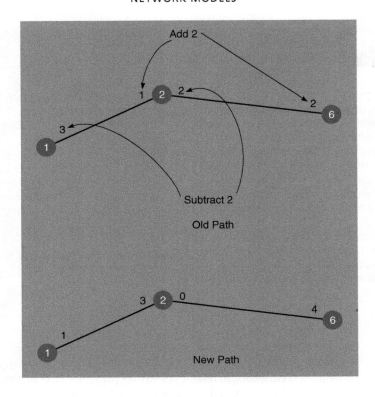

 IN ACTION

Traffic-Control System on the Hanshin Expressway

The Hanshin expressway started with a 2.3-kilometer section of road in Osaka City, Japan, in the 1960s. This small stretch of highway was the first urban toll expressway in Osaka City. The traffic flow was approximately 5,000 cars per day. Today, the expressway includes about 200 kilometers of roadway in a system that connects Osaka and Kobe, Japan. The traffic flow in the early 1990s was more than 800,000 vehicles per day, with peak traffic flows that exceeded 1 million cars per day.

As discussed in this chapter, maximizing the flow of traffic through a network involves an investigation of current and future capacity of the various branches in the network. In addition to capacity analysis, Hanshin decided to use an automated traffic control system to maximize the flow of traffic through the existing expressway and to reduce congestion and bottlenecks caused by accidents, and by road maintenance or disabled cars. It was hoped that the control system would also increase income from the expressway.

Hanshin's management investigated the number of accidents and breakdowns on the expressway to help reduce problems and

further increase traffic flow. The traffic control system provides both direct and indirect control. Direct control includes controlling the number of vehicles entering the expressway at the various on-ramps. Indirect control involves providing comprehensive and up-to-the-minute information concerning traffic flows and the general traffic conditions on the expressway. Information on general traffic conditions is obtained using vehicle detectors, TV cameras, ultrasonic detectors, and automatic vehicle identifiers that read information on license plates. The data gathered from these devices gives people at home and driving the information they need to determine if they will use the Hanshin expressway.

This application reveals that a solution to a problem involves a variety of components, including quantitative analysis, equipment, and other elements, such as providing information to riders.

Source: Based on T. Yoshino, et al. "The Traffic-Control System on the Hanshin Expressway," *Interfaces* 25 (January–February 1995): 94–108.

flow of 2 units from node 6 to node 2 (giving us a total change of 4 units). Looking at the path from node 2 to node 1, we see the number 3 by node 2. This tells us that the total possible change in that direction is 3, and this could come from reducing flows from node 1 to node 2 or increasing flows from node 2 to node 1. Since the flow from node 1 to node 2 is currently 2, we could reduce this by 2, leaving us with the capacity to also allow a flow of 1 unit from node 2 to node 1 (giving us a total change of 3 units). At this stage, we have a flow of 200 cars through the

FIGURE 8   Second Iteration for Waukesha Road System

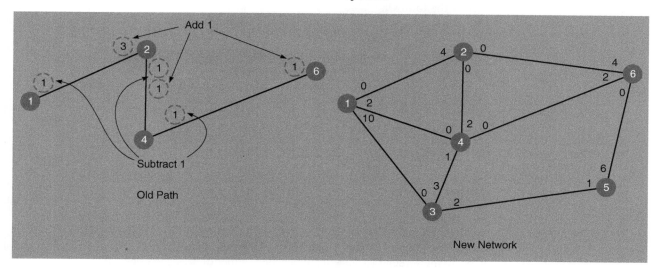

network from node 1 to node 2 to node 6. We have also reflected the new relative capacity, as shown in Figure 7.

Now we repeat the process by picking another path with existing capacity. We will arbitrarily pick path 1–2–4–6. The maximum capacity along this path is 1. In fact, the capacity at every node along this path (1–2–4–6) going from west to east is 1. Remember, the capacity of branch 1–2 is now 1 because 2 units (200 cars per hour) are now flowing through the network. Thus, we increase the flow along path 1–2–4–6 by 1 and adjust the capacity flow (see Figure 8).

The process is repeated.

Now we have a flow of 3 units (300 cars): 200 cars per hour along path 1–2–6 plus 100 cars per hour along path 1–2–4–6. Can we still increase the flow? Yes, along path 1–3–5–6. This is the bottom path. We consider the maximum capacity for each node along this route. The capacity from node 1 to node 3 is 10 units; the capacity from node 3 to node 5 is 2 units; and the capacity from node 5 to node 6 is 6 units. We are limited by the lowest of these, which is the 2 units of flow from node 3 to node 5. The 2-unit increase in flow along this path is shown in Figure 9.

We continue until there are no more paths with unused capacity.

Again we repeat the process, trying to find a path with any unused capacity through the network. If you carefully check the last iteration in Figure 9, you will see that there are no more paths from node 1 to node 6 with unused capacity, even though several other branches

FIGURE 9

Third and Final Iteration for Waukesha Road System

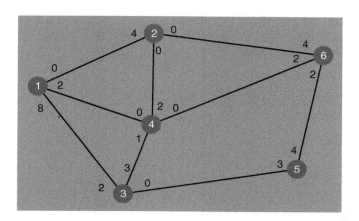

in the network do have unused capacity. The maximum flow of 500 cars per hour is summarized in the following table:

PATH	FLOW (CARS PER HOUR)
1–2–6	200
1–2–4–6	100
1–3–5–6	200
	Total 500

You can also compare the original network to the final network to see the flow between any of the nodes.

This maximal-flow problem can be solved using QM for Windows. Select *Networks* from the Module drop-down menu. Then click *File—New* and select *Maximal Flow* as the type of network. In the screen that appears, enter the number of arcs and click *OK*. The input screen will allow you to enter the starting node, ending node, and the capacity in each direction for each arc. When the problem is solved, one additional column labeled Flow is added to the table, and this column contains the optimal solution, as shown in Program 2.

Linear Program for Maximal Flow

The maximal-flow problem can be modeled as a linear program. This type of problem may be viewed as a special type of transshipment problem with one source, one destination, and a number of transshipment points. The number shipped through the network would be called the *flow*.

The objective is to maximize the flow through the network. There are two types of constraints. The first set of constraints restricts the amount of flow on any arc to the capacity of that arc. The second set of constraints indicates that the amount of flow out of a node will equal the amount of flow into that node. These are the same as the transshipment constraints in the transshipment problem.

PROGRAM 2   **QM for Windows Solution for Waukesha Road Network Maximal-Flow Problem**

Source: 1   Sink: 6

Networks Results

Branch name	Start node	End node	Capacity	Reverse capacity	Flow
Waukesha Road Network Solution					
Maximal Network Flow	5				
Branch 1	1	2	3	1	3
Branch 2	1	3	10	0	2
Branch 3	1	4	2	0	0
Branch 4	2	4	1	1	1
Branch 5	2	6	2	2	2
Branch 6	3	4	3	1	0
Branch 7	3	5	2	1	2
Branch 8	4	6	1	1	1
Branch 9	5	6	6	0	2

The variables are defined as

$$X_{ij} = \text{flow from node } i \text{ to node } j$$

One additional arc will be added to the network, and this arc will go from the sink (node 6) back to the source (node 1). The flow along this arc represents the total flow in the network.

The linear program is

Maximize Flow $= X_{61}$

subject to

$$X_{12} \leq 3$$
$$X_{13} \leq 10$$
$$X_{14} \leq 2$$
$$X_{21} \leq 1$$
$$X_{24} \leq 1$$
$$X_{26} \leq 2$$
$$X_{34} \leq 3$$
$$X_{35} \leq 2$$
$$X_{42} \leq 1$$
$$X_{43} \leq 1$$
$$X_{46} \leq 1$$
$$X_{53} \leq 1$$
$$X_{56} \leq 1$$
$$X_{62} \leq 2$$
$$X_{64} \leq 1$$

$$X_{61} = X_{12} + X_{13} + X_{14} \quad \text{or} \quad X_{61} - X_{12} - X_{13} - X_{14} = 0$$
$$X_{12} + X_{42} + X_{62} = X_{21} + X_{24} + X_{26} \quad \text{or} \quad X_{12} + X_{42} + X_{62} - X_{21} - X_{24} - X_{26} = 0$$
$$x_{13} + X_{43} + X_{53} = X_{34} + X_{35} \quad \text{or} \quad X_{13} + X_{43} + X_{53} - X_{34} - X_{35} = 0$$
$$x_{14} + X_{24} + X_{34} + X_{64} = X_{42} + X_{43} + X_{46} \quad \text{or} \quad X_{14} + X_{24} + X_{34} + X_{64} - X_{42} - X_{43} - X_{46} = 0$$
$$X_{35} = X_{56} + X_{53} \quad \text{or} \quad X_{35} - X_{56} - X_{53} = 0$$
$$X_{26} + X_{46} + X_{56} = X_{61} \quad \text{or} \quad X_{26} + X_{46} + X_{56} = X_{61}$$
$$X_{ij} \geq 0 \text{ and integer}$$

The last six constraints are restricting the flow out of a node to equal the flow into a node. The problem is now ready to solve using the linear programming module in QM for Windows or using Solver in Excel.

4 Shortest-Route Problem

The shortest-route technique minimizes the distance through a network.

The objective of the **shortest-route problem** is to find the shortest distance from one location to another. In a network, this often involves determining the shortest route from one node to each of the other nodes. This problem can be solved either by the shortest-route technique or by modeling this as a linear program with 0–1 variables. We will present an example and demonstrate the shortest-route technique first, and then a linear program will be developed.

Shortest-Route Technique

Every day, Ray Design, Inc., must transport beds, chairs, and other furniture items from the factory to the warehouse. This involves going through several cities. Ray would like to find the route with the shortest distance. The road network is shown in Figure 10.

FIGURE 10

Roads from Ray's Plant to Warehouse

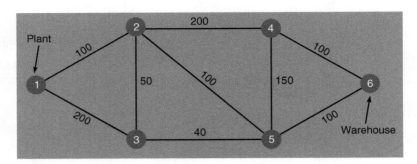

IN ACTION Improving Pupil Transportation

In the early 1990s, North Carolina was spending almost $150 million on transporting students to schools. The state's student transportation system involved some 13,000 buses, 100 school districts, and 700,000 students. In 1989, the General Assembly of the state decided to investigate ways that could be used to save money by developing a better way of transporting students. The General Assembly was committed to funding school districts that transported students efficiently, while only reimbursing justifiable expenses for those districts that were not efficient in terms of how they transported students to and from public schools.

The input data to North Carolina's network model included the number of buses used and the total operating expenses. Total operating expenses included driver salaries, salaries to other transportation personnel, payments to local governments, fuel costs, parts and repair costs, and other related costs. These input values were used to compute an efficiency score for the various districts. These efficiency scores were then used to help in allocating funds to the districts. Those districts with an efficiency score of 0.9 or higher received full funding. Converting efficiency scores to funding was originally received with skepticism. After several years, however, more state officials realized the usefulness of the approach. In 1994–1995, the efficiency-based funding approach was used alone to determine funding.

The use of efficiency-based funding resulted in the elimination of hundreds of school buses, with savings over a three-year period greater than $25 million.

Source: Based on T. Sexton, et al. "Improving Pupil Transportation in North Carolina," *Interfaces* 24 (January–February 1994): 87–103.

The shortest-route technique can be used to minimize total distance from any starting node to a final node. The technique is summarized in the following steps:

The steps of the shortest-route technique.

Steps of the Shortest-Route Technique

1. Find the nearest node to the origin (plant). Put the distance in a box by the node.
2. Find the next-nearest node to the origin (plant), and put the distance in a box by the node. In some cases, several paths will have to be checked to find the nearest node.
3. Repeat this process until you have gone through the entire network. The last distance at the ending node will be the distance of the shortest route. You should note that the distance placed in the box by each node is the shortest route to this node. These distances are used as intermediate results in finding the next-nearest node.

We look for the nearest node to the origin.

Looking at Figure 10, we can see that the nearest node to the plant is node 2, with a distance of 100 miles. Thus we will connect these two nodes. This first iteration is shown in Figure 11.

Now we look for the next-nearest node to the origin. We check nodes 3, 4, and 5. Node 3 is the nearest, but there are two possible paths. Path 1–2–3 is nearest to the origin, with a total distance of 150 miles (see Figure 12).

We repeat the process. The next-nearest node is either node 4 or node 5. Node 4 is 200 miles from node 2, and node 2 is 100 miles from node 1. Thus, node 4 is 300 miles from the origin. There are two paths for node 5, 2–5 and 3–5, to the origin. Note that we don't have to go all the way back to the origin because we already know the shortest route from node 2 and node 3 to the origin. The minimum distances are placed in boxes by these nodes. Path 2–5 is 100 miles,

FIGURE 11

First Iteration for Ray Design

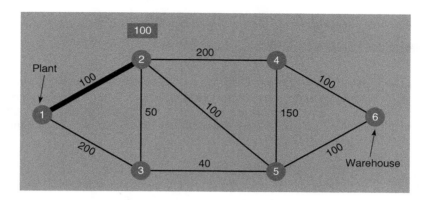

FIGURE 12

Second Iteration for Ray Design

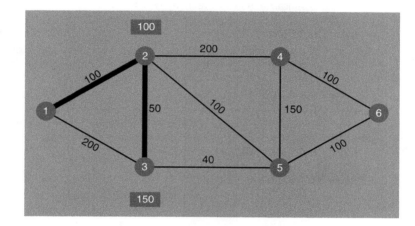

The process is repeated.

and node 2 is 100 miles from the origin. Thus, the total distance is 200 miles. In a similar fashion, we can determine that the path from node 5 to the origin through node 3 is 190 (40 miles between node 5 and 3 plus 150 miles from node 3 to the origin). Thus, we pick node 5 going through node 3 to the origin (see Figure 13).

The next-nearest node will be either node 4 or node 6, as the last remaining nodes. Node 4 is 300 miles from the origin (300 = 200 from node 4 to node 2 plus 100 from node 2 to the origin). Node 6 is 290 miles from the origin (290 = 100 + 190). Node 6 has the minimum distance, and because it is the ending node, we are done (refer to Figure 14). The shortest route is path 1–2–3–5–6, with a minimum distance of 290 miles. This problem can be solved in QM for Windows. The input screen is shown in Program 3A. The solution is shown in Program 3B. Additional information for the optimal solution is available by clicking *Window* after the problem has been solved.

Linear Program for Shortest-Route Problem

The shortest-route problem may be viewed as a special type of transshipment problem with one source having a supply of 1, one destination with a demand of 1, and a number of transshipment points. This type of problem can be modeled as a linear program with 0–1 variables. These variables will indicate whether a particular arc is chosen to be a part of the route taken.

For the Ray Design, Inc., example, the objective is to minimize the total distance (cost) from the start to the finish. The variables are defined as

$$X_{ij} = 1 \text{ if arc from node } i \text{ to node } j \text{ is selected and } X_{ij} = 0 \text{ otherwise}$$

Since the starting point is node 1, we will not include variables going from node 2 or 3 back to node 1. Similarly, since node 6 is the final destination, we will not include any variable that starts at node 6.

MODELING IN THE REAL WORLD — AT&T Solves Network Problems

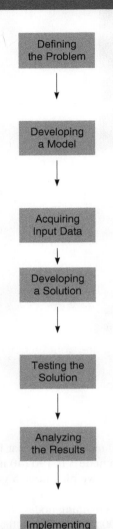

Defining the Problem

↓

Developing a Model

↓

Acquiring Input Data

↓

Developing a Solution

↓

Testing the Solution

↓

Analyzing the Results

↓

Implementing the Results

Defining the Problem

Serving over 80 million customers in the United States and requiring over 40 thousand miles of cable, AT&T's fiber-optic network is the largest in the industry. Handling about 80 billion calls each year, AT&T defined maintaining network reliability, while maximizing network flow and minimizing network resources, as one of its most important problems.

Developing a Model

AT&T developed several comprehensive models to analyze reliability issues. These models investigated two important aspects of network reliability: (1) preventing failures, and (2) responding quickly when failures occur. The models included real time network routing (RTNR), fast automatic restoration (FASTAR), and synchronous optical network (SONET).

Acquiring Input Data

Over 10 months was spent on collecting data for the models. Because of the vast amount of data, AT&T used data aggregation to reduce the size of the network problem to make the solution easier.

Developing a Solution

The solution used an optimization routine to find the best way to route voice and data traffic through the network to minimize the number of message failures and network resources required. Because of the huge amount of data and the large size of the problem, an optimization solution was generated for each set of possible traffic demand and failure possibilities.

Testing the Solution

AT&T performed testing by comparing the solutions obtained by the new optimization approach to the solutions obtained by older planning tools. Improvement expectations of 5% to 10% were established. The company also used computer simulation to test the solution over varying conditions.

Analyizing the Results

To analyze the results, AT&T had to reverse the aggregation steps performed during data collection. Once the disaggregation process was completed, AT&T was able to determine the best routing approach through the vast network. The analysis of the results included an investigation of embedded capacity and spare capacity provided by the solution.

Implementing the Results

When implemented, the new approach was able to reduce network resources by more than 30%, while maintaining high network reliability. During the study, 99.98% of all calls were successfully completed on the first attempt. The successful implementation also resulted in ideas for changes and improvements, including a full optimization approach that could identify unused capacity and place it into operation.

Source: Based on Ken Ambs, et al. "Optimizing Restoration Capacity at the AT&T Network," *Interfaces* 30, 1 (January–February 2000): 26–44.

FIGURE 13

Third Iteration for Ray Design

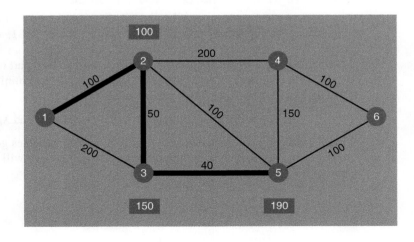

FIGURE 14

Fourth and Final Iteration for Ray Design

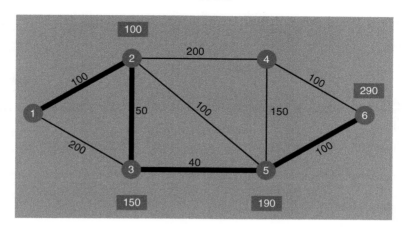

Viewing this as a transshipment problem, the origin node (node 1) must have one unit shipped out of it. This would be

$$X_{12} + X_{13} = 1$$

The final destination node (node 6) must have one unit shipped to it, and this is written

$$X_{46} + X_{56} = 1$$

Each intermediate node will have a constraint requiring the amount coming into the node to equal the amount going out of that node. For node 2 this would be

$$X_{12} + X_{32} = X_{23} + X_{24} + X_{25} \quad \text{or} \quad X_{12} + X_{32} - X_{23} - X_{24} - X_{25} = 0$$

PROGRAM 3A **QM for Windows Input Screen for Ray Design, Inc., Shortest-Route Problem**

Network type: ⊙ Undirected ○ Directed

Origin: 1

Destination: 6

Ray Design, Inc.	Start node	End node	Distance
Branch 1	1	2	100
Branch 2	1	3	200
Branch 3	2	3	50
Branch 4	2	4	200
Branch 5	2	5	100
Branch 6	3	5	40
Branch 7	4	5	150
Branch 8	4	6	100
Branch 9	5	6	100

PROGRAM 3B QM for Windows Solution Screen for Ray Design, Inc., Shortest-Route Problem

Network type
- ● Undirected
- ○ Directed

Origin: ◄ [   ] ► [1]

Destination: ◄ [   ] ► [6]

Networks Results

Ray Design, Inc. Solution				
Total distance = 290	Start node	End node	Distance	Cumulative Distance
Branch 1	1	2	100	100
Branch 3	2	3	50	150
Branch 6	3	5	40	190
Branch 9	5	6	100	290

The other constraints would be constructed in a similar manner. The complete model is

$$\text{Minimize distance} = 100X_{12} + 200X_{13} + 50X_{23} + 50X_{32} + 200X_{24} + 200X_{42}$$
$$+ 100X_{25} + 100X_{52} + 40X_{35} + 40X_{53} + 150X_{45}$$
$$+ 150X_{54} + 100X_{46} + 100X_{56}$$

subject to

$$X_{12} + X_{13} = 1 \qquad \text{Node 1}$$
$$X_{12} + X_{32} - X_{23} - X_{24} - X_{25} = 0 \qquad \text{Node 2}$$
$$X_{13} + X_{23} - X_{32} - X_{35} = 0 \qquad \text{Node 3}$$
$$X_{24} + X_{54} - X_{42} - X_{45} - X_{46} = 0 \qquad \text{Node 4}$$
$$X_{25} + X_{35} + X_{45} - X_{52} - X_{53} - X_{54} - X_{56} = 0 \qquad \text{Node 5}$$
$$X_{46} + X_{56} = 1 \qquad \text{Node 6}$$
$$\text{All variables} = 0 \text{ or } 1$$

This can now be solved with Solver in Excel or with QM for Windows.

Summary

We presented three important network problems—the minimal-spanning tree, the maximal-flow, and the shortest-route problems. All these problems are represented as networks, and specialized solution techniques were provided. The maximal-flow problem and the shortest-route problem may be considered special cases of the transshipment problem, and both of these were modeled using linear programming with variables that were integers or 0–1. These three network problems have a wide variety of applications, and there are many other types of network problems as well.

Glossary

Arc A line in a network that may represent a path or route. An arc or branch is used to connect the nodes in a network.

Maximal-Flow Problem A network problem with the objective of determining the maximum amount that may flow from the origin or source to the final destination or sink.

Minimal-Spanning Tree Problem A network problem with the objective of connecting all the nodes in the network while minimizing the total distance required to do so.

Node A point in a network, often represented by a circle, that is at the beginning or end of an arc.

Shortest-Route Problem A network problem with the objective of finding the shortest distance from one location to another.

Sink The final node or destination in a network.

Source The origin or beginning node in a network.

Solved Problems

Solved Problem 1

Roxie LaMothe, owner of a large horse breeding farm near Orlando, is planning to install a complete water system connecting all of the various stables and barns. The location of the facilities and the distances between them is given in the network shown in Figure 15. Roxie must determine the least expensive way to provide water to each facility. What do you recommend?

FIGURE 15

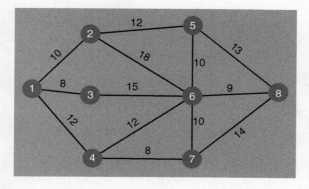

Solution

This is a typical minimum-spanning tree problem that can be solved by hand. We begin by selecting node 1 and connecting it to the nearest node, which is node 3. Nodes 1 and 2 are the next to be connected, followed by nodes 1 and 4. Now we connect node 4 to node 7 and node 7 to node 6. At this point, the only remaining points to be connected are node 6 to node 8 and node 6 to node 5. The final solution can be seen in Figure 16. Table 2 summarizes these steps.

FIGURE 16

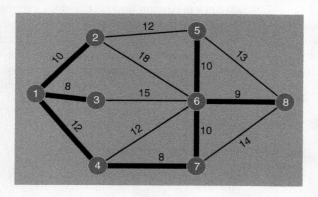

TABLE 2 Summary of Steps in Solved Problem 1 Minimal-Spanning Tree Problem

STEP	CONNECTED NODES	UNCONNECTED NODES	CLOSEST UNCONNECTED NODE	ARC SELECTED	ARC LENGTH	TOTAL DISTANCE
1	1	2, 3, 4, 5, 6, 7, 8	3	1–3	8	8
2	1, 3	2, 4, 5, 6, 7, 8	2	1–2	10	18
3	1, 2, 3	4, 5, 6, 7, 8	4 or 5	1–4	12	30
4	1, 2, 3, 4	5, 6, 7, 8	7	4–7	8	38
5	1, 2, 3, 4, 7	5, 6, 8	6	7–6	10	48
6	1, 2, 3, 4, 6, 7	5, 8	8	6–8	9	57
7	1, 2, 3, 4, 6, 7, 8	5	5	6–5	10	67

Solved Problem 2

PetroChem, an oil refinery located on the Mississippi River south of Baton Rouge, Louisiana, is designing a new plant to produce diesel fuel. Figure 17 shows the network of the main processing centers along with the existing rate of flow (in thousands of gallons of fuel). The management at PetroChem would like to determine the maximum amount of fuel that can flow through the plant, from node 1 to node 7.

FIGURE 17

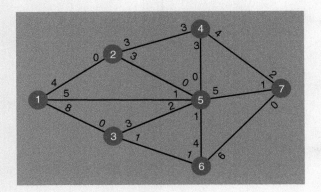

Solution

Using the maximal-flow technique, we arbitrarily choose path 1–5–7, which has a maximum flow of 5. The capacities are then adjusted, leaving the capacities from 1 to 5 at 0, and the capacity from 5 to 7 also at 0. The next path arbitrarily selected is 1–2–4–7, and the maximum flow is 3. When capacities are adjusted, the capacity from 1 to 2 and the capacity from 4 to 7 are 1, and the capacity from 2 to 4 is 0. The next path selected is 1–3–6–7, which has a maximum flow of 1, and the capacity from 3 to 6 is adjusted to 0. The next path selected is 1–2–5–6–7, which has a maximum flow of 1. After this, there are no more paths with any capacity. Arc 5–7 has capacity of 0. While arc 4–7 has a capacity of 1, both arc 2–4 and arc 5–4 have a capacity of 0, so no more flow is available through node 4. Similarly, while arc 6–7 has a capacity of 4 remaining, the capacity for arc 3–6 and the capacity for arc 5–6 are 0. Thus, the maximum flow is 10 (5 + 3 + 1 + 1). The flows are shown in Figure 18.

FIGURE 18

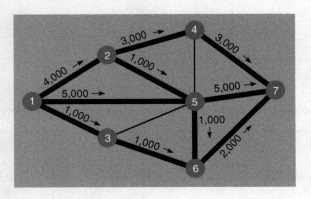

Solved Problem 3

The network of Figure 19 shows the highways and cities surrounding Leadville, Colorado. Leadville Tom, a bicycle helmet manufacturer, must transport his helmets to a distributor based in Dillon, Colorado. To do this, he must go through several cities. Tom would like to find the shortest way to get from Leadville to Dillon. What do you recommend?

FIGURE 19

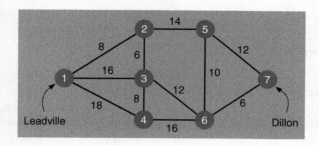

Solution

The problem can be solved using the shortest-route technique. The nearest node to the origin (node 1) is node 2. Give this a distance of 8 and put this in a box next to node 2. Next, consider nodes 3, 4, and 5 since there is an arc to each of these from either node 1 or node 2, and both of these have their distances established. The nearest node to the origin is 3, so the distance to put in the box next to node 3 is 14 (8 + 6). Then consider nodes 4, 5, and 6. The node nearest the origin is node 4, which has a distance of 18 (directly from node 1). Then consider nodes 5 and 6. The node with the least distance from the origin is node 5 (coming through node 2), and this distance is 22. Next, consider nodes 6 and 7, and node 6 is selected since the distance is 26 (coming through node 3). Finally, node 7 is considered, and the shortest distance from the origin is 32 (coming through node 6). The route that gives the shortest distance is 1–2–3–6–7, and the distance is 32. See Figure 20 for the solution.

FIGURE 20

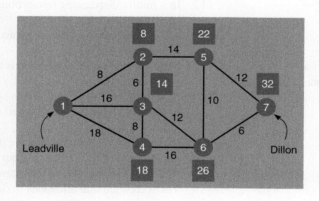

Self-Test

- Before taking the self-test, refer to the learning objectives at the beginning of the chapter, the notes in the margins, and the glossary at the end of the chapter.
- Use the key at the end of the chapter to correct your answers.
- Restudy pages that correspond to any questions that you answered incorrectly or material you feel uncertain about.

1. Which technique is used to connect all points of a network together while minimizing the distance between them?
   a. maximal flow
   b. minimal flow
   c. minimal-spanning tree
   d. shortest route
   e. longest span

2. The first step of the minimal-spanning tree technique is to
   a. select the node with the highest distance between it and any other node.
   b. select the node with the lowest distance between it and any other node.
   c. select the node that is closest to the origin.
   d. select any arc that connects two nodes.
   e. select any node.

3. The first step of the maximal-flow technique is to
   a. select any node.
   b. pick any path from the start to the finish with some flow.
   c. pick the path with the maximum flow.
   d. pick the path with the minimal flow.
   e. pick a path where the flow going into each node is greater than the flow coming out of each node.
4. In which technique do you connect the nearest node to the existing solution that is not currently connected?
   a. maximal tree
   b. shortest route
   c. minimal-spanning tree
   d. maximal flow
   e. minimal flow
5. In the shortest-route technique, the objective is to determine the route from an origin to a destination that passes through the fewest number of other nodes.
   a. True
   b. False
6. Adjusting the flow capacity numbers on a path is an important step in which technique?
   a. maximal flow
   b. minimal flow
   c. maximal-spanning tree
   d. minimal-spanning tree
   e. shortest route
7. Which of the following may be considered a transshipment problem in which there is one source with a supply of 1?
   a. a maximal-flow problem
   b. a minimal-spanning tree problem
   c. a minimal-flow problem
   d. a shortest-route problem
8. If the maximal-flow problem is formulated as a linear program, the objective is to
   a. maximize the flow from the sink to the source.
   b. minimize the total distance.
   c. minimize the flow from the sink to the source.
   d. find the shortest distance from the source to the sink.
9. When the optimal solution has been reached with the maximal-flow technique, every node will be connected with at least one other node.
   a. True
   b. False
10. A large city is planning for delays during rush hour when roads are closed for maintenance. On a normal weekday, 160,000 vehicles travel on a freeway from downtown to a point 15 miles to the west. Which of the techniques discussed in this chapter would help the city planners determine if alternate routes provide sufficient capacity for all the traffic?
    a. minimal-spanning tree technique
    b. maximal-flow technique
    c. shortest-route technique
11. The computing center at a major university is installing new fiber optic cables for a campuswide computer network. Which of the techniques in this chapter could be used to determine the least amount of cable needed to connect the 20 buildings on campus?
    a. minimal-spanning tree technique
    b. maximal-flow technique
    c. shortest-route technique
12. In a minimal-spanning tree problem, the optimal solution has been found when
    a. the start node and the finish node are connected by a continuous path.
    b. the flow from the start node is equal to the flow into the finish node.
    c. all arcs have been selected to be a part of the tree.
    d. all nodes have been connected and are a part of the tree.
13. _____ is a technique that is used to find how a person or an item can travel from one location to another while minimizing the total distance traveled.
14. The technique that allows us to determine the maximum amount of a material that can flow through a network is called _____.
15. The _____ technique can be used to connect all of the points of a network together while minimizing the distance between them.

Discussion Questions and Problems

Discussion Questions

1 What is the minimal-spanning tree technique? What types of problems can be solved using this quantitative analysis technique?
2 Describe the steps of the maximal-flow technique.
3 Give several examples of problems that can be solved using the maximal-flow technique.
4 What are the steps of the shortest-route technique?
5 Describe a problem that can be solved by the shortest-route technique.
6 Is it possible to get alternate optimal solutions with the shortest-route technique? Is there an automatic way of knowing if you have an alternate optimal solution?
7 Describe how the maximal-flow problem is modeled as a transshipment problem.
8 Describe how the shortest-route problem is modeled as a transshipment problem.

Problems*

Q: 9 Bechtold Construction is in the process of installing power lines to a large housing development. Steve Bechtold wants to minimize the total length of wire used, which will minimize his costs. The housing development is shown as a network in Figure 21. Each house has been numbered, and the distances between houses are given in hundreds of feet. What do you recommend? *Minimal-Spanning*

Q: 10 The city of New Berlin is considering making several of its streets one-way. What is the maximum number of cars per hour that can travel from east to west? The network is shown in Figure 22.

Q: 11 Transworld Moving has been hired to move the office furniture and equipment of Cohen Properties to their new headquarters. What route do you recommend? The network of roads is shown in Figure 23. *Shortest Route*

Q• 12 Because of a sluggish economy, Bechtold Construction has been forced to modify its plans for the housing development in Problem 9. The result is that the path from node 6 to 7 now has a distance of 7. What impact does this have on the total length of wire needed to install the power lines?

Q• 13 Due to increased property taxes and an aggressive road development plan, the city of New Berlin has been able to increase the road capacity of two of its roads (see Problem 10). The capacity along the road represented by the path from node 1–node 2 has been increased from 2 to 5. In addition, the capacity from node 1–node 4 has been increased from 1 to 3. What impact do these changes have on the number of cars per hour that can travel from east to west?

Q: 14 The director of security wants to connect security video cameras to the main control site from five potential trouble locations. Ordinarily, cable would simply be run from each location to the main control site. However, because the environment is potentially explosive, the cable must be run in a special conduit that is continually air purged. This conduit is very expensive but large enough to handle five cables (the maximum that might be needed). Use the minimal-spanning tree technique to find a minimum distance route for the conduit between the locations noted in Figure 24. (Note that it makes no difference which one is the main control site.)

Q: 15 One of our best customers has had a major plant breakdown and wants us to make as many widgets

FIGURE 21
Network for Problem 9

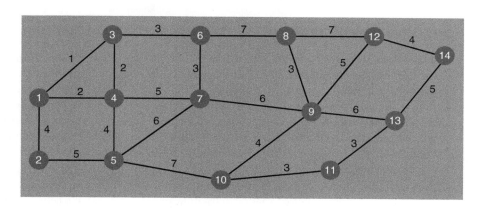

FIGURE 22
Network for Problem 10

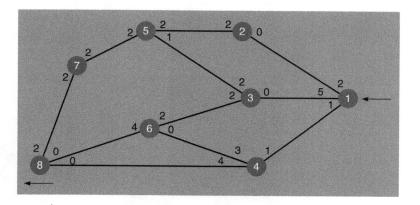

---

*Note: Q means the problem may be solved with QM for Windows.

FIGURE 23
Network for Problem 11

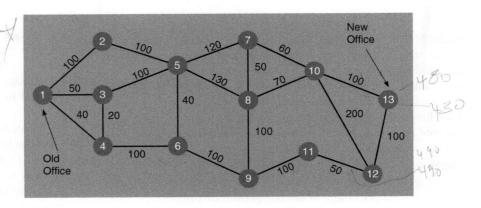

FIGURE 24
Network for Problem 14

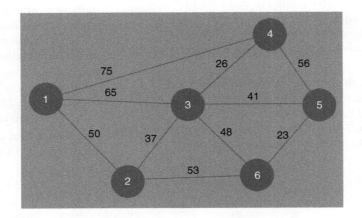

for him as possible during the next few days, until he gets the necessary repairs done. With our general-purpose equipment there are several ways to make widgets (ignoring costs). Any sequence of activities that takes one from node 1 to node 6 in Figure 25 will produce a widget. How many widgets can we produce per day? Quantities given are number of widgets per day.

Q·16 Transworld Moving, like other moving companies, closely follows the impact of road construction to make sure that its routes remain the most efficient. Unfortunately, there has been unexpected road construction due to a lack of planning for road repair

around the town of New Haven, represented by node 9 in the network. (See Problem) All roads leading to node 9, except the road from node 9 to node 11, can no longer be traveled. Does this have any impact on the route that should be used to ship the office furniture and equipment of Cohen Properties to their new headquarters?

Q:17 Solve the minimal-spanning tree problem in the network shown in Figure 26. Assume that the numbers in the network represent distance in hundreds of yards.

Q:18 Refer to Problem 17. What impact would changing the value for path 6–7 to 500 yards have on the solution to the problem and the total distance?

FIGURE 25
Network for Problem 15

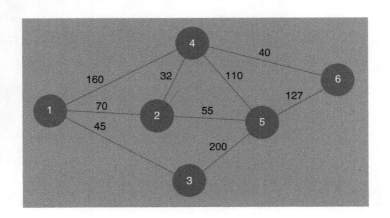

FIGURE 26
Network for Problem 17

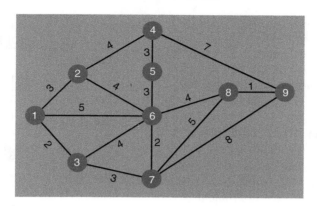

Q: 19 The road system around the hotel complex on International Drive (node 1) to Disney World (node 11) in Orlando, Florida, is shown in the network of Figure 27. The numbers by the nodes represent the traffic flow in hundreds of cars per hour. What is the maximum flow of cars from the hotel complex to Disney World? *maximal - flow problem*

Q: 20 A road construction project would increase the road capacity around the outside roads from International Drive to Disney World by 200 cars per hour (see Problem 19). The two paths affected would be 1–2–6–9–11 and 1–5–8–10– What impact would this have on the total flow of cars? Would the total flow of cars increase by 400 cars per hour?

Q: 21 Refer to Problem 19 and model this problem using linear programming. Solve it with any software.

Q: 22 In Problem 21, a linear program was developed for the road system at Disney World. Modify this linear program to make the changes detailed in Problem 20. Solve this problem and compare it to the solution without the changes.

Q: 23 Solve the maximal-flow problem presented in the network of Figure 28 below. The numbers in the network represent thousands of gallons per hour as they flow through a chemical processing plant.

Q: 24 Two terminals in the chemical processing plant, represented by nodes 6 and 7, require emergency repair (see Problem 23). No material can flow into or out of these nodes. What impact does this have on the capacity of the network?

Q: 25 Solve the shortest-route problem presented in the network of Figure 29 below, going from node 1 to

FIGURE 27
Network for Problem 19

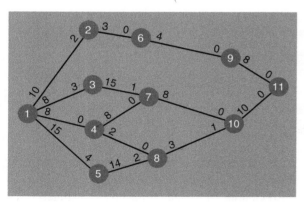

FIGURE 28
Network for Problem 23

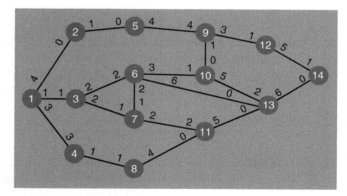

FIGURE 29
Network for Problem 25

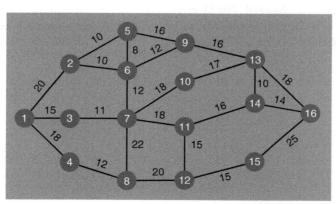

node 16. All numbers represent kilometers between German towns near the Black Forest.

Q: 26 Due to bad weather, the roads going through nodes 7 and 8 have been closed (see Problem 25). No traffic can get onto or off of these roads. Describe the impact that this will have (if any) on the shortest route through this network.

Q: 27 Refer to Problem 25 and model this problem using linear programming. Solve it with any software.

Q: 28 In Problem 27, a linear program was developed for the shortest-route problem. Modify this linear program to make the changes detailed in Problem 26. Solve this problem and compare it to the solution without the changes.

Q: 29 Grey Construction would like to determine the least expensive way of connecting houses it is building with cable TV. It has identified 11 possible branches or routes that could be used to connect the houses. The cost in hundreds of dollars and the branches are summarized in the following table.

(a) What is the least expensive way to run cable to the houses?

BRANCH	START NODE	END NODE	COST ($100s)
Branch 1	1	2	5
Branch 2	1	3	6
Branch 3	1	4	6
Branch 4	1	5	5
Branch 5	2	6	7
Branch 6	3	7	5
Branch 7	4	7	7
Branch 8	5	8	4
Branch 9	6	7	1
Branch 10	7	9	6
Branch 11	8	9	2

(b) After reviewing cable and installation costs, Grey Construction would like to alter the costs for installing cable TV between its houses. The first branches need to be changed. The changes are summarized in the following table. What is the impact on total costs?

BRANCH	START NODE	END NODE	COST ($100s)
Branch 1	1	2	5
Branch 2	1	3	1
Branch 3	1	4	1
Branch 4	1	5	1
Branch 5	2	6	7
Branch 6	3	7	5
Branch 7	4	7	7
Branch 8	5	8	4
Branch 9	6	7	1
Branch 10	7	9	6
Branch 11	8	9	2

Q: 30 In going from Quincy to Old Bainbridge, there are 10 possible roads that George Olin can take. Each road can be considered a branch in the shortest-route problem.

(a) Determine the best way to get from Quincy (node 1) to Old Bainbridge (node 8) that will minimize total distance traveled. All distances are in hundreds of miles.

BRANCH	START NODE	END NODE	DISTANCE (IN HUNDREDS OF MILES)
Branch 1	1	2	3
Branch 2	1	3	2
Branch 3	2	4	3
Branch 4	3	5	3
Branch 5	4	5	1
Branch 6	4	6	4
Branch 7	5	7	2
Branch 8	6	7	2
Branch 9	6	8	3
Branch 10	7	8	6

(b) George Olin made a mistake in estimating the distances from Quincy to Old Bainbridge. The new distances are in the following table. What impact does this have on the shortest route from Quincy to Old Bainbridge?

BRANCH	START NODE	END NODE	DISTANCE (IN HUNDREDS OF MILES)
Branch 1	1	2	3
Branch 2	1	3	2
Branch 3	2	4	3
Branch 4	3	5	1
Branch 5	4	5	1
Branch 6	4	6	4
Branch 7	5	7	2
Branch 8	6	7	2
Branch 9	6	8	3
Branch 10	7	8	6

Q: 31   South Side Oil and Gas, a new venture in Texas, has developed an oil pipeline network to transport oil from exploration fields to the refinery and other locations. There are 10 pipelines (branches) in the network. The oil flow in hundreds of gallons and the network of pipelines is given in the following table.

(a) What is the maximum that can flow through the network?

BRANCH	START NODE	END NODE	CAPACITY	REVERSE CAPACITY	FLOW
Branch 1	1	2	10	4	10
Branch 2	1	3	8	2	5
Branch 3	2	4	12	1	10
Branch 4	2	5	6	6	0
Branch 5	3	5	8	1	5
Branch 6	4	6	10	2	10
Branch 7	5	6	10	10	0
Branch 8	5	7	5	5	5
Branch 9	6	8	10	1	10
Branch 10	7	8	10	1	5

(b) South Side Oil and Gas needs to modify its pipeline network flow patterns. The new data is in the following table. What impact does this have on the maximum flow through the network?

BRANCH	START NODE	END NODE	CAPACITY	REVERSE CAPACITY	FLOW
Branch 1	1	2	10	4	10
Branch 2	1	3	8	2	5
Branch 3	2	4	12	1	10
Branch 4	2	5	0	0	0
Branch 5	3	5	8	1	5
Branch 6	4	6	10	2	10
Branch 7	5	6	10	10	0
Branch 8	5	7	5	5	5
Branch 9	6	8	10	1	10
Branch 10	7	8	10	1	5

Q: 32   The following table represents a network with the arcs identified by their starting and ending nodes. Draw the network and use the minimal-spanning tree to find the minimum distance required to connect these nodes.

ARC	DISTANCE
1–2	12
1–3	8
2–3	7
2–4	10
3–4	9
3–5	8
4–5	8
4–6	11
5–6	9

Q: 33   The network in Figure 30 represents streets of a city with the indicated number of cars per hour that can travel these streets. Find the maximum number of cars that could travel per hour through this system. How many cars would travel on each street (arc) to allow this maximum flow?

Q: 34   Refer to Problem 33. How would the maximum number of cars be affected if the street from node 3 to node 6 were temporarily closed?

Q: 35   Use the shortest route algorithm to determine the minimum distance from node 1 to node 7 in Figure 31. Which nodes are included in this route?

FIGURE 30
Network for Problem 33

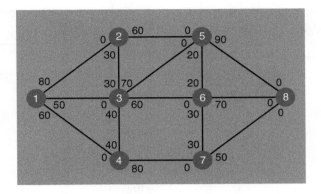

FIGURE 31
Network for Problem 35

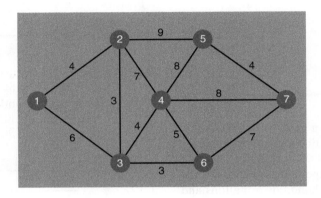

36 Northwest University is in the process of completing a computer bus network that will connect computer facilities throughout the university. The prime objective is to string a main cable from one end of the campus to the other (nodes 1–25) through underground conduits. These conduits are shown in the network of Figure 32; the distance between them is in hundreds of feet. Fortunately, these underground conduits have remaining capacity through which the bus cable can be placed.

(a) Given the network for this problem, how far (in hundreds of feet) is the shortest route from node 1 to node 25?

(b) In addition to the computer bus network, a new phone system is also being planned. The phone system would use the same underground conduits.

If the phone system were installed, the following paths along the conduit would be at capacity and would not be available for the computer bus network: 6–11, 7–12, and 17–20. What changes (if any) would you have to make to the path used for the computer bus if the phone system were installed?

(c) The university *did* decide to install the new phone system before the cable for the computer network. Because of unexpected demand for computer networking facilities, an additional cable is needed for node 1 to node 25. Unfortunately, the cable for the first or original network has completely used up the capacity along its path. Given this situation, what is the best path for the second network cable?

FIGURE 32
Network for Problem 36

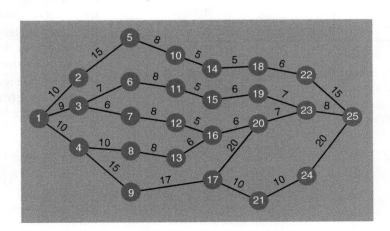

Case Study

Binder's Beverage

Bill Binder's business nearly went under when Colorado almost passed the bottle bill. Binder's Beverage produced soft drinks for many of the large grocery stores in the area. After the bottle bill failed, Binder's Beverage flourished. In a few short years, the company had a major plant in Denver with a warehouse in east Denver. The problem was getting the finished product to the warehouse. Although Bill was not good with distances, he was good with times. Denver is a big city with numerous roads that could be taken from the plant to the warehouse, as shown in Figure 33.

The soft drink plant is located at the corner of North Street and Columbine Street. High Street also intersects North and Columbine Street at the plant. Twenty minutes due north of the plant on North Street is I-70, the major east–west highway in Denver.

North Street intersects I-70 at Exit 135. It takes five minutes driving east on I-70 to reach Exit 136. This exit connects I-70 with High Street and 6th Avenue. Ten minutes east on I-70 is Exit 137. This exit connects I-70 with Rose Street and South Avenue.

From the plant, it takes 20 minutes on High Street, which goes in a northeast direction, to reach West Street. It takes another 20 minutes on High Street to reach I-70 and Exit 136.

It takes 30 minutes on Columbine Street to reach West Street from the plant. Columbine Street travels east and slightly north.

West Street travels east and west. From High Street, it takes 15 minutes to get to 6th Avenue on West Street. Columbine Street also comes into this intersection. From this intersection, it takes an additional 20 minutes on West Street to get to Rose Street, and another 15 minutes to get to South Avenue.

From Exit 136 on 6th Avenue, it takes 5 minutes to get to West Street. Sixth Avenue continues to Rose Street, requiring 25 minutes. Sixth Avenue then goes directly to the warehouse. From Rose Street, it takes 40 minutes to get to the warehouse on 6th Avenue.

At Exit 137, Rose Street travels southwest. It takes 20 minutes to intersect with West Street, and another 20 minutes to get to 6th Avenue. From Exit 137, South Avenue goes due south. It takes 10 minutes to get to West Street and another 15 minutes to get to the Warehouse.

Discussion Question

1. What route do you recommend?

FIGURE 33
Street Map for Binder's Beverage Case

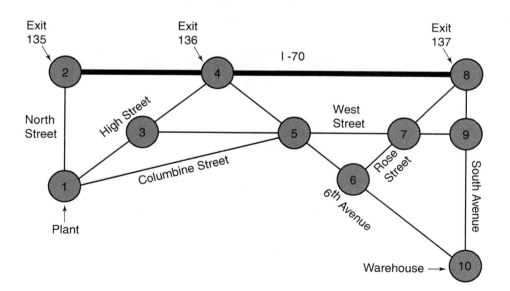

Case Study

Southwestern University Traffic Problems

Southwestern University (SWU), located in the small town of Stephenville, Texas, is experiencing increased interest in its football program now that a big-name coach has been hired. The increase in season ticket sales for the upcoming season means additional revenues, but it also means increased complaints due to the traffic problems associated with the football games. When a new stadium is built, this will only get worse. Marty Starr, SWU's president, has asked the University Planning Committee to look into this problem.

Based on traffic projections, Dr. Starr would like to have sufficient capacity so that 35,000 cars per hour could travel from the stadium to the interstate highway. To alleviate the anticipated traffic problems, some of the current streets leading from the university to the interstate highway are being considered for widening to increase the capacity. The current street capacities with the number of cars (in 1,000s) per hour are shown in Figure 34. Since the major problem will be after the game, only the flows away from the stadium are indicated. These flows include some streets closest to the stadium being transformed into one-way streets for a short period after each game with police officers directing traffic.

Alexander Lee, a member of the University Planning Committee, has said that a quick check of the road capacities in the diagram in Figure 34 indicates that the total number of cars per hour that may leave the stadium (node 1) is 33,000. The number of cars that may pass through nodes 2, 3, and 4 is 35,000 per

hour, and the number of cars that may pass through nodes 5, 6, and 7 is even greater. Therefore, Dr. Lee has suggested that the current capacity is 33,000 cars per hour. He has also suggested that a recommendation be made to the city manager for expansion of one of the routes from the stadium to the highway to permit an additional 2,000 cars per hour. He recommends expanding whichever route is cheapest. If the city chooses not to expand the roads, it is felt that the traffic problem would be a nuisance but would be manageable.

Based on past experience, it is believed that as long as the street capacity is within 2,500 cars per hour of the number that leave the stadium, the problem is not too severe. However, the severity of the problem grows dramatically for each additional 1,000 cars that are added to the streets.

Discussion Questions

1. If there is no expansion, what is the maximum number of cars that may actually travel from the stadium to the interstate per hour? Why is this number not equal to 33,000, as Dr. Lee suggested?
2. If the cost for expanding a street were the same for each street, which street(s) would you recommend expanding to increase the capacity to 33,000? Which streets would you recommend expanding to get the total capacity of the system to 35,000 per hour?

FIGURE 34
Roads from Stadium to interstate

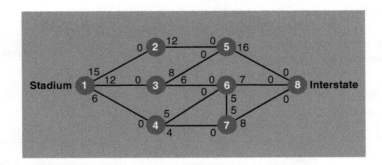

Internet Case Study

See our Internet home page, at **www.pearsonhighered.com/render**, for the additional case study Ranch Development Project, which involves finding the least-cost way to provide water and sewer services to homes in a new housing development.

Bibliography

Ahuja, R. K., T. L. Magnanti, and J. B. Orlin. *Network Flows: Theory, Algorithms, and Applications.* Upper Saddle River, NJ: Prentice Hall, 1993.

Bazlamacci, Cuneyt F., and Khalil S. Hindi. "Minimum-Weight Spanning Tree Algorithms: A Survey and Empirical Study," *Computers and Operations Research* 28, 8 (July 2001): 767–785.

Current, J. "The Minimum-Covering/Shortest Path Problem," *Decision Sciences* 19 (Summer 1988): 490–503.

Erel, Erdal, and Hadi Gokcen. "Shortest-Route Formulation of Mixed-Model Assembly Line Balancing Problem," *European Journal of Operational Research* 116, 1 (1999): 194–204.

Jacobs, T., B. Smith, and E. Johnson. "Incorporating Network Flow Effects into the Airline Fleet Assignment Process," *Transportation Science* 42, 4 (2008): 514–529.

Jain, A., and J. W. Mamer. "Approximations for the Random Minimal Spanning Tree with Application to Network Provisioning," *Operations Research* 36 (July–August 1988): 575–584.

Johnsonbaugh, Richard. *Discrete Mathematics*, 5th ed. Upper Saddle River, NJ: Prentice Hall, 2001.

Kawatra, R., and D. Bricker. "A Multiperiod Planning Model for the Capacitated Minimal Spanning Tree Problem," *European Journal of Operational Research* 121, 2 (2000): 412–419.

Liu, Jinming, and Fred Rahbar. "Project Time–Cost Trade-off Optimization by Maximal Flow Theory," *Journal of Construction Engineering & Management* 130, 4 (July/August 2004): 607–609.

Onal, Hayri, et al. "Two Formulations of the Vehicle Routing Problem," *The Logistics and Transportation Review* (June 1996): 177–191.

Sancho, N. G. F. "On the Maximum Expected Flow in a Network," *Journal of Operational Research Society* 39 (May 1988): 481–485.

Sedeño-Noda, Antonio, Carlos González-Martín, and Sergio Alonso. "A Generalization of the Scaling Max-Flow Algorithm," *Computers & Operations Research* 31, 13 (November 2004): 2183–2198.

Troutt, M. D., and G. P White. "Maximal Flow Network Modeling of Production Bottleneck Problems," *Journal of the Operational Research Society* 52, 2 (February 2001): 182–187.

Solutions to Selected Problems

10 200 on path 1–2–5–7–8, 200 on path 1–3–6–8, and 100 on path 1–4–8. Total = 500.

12 The minimum distance is 47 (4,700 feet).

14 Total distance is 177. Connect 1–2, 2–3, 3–4, 3–5, 5–6.

16 The total distance is 430. Route 1–3–5–7–10–13.

18 The minimal spanning tree length is 23.

20 The maximal flow is 17.

24 The maximal flow is 2,000 gallons.

26 The shortest route is 76. The path is 1–2–6–9–13–16.

30 (a) 1,200 miles (b) 1,000 miles.

32 Total distance = 40.

34 Maximum number = 190.

36 (a) The shortest distance is 49.   (b) The shortest distance is 55.   (c) The shortest distance is 64.

Solutions to Self-Tests

1. c
2. e
3. b
4. c
5. b
6. a
7. d
8. a
9. b
10. b
11. a
12. d
13. shortest route
14. maximal flow
15. minimal spanning tree

Queuing Models

The companion website for this text is www.pearsonhighered.com/balakrishnan.

1 Introduction

A primary goal of queuing analysis is to find the best level of service for an organization.

The study of **queues**,[1] also called *waiting lines*, is one of the oldest and most widely used decision modeling techniques. Queues are an everyday occurrence, affecting people shopping for groceries, buying gasoline, making bank deposits, and waiting on the telephone for the first available customer service person to answer. Queues can also take the form of machines waiting to be repaired, prisoners to be processed in a jail system, or airplanes lined up on a runway for permission to take off.

Most queuing problems focus on finding the ideal level of service that a firm should provide. Supermarkets must decide how many cash register checkout positions should be opened. Gasoline stations must decide how many pumps should be available. Manufacturing plants must determine the optimal number of mechanics to have on duty each shift to repair machines that break down. Banks must decide how many teller windows to keep open to serve customers during various hours of the day. In most cases, this level of service is an option over which management has control. An extra teller, for example, can be borrowed from another chore or can be hired and trained quickly if demand warrants it. This may, however, not always be the case. For example, a plant may not be able to locate or hire skilled mechanics to repair sophisticated electronic machinery.

Approaches for Analyzing Queues

In practice, there are two principal approaches that managers can use to analyze the performance of a queuing system and evaluate its cost-effectiveness. The first approach is based on *analytical modeling*. For several different queuing systems that satisfy certain properties, decisions modelers have derived explicit formulas to calculate various performance measures. These formulas, although rather cumbersome in some cases, are quite straightforward to use, especially if they are coded in a computer software program. In this chapter, we discuss analytical models for a few simple queuing systems. Although we show the mathematical equations needed to compute the performance measures of these queuing systems, we will actually use Excel worksheets (included on the Companion Website) to calculate these values in each case. From a managerial perspective, therefore, the use of these analytical models will be very easy and straightforward.

More sophisticated models exist to handle variations of basic assumptions, but when even these do not apply, we can turn to computer simulation.

Many real-world queuing systems can, however, be so complex that they cannot be modeled analytically at all. When this happens, decision modelers usually turn to the second approach—**computer simulation**—to analyze the performance of these systems.

2 Queuing System Costs

As noted earlier, a primary goal of queuing analysis is to find the best level of service that a firm should provide. In deciding this ideal level of service, managers have to deal with two types of costs:

1. *Cost of providing the service.* This is also known as the **service cost**. Examples of this type of cost include wages paid to servers, the cost of buying an extra machine, and the cost of constructing a new teller window at a bank. As a firm increases the size of its

[1] The word *queue* is pronounced like the letter Q (i.e., "kew").

FIGURE 1
Queuing Costs and Service Levels

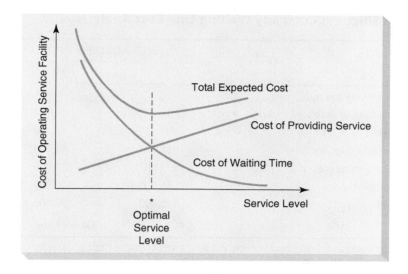

Staff and provides added service facilities, the result could be excellent customer service with seldom more than one or two customers in a queue. While customers may be happy with the quick response, the cost of providing this service can, however, become very expensive.

2. *Cost of* not *providing the service.* This is also known as the **waiting cost** and is typically the cost of customer dissatisfaction. If a facility has just a minimum number of checkout lines, pumps, or teller windows open, the service cost is kept low, but customers may end up with long waiting times in the queue. How many times would you return to a large department store that had only one cash register open every time you shop? As the average length of the queue increases and poor service results, customers and goodwill may be lost.

Managers must deal with the trade-off between the cost of providing service and the cost of customer waiting time. The latter may be hard to quantify.

Total expected cost is the sum of service plus waiting costs.

Most managers recognize the trade-off that must take place between the cost of providing good service and the cost of customer waiting time, and they try to achieve a happy medium between the two. They want queues that are short enough so that customers don't become unhappy and either storm out without buying or buy but never return. But they are willing to allow some waiting in line if this wait is balanced by a significant savings in service costs.

One means of evaluating a service facility is thus to look at a total expected cost, a concept illustrated in Figure 1. Total expected cost is the sum of expected waiting costs and expected costs of providing service.

Service costs increase as a firm attempts to raise its level of service. For example, if three teams of stevedores, instead of two, are employed to unload a cargo ship, service costs are increased by the additional price of wages. As service improves in speed, however, the cost of time spent waiting in lines decreases. This waiting cost may reflect lost productivity of workers while their tools or machines are awaiting repairs or may simply be an estimate of the costs of customers lost because of poor service and long queues.

THREE RIVERS SHIPPING COMPANY EXAMPLE As an illustration of a queuing system, let's look at the case of the Three Rivers Shipping Company. Three Rivers runs a huge docking facility located on the Ohio River near Pittsburgh. Approximately five ships arrive to unload their cargoes of steel and ore during every 12-hour work shift. Each hour that a ship sits idle in line, waiting to be unloaded, costs the firm a great deal of money, about $1,000 per hour. From experience, management estimates that if one team of stevedores is on duty to handle the unloading work, each ship will wait an average of 7 hours to be unloaded. If two teams are working, the average waiting time drops to 4 hours; for three teams, it is 3 hours; and for four teams of stevedores, only 2 hours. But each additional team of stevedores is also an expensive proposition, due to union contracts.

The goal is to find the service level that minimizes total expected cost.

The Three Rivers superintendent would like to determine the optimal number of teams of stevedores to have on duty each shift. The objective is to minimize total expected costs. This analysis is summarized in Table 1. To minimize the sum of service costs and waiting costs, the firm makes the decision to employ two teams of stevedores each shift.

TABLE 1   Three Rivers Shipping Company Waiting Line Cost Analysis

	NUMBER OF TEAMS OF STEVEDORES			
	1	2	3	4
(a) Average number of ships arriving per shift	5	5	5	5
(b) Average time each ship waits to be unloaded (hours)	7	4	3	2
(c) Total ship hours lost per shift ($a \times b$)	35	20	15	10
(d) Estimated cost per hour of idle ship time	$1,000	$1,000	$1,000	$1,000
(e) Value of ship's lost time or waiting cost ($c \times d$)	$35,000	$20,000	$15,000	$10,000
(f) Stevedore team salary,* or service cost	$6,000	$12,000	$18,000	$24,000
(g) Total expected cost ($e + f$)	$41,000	$32,000	$33,000	$34,000
		Optimal cost		

*Stevedore team salaries are computed as the number of people in a typical team (assumed to be 50) multiplied by the number of hours each person works per day (12 hours) multiplied by an hourly salary of $10 per hour. If two teams are employed, the rate is just doubled.

3   Characteristics of a Queuing System

In this section we discuss the three components of a queuing system that are critical for the development of analytical **queuing models**: (1) the arrivals or inputs to the system (sometimes referred to as the *calling population*), (2) the queue or the waiting line itself, and (3) the service facility. Together, these three components define the type of queuing system under consideration.

Arrival Characteristics

With regard to the input source that generates arrivals or customers for a queuing system, it is important to consider the following: (1) size of the **arrival population**, (2) pattern of arrivals (or the arrival distribution) at the queuing system, and (3) behavior of the arrivals.

Unlimited (or infinite) populations *are assumed for most queuing models.*

SIZE OF THE ARRIVAL POPULATION   Population sizes are considered to be either *infinite (unlimited)* or *finite (limited)*. When the number of customers or arrivals on hand at any given moment is just a small portion of potential arrivals, the arrival population is considered an **infinite, or unlimited, population**. For practical purposes, examples of unlimited populations include cars arriving at a highway tollbooth, shoppers arriving at a supermarket, or students arriving to register for classes at a large university. Most queuing models assume such an infinite arrival population. When this is not the case, modeling becomes much more complex. An example of a **finite, or limited, population** is a shop with only eight machines that might break down and require service.

Analytical queuing models typically use the average arrival rate.

ARRIVAL DISTRIBUTION   Arrivals can be characterized either by an average *arrival rate* or by an average *arrival time*. Because both measures occur commonly in practice, it is important to distinguish between the two. An average arrival rate denotes the average number of arrivals in a given interval of time. Examples include two customers per hour, four trucks per minute, two potholes per mile of road, and five typing errors per printed page. In contrast, an average arrival time denotes the average time between successive arrivals. Examples include 30 minutes between customers, 0.25 minutes between trucks, 0.5 miles between potholes, and 0.2 pages between typing errors. It is important to remember that for analytical queuing models, we typically use the average arrival *rate*.

Arrivals are random when they are independent of one another and cannot be predicted exactly.

Customers can arrive at a service facility either according to some known constant schedule (e.g., one patient every 15 minutes, one student for advising every half hour), or they can arrive in a random manner. Arrivals are considered random when they are independent of one another and their occurrence cannot be predicted exactly.

It turns out that in many real-world queuing problems, even when arrivals are random, the actual number of arrivals per unit of time can be estimated by using a probability distribution

The **Poisson distribution** *is used in many queuing models to represent arrival patterns.*

known as the **Poisson distribution**. The Poisson distribution is applicable whenever the following assumptions are satisfied: (1) The average arrival rate over a given interval of time is known, (2) this average rate is the same for all equal-sized intervals, (3) the actual number of arrivals in one interval has no bearing on the actual number of arrivals in another interval, and (4) there cannot be more than one arrival in an interval as the size of the interval approaches zero. For a given average arrival rate, a discrete Poisson distribution can be established by using the following formula:[2]

$$P(X) = \frac{e^{-\lambda}\lambda^X}{X!} \text{ for } X = 0, 1, 2, \cdots \tag{1}$$

where

X = number of arrivals per unit of time (e.g., hour)

$P(X)$ = probability of exactly X arrivals

λ = average arrival *rate* (i.e., average number of arrivals per unit of time)

e = 2.7183 (known as the exponential constant)

These values are easy to compute with the help of a calculator or Excel. Figure 2 illustrates the shape of the Poisson distribution for $\lambda = 2$ and $\lambda = 4$. This means that if the average arrival rate is $\lambda = 2$ customers per hour, the probability of 0 customers arriving in any random hour is 0.1353, the probability of 1 customer is 0.2707, 2 customers is 0.2707, 3 customers is 0.1804, 4 customers is 0.0902 and so on. The chance that 9 or more will arrive in any hour is virtually zero.

All the analytical models discussed in this chapter assume Poisson arrivals. However, in practice, arrivals in queuing systems need not always be Poisson and could follow other probability distributions. The use of statistical goodness of fit tests to identify these distributions and analytical queuing models to analyze such systems are topics discussed in more advanced texts. Of course, we can also analyze such queuing systems by using computer simulation.

Balking *refers to customers who do not join a queue.* **Reneging** *customers join a queue but leave before being served.*

BEHAVIOR OF ARRIVALS Most queuing models assume that an arriving customer is a patient customer. Patient customers are people or machines that wait in the queue until they are served and do not switch between lines. Unfortunately, life and decision models are complicated by the fact that people have been known to balk or renege. **Balking** refers to customers refusing to

FIGURE 2 **Two Examples of the Poisson Distribution for Arrival Times**

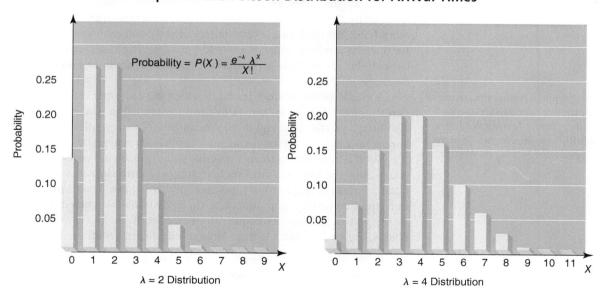

[2] The term $X!$, called X *factorial*, is defined as $(X)(X - 1)(X - 2) \ldots (3)(2)(1)$. For example, $5! = (5)(4)(3)(2)(1) = 120$. By definition, $0! = 1$.

join a queue because it is too long to suit their needs or interests. **Reneging** customers are those who enter the queue but then become impatient and leave without completing their transaction. Actually, both of these situations serve to accentuate the need for queuing models. How many times have you seen a shopper with a basket full of groceries, including perishables such as milk, frozen food, or meats, simply abandon the shopping cart before checking out because the queue was too long? This expensive occurrence for the store makes managers acutely aware of the importance of service-level decisions.

Queue Characteristics

The models in this chapter assume unlimited queue length.

The queue itself is the second component of a queuing system. The *length* of a queue can be either limited (finite) or unlimited (infinite). A queue is said to be limited when it cannot increase to an infinite length due to physical or other restrictions. For example, the queue at a bank's drive-up window may be limited to 10 cars due to space limitations. Or, the number of people waiting for service in an airline's phone reservation system may be limited to 30 due to the number of telephone lines available. In contrast, a queue is defined as unlimited when its size is unrestricted, as in the case of the tollbooth serving arriving automobiles. In all the analytic queuing models we discuss in this chapter, we assume that queue lengths are *unlimited*.

Most queuing models use the first-in, first-out rule. This is obviously not appropriate in all service systems, especially those dealing with emergencies.

A second waiting line characteristic deals with **queue discipline**. This refers to the rule by which customers in the line are to receive service. Most systems use a queue discipline known as the **first-in, first-out (FIFO)** rule. However, in places such as a hospital emergency room or an express checkout line at a supermarket, various assigned priorities may preempt FIFO. Patients who are critically injured will move ahead in treatment priority over patients with broken fingers or noses. Shoppers with fewer than 10 items may be allowed to enter the express checkout queue but are then treated as first-come, first-served. Computer programming runs are another example of queuing systems that operate under priority scheduling. In many large companies, when computer-produced paychecks are due out on a specific date, the payroll program has highest priority over other runs.[3]

Service Facility Characteristics

The third part of a queuing system is the service facility itself. It is important to examine two basic properties: (1) the configuration of the service facility and (2) the pattern of service times (or the service distribution) at the facility.

Service facilities can either have a single server or multiple servers.

CONFIGURATION OF THE SERVICE FACILITY Service facilities are usually classified in terms of the number of servers (or channels) and the number of phases (or service stops) that must be made. A **single-server queuing system** is typified by the drive-in bank that has only one open teller or by the type of a drive-through fast-food restaurant that has a similar setup. If, on the other hand, the bank has several tellers on duty and each customer waits in one common line for the first available teller, we would have a **multiple-server queuing system** at work. Many banks today are multiple-server service systems, as are most post offices and many airline ticket counters.

Single-phase means the customer receives service at only one station before leaving the system. Multiphase implies two or more stops before leaving the system.

A **single-phase system** is one in which the customer receives service from only one station and then exits the system. A fast-food restaurant in which the person who takes your order also brings you the food and takes your money is a single-phase system. So is a driver's license bureau in which the person taking your application also grades your test and collects the license fee. But if a fast-food restaurant requires you to place your order at one station, pay at a second, and pick up the food at a third service stop, it is a **multiphase system**. Similarly, if the driver's license bureau is large or busy, you will probably have to wait in line to complete the application (the first service stop), queue again to have the test graded (the second service stop), and finally go to a third service counter to pay the fee. To help you relate the concepts of servers and phases, Figure 3 presents four possible service facility configurations.

Service times often follow the exponential distribution.

SERVICE DISTRIBUTION Service patterns are like arrival patterns in that they can be either constant or random. If the service time is constant, it takes the same amount of time to take care

---

[3] The term FIFS (*first-in, first-served*) is often used in place of FIFO. Another discipline, LIFS (*last-in, first-served*), is commonly used when material is stacked or piled and the items on top are used first.

FIGURE 3 **Four Basic Queuing System Configurations**

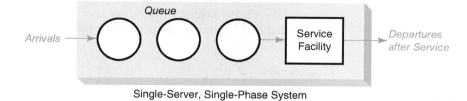

Single-Server, Single-Phase System

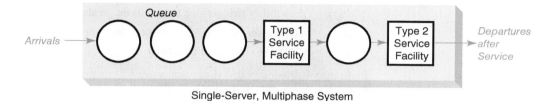

Single-Server, Multiphase System

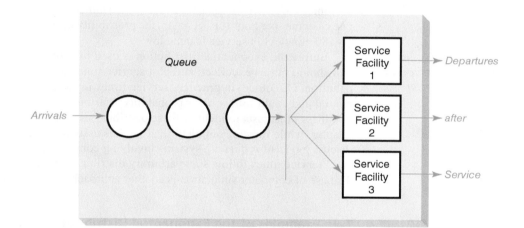

Multiple-Server, Single-Phase System

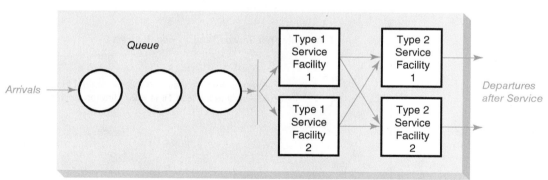

Multiple-Server, Multiphase System

of each customer. This is the case, for example, in a machine-performed service operation such as an automatic car wash. More often, however, service times are randomly distributed. Even in such situations, it turns out that we can estimate service times in many real-world queuing problems by using a probability distribution known as the **exponential distribution**.

The Poisson and exponential probability distributions are directly related to each other. If the number of arrivals follows a Poisson distribution, it turns out that the time between successive arrivals follows an exponential distribution. Processes that follow these distributions are commonly referred to as *Markovian* processes.

Just as we did with arrivals, we need to distinguish here between service rate and service time. While the service rate denotes the number of units served in a given interval of time, the service time denotes the length of time taken to actually perform the service. Although the exponential distribution estimates the probability of service times, the parameter used in this computation is the average service rate. For any given average service rate, such as two customers per hour, or four trucks per minute, the exponential distribution can be established using the formula

$$P(t) = e^{-\mu t} \quad \text{for } t \geq 0 \tag{2}$$

where

t = service time

$P(t)$ = probability that service time will be greater than t

μ = average service rate (i.e., average number of customers served per unit of time)

e = 2.7183 (exponential constant)

Figure 4 illustrates that if service times follow an exponential distribution, the probability of any very long service time is low. For example, when the average service *rate* is 3 customers per hour (i.e., the average service *time* is 20 minutes per customer), seldom, if ever, will a customer require more than 1.5 hours (= 90 minutes). Likewise, if the average service rate is one customer per hour (i.e., $\mu = 1$), the probability of the customer spending more than 3 hours (=180 minutes) in service is quite low.

It is important to verify that the assumption of exponential service times is valid before applying the model.

Before the exponential distribution is used in a queuing model, the decision modeler can and should observe, collect, and plot service time data to determine whether they fit the distribution. Of course, in practice, service times in queuing systems need not always be exponential and could follow other probability distributions. As with arrivals, the use of statistical goodness of fit tests to identify these distributions is discussed in more advanced texts. In this chapter, while most of our analytical models assume exponential service times, we will also discuss models for queuing systems involving constant service times and general service times (i.e., service times follow some arbitrary distribution with mean μ and standard deviation σ). The use of computer simulation is another approach for analyzing such queuing systems.

FIGURE 4   Two Examples of the Exponential Distribution for Service Times

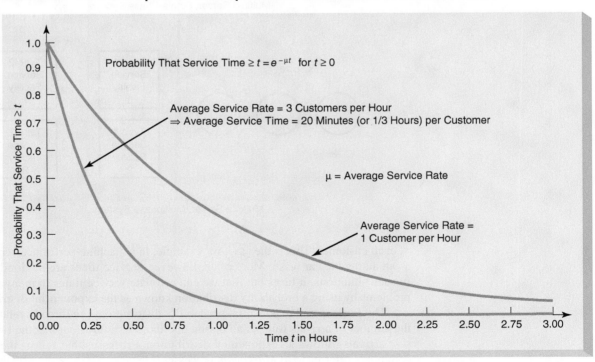

Measuring the Queue's Performance

Queuing models can help a manager obtain many performance measures (also known as **operating characteristics**) of a waiting line system. We list here some of the measures commonly used in practice. For each performance measure, we also list the standard notation that is used:

Here is a list of the key operating characteristics of a queuing system.

- ρ = **utilization factor** of the system (i.e., the probability that all servers are busy)
- L_q = average length (i.e., the number of customers) of the queue
- L = average number of customers in the system (i.e., the number in the queue plus the number being served)
- W_q = average time that each customer spends in the queue
- W = average time that each customer spends in the system (i.e., the time spent waiting plus the time spent being served)
- P_0 = probability that there are no customers in the system (i.e., the probability that the service facility will be idle)
- P_n = probability that there are exactly n customers in the system

Kendall's Notation for Queuing Systems

Kendall's notation is used to classify queuing systems.

In queuing theory we commonly use a three-symbol notation, known as *Kendall's notation*, to classify the wide variety of queuing models that are possible in practice. The three-symbol notation is as follows:

$$A/B/s$$

where

- A = the arrival probability distribution. Typical choices are M (Markovian) for a Poisson distribution, D for a constant or deterministic distribution, or G for a general distribution with known mean and variance.
- B = the service time probability distribution. Typical choices are M for an exponential distribution, D for a constant or deterministic distribution, or G for a general distribution with known mean and variance.
- s = number of servers.

Using Kendall's notation, we would denote a single-server queuing system with Poisson arrival and exponential service time distributions as an M/M/1 system. If this system had two servers, we would then classify it as an M/M/2 system.

Kendall's three-symbol notation is sometimes extended to include five symbols.

Kendall's notation has sometimes been extended to include five symbols. The first three symbols are the same as just discussed. The fourth symbol denotes the maximum allowable length of the queue. It is used in systems in which there is a **finite, or limited, queue length**. The fifth symbol denotes the size of the arrival population. It is used in systems in which the size of the arrival population is finite. By default, if these two symbols are omitted, their values are assumed to be infinity. Hence, the M/M/1 notation discussed previously corresponds to an M/M/1/∞/∞ queuing system.

Variety of Queuing Models Studied Here

We study five commonly used queuing models here.

Although a wide variety of queuing models can be applied in practice, we introduce you to five of the most widely used models in this chapter. These are outlined in Table 2, and examples of each follow in the next few sections. More complex models are described in queuing theory textbooks[4] or can be developed through the use of computer simulation. Note that all five of the queuing models listed in Table 2 have five characteristics in common. They all assume the following:

1. Arrivals that follow the Poisson probability distribution.
2. FIFO queue discipline.
3. A single-phase service facility.

---

[4] See, for example, B. D. Bunday. *An Introduction to Queuing Theory.* New York: Halsted Press, 1996, or C. H. Ng. *Queuing Modeling Fundamentals.* New York: Wiley, 1997.

TABLE 2 Queuing Models Described in This Chapter

NAME (KENDALL NOTATION)	EXAMPLE	NUMBER OF SERVERS	NUMBER OF PHASES	ARRIVAL RATE PATTERN	SERVICE TIME PATTERN	POPLN. SIZE	QUEUE DISCIP.
Simple system (M/M/1)	Information counter at department store	Single	Single	Poisson	Exponential	Unlimited	FIFO
Multiple-server (M/M/s)	Airline ticket counter	Multiple	Single	Poisson	Exponential	Unlimited	FIFO
Constant service (M/D/1)	Automated car wash	Single	Single	Poisson	Constant	Unlimited	FIFO
General service (M/G/1)	Auto repair shop	Single	Single	Poisson	General	Unlimited	FIFO
Limited population (M/M/s/∞/N)	Shop with exactly ten machines that might break	Multiple	Single	Poisson	Exponential	Limited	FIFO

4. **Infinite, or unlimited, queue length.** That is, the fourth symbol in Kendall's notation is ∞.
5. Service systems that operate under steady, ongoing conditions. This means that both arrival rates and service rates remain stable during the analysis.

4 Single-Server Queuing System with Poisson Arrivals and Exponential Service Times (M/M/1 Model)

In this section we present a decision model to determine the operating characteristics of an **M/M/1** queuing system. After these numeric measures have been computed, we then add in cost data and begin to make decisions that balance desirable service levels with queuing costs.

Assumptions of the M/M/1 Queuing Model

The single-server, single-phase model we consider here is one of the most widely used and simplest queuing models. It assumes that seven conditions exist:

These seven assumptions must be met if the single-server, single-phase model is to be applied.

1. Arrivals are served on a FIFO basis.
2. Every arrival waits to be served, regardless of the length of the line; that is, there is no balking or reneging.

 IN ACTION

IBM Uses Queuing Analysis to Improve Semiconductor Production

IBM's 300 mm fabrication (fab) facility in East Fishkill, New York cost more than $4 billion to build. High capacity utilization and short lead times are keys to reducing the cost per wafer, expediting time to market, and improving profitability and yield. IBM's managers and engineers therefore maintain constant focus on balancing future demand, equipment utilization, bottlenecks, and lead times.

To help in this effort, IBM developed an advanced queuing network model called Enterprise Production Planning and Optimization System (EPOS) to address both short-term tactical capacity planning and long-term strategic capital investment planning.

EPOS enhances prior queuing network models by not only adding the ability to model product-specific batch arrivals and service, but also by embedding a linear program to help decide which lot to allocate to which queue when route choices are present.

Since its implementation, EPOS has become an integral part of IBM's efforts to improve factory performance by predicting bottlenecks, managing lead times, prioritizing continuous-improvement efforts, and planning capital equipment investments, thus helping IBM reduce expenses by tens of millions of dollars.

Source: Based on S. M. Brown et al. "Queuing Model Improves IBM's Semiconductor Capacity and Lead-Time Management," *Interfaces* 40, 5 (September–October 2010): 397–407.

3. Arrivals are independent of preceding arrivals, but the average number of arrivals (the arrival rate) does not change over time.
4. Arrivals are described by a Poisson probability distribution and come from an infinite or very large population.
5. Service times also vary from one customer to the next and are independent of one another, but their average rate is known.
6. Service times occur according to the exponential probability distribution.
7. The average service rate is greater than the average arrival rate; that is, $\mu > \lambda$. If this condition does not hold (and $\mu \leq \lambda$), the queue length will grow indefinitely because the service facility does not have the capacity to handle the arriving customers (on average).

When these seven conditions are met, we can develop equations that define the system's operating characteristics. The mathematics used to derive each equation is rather complex and beyond the scope of this text, so we will just present the resulting equations here.

We use Excel templates to calculate operating characteristics for our queuing models.

Although we could calculate the operating characteristic equations for *all* the queuing systems discussed in this chapter by hand, doing so can be quite cumbersome. An easier approach is to develop Excel worksheets for these formulas and use them for all calculations. This allows us to focus on what is really important for managers: the interpretation and use of the results of queuing models. Therefore, we adopt this approach in our discussions in this chapter.

Operating Characteristic Equations for an M/M/1 Queuing System
We let

$$\lambda = \text{average number of arrivals per time period (e.g., per hour)}$$
$$\mu = \text{average number of people or items served per time period}$$

λ and μ must both be rates and be defined for the same time interval.

It is very important to note two issues here. First, both λ and μ must be rates. That is, they must denote the average number of occurrences per a given time interval. Second, both λ and μ must be defined for the *same time interval*. That is, if λ denotes the average number of units arriving *per hour*, then μ must denote the average number of units served *per hour*. As noted earlier, it is necessary for the average service rate to be greater than the average arrival rate (i.e., $\mu > \lambda$). The operating characteristic equations for the M/M/1 queuing system are as follows:

These seven queuing equations for the single-server, single-phase model describe the important operating characteristics of the service system.

1. Average server utilization in the system:

$$\rho = \lambda/\mu \tag{3}$$

2. Average number of customers or units waiting in line for service:

$$L_q = \frac{\lambda^2}{\mu(\mu - \lambda)} \tag{4}$$

3. Average number of customers or units in the system:

$$L = L_q + \lambda/\mu \tag{5}$$

4. Average time a customer or unit spends waiting in line for service:

$$W_q = \frac{L_q}{\lambda} = \frac{\lambda}{\mu(\mu - \lambda)} \tag{6}$$

5. Average time a customer or unit spends in the system (namely, in the queue or being served):

$$W = W_q + 1/\mu \tag{7}$$

6. Probability that there are zero customers or units in the system:

$$P_0 = 1 - \lambda/\mu \tag{8}$$

7. Probability that there are n customers or units in the system:

$$P_n = (\lambda/\mu)^n P_0 \tag{9}$$

Arnold's Muffler Shop Example

We now apply these formulas to the queuing problem faced by Arnold's Muffler Shop in New Orleans. Customers needing new mufflers arrive at the shop on the average of two per hour. Arnold's mechanic, Reid Blank, is able to perform this service at an average rate of three per hour, or about one every 20 minutes. Larry Arnold, the shop owner, studied queuing models in an MBA program and feels that all seven of the conditions for a single-server queuing model are met. He proceeds to calculate the numeric values of the operating characteristics of his queuing system.

Using ExcelModules for Queuing Model Computations

ExcelModules includes worksheets for all the queuing models discussed in this chapter.

Excel Note

- The Companion Website for this text, at www.pearsonhighered.com/balakrishnan, contains a set of Excel worksheets, bundled together in a software package called ExcelModules.
- The Companion Website also provides the Excel file for each sample problem discussed here. The relevant file name is shown in the margin next to each example.
- For clarity, all worksheets for queuing models in ExcelModules are color coded as follows:
  - *Input cells*, where we enter the problem data, are shaded yellow.
  - *Output cells*, which show results, are shaded green.

When we run the ExcelModules program, we see a new tab titled ExcelModules in Excel's Ribbon. We select this tab and then click the Modules icon followed by the Queuing Models menu. The choices shown in Screenshot 1A are displayed. From these choices, we select the appropriate queuing model.

When *any* of the queuing models is selected in ExcelModules, we are first presented with an option to specify a title for the problem (see Screenshot 1B). The default title is Problem Title.

To analyze M/M/1 systems, we use the M/M/s worksheet in ExcelModules and set s = 1.

EXCELMODULES SOLUTION FOR ARNOLD'S MUFFLER SHOP The M/M/1 queuing model is included in ExcelModules as a special case of the M/M/s model with s = 1. Hence, to analyze Arnold's problem, we select the choice labeled Exponential Service Times (M/M/s), shown in

SCREENSHOT 1A   Queuing Models Menu in ExcelModules

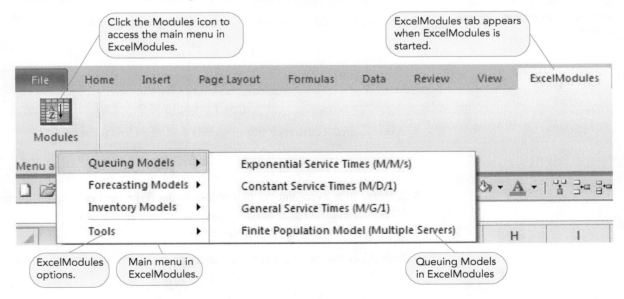

**SCREENSHOT 1B
Input Window for
Optional Problem Title**

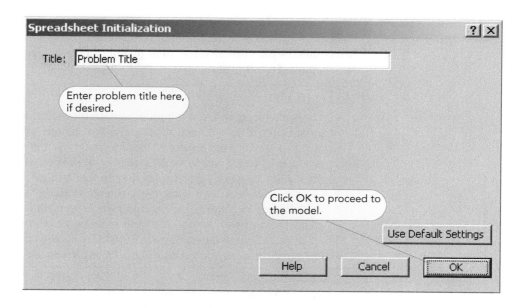

Title: Problem Title

Enter problem title here, if desired.

Click OK to proceed to the model.

Use Default Settings

Help   Cancel   OK

File: 9-2.xls, sheet: 9-2A

Screenshot 1A. When we click OK after entering the problem title, we get the screen shown in Screenshot 2A. Each queuing worksheet in ExcelModules includes one or more messages specific to that model. It is important to note and follow the messages. For example, the M/M/s worksheet includes the following two messages:

1. Both λ and μ must be RATES and use the same time unit. For example, given a service time such as 10 minutes per customer, convert it to a service rate such as 6 per hour.
2. The total service rate (rate × servers) must be greater than the arrival rate.

SCREENSHOT 2A   M/M/s Worksheet in ExcelModules

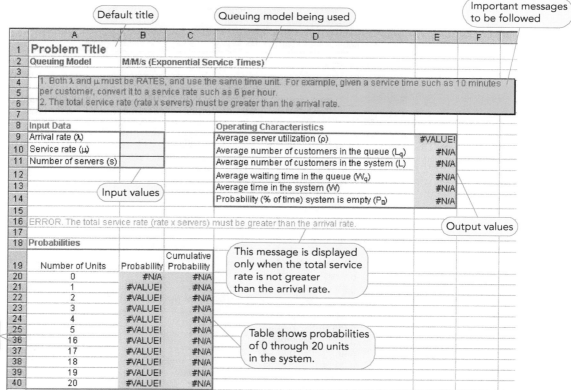

Important: *The total service rate must exceed the arrival rate.*

If the total average service rate ($\mu \times$ s) does *not* exceed the average arrival rate (λ), the worksheet will automatically print the error message shown in row 16. This message is seen in Screenshot 2A because the values of λ, μ, and number of servers (s) have not been input yet and have defaulted to zero values.

Excel Notes

- The worksheets in ExcelModules contain formulas to compute the operating characteristics for different queuing models. The default values of zero for input data such as λ and μ cause the results of these formulas to initially appear as #N/A, #VALUE!, or #DIV/0! (see Screenshot 2A). However, as soon as we enter valid values for these input data, the worksheets display the formula results.
- Once ExcelModules has been used to create an Excel worksheet for a particular queuing model (such as M/M/s), the resulting worksheet can be used to compute the operating characteristics with several different input parameter values. For example, we can enter different input values in cells B9:B11 of Screenshot 2A and compute the resulting operating characteristic values without having to create a *new* M/M/s worksheet each time.

File: 9-2.xls, sheet: 9-2B

In Larry Arnold's case, the average arrival rate (λ) is two cars per hour. The average service rate (μ) is three mufflers per hour. We therefore enter these values in cells B9 and B10, respectively, as shown in Screenshot 2B. The number of servers (cell B11) equals one here because there is only one mechanic.

SCREENSHOT 2B **Operating Characteristics with μ = 3 for Arnold's Muffler Shop: M/M/1 Queuing System**

Problem title

M/M/s with s = 1 is the M/M/1 model.

	A	B	C	D	E	F
1	Arnold's Muffler Shop					
2	Queuing Model	M/M/s (Exponential Service Times)				
3						
4	1. Both λ and μ must be RATES, and use the same time unit. For example, given a service time such as 10 minutes					
5	per customer, convert it to a service rate such as 6 per hour.					
6	2. The total service rate (rate x servers) must be greater than the arrival rate.					
7						
8	Input Data			Operating Characteristics		
9	Arrival rate (λ)	2		Average server utilization (ρ)	0.6667	
10	Service rate (μ)	3		Average number of customers in the queue (L_q)	1.3333	
11	Number of servers (s)	1		Average number of customers in the system (L)	2.0000	
12				Average waiting time in the queue (W_q)	0.6667	
13				Average time in the system (W)	1.0000	
14				Probability (% of time) system is empty (P_0)	0.3333	
15						
16						
17						
18	Probabilities					
19	Number of Units	Probability	Cumulative Probability			
20	0	0.3333	0.3333			
21	1	0.2222	0.5556			
22	2	0.1481	0.7037			
23	3	0.0988	0.8025			
24	4	0.0658	0.8683			
25	5	0.0439	0.9122			
36	16	0.0005	0.9990			
37	17	0.0003	0.9993			
38	18	0.0002	0.9995			
39	19	0.0002	0.9997			
40	20	0.0001	0.9998			

2 cars per hour

One mechanic

3 mufflers per hour

Mechanic is busy 67% of the time.

0.67 hours = 40 minutes

= 60 minutes

This is the probability that there are ≤ 4 cars in the system.

The worksheet now displays the operating characteristics of this queuing system in cells E9:E14. In addition, the worksheet computes the probability that there are exactly n customers in the system, for $n = 0$ through 20. Cumulative probabilities (i.e., the probability that there are n or *fewer* customers) are also calculated. These values are shown in cells A19:C40.

We get the results for the Arnold's Muffler Shop problem.

The results show that there are, on average, two cars in the system (i.e., $L = 2$), and each car spends an average of one hour in the system (i.e., $W = 1$ hour). The corresponding values for the waiting line alone (not including the server) are $L_q = 1.33$ cars, and $W_q = 0.667$ hours (or 40 minutes). The mechanic (server) is busy 67% of the time (i.e., the utilization factor $\rho = 0.67$). The fact that there is only one mechanic implies that an arriving car has a 33% chance of not having to wait ($P_0 = 0.33$).

Cost Analysis of the Queuing System

Conducting an economic analysis is the next step. It permits cost factors to be included.

Now that the operating characteristics of the queuing system have been computed, Arnold decides to do an economic analysis of their impact. The queuing model was valuable in predicting potential waiting times, queue lengths, idle times, and so on. But it did not identify optimal decisions or consider cost factors. As stated earlier, the solution to a queuing problem may require a manager to make a trade-off between the increased cost of providing better service and the decreased waiting costs derived from providing that service.

Customer waiting time is often considered the most important factor.

Arnold estimates that the cost of customer waiting time, in terms of customer dissatisfaction and lost goodwill, is $10 per hour spent in his shop. Observe that this time includes the time a customer's car is waiting in the queue for service as well as the time when the car is actually being serviced. The only cost of providing service that Arnold can identify is the salary of Reid Blank, the mechanic, who is paid $12 per hour.

Waiting costs plus service costs equal total cost.

The total cost, defined as the sum of the waiting cost and the service cost, is calculated as follows:

$$\text{Total cost} = C_w \times L + C_s \times s \tag{10}$$

where

C_w = customer waiting cost per unit time period

L = average number of customers in the system

C_s = cost of providing service per server per unit time period

s = number of servers in the queuing system

In Arnold's case, $C_w = \$10$ per hour, $L = 2$ (see Screenshot 2B), $C_s = \$12$ per hour, and $s = 1$ (because there is only one mechanic). Hence, Arnold computes his total cost as $\$10 \times 2 + \$12 \times 1 = \$32$ per hour.

Increasing the Service Rate

Now Arnold faces a decision. He finds out through the muffler business grapevine that Rusty Muffler Shop, a crosstown competitor, employs a mechanic named Jimmy Smith who can install new mufflers at an average rate of four per hour. Larry Arnold contacts Smith and inquires as to his interest in switching employers. Smith says that he would consider leaving Rusty Muffler Shop but only if he were paid a $15 per hour salary. Arnold, being a crafty businessman, decides to check whether it would be worthwhile to fire Blank and replace him with the speedier but more expensive Smith.

Arnold first recomputes all the operating characteristics, using a new average service rate (μ) of four mufflers per hour. The average arrival rate (λ) remains at two cars per hour. The revised characteristic values if Smith is employed are shown in Screenshot 2C.

File: 9-2.xls, sheet: 9-2C

It is quite evident that Smith's higher average rate (four mufflers per hour compared to Blank's three mufflers per hour) will result in shorter queues and waiting times. For example, a customer would now spend an average of only 0.5 hours in the system (i.e., $W = 0.5$) and 0.25 hours waiting in the queue ($W_q = 0.25$) as opposed to 1 hour in the system and 0.67 hours in the queue with Blank as the mechanic. The average number of customers in the system (L) decreases from two units to one unit.

SCREENSHOT 2C Revised Operating Characteristics with $\mu = 4$ for Arnold's Muffler Shop: M/M/1 Queuing System

	A	B	C	D	E	F
1	Arnold's Muffler Shop					
2	Queuing Model	M/M/s (Exponential Service Times)				
3						
4	1. Both λ and μ must be RATES, and use the same time unit. For example, given a service time such as 10 minutes					
5	per customer, convert it to a service rate such as 6 per hour.					
6	2. The total service rate (rate x servers) must be greater than the arrival rate.					
7						
8	Input Data			Operating Characteristics		
9	Arrival rate (λ)	2		Average server utilization (ρ)	0.5000	
10	Service rate (μ)	4		Average number of customers in the queue (L_q)	0.5000	
11	Number of servers (s)	1		Average number of customers in the system (L)	1.0000	
12				Average waiting time in the queue (W_q)	0.2500	
13		New service rate		Average time in the system (W)	0.5000	
14				Probability (% of time) system is empty (P_0)	0.5000	
15						0.25 hours = 15 minutes
16				= 30 minutes		
17						
18	Probabilities					
19	Number of Units	Probability	Cumulative Probability			
20	0	0.5000	0.5000			
21	1	0.2500	0.7500			
22	2	0.1250	0.8750			
23	3	0.0625	0.9375			
24	4	0.0313	0.9688			
25	5	0.0156	0.9844			
36	16	0.0000	1.0000			
37	17	0.0000	1.0000			
38	18	0.0000	1.0000			
39	19	0.0000	1.0000			
40	20	0.0000	1.0000			

Here is a comparison of total costs, using the two different mechanics.

Arnold revises his economic analysis with the new information. The revised values are $C_w = \$10$ per hour, $L = 1$ (see Screenshot 2C), $C_s = \$15$ per hour, and $s = 1$ (because there is still only one mechanic). Hence, Arnold's revised total cost with Smith as the mechanic is $\$10 \times 1 + \$15 \times 1 = \$25$ per hour. Because the total cost with Blank as the mechanic was $32 per hour, Arnold may very well decide to hire Smith and reduce his cost by $7 per hour (or $56 per 8-hour day).

5 Multiple-Server Queuing System with Poisson Arrivals and Exponential Service Times (M/M/S Model)

The next logical step is to look at a multiple-server queuing system, in which two or more servers are available to handle arriving customers. Let us still assume that customers awaiting service form one single line and then proceed to the first available server. An example of such a multiple-server, single-phase waiting line is found in many banks or post offices today. A common line is formed, and the customer at the head of the line proceeds to the first free teller or clerk. (Refer to Figure 3 for a typical multiple-server configuration.)

The multiple-server model also assumes Poisson arrivals and exponential services.

The multiple-server system presented here again assumes that arrivals follow a Poisson probability distribution and that service times are distributed exponentially. Service is first come, first served, and all servers are assumed to perform at the same average rate.[5] Other assumptions listed earlier for the single-server model apply as well.

---

[5]Analytical models for multiserver queuing systems where different servers perform at different average rates are beyond the scope of this text.

Operating Characteristic Equations for an M/M/s Queuing System

We let

$$\lambda = \text{average number of arrivals per time (e.g., per hour)}$$

$$\mu = \text{average number of customers served per time } per\ server$$

$$s = \text{number of servers}$$

As with the M/M/1 system, with an **M/M/s** system, it is very important that we define both λ and μ for the *same time interval*. It is also important to note that the average service rate μ is defined *per server*. That is, if there are two servers and each server is capable of handling an average of three customers per hour, μ is defined as three per hour, *not* six per hour ($= 2 \times 3$). Finally, as noted earlier, it is necessary for the average total service rate to be greater than the average arrival rate (that is, $s\mu > \lambda$).

The operating characteristic equations for the M/M/s queuing system are as follows:

1. Average server utilization in the system:

$$\rho = \lambda/(s\mu) \tag{11}$$

2. Probability that there are zero customers or units in the system:

$$P_0 = \frac{1}{\left[\sum_{k=0}^{s-1}\frac{1}{k!}\left(\frac{\lambda}{\mu}\right)^k\right] + \frac{1}{s!}\left(\frac{\lambda}{\mu}\right)^s\frac{s\mu}{(s\mu - \lambda)}} \tag{12}$$

3. Average number of customers or units waiting in line for service:

$$L_q = \frac{(\lambda/\mu)^s\lambda\mu}{(s-1)!(s\mu - \lambda)^2}P_0 \tag{13}$$

4. Average number of customers or units in the system:

$$L = L_q + \lambda/\mu \tag{14}$$

5. Average time a customer or unit spends waiting in line for service:

$$W_q = L_q/\lambda \tag{15}$$

6. Average time a customer or unit spends in the system:

$$W = W_q + 1/\mu \tag{16}$$

7. Probability that there are n customers or units in the system:

$$P_n = \frac{(\lambda/\mu)^n}{n!}P_0 \quad \text{for } n \le s \tag{17}$$

$$P_n = \frac{(\lambda/\mu)^n}{s!s^{(n-s)}}P_0 \quad \text{for } n > s \tag{18}$$

These equations are more complex than the ones used in the single-server model. Yet they are used in exactly the same fashion and provide the same type of information as those in the simpler M/M/1 model.

Arnold's Muffler Shop Revisited

For an application of the multiple-server queuing model, let us return to Arnold's Muffler Shop problem. Earlier, Larry Arnold examined two options. He could retain his current mechanic, Reid Blank, at a total system cost of $32 per hour, or he could fire Blank and hire a slightly more expensive but faster worker named Jimmy Smith. With Smith on board, the system cost could be reduced to $25 per hour.

The muffler shop considers opening a second muffler service bay that operates at the same speed as the first one.

Arnold now explores a third option. He finds that at minimal after-tax cost, he can open a second service bay in which mufflers can be installed. Instead of firing his first mechanic, Blank, he would hire a second mechanic, Joel Simpson. The new mechanic would be able to install mufflers at the same average rate as Blank ($\mu = 3$ per hour) and be paid the same salary as Blank ($12 per hour). Customers, who would still arrive at the average rate of $\lambda = 2$ per hour, would wait in a single line until one of the two mechanics became available. To find out how this option compares with the old single-server queuing system, Arnold computes the operating characteristics for the M/M/2 system.

File: 9-3.xls

Remember that in the M/M/s model, the average service rate is μ per server.

We dramatically lower waiting time results by opening the second service bay.

EXCELMODULES SOLUTION FOR ARNOLD'S MUFFLER SHOP WITH TWO MECHANICS Once again, we select the choice titled Exponential Service Times (M/M/s) from the Queuing Models menu in ExcelModules (see Screenshot 1A). After entering the optional title, we enter the input data as shown in Screenshot 3. For Arnold's problem, observe that the average arrival rate (λ) is two cars per hour. The average service rate (μ) is three mufflers per hour *per mechanic*. We enter these values in cells B9 and B10, respectively. The number of servers (cell B11) is two because there are now two mechanics.

The worksheet now displays the operating characteristics of this queuing system in cells E9:E14. Probabilities of having a specific number of units in the system are shown in cells A19:C40. Arnold first compares these results with the earlier results. The information is summarized in Table 3. The increased service from opening a second bay has a dramatic effect on almost all results. In particular, average time spent waiting in line (W_q) drops down from 40 minutes with only Blank working or 15 minutes with only Smith working, to only 2.5 minutes with Blank and Simpson working! Similarly, the average number of cars in the system (L) falls to 0.75.[6] But does this mean that a second bay should be opened?

SCREENSHOT 3   Revised Operating Characteristics for Arnold's Muffler Shop: M/M/2 Queuing System

M/M/s with s = 2 is the M/M/2 model.

	A	B	C	D	E	F
1	Arnold's Muffler Shop					
2	Queuing Model	M/M/s (Exponential Service Times)				
3						
4	1. Both λ and μ must be RATES, and use the same time unit. For example, given a service time such as 10 minutes					
5	per customer, convert it to a service rate such as 6 per hour.					
6	2. The total service rate (rate x servers) must be greater than the arrival rate.					
7						
8	Input Data			Operating Characteristics		
9	Arrival rate (λ)	2		Average server utilization (ρ)	0.3333	
10	Service rate (μ)	3		Average number of customers in the queue (Lq)	0.0833	
11	Number of servers (s)	2		Average number of customers in the system (L)	0.7500	
12				Average waiting time in the queue (Wq)	0.0417	
13				Average time in the system (W)	0.3750	
14				Probability (% of time) system is empty (P0)	0.5000	
15						
16						
17						
18	Probabilities					
19	Number of Units	Probability	Cumulative Probability			
20	0	0.5000	0.5000			
21	1	0.3333	0.8333			
22	2	0.1111	0.9444			
23	3	0.0370	0.9815			
24	4	0.0123	0.9938			
25	5	0.0041	0.9979			
36	16	0.0000	1.0000			
37	17	0.0000	1.0000			
38	18	0.0000	1.0000			
39	19	0.0000	1.0000			
40	20	0.0000	1.0000			

Servers are busy only 33.3% of the time.

Two mechanics on duty

Equal service rate for both mechanics. Rate shown is *per mechanic.*

0.0417 hours = 2.5 minutes

Hidden rows. See Companion Website for full file.

---

[6] Note that adding a second mechanic cuts queue waiting time and length by more than half; that is, the relationship between the number of servers and queue characteristics is *nonlinear*. This is because of the random arrival and service processes. When there is only one mechanic, and two customers arrive within a minute of each other, the second will have a long wait. The fact that the mechanic may have been idle for 30 minutes before they both arrive does not change the average waiting time. Thus, single-server models often have high wait times compared to multiple-server models.

TABLE 3 Effect of Service Level on Arnold's Operating Characteristics

OPERATING CHARACTERISTIC	LEVEL OF SERVICE		
	ONE MECHANIC ($\mu = 3$)	TWO MECHANICS ($\mu = 3$ EACH)	ONE FASTER MECHANIC ($\mu = 4$)
Probability that the system is empty (P_0)	0.33	0.50	0.50
Average number of cars in the system (L)	2 cars	0.75 cars	1 car
Average time spent in the system (W)	60 minutes	22.5 minutes	30 minutes
Average number of cars in the queue (L_q)	1.33 cars	0.083 cars	0.50 cars
Average time spent in the queue (W_q)	40 minutes	2.5 minutes	15 minutes

Cost Analysis of the Queuing System

We do an economic analysis with two service bays.

To complete his economic analysis of the M/M/2 queuing system, Arnold notes that the relevant values are $C_w = \$10$ per hour, $L = 0.75$ (see Screenshot 3), $C_s = \$12$ per hour, and $s = 2$ (because there are two mechanics). The total cost is, therefore, $\$10 \times 0.75 + \$12 \times 2 = \$31.50$ per hour.

As you recall, total cost with just Blank as the mechanic was found to be $32 per hour. Total cost with just the faster but more expensive Smith was $25 per hour. Although opening a second bay would be likely to have a positive effect on customer goodwill and hence lower the cost of waiting time (i.e., lower C_w), it does mean an increase in the total cost of providing service. Look back to Figure 1, and you will see that such trade-offs are the basis of queuing theory. Based on his analysis, Arnold decides to replace his current worker Blank with the speedier Smith and not open a second service bay.

6 Single-Server Queuing System with Poisson Arrivals and Constant Service Times (M/D/1 Model)

Constant service rates speed up the process compared to exponentially distributed service times with the same value of μ.

When customers or equipment are processed according to a fixed cycle, as in the case of an automatic car wash or an amusement park ride, constant service rates are appropriate. Because constant service rates are certain, the values for L_q, W_q, L, and W in such a queuing system are always less than they would be in an equivalent M/M/s system, which have variable service

IN ACTION Using Queuing Models in a Hospital Eye Clinic

The hospital outpatient eye clinic at the United Kingdom's Royal Preston Hospital is not unlike other clinics at hospitals throughout the rest of the world: It is regularly overbooked and overrun, and it has excessive patient waiting times. Even though its patient charter states that no one should wait to be seen for more than 30 minutes past their appointment time, patients, on average, waited over 50 minutes.

Many problems in hospital clinics can be explained as a vicious cycle of events: (1) appointments staff overbook every clinic session because of the large patient volume; (2) patients therefore wait in long queues; (3) doctors are overburdened; and (4) when a doctor is ill, the staff spends much time canceling and rescheduling appointments.

To break out of this cycle, the clinic at Royal Preston needed to reduce patient waiting times. This was done by applying computer-driven queuing models and attempting to reduce the patient time variability. The hospital used queuing software

to specifically address the 30-minute statistic in the patient charter. Researchers assumed that (1) each patient arrived on time, (2) the service distribution was known from past history, (3) 12% of patients missed their appointments, and (4) 33% of the patients queued for a second consultation.

Making a list of 13 recommendations (many nonquantitative) to the clinic, researchers returned two years later to find that most of their suggestions were followed (or at least seriously attempted), yet performance of the clinic had shown no dramatic improvement. Patient waiting times were still quite long, the clinic was still overbooked, and appointments sometimes had to be canceled. The conclusion: Even though models can often help *understand* a problem, some problems, like those in the outpatient clinic, are messy and hard to fix.

Source: Based on J. C. Bennett and D. J. Worthington. "An Example of a Good but Partially Successful OR Engagement: Improving Outpatient Clinic Operations," *Interfaces* (September–October 1998): 56–69.

times. As a matter of fact, both the average queue length and the average waiting time in the queue are *halved* with the constant service rate model.

Operating Characteristic Equations for an M/D/1 Queuing System

In the *M/D/1* queuing system we let

$$\lambda = \text{average number of arrivals per time (e.g., per hour)}$$
$$\mu = \text{constant number of people or items served per time period}$$

The operating characteristic equations for the M/D/1 queuing system are as follows:

1. Average server utilization in the system:

$$\rho = \lambda/\mu \tag{19}$$

2. Average number of customers or units waiting in line for service:

$$L_q = \frac{\lambda^2}{2\mu(\mu - \lambda)} \tag{20}$$

3. Average number of customers or units in the system:

$$L = L_q + \lambda/\mu \tag{21}$$

4. Average time a customer or unit spends waiting in line for service:

$$W_q = L_q/\lambda = \frac{\lambda}{2\mu(\mu - \lambda)} \tag{22}$$

5. Average time a customer or unit spends in the system (namely, in the queue or being served):

$$W = W_q + 1/\mu \tag{23}$$

6. Probability that there are zero customers or units in the system:

$$P_0 = 1 - \lambda/\mu \tag{24}$$

Garcia-Golding Recycling, Inc.

Garcia-Golding Recycling, Inc., collects and compacts aluminum cans and glass bottles in New York City. Its truck drivers, who arrive to unload these materials for recycling, currently wait an average of 15 minutes before emptying their loads. The cost of the driver and truck time wasted while in queue is valued at $60 per hour. Garcia-Golding is considering purchasing a new automated compactor. The new compactor will be able to process truckloads at a constant rate of 12 trucks per hour (i.e., 5 minutes per truck), and its cost will be amortized at a rate of $3 per truck unloaded. Trucks arrive according to a Poisson distribution at an average rate of 8 per hour. Should Garcia-Golding purchase the new compactor?

EXCELMODULES SOLUTION FOR GARCIA-GOLDING RECYCLING We select the choice titled Constant Service Times (M/D/1) from the Queuing Models menu in ExcelModules (see Screenshot 1A). After entering the optional title, we enter the input data as shown in Screenshot 4. For Garcia-Golding's problem, the average arrival rate (λ) is 8 trucks per hour. The constant service rate (μ) is 12 trucks per hour. We enter these values in cells B9 and B10, respectively. The worksheet now displays the operating characteristics of this queuing system in cells E9:E14.

Cost Analysis of the Queuing System

We do a cost analysis for the recycling example.

The *current* system makes drivers wait an average of 15 minutes before emptying their trucks. The waiting cost per trip is

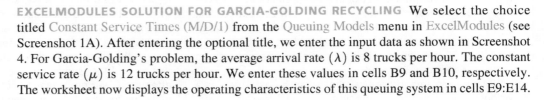

Current waiting cost per trip = (0.25 hours waiting) × $60/hour
= $15 per trip

SCREENSHOT 4 **Operating Characteristics for Garcia-Golding Recycling: M/D/1 Queuing System**

The average waiting time in the queue (W_q) with the new automated compactor is only 0.0833 hours, or 5 minutes. Therefore, the revised waiting cost per trip is

$$\text{Revised waiting cost per trip} = (0.0833 \text{ hours waiting}) \times \$60/\text{hour}$$
$$= \$5 \text{ per trip}$$
$$\text{Savings with new equipment} = \$15 - \$5 = \$10 \text{ per trip}$$
$$\text{Amortized cost of equipment} = \$3 \text{ per trip}$$
$$\text{Hence, net savings} = \$10 - \$3 = \$7 \text{ per trip}$$

Garcia-Golding should therefore purchase the new compactor.

7 Single-Server Queuing System with Poisson Arrivals and General Service Times (M/G/1 Model)

So far, we have studied systems in which service times are either exponentially distributed or constant. In many cases, however, service times could follow some **arbitrary, or general, distribution** with mean μ and standard deviation σ. In such cases, we refer to the model as a *general* service time model. Real-world examples of general service times include time required to service vehicles at an auto repair shop (e.g., an oil change service) and time required by a store clerk to complete a sales transaction.

General service time models assume arbitrary distributions for service times.

The single-server system presented here assumes that arrivals follow a Poisson probability distribution. As in earlier models, with the **M/G/1** model we also assume that (1) service is on a first-come, first-served basis, (2) there is no balking or reneging, and (3) the average service rate is greater than the average arrival rate.

Operating Characteristic Equations for an M/G/1 Queuing System

For the M/G/1 system we let

λ = average number of arrivals per time (e.g., per hour)

μ = average number of people or items served per time period

σ = standard deviation of service time

λ and μ are rates and must be for the same time interval. The standard deviation, σ, must also be measured in the same time unit.

As with the M/M/s models, with the M/G/1 model, λ and μ must be defined for the *same time interval*. Also, it is important to note that while λ and μ are rates (i.e., number of occurrences in a specified time interval), σ is the standard deviation of the service time. The units for σ should, however, be consistent with λ and μ. For example, if λ and μ are expressed as average rates per hour, σ should also be measured in hours.

The operating characteristic equations for the M/G/1 model are as follows:

1. Average server utilization in the system:

$$\rho = \lambda/\mu \tag{25}$$

2. Average number of customers or units waiting in line for service:

$$L_q = \frac{\lambda^2\sigma^2 + (\lambda/\mu)^2}{2(1 - (\lambda/\mu))} \tag{26}$$

3. Average number of customers or units in the system:

$$L = L_q + \lambda/\mu \tag{27}$$

4. Average time a customer or unit spends waiting in line for service:

$$W_q = L_q/\lambda \tag{28}$$

5. Average time a customer or unit spends in the system:

$$W = W_q + 1/\mu \tag{29}$$

6. Probability that there are zero customers or units in the system:

$$P_0 = 1 - \lambda/\mu \tag{30}$$

Meetings with Professor Crino

This is an example of a general service time model.

Professor Michael Crino advises all honors students at Central College. During the registration period, students meet with Professor Crino to decide courses for the following semester and to discuss any other issues they may be concerned about. Rather than have students set up specific appointments to see him, Professor Crino prefers setting aside two hours each day during the registration period and having students drop in on an informal basis. This approach, he believes, makes students feel more at ease with him.

Based on his experience, Professor Crino thinks that students arrive at an average rate of one every 12 minutes (or five per hour) to see him. He also thinks the Poisson distribution is appropriate to model the arrival process. Advising meetings last an average of 10 minutes each; that is, Professor Crino's service rate is six per hour. However, because some students have concerns that they wish to discuss with Professor Crino, the length of these meetings varies. Professor Crino estimates that the standard deviation of the service time (i.e., the meeting length) is 5 minutes.

File: 9-5.xls, sheet: 9-5A

EXCELMODULES SOLUTION FOR PROFESSOR CRINO'S PROBLEM We select the choice titled General Service Times (M/G/1) from the Queuing Models menu in ExcelModules (see Screenshot 1A). After entering the optional title, we enter the input data in the screen as shown in Screenshot 5A. For Professor Crino's problem, the average arrival rate (λ) is five students per hour. The average service rate (μ) is six students per hour. Observe that, as required, μ exceeds λ, and both are for the same time interval (per hour, in this case). The standard deviation (σ) of the service time is 5 minutes. However, because λ and μ are expressed per hour, we also express σ in hours and write it as 0.0833 hours ($= 5$ minutes).

We enter the values of λ, μ, and σ in cells B9, B10, and B11, respectively, as shown in Screenshot 5A. The worksheet now displays the operating characteristics of this queuing system in cells E9:E14.

The results indicate that, on average, Professor Crino is busy during 83.3% of his advising period. There are 2.60 students waiting to see him on average, and each student waits an average of 0.52 hours (or approximately 31 minutes).

SCREENSHOT 5A **Operating Characteristics for Professor Crino's Problem: M/G/1 Queuing System**

	A	B	C	D	E
1	Professor Crino's Problem				
2	Queuing Model	M/G/1 (General Service Times)			
3					
4	1. Both λ and μ must be RATES, and use the same time unit. However, the standard deviation (σ)				
5	must be for the service TIME, not the service rate.				
6	2. The service rate must be greater than the arrival rate.				
7					
8	Input Data			Operating Characteristics	
9	Arrival rate (λ)	5		Average server utilization (ρ)	0.8333
10	Service rate (μ)	6		Average number of customers in the queue (Lq)	2.6038
11	Standard deviation (σ)	0.0833		Average number of customers in the system (L)	3.4371
12				Average waiting time in the queue (Wq)	0.5208
13				Average time in the system (W)	0.6874
14				Probability (% of time) system is empty (P0)	0.1667

0.5208 hours = 31.2 minutes

0.6874 hours = 41.25 minutes

Standard deviation of service *time*, in hours

Service *rate*, per hour

Using Excel's Goal Seek to Identify Required Model Parameters

Looking at the results in Screenshot 5A, Professor Crino realizes that making students wait an average of 31 minutes is unacceptable. Ideally, he would like to speed up these meetings so that students wait no more than 15 minutes (or 0.25 hours) on average. He realizes that he has little control over the standard deviation of the service time. However, by insisting that students come prepared (e.g., decide ahead of time which courses they want to take) for these meetings, Professor Crino thinks he can decrease the average meeting length. The question is this: What should be the average meeting length that will enable Professor Crino to meet his goal of a 15-minute average waiting time?

One way to solve this problem is to plug in different values for the average service rate μ in cell B10 of Screenshot 5A and keep track of the W_q value in cell E12 until it drops below 0.25. An alternate, and preferred, approach is to use a procedure in Excel called Goal Seek to automate the search process for the value of μ. We use Goal Seek to find the break-even point. The Goal Seek procedure allows us to specify a desired value for a *target cell*. This target cell should contain a formula that involves a different cell, called the *changing cell*. Once we specify the target cell, its desired value, and the changing cell in Goal Seek, the procedure automatically manipulates the changing cell value to try to make the target cell achieve its desired value.

In our model, the changing cell is the average service rate μ (cell B10). The target cell is the average waiting time W_q (cell E12). We want the target cell to achieve a value of 15 minutes (which we specify as 0.25 hours because μ and λ are per hour). After bringing up the General Service Times (M/G/1) worksheet in ExcelModules (see Screenshot 5A), we invoke the Goal Seek procedure by clicking the Data tab on Excel's Ribbon, followed by the What-If Analysis button (found in the Data Tools group within the Data tab), and then finally on Goal Seek. The window shown in Screenshot 5B is now displayed.

We specify cell E12 as the target cell in the Set cell box, a desired value of 0.25 for this cell in the To value box, and cell B10 in the box labeled By changing cell. When we click OK, we get the windows shown in Screenshot 5C. The results indicate that if Professor Crino can increase his service rate to 6.92 students per hour, the average waiting time drops to around 15 minutes. That is, Professor Crino needs to reduce his average meeting length to approximately 8.67 minutes (= 6.92 students per 60 minutes).

We can use Goal Seek in any of the queuing models discussed here to determine the value of an input parameter (e.g., μ or λ) that would make an operating characteristic reach a desired value. For example, we could use it in the M/M/1 worksheet (section 4) to find the value of

Excel's Goal Seek *procedure allows us to find the required value of a queue parameter to achieve a stated goal.*

File: 9-5.xls, sheet: 9-5C

SCREENSHOT 5B
Goal Seek Input Window in Excel

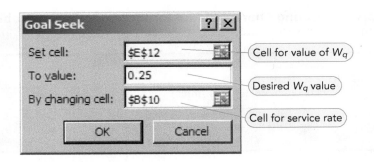

Goal Seek ? ✕

Set cell: $E$12 ← Cell for value of W_q

To value: 0.25 ← Desired W_q value

By changing cell: $B$10 ← Cell for service rate

OK   Cancel

SCREENSHOT 5C   Goal Seek Status Window and Revised Operating Characteristics for Professor Crino's Problem: M/G/1 Queuing System

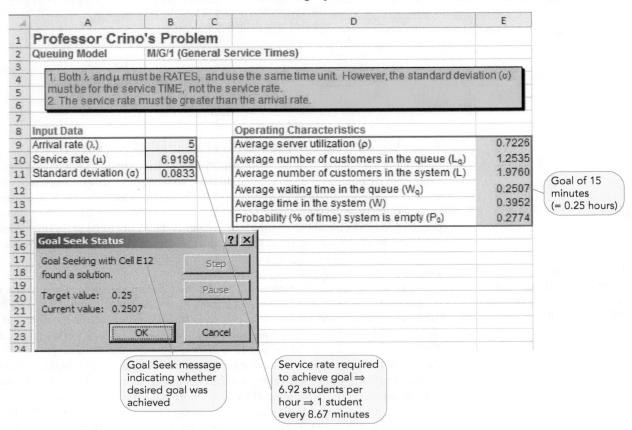

	A	B	C	D	E
1	**Professor Crino's Problem**				
2	Queuing Model	M/G/1 (General Service Times)			
3					
4	1. Both λ and μ must be RATES, and use the same time unit. However, the standard deviation (σ)				
5	must be for the service TIME, not the service rate.				
6	2. The service rate must be greater than the arrival rate.				
7					
8	Input Data			Operating Characteristics	
9	Arrival rate (λ)	5		Average server utilization (ρ)	0.7226
10	Service rate (μ)	6.9199		Average number of customers in the queue (L_q)	1.2535
11	Standard deviation (σ)	0.0833		Average number of customers in the system (L)	1.9760
12				Average waiting time in the queue (W_q)	0.2507
13				Average time in the system (W)	0.3952
14				Probability (% of time) system is empty (P_0)	0.2774
15					

Goal Seek Status ? ✕

Goal Seeking with Cell E12 found a solution.

Step
Pause

Target value: 0.25
Current value: 0.2507

OK   Cancel

Goal of 15 minutes (= 0.25 hours)

Goal Seek message indicating whether desired goal was achieved

Service rate required to achieve goal ⇒ 6.92 students per hour ⇒ 1 student every 8.67 minutes

μ that would allow Arnold to offer his customers a guarantee of having to wait no more than 5 minutes (or 0.0833 hours). The answer turns out to be six mufflers per hour. See if you can verify this by using Goal Seek and the Exponential Service Times (M/M/s) queuing model in ExcelModules.

8   Multiple-Server Queuing System with Poisson Arrivals, Exponential Service Times, and Finite Population Size (M/M/S/∞/N Model)

All the queuing models we have studied so far have assumed that the size of the calling population is infinite. Hence, as customers arrive at the queuing system, the potential number of customers left in the population is still large, and the average arrival rate does not change. However, when there is a limited population of potential customers for a service facility, we need to consider a different queuing model. This model would be used, for example, if we

Queuing Analysis Helps the Israeli Army Redesign Recruitment Procedures

Israel has compulsory army service starting at age 18. To examine candidates for service, the army was using a two-day process at six recruitment offices located around the country. Even though the staff worked at peak capacity, over 70 percent of candidates did not finish the process within two days and had to be recalled for extra visits. Before building a new recruitment office to meet this growing problem, the army wanted to investigate whether it was possible to improve performance in the recruiting offices.

The research team developed a queuing model to study this problem based on the following parameters: arrival-time distribution, routes, station data, and the order in which rooms are filled. The model helped them arrive at a configuration that processed about 99 percent of candidates completely in just one day with shortened waiting times at various stations, but was still economical in terms of personnel capacity and usage. Savings of over $3.3 million resulted from closed offices as well as decreased costs for personnel, traveling, and office expenses.

Source: Based on O. Shtrichman, R. Ben-Haim, and M. A. Pollatschek. "Using Simulation to Increase Efficiency in an Army Recruitment Office," *Interfaces* 31, 4 (July–August 2001): 61–70.

were considering equipment repairs in a factory that has 5 machines, if we were in charge of maintenance for a fleet of 10 commuter airplanes, or if we ran a hospital ward that has 20 beds. The limited population model permits any number of servers to be considered.

In the finite population model, the arrival rate is dependent on the length of the queue.

The reason the M/M/s/∞/N model differs from the earlier queuing models is that there is now a dependent relationship between the length of the queue and the arrival rate. To illustrate this situation, we can assume that our factory has five machines. If all five are broken and awaiting repair, the arrival rate drops to zero. In general, as the waiting time becomes longer in a limited population queuing system, the arrival rate of customers drops lower.

In this section, we describe a finite arrival population model that has the following assumptions:

1. There are s servers with *identical* service time distributions.
2. The population of units seeking service is finite, of size N.[7]
3. The arrival distribution of *each customer* in the population follows a Poisson distribution, with an average rate of λ.
4. Service times are exponentially distributed, with an average rate of μ.
5. Both λ and μ are specified for the same time period.
6. Customers are served on a first-come, first-served basis.

Arrival rate, λ is per customer or unit.

Operating Characteristic Equations for the Finite Population Queuing System

For the M/M/s/∞/N model we let

λ = average number of arrivals per time (e.g., per hour)

μ = average number of people or items served per time period

s = number of servers

N = size of the population

The operating characteristic equations for the M/M/s/∞/N model are as follows:

1. Probability that there are zero customers or units in the system:

$$P_0 = \frac{1}{\sum_{n=0}^{s-1} \frac{N!}{(N-n)!n!}\left(\frac{\lambda}{\mu}\right)^n + \sum_{n=s}^{N} \frac{N!}{(N-n)!s!s^{n-s}}\left(\frac{\lambda}{\mu}\right)^n} \qquad (31)$$

---

[7] Although there is no definite number that we can use to divide finite from infinite arrival populations, the general rule of thumb is this: If the number in the queue is a significant proportion of the arrival population, we should use a finite queuing model.

2. Probability that there are exactly n customers in the system:

$$P_n = \frac{N!}{(N-n)!n!}\left(\frac{\lambda}{\mu}\right)^n P_0, \quad \text{if } 0 \le n \le s \tag{32}$$

$$P_n = \frac{N!}{(N-n)!s!s^{n-s}}\left(\frac{\lambda}{\mu}\right)^n P_0, \quad \text{if } s < n \le N \tag{33}$$

$$P_n = 0, \quad \text{if } n > N \tag{34}$$

3. Average number of customers or units in line, waiting for service:

$$L_q = \sum_{n=s}^{N}(n-s)P_n \tag{35}$$

4. Average number of customers or units in the system:

$$L = \sum_{n=0}^{s-1}nP_n + L_q + s\left(1 - \sum_{n=0}^{s-1}P_n\right) \tag{36}$$

5. Average time a customer or unit spends in the queue waiting for service:

$$W_q = \frac{L_q}{\lambda(N-L)} \tag{37}$$

6. Average time a customer or unit spends in the system:

$$W = \frac{L}{\lambda(N-L)} \tag{38}$$

Department of Commerce Example

We look at an example of a finite population model.

The U.S. Department of Commerce (DOC) in Washington, DC, uses five high-speed printers to print all documents. Past records indicate that each of these printers needs repair after about 20 hours of use. Breakdowns have been found to be Poisson distributed. The one technician on duty can repair a printer in an average of 2 hours, following an exponential distribution.

EXCELMODULES SOLUTION FOR THE DOC'S PROBLEM We select the choice titled Finite Population Model (Multiple Servers) from the Queuing Models menu in ExcelModules (see Screenshot 1A). After entering the optional title, we get the screen shown in Screenshot 6A. For the DOC's problem, the average arrival rate (λ) for *each printer* is $1/20 = 0.05$ per hour. The average service rate (μ) is one every two hours, or 0.50 printers per hour. As before, both μ and λ are expressed for the same time period (per hour, in this case). The number of servers (s) is one because there is only one technician on duty. Finally, the population size (N) is five because there are five printers at the DOC.

We enter the values of λ, μ, s, and N in cells B9, B10, B11, and B12, respectively, as shown in Screenshot 6A. The worksheet now displays the operating characteristics of this queuing system in cells E9:E15. Probability values (P_n) are shown in cells B19:B24.

Cost Analysis of the Queuing System

The results indicate that there are 0.64 printers down, on average, in the system. If printer downtime is estimated at $120 per hour, and the technician is paid $25 per hour, we can compute the total cost per hour as

This is the total cost computation.

$$\text{Total cost} = (\text{Average number of printers down}) \times (\text{Cost of downtime hour})$$
$$+ (\text{Cost of technician hour})$$
$$= 0.64 \times \$120 + \$25 = \$101.80 \text{ per hour}$$

The office manager is willing to consider hiring a second printer technician, provided that doing so is cost-effective. To check this, we compute the DOC queue's operating characteristics again. However, the number of servers this time (cell B11) is two. The results are shown in Screenshot 6B.

SCREENSHOT 6A Operating Characteristics for the Department of Commerce Problem: M/M/1 Queuing System with Finite Population

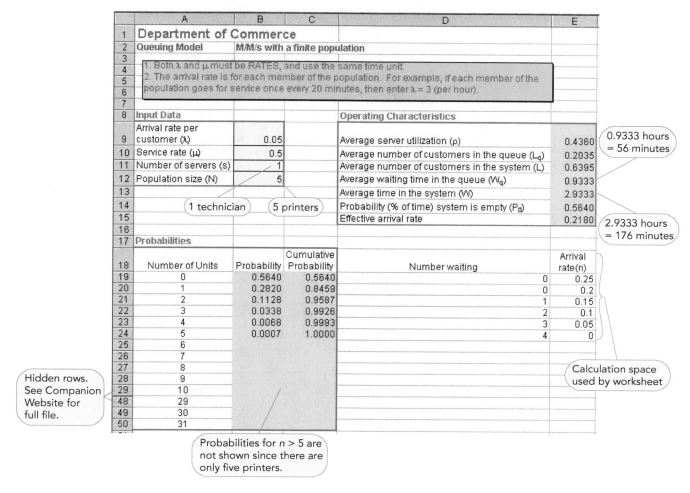

Screenshot 6B indicates that there are now only 0.46 printers, on average, in the system. We can compute the revised total cost per hour as

This is the total cost with two technicians.

Total cost = (Average number of printers down) × (Cost of downtime hour)
+ (Cost of technician hour) × (Number of technicians)
= 0.64 × $120 + $25 × 2 = $105.20 per hour

Because the total cost is higher in this case ($105.20 versus $101.80 per hour), the office manager should not hire a second technician.

9 More Complex Queuing Systems

Many queuing systems that occur in real-world situations have characteristics like those of Arnold's Muffler Shop, Garcia-Golding Recycling, Inc., Professor Crino's advising meetings, and the Department of Commerce examples. This is true when the situation calls for issues such as (1) single or multiple servers, (2) Poisson arrivals, (3) exponential, constant, or arbitrary service times, (4) a finite or an infinite arrival population, (5) infinite queue length, (6) no balking or reneging, and (7) first-in, first-out service.

SCREENSHOT 6B Revised Operating Characteristics for the Department of Commerce Problem: M/M/2 Queuing System with Finite Population

	A	B	C	D	E
1	Department of Commerce				
2	Queuing Model	M/M/s with a finite population			
3					
4	1. Both λ and μ must be RATES, and use the same time unit.				
5	2. The arrival rate is for each member of the population. For example, if each member of the population goes for service once every 20 minutes, then enter λ = 3 (per hour).				
6					
7					
8	Input Data			Operating Characteristics	
9	Arrival rate per customer (λ)	0.05		Average server utilization (ρ)	0.2268
10	Service rate (μ)	0.5		Average number of customers in the queue (L_q)	0.0113
11	Number of servers (s)	2		Average number of customers in the system (L)	0.4648
12	Population size (N)	5		Average waiting time in the queue (W_q)	0.0497
13				Average time in the system (W)	2.0497
14		2 technicians		Probability (% of time) system is empty (P_0)	0.6186
15				Effective arrival rate	0.2268
16					
17	Probabilities				
18	Number of Units	Probability	Cumulative Probability	Number waiting	Arrival rate(n)
19	0	0.6186	0.6186	0	0.25
20	1	0.3093	0.9279	0	0.2
21	2	0.0619	0.9897	0	0.15
22	3	0.0093	0.9990	1	0.1
23	4	0.0009	1.0000	2	0.05
24	5	0.0000	1.0000	3	0
25	6				
26	7				
27	8				
28	9				
29	10				
48	29				
49	30				
50	31				

Callouts: L drops to 0.46 with two technicians. • System is empty 62% of the time—that is, no printers are broken. • Calculation space used by worksheet. • Hidden rows. See Companion Website for full file.

Often, however, *variations* of this specific case are present in a queuing system. Arrival times, for example, may not be Poisson distributed. A college registration system in which seniors have first choice of courses and hours over all other students is an example of a first-come, first-served model with a preemptive priority queue discipline. A physical examination for military recruits is an example of a multiphase system—one that differs from the single-phase models discussed in this chapter. Recruits first line up to have blood drawn at one station, then wait to take an eye exam at the next station, talk to a psychiatrist at the third, and are examined by a doctor for medical problems at the fourth. At each phase, the recruits must enter another queue and wait their turn. An airline reservation system with a finite number of phone lines is an example of a system with a limited queue length.

It turns out that for many of these more complex queuing systems also, decision modelers have developed analytical models to compute their operating characteristics. Not surprisingly, the mathematical expressions for these computations are somewhat more cumbersome than the ones covered in this chapter.[8] However, as noted previously, real-world queuing systems can often be so complex that they cannot be modeled analytically at all. When this happens, decision modelers usually turn to a different approach—*computer simulation*—to analyze the performance of these systems.

More sophisticated models exist to handle variations of basic assumptions, but when even these do not apply, we can turn to computer simulation.

---

[8] Often, the qualitative results of queuing models are as useful as the quantitative results. Results show that it is inherently more efficient to pool resources, use central dispatching, and provide single multiple-server systems rather than multiple single-server systems.

Summary

Queuing systems are an important part of the business world. This chapter describes several common queuing situations and presents decision models for analyzing systems that follow certain assumptions: (1) The queuing system involves just a single phase of service, (2) arrivals are Poisson distributed, (3) arrivals are treated on a first-in, first-out basis and do not balk or renege, (4) service times follow the exponential distribution, an arbitrary distribution, or are constant, and (5) the average service rate is faster than the average arrival rate.

The models illustrated in this chapter are for single-server, single-phase and for multiple-server, single-phase problems. We show how to compute a series of operating characteristics in each case using Excel worksheets and then study total expected costs. Total cost is the sum of the cost of providing service plus the cost of waiting time.

Key operating characteristics for a system are (1) utilization rate, (2) percentage of idle time, (3) average time spent waiting in the system and in the queue, (4) average number of customers in the system and in the queue, and (5) probabilities of various numbers of customers in the system.

We emphasize that a variety of queuing situations exist that do not meet all the assumptions of the traditional models considered here. In such cases, we need to use more complex analytical models or turn to a technique called computer simulation.

Glossary

Arbitrary, or General, Distribution   A probability distribution that is sometimes used to describe random service times in a queuing system.

Arrival Population   The population from which arrivals at the queuing system come. Also known as the *calling population.*

Balking   The case in which arriving customers refuse to join the waiting line.

Computer Simulation   A technique for representing queuing models that are complex and difficult to model analytically.

Exponential Distribution   A probability distribution that is often used to describe random service times in a queuing system.

Finite, or Limited, Population   A case in which the number of customers in the system is a significant proportion of the calling population.

Finite, or Limited, Queue Length   A queue that cannot increase beyond a specific size.

First-In, First-Out (FIFO)   A queue discipline in which the customers are served in the strict order of arrival.

Goal Seek   A procedure in Excel that can be used to identify the value of a queuing system parameter required to achieve a desired value of an operating characteristic.

Infinite, or Unlimited, Population   A calling population that is very large relative to the number of customers currently in the system.

Infinite, or Unlimited, Queue Length   A queue that can increase to an infinite size.

M/D/1   Kendall's notation for the constant service time model.

M/G/1   Kendall's notation for the arbitrary, or general, service time model.

M/M/1   Kendall's notation for the single-server model with Poisson arrivals and exponential service times.

M/M/s   Kendall's notation for the multiple-server queuing model (with s servers), Poisson arrivals, and exponential service times.

Multiphase System   A system in which service is received from more than one station, one after the other.

Multiple-Server Queuing System   A system that has more than one service facility, all fed by the same single queue.

Operating Characteristics   Descriptive characteristics of a queuing system, including the average number of customers in a line and in the system, the average waiting times in a line and in the system, and the percentage of idle time.

Poisson Distribution   A probability distribution that is often used to describe random arrivals in a queue.

Queue   One or more customers or units waiting to be served. Also called a *waiting line.*

Queue Discipline   The rule by which customers in a line receive service.

Queuing Model   A mathematical model that studies the performance of waiting lines or queues.

Reneging   The case in which customers enter a queue but then leave before being served.

Service Cost   The cost of providing a particular level of service.

Single-Phase System   A queuing system in which service is received at only one station.

Single-Server Queuing System   A system with one service facility fed by one queue. Servers are also referred to as *channels.*

Utilization Factor (ρ)   The proportion of time that a service facility is in use.

Waiting Cost.   The cost to a firm of having customers or units waiting in line to be served.

Solved Problems

Solved Problem 1

The Maitland Furniture store gets an average of 50 customers per shift. The manager of Maitland wants to calculate whether she should hire one, two, three, or four salespeople. She has determined that average waiting times will be seven minutes with one salesperson, four minutes with two salespeople, three minutes with three salespeople, and two minutes with four salespeople. She has estimated the cost per minute that customers wait at $1. The cost per salesperson per shift (including fringe benefits) is $70. How many salespeople should be hired?

Solution

The manager's calculations are as follows:

	NUMBER OF SALESPEOPLE			
	1	2	3	4
(a) Average number of customers per shift	50	50	50	50
(b) Average waiting time (minutes) per customer	7	4	3	2
(c) Total waiting time (minutes) per shift (a × b)	350	200	150	100
(d) Cost per minute of waiting time (estimated)	$1	$1	$1	$1
(e) Value of lost time per shift (c × d)	$350	$200	$150	$100
(f) Salary cost per shift	$70	$140	$210	$280
(g) Total cost per shift	$420	$340	$360	$380

Because the minimum total cost per shift relates to two salespeople, the manager's optimum strategy is to hire two salespeople.

Solved Problem 2

Marty Schatz owns and manages a chili dog and soft drink store near the campus. Although Marty can service 30 customers per hour on the average (μ), he gets only 20 customers per hour (λ). Because Marty could wait on 50% more customers than actually visit his store, it doesn't make sense to him that he should have any waiting lines.

Marty hires you to examine the situation and to determine some characteristics of his queue. After looking into the problem, you make the seven assumptions listed in section 4. What are your findings?

Solution

File: 9-7.xls

For this problem, we use the Exponential Service Times (M/M/s) queuing worksheet in ExcelModules. The arrival rate (λ) is 20 customers per hour, the service rate (μ) is 30 customers per hour, and there is one server. We enter these values in cells B9, B10, and B11, respectively, as shown in Screenshot 7.

The operating characteristics of this queuing system are displayed in cells E9:E14. The probabilities that there are exactly n customers in the system, for $n = 0$ through 20, are shown in cells B20:B40.

Solved Problem 3

Refer to Solved Problem 2. Marty agreed that these figures seemed to represent his approximate business situation. You are quite surprised at the length of the lines and elicit from him an estimated value of the customer's waiting time (in the queue, not being waited on) at 10 cents per minute. During the 12 hours that Marty is open, he gets 12 × 20 = 240 customers. The average customer is in a queue 4 minutes, so the total customer waiting time is 240 × 4 minutes = 960 minutes. The value of 960 minutes is $0.10 × 960 minutes = $96.

SCREENSHOT 7 **Operating Characteristics for Solved Problem 2: M/M/1 Queuing System**

	A	B	C	D	E	F
1	**Solved Problem 9-2**					
2	Queuing Model	M/M/s (Exponential Service Times)		— M/M/s with s = 1		
3						
4	1. Both λ and μ must be RATES, and use the same time unit. For example, given a service time such as 10 minutes					
5	per customer, convert it to a service rate such as 6 per hour.					
6	2. The total service rate (rate x servers) must be greater than the arrival rate.					
7						
8	**Input Data**			**Operating Characteristics**		
9	Arrival rate (λ)	20		Average server utilization (ρ)	0.6667	0.0667 hours
10	Service rate (μ)	30		Average number of customers in the queue (Lq)	1.3333	= 4 minutes
11	Number of servers (s)	1		Average number of customers in the system (L)	2.0000	
12				Average waiting time in the queue (Wq)	0.0667	
13		1 server		Average time in the system (W)	0.1000	
14				Probability (% of time) system is empty (P0)	0.3333	
15						
16						= 6 minutes
17						
18	**Probabilities**					
19	Number of Units	Probability	Cumulative Probability			
20	0	0.3333	0.3333			
21	1	0.2222	0.5556			
22	2	0.1481	0.7037			
23	3	0.0988	0.8025			
24	4	0.0658	0.8683			
25	5	0.0439	0.9122			
36	16	0.0005	0.9990			
37	17	0.0003	0.9993			
38	18	0.0002	0.9995			
39	19	0.0002	0.9997			
40	20	0.0001	0.9998			

Hidden rows. See Companion Website for full file.

You tell Marty that not only is 10 cents per minute quite conservative, but he could probably save most of that $96 of customer ill will if he hired another salesclerk. After much haggling, Marty agrees to provide you with all the chili dogs you can eat during a week-long period in exchange for your analysis of the results of having two clerks wait on the customers.

Assuming that Marty hires one additional salesclerk whose service rate equals Marty's rate, complete the analysis.

Solution

File: 9-8.xls

We once again use the Exponential Service Times (M/M/s) queuing worksheet in ExcelModules. The arrival rate (λ) is 20 customers per hour, and the service rate (μ) is 30 customers per hour. There are, however, two servers now. We enter these values in cells B9, B10, and B11, respectively, as shown in Screenshot 8.

The operating characteristics of this queuing system are displayed in cells E9:E14. The probabilities that there are exactly *n* customers in the system, for *n* = 0 through 20, are shown in cells B20:B40.

You now have (240 customers) × (0.0042 hours) = 1 hour total customer waiting time per day. The total cost of 1 hour of customer waiting time is (60 minutes) × ($0.10 per minute) = $6.

You are ready to point out to Marty that hiring one additional clerk will save $96 − $6 = $90 of customer ill will per 12-hour shift. Marty responds that the hiring should also reduce the number of people who look at the line and leave as well as those who get tired of waiting in line and leave. You tell Marty that you are ready for two chili dogs, extra hot.

SCREENSHOT 8 Operating Characteristics for Solved Problem 3: M/M/2 Queuing System

	A	B	C	D	E	F
1	Solved Problem 9-3					
2	Queuing Model	M/M/s (Exponential Service Times)				
3						
4	1. Both λ and μ must be RATES, and use the same time unit. For example, given a service time such as 10 minutes					
5	per customer, convert it to a service rate such as 6 per hour.					
6	2. The total service rate (rate x servers) must be greater than the arrival rate.					
7						
8	Input Data			Operating Characteristics		
9	Arrival rate (λ)	20		Average server utilization (ρ)	0.3333	
10	Service rate (μ)	30		Average number of customers in the queue (L_q)	0.0833	
11	Number of servers (s)	2		Average number of customers in the system (L)	0.7500	
12				Average waiting time in the queue (W_q)	0.0042	
13		2 servers		Average time in the system (W)	0.0375	
14				Probability (% of time) system is empty (P_0)	0.5000	
15						
16						
17						
18	Probabilities					
19	Number of Units	Probability	Cumulative Probability			
20	0	0.5000	0.5000			
21	1	0.3333	0.8333			
22	2	0.1111	0.9444			
23	3	0.0370	0.9815			
24	4	0.0123	0.9938			
25	5	0.0041	0.9979			
36	16	0.0000	1.0000			
37	17	0.0000	1.0000			
38	18	0.0000	1.0000			
39	19	0.0000	1.0000			
40	20	0.0000	1.0000			

W_q drops from 0.0667 hours to 0.0042 hours (= 0.25 minutes) with two servers.

Hidden rows. See Companion Website for full file.

Discussion Questions and Problems

Discussion Questions

1 What is a queuing problem? What are the components in a queuing system?

2 What are the assumptions underlying common queuing models?

3 Describe the important operating characteristics of a queuing system.

4 Why must the service rate be greater than the arrival rate in a single-server queuing system?

5 Briefly describe three situations in which the FIFO discipline rule is not applicable in queuing analysis.

6 Provide examples of four situations in which there is a limited, or finite, waiting line.

7 What are the components of the following systems? Draw and explain the configuration of each.
 (a) Barbershop
 (b) Car wash
 (c) Laundromat
 (d) Small grocery store

8 Do doctors' offices generally have random arrival rates for patients? Are service times random? Under what circumstances might service times be constant?

9 Do you think the Poisson distribution, which assumes independent arrivals, is a good estimation of arrival rates in the following queuing systems? Defend your position in each case.
 (a) Cafeteria in your school
 (b) Barbershop
 (c) Hardware store
 (d) Dentist's office
 (e) College class
 (f) Movie theater

Problems

10 The Edge Convenience Store has approximately 300 customers shopping in its store between 9 A.M. and 5 P.M. on Saturdays. In deciding how many cash registers to keep open each Saturday, Edge's manager considers two factors: customer waiting time (and the associated waiting cost) and

the service costs of employing additional checkout clerks. Checkout clerks are paid an average of $10 per hour. When only one is on duty, the waiting time per customer is about 10 minutes (or $\frac{1}{6}$ hour); when two clerks are on duty, the average checkout time is 6 minutes per person; 4 minutes when three clerks are working; and 3 minutes when four clerks are on duty.

Edge's management has conducted customer satisfaction surveys and has been able to estimate that the store suffers approximately $13 in lost sales and goodwill for every *hour* of customer time spent waiting in checkout lines. Using the information provided, determine the optimal number of clerks to have on duty each Saturday to minimize the store's total expected cost.

11 From historical data, Harry's Car Wash estimates that dirty cars arrive at a rate of 10 per hour all day Saturday. With a crew working the wash line, Harry figures that cars can be cleaned at a rate of one every five minutes. One car at a time is cleaned in this example of a single-server waiting line. Assuming Poisson arrivals and exponential service times, find the
(a) average number of cars in line
(b) average time a car waits before it is washed
(c) average time a car spends in the service system
(d) utilization rate of the car wash
(e) probability that no cars are in the system

12 Rockwell Electronics Corporation retains a service crew to repair machine breakdowns that occur on an average of $\lambda = 3$ per day (approximately Poisson in nature). The crew can service an average of $\mu = 8$ machines per day, with a repair time distribution that resembles the exponential distribution.
(a) What is the utilization rate of this service system?
(b) What is the average downtime for a machine that is broken?
(c) How many machines are waiting to be serviced at any given time?
(d) What is the probability that more than one machine is in the system? What is the probability that more than two machines are broken and waiting to be repaired or being serviced? More than three? More than four?

13 The people staffing the ticket booth at an aquarium are able to distribute tickets and brochures to 440 patrons every hour, according to an exponential distribution. On a typical day, an average of 352 people arrive every hour to gain entrance to the aquarium. The arrivals have been found to follow a Poisson distribution. The aquarium's manager wants to make the arrival process as convenient as possible for the patrons and so wishes to examine several queue operating characteristics.

(a) Find the average number of patrons waiting in line to purchase tickets.
(b) What percentage of the time is the ticket window busy?
(c) What is the average time that a visitor to the aquarium spends in the system?
(d) What is the average time spent waiting in line to get to the ticket window?
(e) What is the probability that there are more than two people in the system? More than three people?
(f) What is the probability that there are more than two people in line? More than three people?

14 A computer processes jobs on a first-come, first-served basis in a time-sharing environment. The jobs have Poisson arrival rates, with an average of six minutes between arrivals. The objective in processing these jobs is that they spend no more than eight minutes, on average, in the system. How fast does the computer have to process jobs, on average, to meet this objective?

15 An agent in a train station sells tickets and provides information to travelers. An average of two travelers approach the agent for assistance each minute. Their arrival is distributed according to a Poisson distribution. The agent is able to meet the travelers' needs in approximately 20 seconds, distributed exponentially.
(a) What is the probability that there are more than two travelers in the system? More than three? More than four?
(b) What is the probability that the system is empty?
(c) How long will the average traveler have to wait before reaching the agent?
(d) What is the expected number of travelers in the queue?
(e) What is the average number in the system?
(f) If a second agent is added (who works at the same pace as the first), how will the operating characteristics computed in parts (b), (c), (d), and (e) change? Assume that travelers wait in a single line and go to the first available agent.

16 The wheat harvesting season in the U.S. Midwest is short, and most farmers deliver their truckloads of wheat to a giant central storage bin within a two-week span. Because of this, wheat-filled trucks waiting to unload and return to the fields have been known to back up for a block at the receiving bin. The central bin is owned cooperatively, and it is to every farmer's benefit to make the unloading/storage process as efficient as possible. The cost of grain deterioration caused by unloading delays and the cost of truck rental and idle driver time are significant concerns to the cooperative members. Although farmers have difficulty quantifying crop

damage, it is easy to assign a waiting and unloading cost for truck and driver of $18 per hour. The storage bin is open and operated 16 hours per day, seven days per week during the harvest season and is capable of unloading 35 trucks per hour, according to an exponential distribution. Full trucks arrive all day long (during the hours the bin is open), at a rate of about 30 per hour, following a Poisson pattern.

To help the cooperative get a handle on the problem of lost time while trucks are waiting in line or unloading at the bin, find the

(a) average number of trucks in the unloading system
(b) average time per truck in the system
(c) utilization rate for the bin area
(d) probability that there are more than three trucks in the system at any given time
(e) total daily cost to the farmers of having their trucks tied up in the unloading process
(f) The cooperative, as mentioned, uses the storage bin only two weeks per year. Farmers estimate that enlarging the bin would cut unloading costs by 50% next year. It will cost $9,000 to do so during the off-season. Would it be worth the cooperative's while to enlarge the storage area?

17 A restaurant's reservation agent takes reservations for dinner by telephone. If he is already on the phone when a patron calls to make a reservation, the incoming call is answered automatically, and the customer is asked to wait for the agent. As soon as the agent is free, the patron who has been on hold the longest is transferred to the agent to be served. Calls for reservations come in at a rate of about 15 per hour. The agent is able to make a reservation in an average of three minutes. Calls tend to follow a Poisson distribution, and the times to make a reservation tend to be exponential. The agent is paid $15 per hour. The restaurant estimates that every minute a customer must wait to speak to the agent costs the restaurant $1.

(a) What is the average time that diners must wait before their calls are transferred to the agent?
(b) What is the average number of callers waiting to make a reservation?
(c) The restaurant is considering adding a second agent to take calls, who would be paid the same $15 per hour. Should it hire another agent? Explain.

18 Sal's International Barbershop is a popular haircutting and styling salon near the campus of the University of New Orleans. Four barbers work full time and spend an average of 15 minutes on each customer. Customers arrive all day long, at an average rate of 12 per hour. When they enter, they take a number to wait for the first available barber.

Arrivals tend to follow the Poisson distribution, and service times are exponentially distributed.
(a) What is the probability that the shop is empty?
(b) What is the average number of customers in the barbershop?
(c) What is the average time spent in the shop?
(d) What is the average time that a customer spends waiting to be called to a chair?
(e) What is the average number of customers waiting to be served?
(f) What is the shop's utilization factor?
(g) Sal's is thinking of adding a fifth barber. How will this affect the utilization rate?

19 Sal (see Problem 18) is considering changing the queuing characteristics of his shop. Instead of selecting a number for the first available barber, a customer will be able to select which barber he or she prefers upon arrival. Assuming that this selection does not change while the customer is waiting for his or her barber to become available and that the requests for each of the four barbers are evenly distributed, answer the following:
(a) What is the average number of customers in the barber shop?
(b) What is the average time spent in the shop?
(c) What is the average time a customer spends waiting to be called to a chair?
(d) What is the average number of customers waiting to be served?
(e) Explain why the results from Problems 18 and 19 differ.

20 Carlos Gomez is the receiving supervisor for a large grocery store. Trucks arrive to the loading dock at an average rate of four per hour, according to a Poisson distribution, for 8 hours each day. The cost of operating a truck is estimated to be $80 per hour. Trucks are met by a three-person crew, which is able to unload a truck in an average of 12 minutes, according to an exponential distribution. The payroll cost associated with hiring a crew member, including benefits, is $22 per hour. Carlos is now considering the installation of new equipment to help the crew, which would decrease the average unloading time from 12 minutes to 9 minutes. The cost of this equipment would be about $500 per day. Is the installation of the new equipment economically feasible?

21 A local office of the Department of Motor Vehicles (DMV) wishes to overcome the reputation of making citizens wait in line for extremely long times before being able to conduct their business. Accordingly, the DMV is analyzing how best to serve the driving public. Its goal is to make sure that citizens will not have to wait more than five minutes before they are engaged in service with a clerk. The DMV currently has eight clerks to serve people. If a

clerk is not busy with customers, he can fill his time with filing or processing mailed-in requests for service. On a typical day, drivers come into the DMV according to the following pattern:

TIME	ARRIVAL RATE (CUSTOMERS/HOUR)
8 A.M.–10 A.M.	20
10 A.M.–2 P.M.	40
2 P.M.–5 P.M.	25

Arrivals follow a Poisson distribution. Service times follow an exponential distribution, with an average of 10 minutes per customer. How many clerks should be on duty during each period to maintain the desired level of service? You may use Excel's Goal Seek procedure to find the answer.

22 Julian Argo is a computer technician in a large insurance company. He responds to a variety of complaints from agents regarding their computers' performance. He receives an average of one computer per hour to repair, according to a Poisson distribution. It takes Julian an average of 50 minutes to repair any agent's computer. Service times are exponentially distributed.
   (a) Determine the operating characteristics of the computer repair facility. What is the probability that there will be more than two computers waiting to be repaired?
   (b) Julian believes that adding a second repair technician would significantly improve his office's efficiency. He estimates that adding an assistant, but still keeping the department running as a single-server system, would double the capacity of the office from 1.2 computers per hour to 2.4 computers per hour. Analyze the effect on the waiting times for such a change and compare the results with those found in part (a).
   (c) Insurance agents earn $30 for the company per hour, on average, while computer technicians earn $18 per hour. An insurance agent who does not have access to his computer is unable to generate revenue for the company. What would be the hourly savings to the firm associated with employing two technicians instead of one?

23 Julian is considering putting the second technician in another office on the other end of the building, so that access to a computer technician is more convenient for the agents. Assume that the other agent will also have the ability to repair a computer in 50 minutes and that each faulty computer will go to the next available technician. Is this approach more cost-effective than the two approaches considered in Problem 22?

24 Bru-Thru is a chain of drive-through beer and wine outlets where customers arrive, on average, every five minutes. Management has a goal that customers will be able to complete their transaction, on average, in six minutes with a single server. Assume that this system can be described as an M/M/1 configuration. What is the average service time that is necessary to meet this goal?

25 Recreational boats arrive at a single gasoline pump located at the dock at Trident Marina at an average rate of 10 per hour on Saturday mornings. The fill-up time for a boat is normally distributed, with an average of 5 minutes and a standard deviation of 1.5 minutes. Assume that the arrival rate follows the Poisson distribution.
   (a) What is the probability that the pump is vacant?
   (b) On average, how long does a boat wait before the pump is available?
   (c) How many boats, on average, are waiting for the pump?

26 A chemical plant stores spare parts for maintenance in a large warehouse. Throughout the working day, maintenance personnel go to the warehouse to pick up supplies needed for their jobs. The warehouse receives a request for supplies, on average, every 2 minutes. The average request requires 1.7 minutes to fill. Maintenance employees are paid $20 per hour, and warehouse employees are paid $12 per hour. The warehouse is open 8 hours each day. Assuming that this system follows the M/M/s requirements, what is the optimal number of warehouse employees to hire?

27 During peak times the entry gate at a large amusement park experiences an average arrival of 500 customers per minute, according to a Poisson distribution. The average customer requires four seconds to be processed through the entry gate. The park's goal is to keep the waiting time less than five seconds. How many entry gates are necessary to meet this goal?

28 Customers arrive at Valdez's Real Estate at an average rate of one per hour. Arrivals can be assumed to follow the Poisson distribution. Juan Valdez, the agent, estimates that he spends an average of 30 minutes with each customer. The standard deviation of service time is 15 minutes, and the service time distribution is arbitrary.
   (a) Calculate the operating characteristics of the queuing system at Valdez's agency.
   (b) What is the probability that an arriving customer will have to wait for service?

29 If Valdez wants to ensure that his customers wait an average of around 10 minutes, what should be his average service time? Assume that the standard deviation of service time remains at 15 minutes.

30 Customers arrive at an automated coffee vending machine at a rate of 4 per minute, following a Poisson distribution. The coffee machine dispenses a cup of coffee at a constant rate of 10 seconds.
   (a) What is the average number of people waiting in line?
   (b) What is the average number of people in the system?
   (c) How long does the average person wait in line before receiving service?

31 Chuck's convenience store has only one gas pump. Cars pull up to the pump at a rate of one car every eight minutes. Depending on the speed at which the customer works, the pumping time varies. Chuck estimates that the pump is occupied for an average of five minutes, with a standard deviation of one minute. Calculate Chuck's operating characteristics. Comment on the values obtained. What, if anything, would you recommend Chuck should do?

32 Get Connected, Inc., operates several Internet kiosks in Atlanta, Georgia. Customers can access the Web at these kiosks, paying $2 for 30 minutes or a fraction thereof. The kiosks are typically open for 10 hours each day and are always full. Due to the rough usage these PCs receive, they break down frequently. Get Connected has a central repair facility to fix these PCs. PCs arrive at the facility at an average rate of 0.9 per day. Repair times take an average of 1 day, with a standard deviation of 0.5 days.

   Calculate the operating characteristics of this queuing system. How much is it worth to Get Connected to increase the average service rate to 1.25 PCs per day?

33 A construction company owns six backhoes, which each break down, on average, once every 10 working days, according to a Poisson distribution. The mechanic assigned to keeping the backhoes running is able to restore a backhoe to sound running order in 1 day, according to an exponential distribution.
   (a) How many backhoes are waiting for service, on average?
   (b) How many are currently being served?
   (c) How many are in running order, on average?
   (d) What is the average waiting time in the queue?
   (e) What is the average wait in the system?

34 A technician monitors a group of five computers in an automated manufacturing facility. It takes an average of 15 minutes, exponentially distributed, to adjust any computer that develops a problem. The computers run for an average of 85 minutes, Poisson distributed, without requiring adjustments. Compute the following measures:
   (a) average number of computers waiting for adjustment
   (b) average number of computers not in working order

(c) probability the system is empty
(d) average time in the queue
(e) average time in the system

35 A copier repair person is responsible for servicing the copying machines for seven companies in a local area. Repair calls come in at an average of one call every other day. The arrival rate follows the Poisson distribution. Average service time per call, including travel time, is exponentially distributed, with a mean of two hours. The repair person works an eight-hour day.
   (a) On average, how many hours per day is the repair person involved with service calls?
   (b) How many hours, on average, does a customer wait for the repair person to arrive after making a call?
   (c) What is the probability that more than two machines are out of service at the same time?

36 The Johnson Manufacturing Company operates six identical machines that are serviced by a single technician when they break down. Breakdowns occur according to the Poisson distribution and average 0.03 breakdowns per machine operating hour. Average repair time for a machine is five hours and follows the exponential distribution.
   (a) What percentage of the technician's time is spent repairing machines?
   (b) On average, how long is a machine out of service because of a breakdown?
   (c) On average, how many machines are out of service?
   (d) Johnson wants to investigate the economic feasibility of adding a second technician. Each technician costs the company $18 per hour. Each hour of machine downtime costs $120. Should a second technician be added?

37 A typical subway station in Washington, DC, has six turnstiles, each of which can be controlled by the station manager to be used for either entrance or exit control—but never for both. The manager must decide at different times of the day how many turnstiles to use for entering passengers and how many to use to allow passengers to exit.

   At the Washington College Station, passengers enter the station at a rate of about 84 per minute between the hours of 7 and 9 A.M. Passengers exiting trains at the stop reach the exit turnstile area at a rate of about 48 per minute during the same morning rush hour. Each turnstile can allow an average of 30 passengers per minute to enter or exit. Arrival and service times have been thought to follow Poisson and exponential distributions, respectively. Assume that riders form a common queue at both entry and exit turnstile areas and proceed to the first empty turnstile.

The Washington College Station manager does not want the average passenger at his station to have to wait in a turnstile line for more than six seconds, nor does he want more than eight people in any queue at any average time.

(a) How many turnstiles should be opened in each direction every morning?

(b) Discuss the assumptions underlying the solution of this problem, using queuing theory.

38 A clerk of court is responsible for receiving and logging legal documents that are to be placed before the various judges to review and sign. She receives these documents on a first-come, first-served basis. Lawyers' couriers arrive before the clerk at an average rate of eight per hour, according to a Poisson distribution. The time it takes the clerk to process the documents is normally distributed, with an average of six minutes and a standard deviation of two minutes.

(a) What is the probability that a courier will have to wait for service?

(b) On average, how many couriers will be waiting for service?

(c) How long is the average wait for service?

39 County General Hospital's cardiac care unit (CCU) has seven beds, which are virtually always occupied by patients who have just undergone heart surgery. Two registered nurses are on duty at the CCU in each of the three 8-hour shifts. On average, a patient requires a nurse's attention every 66 minutes. The arrival rate follows a Poisson distribution. A nurse will spend an average of 19 minutes (exponentially distributed) assisting a patient and updating medical records regarding the care provided.

(a) What percentage of the nurses' time is spent responding to these requests?

(b) What is the average time a patient spends waiting for one of the nurses to arrive at bedside?

(c) What is the average number of patients waiting for a nurse to arrive?

(d) What is the probability that a patient will not have to wait for a nurse to arrive?

Case Study

New England Foundry

For more than 75 years, New England Foundry, Inc., has manufactured woodstoves for home use. In recent years, with increasing energy prices, George Mathison, president of New England Foundry, has seen sales triple. This dramatic increase in sales has made it even more difficult for George to maintain quality in all the woodstoves and related products.

Unlike other companies manufacturing woodstoves, New England Foundry is *only* in the business of making stoves and stove-related products. Its major products are the Warmglo I, the Warmglo II, the Warmglo III, and the Warmglo IV. The Warmglo I is the smallest woodstove, with a heat output of 30,000 Btu, and the Warmglo IV is the largest, with a heat output of 60,000 Btu. In addition, New England Foundry, Inc., produces a large array of products that have been designed to be used with their four stoves. These products include warming shelves, surface thermometers, stovepipes, adaptors, stove gloves, trivets, mitten racks, andirons, chimneys, and heat shields. New England Foundry also publishes a newsletter and several paperback books on stove installation, stove operation, stove maintenance, and wood sources. It is George's belief that the company's wide assortment of products is a major contributor to the sales increases.

The Warmglo III outsells all the other stoves by a wide margin. The heat output and available accessories are ideal for the typical home. The Warmglo III also has a number of outstanding features that make it one of the most attractive and heat-efficient stoves on the market. Each Warmglo III also has a thermostatically controlled primary air intake valve that allows the stove to adjust itself automatically to produce the correct heat output for varying weather conditions. A secondary air opening is used to increase the heat output in case of very cold weather. The internal stove parts produce a horizontal flame path for more efficient burning, and the output gases are forced to take an S-shaped path through the stove. The S-shaped path allows more complete combustion of the gases and better heat transfer from the fire and gases through the cast iron to the area to be heated. These features, along with the accessories, resulted in expanding sales and prompted George to build a new factory to manufacture Warmglo III stoves. An overview diagram of the factory is shown in Figure 5.

The new foundry uses the latest equipment, including a new Disamatic that helps in manufacturing stove parts. Regardless of new equipment or procedures, casting operations have remained basically unchanged for hundreds of years. To begin with, a wooden pattern is made for every cast iron piece in the stove. The wooden pattern is an exact duplication of the cast iron piece that is to be manufactured. New England Foundry has all its patterns made by Precision Patterns, Inc., and these patterns are stored in the pattern shop and maintenance room. Then a specially formulated sand is molded around the wooden pattern. There can be two or more sand molds for each pattern. Mixing the sand and making the molds are done in the molding room. When the wooden pattern is removed, the resulting sand molds form a negative image of the desired casting. Next, the molds are transported to the casting room, where molten iron is poured into the molds and allowed to cool. When the iron has solidified, the molds are moved into the cleaning, grinding,

FIGURE 5 Overview of the Factory

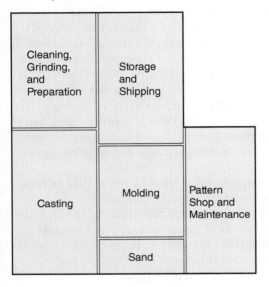

FIGURE 6 Overview of the Factory after Changes

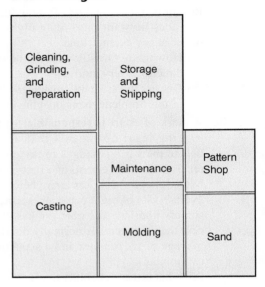

and preparation room. The molds are dumped into large vibrators that shake most of the sand from the casting. The rough castings are then subjected to both sandblasting to remove the rest of the sand and grinding to finish some of the surfaces of the castings. The castings are then painted with a special heat-resistant paint, assembled into workable stoves, and inspected for manufacturing defects that may have gone undetected thus far. Finally, the finished stoves are moved to storage and shipping, where they are packaged and shipped to the appropriate locations.

At present, the pattern shop and the maintenance department are located in the same room. One large counter is used both by maintenance personnel to get tools and parts and by sand molders who need various patterns for the molding operation. Pete Nawler and Bob Bryan, who work behind the counter, are able to service a total of 10 people per hour (or about 5 per hour each). On average, 4 people from maintenance and 3 people from the molding department arrive at the counter per hour. People from the molding department and from maintenance arrive randomly, and to be served, they form a single line. Pete and Bob have always had a first-come, first-served policy. Because of the location of the pattern shop and maintenance department, it takes about three minutes for a person from the maintenance department to walk to the pattern

and maintenance room, and it takes about one minute for a person to walk from the molding department to the pattern and maintenance room.

After observing the operation of the pattern shop and maintenance room for several weeks, George decided to make some changes to the layout of the factory. An overview of these changes is shown in Figure 6.

Separating the maintenance shop from the pattern shop had a number of advantages. It would take people from the maintenance department only one minute instead of three to get to the new maintenance department. Using time and motion studies, George was also able to determine that improving the layout of the maintenance department would allow Bob to serve 6 people from the maintenance department per hour, and improving the layout of the pattern department would allow Pete to serve 7 people from the molding shop per hour.

Discussion Questions

1. How much time would the new layout save?
2. If maintenance personnel were paid $9.50 per hour and molding personnel were paid $11.75 per hour, how much could be saved per hour with the new factory layout?

Case Study

Winter Park Hotel

Donna Shader, manager of the Winter Park Hotel, is considering how to restructure the front desk to reach an optimum level of staff efficiency and guest service. At present, the hotel has five clerks on duty, each with a separate waiting line, during the peak check-in time of 3:00 P.M. to 5:00 P.M. Observation

of arrivals during this time shows that an average of 90 guests arrive each hour (although there is no upward limit on the number that could arrive at any given time). It takes an average of 3 minutes for the front-desk clerk to register each guest.

Ms. Shader is considering three plans for improving guest service by reducing the length of time guests spend waiting in line. The first proposal would designate one employee as a quick-service clerk for guests registering under corporate accounts, a market segment that fills about 30% of all occupied rooms. Because corporate guests are preregistered, their registration takes just 2 minutes. With these guests separated from the rest of the clientele, the average time for registering a typical guest would climb to 3.4 minutes. Under plan 1, noncorporate guests would choose any of the remaining four lines.

The second plan is to implement a single-line system. All guests could form a single waiting line to be served by whichever of five clerks became available. This option would require sufficient lobby space for what could be a substantial queue.

The use of an automatic teller machine (ATM) for check-ins is the basis of the third proposal. This ATM would provide approximately the same service rate as would a clerk. Given

that initial use of this technology might be minimal, Shader estimated that 20% of customers, primarily frequent guests, would be willing to use the machines. (This might be a conservative estimate if the guests perceive direct benefits from using the ATM, as bank customers do. Citibank reports that some 95% of its Manhattan customers use its ATMs.) Ms. Shader would set up a single queue for customers who prefer human check-in clerks. This queue would be served by the five clerks, although Shader is hopeful that the machine will allow a reduction to four.

Discussion Questions

1. Determine the average amount of time that a guest spends checking in. How would this change under each of the stated options?
2. Which option do you recommend?

 Internet Case Studies

See the Companion Website for this text, at www.pearsonhighered.com/balakrishnan, for additional case studies.

Brief Solutions to Odd-Numbered End-of-Chapter Problems

11 (a) 4.1667. (b) 25 minutes. (c) 30 minutes. (d) 0.8333. (e) 0.1667.

13 (a) 3.2 patrons. (b) 0.8. (c) 0.0114 hours. (d) 0.0091 hours. (e) 0.5120, 0.4096,

15 (a) 0.2963, 0.1975, 0.1317. (b) 0.3333. (c) 0.6667 minutes. (d) 1.333 travelers. (e) 2 travelers. (f) $P_0 = 0.5$, $W_q = 0.0417$ minutes, $L_q = 0.08333$ travelers, $L = 0.75$ travelers.

17 (a) 0.15 hours (9 minutes). (b) 2.25. (c) Do not add second server. Costs increase by $6.49 per hour.

19 (a) 12 total (3 per queue). (b) 1 hour. (c) 0.75 hours. (d) 9 total (2.25 per queue). (e) Single M/M/4 system is more efficient than 4 parallel independent M/M/1 systems.

21 8 A.M.–10 A.M.: 5 clerks, 10 A.M.–2 P.M.: 8 clerks, 2 P.M.–5 P.M.: 6 clerks.

23 Cost is $8.82 higher than the single-server system with two servers.

25 (a) 0.1667. (b) 0.2271 hours. (c) About 2 boats.

27 7 gates.

29 About 23 minutes per customer.

31 $L_q = 0.5417$ cars, $L = 1.1667$ cars, $W_q = 4.33$ minutes, $W = 9.33$ minutes. Consider adding a second pump.

33 (a) 0.3297. (b) 0.8431. (c) 5.1569. (d) 0.6395 days. (e) 1.6355 days.

35 (a) 5.53 hours. (b) 2.236 hours. (c) 0.22.

37 4 entry, 2 exit.

39 (a) 71.90%. (b) 0.1249 hours. (c) 0.5673 patients. (d) 57.79%.

Simulation Modeling

Summary • Glossary • Solved Problems • Discussion Questions and Problems • Case Study: Alabama Airlines • Case Study: Abjar Transport Company • Internet Case Studies

The companion website for this text is www.pearsonhighered.com/balakrishnan.

From Chapter 10 of *Managerial Decision Modeling with Spreadsheets*, Third Edition. Nagraj Balakrishnan, Barry Render, Ralph M. Stair, Jr.
Copyright © 2013 by Pearson Education, Inc. All rights reserved.

1 Introduction

We are all aware to some extent of the importance of simulation models in our world. Boeing Corporation and Airbus Industries, for example, commonly build simulation models of their proposed jet airplanes and then test the aerodynamic properties of the models. Your local civil defense organization may carry out rescue and evacuation practices as it simulates the natural disaster conditions of a hurricane or tornado. The U.S. Army simulates enemy attacks and defense strategies in war games played on computers. Business students take courses that use management games to simulate realistic competitive business situations. And thousands of organizations develop simulation models to assist in making decisions involving their supply chain, inventory control, maintenance scheduling, plant layout, investments, and sales forecasting. Simulation is one of the most widely used decision modeling tools. Various surveys of the largest U.S. corporations reveal that most use simulation in corporate planning.

Simulation sounds like it may be the solution to all management problems. This is, unfortunately, by no means true. Yet we think you may find it one of the most flexible and fascinating of the decision modeling techniques in your studies. Let's begin our discussion of simulation with a simple definition.

What Is Simulation?

To simulate *means to duplicate the features of a real system. The idea is to imitate a real-world situation with a mathematical model that does not affect operations.*

To *simulate* is to try to duplicate the features, appearance, and characteristics of a real system. In this chapter we show how to simulate a business or management system by building a *mathematical model* that comes as close as possible to representing the reality of the system. We won't build any *physical* models, as might be used in airplane wind tunnel simulation tests. But just as physical model airplanes are tested and modified under experimental conditions, our mathematical models need to be experimented with to estimate the effects of various actions. The idea behind **simulation** is to imitate a real-world situation mathematically, to then study its properties and operating characteristics, and, finally, to draw conclusions and make action decisions based on the results of the simulation. In this way, the real-life system is not touched until the advantages and disadvantages of what may be a major policy decision are first measured on the system's model.

To use simulation, a manager should (1) define a problem, (2) introduce the variables associated with the problem, (3) construct a mathematical model, (4) set up possible courses of action for testing, (5) run the experiment, (6) consider the results (possibly deciding to modify the model or change data inputs), and (7) decide what course of action to take. These steps are illustrated in Figure 1.

The problems tackled by simulation can range from very simple to extremely complex, from bank teller lines to an analysis of the U.S. economy. Although very small simulations can be conducted by hand, effective use of this technique requires some automated means of calculation—namely, a computer. Even large-scale models, simulating perhaps years of business decisions, can be handled in a reasonable amount of time by computer. Though simulation is one of the oldest decision modeling tools (see the *History* box), it was not until the

FIGURE 1
Process of Simulation

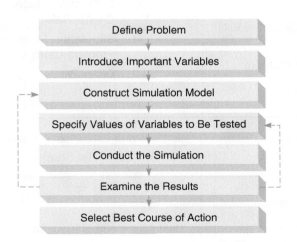

Define Problem

Introduce Important Variables

Construct Simulation Model

Specify Values of Variables to Be Tested

Conduct the Simulation

Examine the Results

Select Best Course of Action

HISTORY   Simulation

The history of simulation goes back 5,000 years to Chinese war games, called *weich'i*, and continues through 1780, when the Prussians used the games to help train their army. Since then, all major military powers have used war games to test military strategies under simulated environments.

From military or operational gaming, a new concept, *Monte Carlo simulation*, was developed as a decision modeling technique by the great mathematician John von Neumann during World War II. Working with neutrons at the Los Alamos Scientific Laboratory, von Neumann used simulation to solve physics problems that were too complex or expensive to analyze by hand or with physical models. The random nature of the neutrons suggested the use of a roulette wheel in dealing with probabilities. Because of the gaming nature, von Neumann called it the Monte Carlo model of studying laws of chance.

With the advent and common use of business computers in the 1950s, simulation grew as a management tool. Specialized computer languages (GPSS and SIMSCRIPT) were developed in the 1960s to handle large-scale problems more effectively. In the 1980s, prewritten simulation programs to handle situations ranging from queuing to inventory were developed. A few of them are ProModel, SLAM, and WITNESS.

introduction of computers in the mid-1940s and early 1950s that it became a practical means of solving management and military problems.

In this chapter, we explain the Monte Carlo simulation method and use it to model a variety of problems. For each simulation model, we show how Excel can be used to set up and solve the problem. In this regard, we discuss two approaches in this chapter:

We discuss two ways of using Excel for simulation here: with and without add-ins.

- *Simulation using Excel's standard built-in functions.* This approach is adequate for many applications and is especially useful if you are operating in a computer environment, such as in a university network, where the installation of additional software on individual computers is not preferred or convenient.
- *Simulation using* Crystal Ball. Several add-ins are available that make setting up and solving simulation models on Excel even easier. In this approach, we illustrate the use of one of the more powerful add-ins, Crystal Ball.

We end this chapter by briefly discussing two other types of simulation models besides the Monte Carlo approach.

Advantages and Disadvantages of Simulation

Simulation is a tool that has become widely accepted by managers for several reasons. The main advantages of simulation are as follows:

These advantages of simulation make it one of the most widely used decision modeling techniques in corporations.

1. It is relatively straightforward and flexible. Properly implemented, a simulation model can be made flexible enough to easily accommodate several changes to the problem scenario.
2. It can be used to analyze large and complex real-world situations that cannot be solved by using conventional decision models. For example, it may not be possible to build and solve a purely mathematical model of a city government system that incorporates important economic, social, environmental, and political factors. But simulation has been used successfully to model urban systems, hospitals, educational systems, national and state economies, and even world food systems.
3. Simulation allows what-if types of questions. With a simulation model, a manager can try out several policy decisions within a matter of minutes.
4. Simulations do not interfere with the real-world system. It may be too disruptive, for example, to experiment with new policies or ideas in a hospital, school, or manufacturing plant. With simulation, experiments are done with the model, not on the system itself.
5. Simulation allows us to study the interactive effects of individual components or variables to determine which ones are important. In any given problem scenario, not all inputs are equally important. We can use simulation to selectively vary each input (or combination of inputs) to identify the ones that most affect the results.
6. "Time compression" is possible with simulation. The effects of ordering, advertising, or other policies over many months or years can be obtained by a computer simulation model in a short time.

7. Simulation allows for the inclusion of real-world complications that most decision models cannot permit. For example, some of the queuing models require exponential or Poisson distributions; the PERT analysis requires normal distributions. But simulation can use any probability distribution that the user defines.

The disadvantages of simulation include cost, its trial-and-error nature, and its uniqueness.

The main disadvantages of simulation are as follows:

1. Good simulation models can be very expensive. It is often a long, complicated process to develop a model. A corporate planning model, for example, can take months or even years to develop.
2. Simulation does not generate optimal solutions to problems, as do other decision modeling techniques, such as linear programming or integer programming. It is a trial-and-error approach that can produce different solutions in repeated runs.
3. Managers must generate all the conditions and constraints for solutions that they want to examine. The simulation model does not produce answers by itself.
4. Each simulation model is unique. Its solutions and inferences are not usually transferable to other problems.

2 Monte Carlo Simulation

Monte Carlo simulation can be used with variables that are probabilistic.

When a problem contains elements that exhibit chance or probability in their behavior, **Monte Carlo simulation** may be applied. The basic idea in Monte Carlo simulation is to randomly generate values for the unknown elements (i.e., variables) in the model through random sampling. The technique breaks down into simple steps. This section examines each of these steps in turn.

Steps of Monte Carlo Simulation

1. Establish a probability distribution for each variable in the model that is subject to chance.
2. Using random numbers, simulate values from the probability distribution for each variable in step 1.
3. Repeat the process for a series of **replications** (also called *runs*, or *trials*).

Step 1: Establish a Probability Distribution for Each Variable

Variables we may want to simulate abound in business problems because very little in life is certain.

Many variables in real-world systems are probabilistic in nature, and we might want to simulate them. A few of these variables are as follows:

- Product demand
- Lead time for orders to arrive
- Time between machine breakdowns
- Time between arrivals at a service facility
- Service time
- Time to complete a project activity
- Number of employees absent from work on a given day
- Stock market performance

To establish a probability distribution for a variable, we often assume that historical behavior is a good indicator of future outcomes.

There are several ways in which we can establish a *probability distribution* for a given variable. One common approach is to examine the historical outcomes of that variable. Then, we can compute the probability of each possible outcome of the variable by dividing the frequency of each observation by the total number of observations. Alternatively, we can use statistical goodness-of-fit tests to identify a commonly known probability distribution (e.g., normal, uniform, exponential, Poisson, binomial) that best characterizes the behavior of the variable. In practice, there are hundreds of probability distributions available to characterize the behavior of the various variables in a simulation model. In our study here, however, we will examine only a few of these probability distributions.

HARRY'S AUTO SHOP EXAMPLE To illustrate how to establish a probability distribution for a variable, let us consider, for example, the monthly demand for radial tires at Harry's Auto Shop over the past 60 months. The data are shown in the first two columns of Table 1. If we

TABLE 1
Historical Monthly Demand for Radial Tires at Harry's Auto Shop

DEMAND	FREQUENCY	PROBABILITY
300	3	3/60 = 0.05
320	6	6/60 = 0.10
340	12	12/60 = 0.20
360	18	18/60 = 0.30
380	15	15/60 = 0.25
400	6	6/60 = 0.10

assume that past demand rates will hold in the future, we can convert these data to a probability distribution for tire demand. To do so, we divide each demand frequency by the total number of months, 60. This is illustrated in the third column of Table 1.

Step 2: Simulate Values from the Probability Distributions

Once we have established the probability distribution for a variable, how do we simulate random values from this distribution? As we shall see shortly, the procedure to do so varies, based on the type of probability distribution. In this section, let us see how we can use the probability distribution identified in Table 1 to simulate Harry's tire demand for a *specific* month in the future. Note that in simulating the demand for any given month, we need to ensure the following:

- The actual monthly demand value is 300, 320, 340, 360, 380, or 400.
- There is a 5% chance that the monthly demand is 300, 10% chance that it is 320, 20% chance that it is 340, 30% chance that it is 360, 25% chance that it is 380, and 10% chance that it is 400.

Probabilities reflect long-term behavior.

These probability values, however, reflect only the long-term behavior. That is, if we simulate tire demand for many months (several hundred, or, better yet, several thousand), the demand will be 300 for exactly 5% of the months, 320 for exactly 10% of the months, and so on. Based on our knowledge of probability distributions, we can also use these probability values to compute Harry's expected value (or average) of monthly demand, as follows:

$$\text{Expected monthly demand} = \sum_i (i\text{th demand value}) \times (\text{Probability of } i\text{th demand value})$$
$$= 300 \times 0.05 + 320 \times 0.10 + 340 \times 0.20 + 360 \times 0.30$$
$$+ 380 \times 0.25 + 400 \times 0.10$$
$$= 358 \text{ tires}$$

Simulated results can differ from analytical results in a short simulation.

In the short term, however, the occurrence of demand may be quite different from these probability values. For example, if we simulate demand for just five months, it is entirely possible (and logical) for the demand to be 320 tires per month for *all* five months. The average demand for these five months would then be 320 tires per month, which is quite different from the expected value of 358 tires per month we just calculated. Hence, what we need is a procedure that will achieve the following objectives:

- Generate, in the *short term*, random demand values that do not exhibit any specific pattern. The expected value need not necessarily equal 358 tires per month.
- Generate, in the *long term*, random demand values that conform exactly to the required probability distribution. The expected value must equal 358 tires per month.

In simulation, we achieve these objectives by using a concept called *random numbers*.

There are several ways to pick random numbers—using a computer, a table, a roulette wheel, and so on.

RANDOM NUMBERS A **random number** is a number that has been selected through a totally random process. For example, assume that we want to generate a series of random numbers from a set consisting of 100 integer-valued numbers: 0, 1, 2, … , 97, 98, 99. There are several ways to do so. One simple way would be as follows:

1. Mark each of 100 identical balls with a unique number between 0 and 99. Put all the balls in a large bowl and mix thoroughly.
2. Select *any* ball from the bowl. Write down the number.
3. Replace the ball in the bowl and mix again. Go back to step 2.

Instead of balls in a bowl, we could have accomplished this task by using the spin of a roulette wheel with 100 slots, or by using tables of random digits that are commonly available.[1] Also, as we shall see shortly, it turns out that most computer software packages (including Excel) and many handheld calculators have built-in procedures for generating an endless set of random numbers.

Cumulative probabilities are found by summing all the previous probabilities up to the current demand.

USING RANDOM NUMBERS TO SIMULATE DEMAND IN HARRY'S AUTO SHOP How do we use random numbers to simulate Harry's tire demand? We begin by converting the probability distribution in Table 1 to a *cumulative probability* distribution. As shown in Table 2, the cumulative probability for each demand value is the sum of the probability of that demand and all demands *less than* that demand value. For example, the cumulative probability for a demand of 340 tires is the sum of the probabilities for 300, 320, or 340 tires. Obviously, the cumulative probability for a demand of 400 tires (the maximum demand) is 1.

We create a random number interval for each value of the variable. The specific numbers assigned to an interval are not relevant as long as the right proportion of unique numbers is assigned to the interval.

Consider the set of 100 integer-valued numbers ranging from 0 to 99. We now use the cumulative probabilities computed in Table 2 to create *random number intervals* by assigning these 100 numbers to represent the different possible demand values. Because there is a 5% probability that demand is 300 tires, we assign 5% of the numbers (i.e., 5 of the 100 numbers between 0 and 99) to denote this demand value. For example, we could assign the first 5 numbers possible (i.e., 0, 1, 2, 3, and 4) to denote a demand of 300 tires. Every time the random number drawn is one of these five numbers, the implication is that the simulated demand that month is 300 tires. Likewise, because there is a 10% chance that demand is 320 tires, we could let the next 10 numbers (i.e., 5 to 14) represent that demand—and so on for the other demand values. The complete random number intervals for the Harry's Auto Shop problem are shown in Table 3. It is important to note that the specific random numbers assigned to denote a demand value are not relevant, as long as the assignment is unique and includes the right proportion of numbers. That is, for example, we can use any set of 5 random numbers between 0 and 99 to denote a demand value of 300 tires, as long as these numbers are not assigned to denote any other demand level.

We simulate values by comparing the random numbers against the random number intervals.

To simulate demand using the random number intervals, we need to generate random numbers between 0 and 99. Suppose we use a computer for this purpose (we will see how to do so shortly). Assume that the first random number generated is 52. Because this is between 35 and

TABLE 2
Cumulative Probabilities for Radial Tires at Harry's Auto Shop

DEMAND	PROBABILITY	CUMULATIVE PROBABILITY
300	0.05	0.05
320	0.10	0.05 + 0.10 = 0.15
340	0.20	0.15 + 0.20 = 0.35
360	0.30	0.35 + 0.30 = 0.65
380	0.25	0.65 + 0.25 = 0.90
400	0.10	0.90 + 0.10 = 1.00

TABLE 3
Random Number Intervals for Radial Tires at Harry's Auto Shop

DEMAND	PROBABILITY	CUMULATIVE PROBABILITY	RANDOM NUMBER INTERVAL
300	0.05	0.05	0 to 4
320	0.10	0.15	5 to 14
340	0.20	0.35	15 to 34
360	0.30	0.65	35 to 64
380	0.25	0.90	65 to 89
400	0.10	1.00	90 to 99

---

[1]See, for example, *A Million Random Digits with 100,000 Normal Deviates*. New York: The Free Press, 1955, p. 7.

IN ACTION   Simulating a Production Line at Delphi

Delphi Corporation, a major supplier of fuel injectors to automobile manufacturers, was considering a new line that would produce the next generation of fuel injectors. In order for the line to be financially viable, it needed to have a high throughput, be cost effective to build, and be able to fit in the available space. To address this issue, Delphi used a simulation model at a very early design stage to serve as a test bed for several candidate line designs.

Simulating a line design involves fully specifying various details such as which machines to use, in what order, conveyor lengths, machine process rates, failure and repair distributions for each machine, etc. Although such detailed information is typically not available at the concept stage of a line design, this is precisely when

simulation helps to assess a line's potential performance characteristics. A major advantage of using simulation at such an early stage is that implementing the model's recommendations is inexpensive because the equipment has not yet been built. In contrast, the model's recommendations may be more difficult to cost justify after the equipment has been built since much of the cost has already been sunk.

The simulation analysis has provided and continues to provide Delphi with valuable guidance for the layout, loading and staffing of the new production line.

Source: Based on M. H. Tongarlak et al. "Using Simulation Early in the Design of a Fuel Injector Production Line," *Interfaces* 40, 2 (March-April 2010): 105–117.

64, it implies that the simulated demand in month 1 is 360 tires. Now assume that the second random number generated is 6. Because this is between 5 and 14, it implies that the simulated demand in month 2 is 320 tires. The procedure continues in this fashion.

Step 3: Repeat the Process for a Series of Replications

A simulation process must be repeated numerous times to get meaningful results.

As noted earlier, although the long-term average demand is 358 tires per month in Harry's example, it is likely that we will get different average values from a short-term simulation of just a few months. It would be very risky to draw any hard-and-fast conclusion regarding any simulation model from just a few simulation replications. We need to run the model for several thousand replications (also referred to as *runs*, or *trials*) in order to gather meaningful results.

3   Role of Computers in Simulation

Although it is possible to simulate small examples such as the Harry's Auto Shop problem by hand, it is easier and much more convenient to conduct most simulation exercises by using a computer. Three of the primary reasons for this follow:

Software packages have built-in procedures for simulating from several different probability distributions.

1. It is quite cumbersome to use hand-based random number generation procedures for even common probability distributions, such as the normal, uniform, and exponential distributions. As noted earlier, most computer software packages (including Excel) have built-in procedures for generation of random numbers. It is quite easy to simulate values from many probability distributions by using a software package's random number generator.

2. In order for the simulation results to be valid and useful, it is necessary to replicate the process hundreds (or even thousands) of times. Doing this by hand is laborious and time-consuming. In contrast, it is possible to simulate thousands of replications for a model in just a matter of seconds by using most software packages.

Software packages allow us to easily replicate a model and keep track of several output measures.

3. During the simulation process, depending on the complexity and scope of the model, we may need to manipulate many input parameters and keep track of several output measures. Here again, doing so by hand could become very cumbersome. Software packages, on the other hand, can be used to easily change multiple input values and track as many output measures as required in any simulation model.

Types of Simulation Software Packages

Three types of software packages are available to help set up and run simulation models on computers, as discussed in the following sections.

The use of simulation has been broadened by the availability of computing technology.

GENERAL-PURPOSE PROGRAMMING LANGUAGES General-purpose programming languages that can be used to set up and run simulation models include standard programming languages such as Visual Basic, C++, and FORTRAN. The main advantage of these languages is that an experienced programmer can use them to develop simulation models for many diverse situations. The big disadvantage, however, is that a program written for a simulation model is specific to that model and is not easily portable. That is, a simulation model developed for one problem or situation may not be easily transferable to a different situation.

Special-purpose simulation languages have several advantages over general-purpose languages.

SPECIAL-PURPOSE SIMULATION LANGUAGES AND PROGRAMS Languages such as GPSS, Simscript III, and Visual SLAM and programs such as Extend, MicroSaint Sharp, BuildSim, AweSim, ProModel, and Xcell can be used to set up and run simulation models. Using such special-purpose languages and programs has three advantages compared with using general-purpose languages: (1) They require less programming time for large simulations, (2) they are usually more efficient and easier to check for errors, and (3) they have built-in procedures to automate many of the tasks in simulation modeling. However, because of the significant learning curve associated with these languages, they are typically likely to be most useful to experienced modelers dealing with extremely complex simulation models.

We focus on building simulation models using Excel in this chapter.

SPREADSHEET MODELS The built-in ability to generate random numbers and use them to select values from several probability distributions makes spreadsheets excellent tools for conducting simple simulations. Spreadsheets are also very powerful for quickly tabulating results and presenting them using graphs. In keeping with the focus of this text, we therefore use Excel (and an Excel add-in, Crystal Ball) in the remainder of this chapter to develop several simulation models.

Random Generation from Some Common Probability Distributions Using Excel

In the following pages, we discuss how we can use Excel's built-in functions to generate random values from seven commonly used probability distributions in simulation models: (1) continuous uniform, (2) discrete uniform, (3) normal, (4) exponential, (5) binomial, (6) discrete general with two outcomes, and (7) discrete general with more than two outcomes.

Excel's RAND function generates random numbers.

GENERATING RANDOM NUMBERS IN EXCEL Excel uses the RAND function to generate random numbers. The format for using this function is

$$=RAND()$$

Note that the $=$ sign before the RAND function implies that the cell entry is a formula. Also, there is no argument within the parentheses; that is, the left parenthesis is immediately followed by the right parenthesis.

If we enter =RAND() in any cell of a spreadsheet, it will return a random value between 0 and 1 (actually, between 0 and 0.9999 ...) *each time you press the calculate key* (i.e., the F9 key). The RAND function can be used either by itself in a cell or as part of a formula. For example, to generate a random number between 0 and 4.9999 ... , the appropriate formula to use would simply be

$$=5*RAND()$$

Uniform distributions can be either discrete or continuous.

CONTINUOUS UNIFORM DISTRIBUTION A variable follows a continuous uniform distribution between a lower limit a and an upper limit b if all values between a and b, including fractional values, are equally likely. To simulate a variable that follows this distribution, we use the following formula:

$$=a+(b-a)*RAND()$$

For example, if $a = 3$ and $b = 9$, we know that $=(9-3)*RAND()$ will generate a random value between 0 and 5.9999.... . If we add this to 3, we will get a random value between 3 and 8.999 ... (which, for all practical purposes, is 9).

DISCRETE UNIFORM DISTRIBUTION If all values between a and b are equally likely, but the variable is allowed to take on only integer values between a and b (inclusive), we refer to this

There are two ways of simulating from a discrete uniform distribution.

as a discrete uniform distribution. To generate values randomly from this distribution, there are two different approaches we can use in Excel. First, we can extend the preceding formula for continuous uniform distributions by including Excel's INT function. The resulting formula is

$$=\text{INT}(a+(b-a+1)*\text{RAND}())$$

Note that we need to add 1 to the $(b - a)$ term in this formula because the INT function always rounds down (that is, it just drops the fractional part from the value).

Alternatively, Excel has a built-in function called RANDBETWEEN that we can use to generate random values from discrete uniform distributions between a and b. The format for this function is

$$=\text{RANDBETWEEN}(a, b)$$

So, for example, if we want to generate random integers between 0 and 99 (as we did in the Harry's Auto Shop example earlier), we can use either of these two Excel formulas:

$$=\text{INT}(100*\text{RAND}()) \quad \text{or} \quad =\text{RANDBETWEEN}(0,99)$$

Excel's NORMINV function can be used to simulate from a normal distribution.

NORMAL DISTRIBUTION The normal distribution is probably one of the most commonly used distributions in simulation models. The normal distribution is always identified by two parameters: mean μ and standard deviation σ (or variance σ^2). To simulate a random value from a normal distribution with mean μ and standard deviation σ, we use the NORMINV function in Excel as follows:

$$=\text{NORMINV}(\text{RAND}(),\mu,\sigma)$$

For example, the formula $=\text{NORMINV}(\text{RAND}(),30,5)$ will generate a random value from a normal distribution with a mean of 30 and a standard deviation of 5. If we repeat this process several thousand times, 50% of the values will be below 30 and 50% will be above 30, 68.26% will be between 25 and 35 ($=$mean $\pm$ 1 standard deviation), and so on. Note that a normally distributed random value will include fractions because the normal distribution is a continuous distribution. If we need to convert normally distributed random values to integers, we can do so by using Excel's ROUND function as follows:

$$=\text{ROUND}(\text{NORMINV}(\text{RAND}(),\mu,\sigma),0)$$

The argument of 0 in the ROUND function specifies that we want to round off fractional values to the nearest number with zero decimal places (i.e., integer). In this case, fractional values of 0.5 and above are rounded up, while fractional values below 0.5 are rounded down.

In some situations, we may need to truncate the value generated from a normal distribution. For example, if we randomly generate demand values from a normal distribution with a mean of 10 and a standard deviation of 4, it is possible that the generated value is sometimes negative. Because demand cannot be negative, we may need to truncate the generated demand by setting any negative value to zero. A simple way of doing so is to use Excel's MAX function, as follows:

$$=\text{MAX}(0,\text{NORMINV}(\text{RAND}(),10,4))$$

Excel's LN function can be used to simulate from an exponential distribution.

EXPONENTIAL DISTRIBUTION The exponential distribution is commonly used to model arrival and service times in queuing systems. The exponential distribution can be described by a single parameter, μ, which describes the average *rate* of occurrences. (Alternatively, $1/\mu$ describes the mean time between successive occurrences.) To simulate a random value from an exponential distribution with average rate μ, we use the following formula in Excel:

$$=-(1/\mu)*\text{LN}(\text{RAND}())$$

where LN in the formula refers to the natural logarithmic function. For example, if the average service rate in a queuing system is 10 customers per hour, the service *time* (in hours) for a specific customer may be randomly generated by using the following formula:

$$=-(1/10)*\text{LN}(\text{RAND}())$$

*Excel's **CRITBINOM** function can be used to simulate from a binomial distribution.*

BINOMIAL DISTRIBUTION The binomial distribution models the probability of the number of successes occurring in n independent events (called trials), where each event has the same two outcomes, which we will label success and failure, and the probability of success in each event is the same value, p. To simulate a random number of successes in the n trials, we use the CRITBINOM function in Excel as follows:[2]

$$=\text{CRITBINOM}(n,p,\text{RAND}())$$

Excel's IF function can be used to select from two possible outcomes.

DISCRETE GENERAL DISTRIBUTION WITH TWO OUTCOMES If the outcomes of a probability distribution are discrete but the probabilities of the various outcomes are *not* the same, we refer to this as a **discrete general distribution** (as opposed to a discrete uniform distribution, where all outcomes have the same probability).

Let us first consider a discrete general distribution with only two outcomes. Suppose we want to randomly select individuals from a population where there are 55% males and 45% females. This implies that in the long term, our selected group will have exactly 55% males and 45% females. However, in the short term, any combination of males and females is possible and logical. To simulate these random draws in Excel, we can use the IF function as follows:

$$=\text{IF}(\text{RAND}()<0.55,\text{"Male"},\text{"Female"})$$

Note that the quotes are needed in the IF function because Male and Female are both text characters. If we use numeric codes (e.g., $1 = \text{Male}, 2 = \text{Female}$) instead of text characters, the formula is then

$$=\text{IF}(\text{RAND}()<0.55,1,2)$$

Random numbers can actually be assigned in many different ways, as long as they represent the correct proportion of the outcomes.

Because RAND() has a 55% chance of returning a value between 0 and 0.55 (which implies it has a 45% chance of returning a value between 0.55 and 0.999 ...), the preceding formula is logical. Note that we could have set up the IF function such that *any* 55% of values between 0 and 1 denotes male and the other 45% denotes female. For example, we could have expressed the formula as follows:

$$=\text{IF}(\text{RAND}()<0.45,\text{"Female"},\text{"Male"})$$

If we replicate the simulation enough times, the male-to-female split will be the same (i.e., 55% male and 45% female), regardless of how the IF function is set up.

DISCRETE GENERAL DISTRIBUTION WITH MORE THAN TWO OUTCOMES Let us now consider a discrete general distribution with more than two outcomes by revisiting the Harry's Auto Shop example. (Table 1 is repeated in the margin for your convenience.) The demand for tires is one of six values: 300, 320, 340, 360, 380, or 400. However, unlike with the discrete uniform distribution, in this case the probability of demand for each value is not the same.

We want to use Excel to simulate demands randomly from this distribution, just as we did manually in Table 3 using random number intervals. To do so, a more experienced Excel user could use a *nested* IF function (i.e., IF function within IF function). However, it is probably more convenient to use Excel's LOOKUP, VLOOKUP, or HLOOKUP functions to randomly select values from this type of probability distribution. In our discussion here, we illustrate the use of the LOOKUP function.

Distribution of Tire Demand

Demand	Probability
300	0.05
320	0.10
340	0.20
360	0.30
380	0.25
400	0.10

Excel Notes

- The Companion Website for this text, at www.pearsonhighered.com/balakrishnan, contains the Excel file for each sample problem discussed here. The relevant file name is shown in the margin next to each example.
- For clarity, our simulation worksheets are color coded as follows:
  - *Input cells*, where we enter known data, are shaded yellow.
  - *Simulation cells*, which show simulated values, are shaded blue.
  - *Output cells*, where the results are shown, are shaded green.

---

[2] Excel 2010 includes an additional function called BINOM.INV, which is an improved version of CRITBINOM and uses the same arguments.

- When you open any of the Excel files for the examples in this chapter, if the Calculation Options in Excel is set to automatic (click Formulas|Calculation Options|Automatic), Excel will automatically recalculate all random numbers in the model. This, in turn, may cause all simulated values in the worksheet to change. Hence, the values you see in the Excel file may not be the same as those shown in the screenshots included in the text.
- *Tip:* After creating a simulation model, if you wish to save your results in such a way that the values do *not* change each time you open the Excel file, you can set the Calculation Options in Excel to manual (click Formulas|Calculation Options|Manual). Alternatively, you can use the Paste Values feature in Excel. You can copy the cells showing the results and use Paste Values to save your answers as values rather than as formulas. Remember, however, that any cell overwritten in this manner will no longer contain the formula.

File: 10-1.xls, sheet: 10-1A

Excel's LOOKUP function can be used to simulate from a discrete general distribution.

File: 10-1.xls, sheet: 10-1B

Screenshot 1A shows the Excel layout showing the formulas for setting up a LOOKUP function. We begin by arranging all the demand values in a column (say, column A). Titles, like the ones shown in row 1, are optional. We then list the probability of each demand in another column (say, column B). In Screenshot 1A, we have shown the demand values in cells A2:A7 and the corresponding probabilities in cells B2:B7.

Just as we did in Table 3, we now create the *random number intervals*. The only difference is that instead of using two-digit random numbers from 0 to 99, we use continuous-valued random numbers from 0 to 0.9999. The formulas to compute the random number intervals for Harry's example are shown in cells C2:D7 of Screenshot 1A. The actual values are shown in Screenshot 1B. Notice that the lower-limit numbers in cells C2:C7 are identical to the ones

SCREENSHOT 1A
Excel Layout and Formulas for a LOOKUP Function

SCREENSHOT 1B
Simulation Using a LOOKUP Function

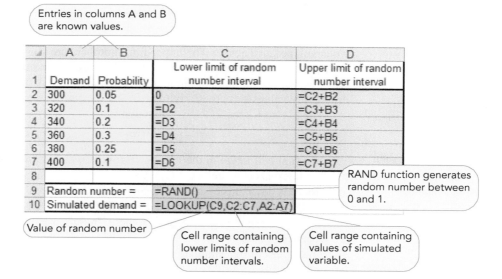

TABLE 4
Simulation from Various Probability Distributions Using Excel's Built-in Formulas

TO SIMULATE	USE BUILT-IN EXCEL FORMULA
Random number	$=\text{RAND}()$
Continuous uniform distribution Between a and b	$=a+(b-a)*\text{RAND}()$
Discrete uniform distribution Between a and b	$=\text{INT}(a+(b-a+1)*\text{RAND}())$ or $=\text{RANDBETWEEN}(a,b)$
Normal distribution Mean $=\mu$; Standard deviation $=\sigma$	$=\text{NORMINV}(\text{RAND}(),\mu,\sigma)$
Exponential distribution Mean rate $=\mu$	$=-(1/\mu)*\text{LN}(\text{RAND}())$
Binomial distribution Number of events $=n$ Probability of success in each event $=p$	$=\text{CRITBINOM}(n,p,\text{RAND}())$
Discrete general distribution with two outcomes only: A and B Probability of outcome $A=p$	$=\text{IF}(\text{RAND}()<p,A,B)$
Discrete general distribution with more than two outcomes: $Range1=$ Cell range containing lower limits of the random number intervals $Range2=$ Cell range containing the variable values	$=\text{LOOKUP}(\text{RAND}(),Range1,Range2)$

we developed in Table 3. The upper-limit numbers are slightly different because we used discrete random numbers in Table 3 and we are using continuous random numbers here. Although we have shown the random number intervals in columns that are adjacent to the demand and probability values here, these could be in any location of the spreadsheet.

We use random number intervals in this simulation.

The format for the LOOKUP function is

$$=\text{LOOKUP}(\text{RAND}(),\text{C2:C7},\text{A2:A7})$$

The first range in the LOOKUP function must contain the lower limits of the random number intervals.

The first cell range in the LOOKUP function must contain the *lower limits* of the random number intervals (i.e., cells C2:C7). Excel takes the value generated by the RAND() function and proceeds down this column to identify the entry where the RAND() value exceeds the lower limit. It then moves to the other range specified in the LOOKUP function (i.e., cells A2:A7) and selects the corresponding entry shown there. In our case, this range has the demand value that we wish to simulate.[3]

The values of this simulation are shown in Screenshot 1B. Let's suppose the random number generated is 0.715 (shown in cell C9). Using the preceding logic, the LOOKUP function compares this number to the entries in the cell range C2:C7. Having recognized that 0.715 exceeds the fifth entry (0.65) in the range but not the sixth (0.90), it returns the fifth entry in the cell range A2:A7. This is cell A6 (also shown in cell A10), which corresponds to a demand value of 380 tires.[4]

Summary of some of Excel's built-in functions used in simulation.

For your convenience, Table 4 presents a summary of the Excel formulas we have presented so far for simulating random values from various probability distributions. In the following sections, we describe four simulation models that use these formulas for their implementation.

---

[3] Note that the upper limit of the random number interval (cells D2:D7) play no role in the LOOKUP function. In fact, it is not necessary to even show this column, and we can safely delete it. However, we have included these entries in all our models here to make it easier to understand the use of the LOOKUP function.

[4] In this example, we have shown the value of the random number separately in cell C9 and used this number in the formula in cell C10. Note that the RAND() function could have been directly embedded in the LOOKUP formula itself. Except for the simulation model discussed in section 4, we do not show the random number values separately in our models.

4 Simulation Model to Compute Expected Profit

Table 1 Revisited

Demand	Probability
300	0.05
320	0.10
340	0.20
360	0.30
380	0.25
400	0.10

Demand, selling price, and profit margin are all probabilistic.

Let us set up the Harry's Auto Shop example as our first simulation model. Recall from Table 1 that Harry's monthly demand of tires is 300, 320, 340, 360, 380, or 400, with specific probabilities for each value. Now let us assume that the following additional information is known regarding Harry's operating environment:

- Depending on competitors' prices and other market conditions, Harry estimates that his average selling price per tire each month follows a discrete uniform distribution between $60 and $80 (in increments of $1).
- Harry's variable cost per tire also varies each month, depending on material costs and other market conditions. This causes Harry's average profit margin per tire (calculated as a percentage of the selling price) to vary each month. Using past data, Harry estimates that his profit margin per tire follows a continuous uniform distribution between 20% and 30% of the selling price.
- Harry estimates that his fixed cost of stocking and selling tires is $2,000 per month.

Using this information, let us simulate and calculate Harry's *average profit* per month from the sale of auto tires.

Setting Up the Model

The first issue to understand in any simulation model is what we mean by **one replication** *of the model.*

File: 10-2.xls, sheet: 10-2A

In any simulation model, the first issue we need to understand is what we mean by *one replication* of the model. In Harry's case, each replication corresponds to simulating one month of tire sales. That is, we will set up the model to simulate one month of tire sales at Harry's Auto Shop and then run the model repeatedly for as many replications as desired. The logic of Harry's simulation process is presented in Figure 2. Such **flow diagrams**, or **flowcharts**, are very useful in understanding the logical sequence of events in simulation models, especially in complex problem scenarios.

Let us now translate the flowchart in Figure 2 into a simulation model, using Excel. Screenshot 2A shows the formula view of the Excel layout for Harry's model. All titles, like the ones shown in rows 1 and 3, are optional. For a given replication, the spreadsheet is organized as follows:

- Cell A4 generates the random number used to simulate the demand that month. For this model alone, we show the actual value of the random number used to simulate each variable value.
- The random number in cell A4 is used in a LOOKUP function to simulate the monthly demand in cell B4. The data (demands, probabilities, and random number intervals) of the LOOKUP function are shown in cells I4:L9.

FIGURE 2
Flowchart for Harry's Auto Shop Simulation Model

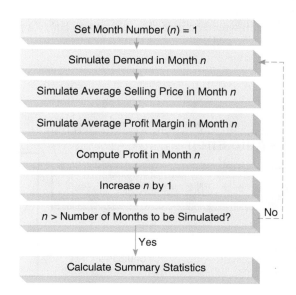

SCREENSHOT 2A Excel Layout and Formulas for Harry's Auto Shop

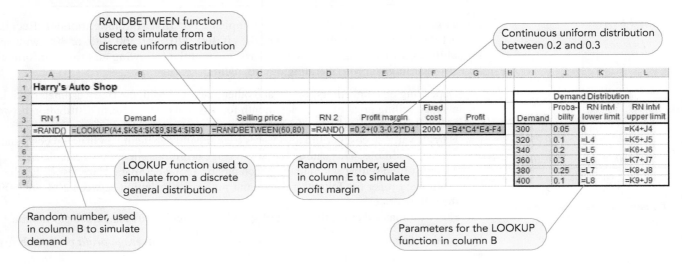

RANDBETWEEN function used to simulate from a discrete uniform distribution

Continuous uniform distribution between 0.2 and 0.3

LOOKUP function used to simulate from a discrete general distribution

Random number, used in column E to simulate profit margin

Random number, used in column B to simulate demand

Parameters for the LOOKUP function in column B

- In cell C4, we simulate the average selling price per tire by using the RANDBETWEEN function (with $a = 60$ and $b = 80$). The formula is =RANDBETWEEN(60,80).
- Cell D4 generates the random number used to simulate the average profit margin per tire.
- The random number in cell D4 is used in cell E4 to simulate the average profit margin per tire. For this, we use the continuous uniform distribution formula, with $a = 0.2$ and $b = 0.3$. The formula is =0.2+(0.3−0.2)*D4.
- Cell F4 shows the fixed cost, equal to $2,000 per month.
- Using these simulated values, Harry's monthly profit is calculated in cell G4 as

$$\text{Profit} = (\text{Demand for tires}) \times (\text{Average selling price per tire})$$
$$\times (\text{Average profit margin per tire}) - (\text{Monthly fixed cost})$$

That is, the formula in cell G4 is =B4*C4*E4−F4.

Screenshot 2B shows the result for a single replication of Harry's simulation model. This result indicates that Harry will earn a profit of $4,125.52 per month. It is important to remember, however, that each randomly simulated value only represents something that *could* occur. As such, there is no guarantee that the specific values simulated in Screenshot 2B will actually occur. Due to the presence of random numbers, these simulated values will change each time the model is replicated (i.e., they will change each time the F9 key is pressed in Excel). Hence, it would be incorrect to estimate Harry's profit based on just one replication (month).

File: 10-2.xls, sheet: 10-2B

SCREENSHOT 2B
Results for the
Simulation Model of
Harry's Auto Shop

Profit for current replication

	RN 1	Demand	Selling price	RN 2	Profit margin	Fixed cost	Profit		Demand	Proba-bility	RN intvl lower limit	RN intvl upper limit
1	**Harry's Auto Shop**											
2									Demand Distribution			
3												
4	0.001	300	$72.00	0.836	28.36%	$2,000	$4,125.52		300	0.05	0.00	0.05
5									320	0.10	0.05	0.15
6									340	0.20	0.15	0.35
7									360	0.30	0.35	0.65
8									380	0.25	0.65	0.90
9									400	0.10	0.90	1.00

RN of 0.001 is between 0.00 and 0.05, implying a demand of 300.

RN of 0.836 implies profit margin is 28.36%.

We need to replicate a simulation model at least a few thousand times to get consistent summary results.

To calculate Harry's *average* monthly profit, we need to replicate the simulation model several thousand times. However, in order to keep the computation times reasonable (especially in a classroom setting) and to keep the size of the resulting Excel files relatively small, we illustrate only 200 replications in most of our models in this chapter. We then compute summary statistics just from these 200 replications. It is important to note that 200 replications are not enough for a simulation model to yield consistent summary results. That is, an average based on just 200 replications, for example, will be different each time we run the simulation model. Therefore, in practice, we should replicate a model as many times as convenient.

Replication by Copying the Model

If the simulation model is very compact, we can perform replications by simply copying the model several times.

In simulation models where each replication consists of just a single row of computations in Excel (such as in Harry's model), an easy way to perform 200 replications is to copy all formulas and values in that row to 199 other rows. For example, we can copy cells A4:G4 in Screenshot 2B to cells A5:G203. (*Note:* For your convenience, a worksheet illustrating this way of replicating Harry's model is included in the Excel file *10-2.xls* on the Companion Website; see the sheet named *10-2B1*.) Due to the use of random numbers in the formulas, the values of the simulated variables will be different in each replication. Hence, each of the 200 entries computed in cells G4:G203, which represents the monthly profit that *could* result in a given month, will be different. Once we have simulated these 200 monthly profit values, we can compute the average monthly profit by using the Excel formula =AVERAGE(G4:G203).

Replicating a model by copying it multiple times could make the Excel file very large.

A clear drawback of this approach for replicating a simulation model is that it could make the resulting Excel file quite large and unwieldy. In fact, for models where each replication consists of computations spanning several rows in Excel (as we will see shortly), it is impractical to even consider copying the entire model 200 or more times. For this reason, we next illustrate a different approach—one that replicates a model multiple times without requiring us to copy the entire model each time.

Replication Using Data Table

*Using **Data Table** in Excel is a convenient way of replicating a large model several times.*

For replicating a simulation model, we can use an Excel procedure called Data Table. The primary use of this procedure in Excel is to plug in different values for a variable in a formula and compute the result each time. For example, if the formula is $(2a + 5)$, we can set up Data Table to plug in several values for the variable a and report the result of the formula each time. In a simulation model, however, we don't really have a "variable" and a "formula" to use in Data Table. So, as explained next, we make Data Table plug in multiple values for a dummy variable in a dummy formula (both of which have nothing to do with the simulation model) and report the "result" each time. The key here is that each time Data Table computes the formula's result, it automatically updates all calculations on the Excel sheet (i.e., it activates the F9 key). As a consequence, all random numbers in the simulation model change, and the result is a new replication of the model, with new values for all simulated entries.

File: 10-2.xls, sheet: 10-2C

We illustrate the use of Data Table to replicate Harry's simulation model 200 times in Screenshot 2C. Here again, we have chosen 200 replications just for convenience. The procedure is as follows:

This is how we set up Data Table.

1. We first use 200 cells in an empty column in the spreadsheet to represent the 200 values of the *dummy* variable. If we wish, we can leave these cells blank because they have no real role to play in the simulation model. However, as we have done in cells N4:N203 in Screenshot 2C, it is convenient to fill these cells with numbers from 1 to 200, to indicate we are performing 200 replications. If we wish, we can title this column *Replication* or *Run* (as shown in cell N3). *Note:* A convenient way to enter a series of numbers in Excel is to click Fill│Series found within the Home tab.

2. In the cell adjacent to the *first* cell in the range N4:N203 (i.e., in cell O4), we specify the cell reference for the output measure we want replicated 200 times. In Harry's model, this corresponds to cell G4, the monthly profit value. Hence, the formula in cell O4 would be =G4. We can title this column *Profit* if we wish (as shown in cell O3). We leave cells O5:O203 blank. Data Table will fill in these cells automatically when we run it.

SCREENSHOT 2C Data Table for Harry's Auto Shop

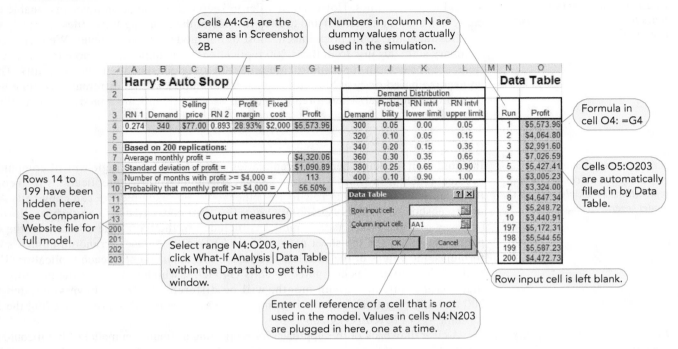

3. We now use the mouse or keyboard to select the range N4:O203 (i.e., both columns). *After* selecting this range, we click the Data tab and choose What-If Analysis | Data Table. The window titled Data Table, shown in Screenshot 2C, is now displayed.

4. Because our table is arranged in columns, we leave the Row input cell box blank. We then select any arbitrary cell that has nothing to do with the simulation model and enter this cell reference in the Column input cell box. It is important to make sure this selected cell (AA1, in Screenshot 2C) has no role to play in the simulation model. In effect, we are telling Data Table that cell AA1 contains our *dummy* formula.

5. Finally, we click OK to run Data Table. The procedure now takes the 200 entries in cells N4:N203, plugs them one at a time in cell AA1, and reports the value of cell G4 each time in cells O4:O203. As noted earlier, even though the variable values in cells N4:N203 and the formula in cell AA1 are dummies, Excel generates new random numbers for each replication of the model. The simulated results in cells O4:O203 are therefore different for each replication.

Excel Notes

- All entries in a simulation model, including columns in Data Table, can be formatted in any manner desired. For example, the profit value can be formatted to display as currency.

- It is usually a good idea to change the Calculation Options in Excel to Manual or Automatic Except for Data Tables when using Data Table (click Calculation Options, found within the Formulas tab). Otherwise, Excel will recalculate the entire Data Table each time we make *any* change in the spreadsheet. Depending on the size of the simulation model and the table, this could be time-consuming.

- For the same reason, it is a good idea to set up each simulation model in a separate Excel file rather than in a different sheet of the same file.

- If we change the Calculation Options to manual, remember that Excel will recalculate values only when we press the F9 key. Likewise, Data Table will initially show the same result value for every replication. We need to press F9 to get the final values.

- Once we have set up and run Data Table, we cannot edit parts of it (if we try to change any entry in the table, Excel will return the message "Cannot change part of a data table.").

To edit a Data Table, we select all cells that were automatically filled in by the Data Table procedure (e.g., cells O5:O203 in Screenshot 2C) and delete those cells. Now we make any changes we wish to the table (such as changing the number of replications) and run the Data Table procedure again.

- Although Data Table shows the value of the final output measure for each replication, the simulation model itself does not show details (e.g., monthly demand, selling price) for these replications. If we want to see complete details for each replication, we need to copy the entire model as many times as desired.

Analyzing the Results

Cells O4 to O203 show the monthly profit for 200 replications (months). We can now calculate the following statistics:

Cell G7: =AVERAGE(O4l:O203)   Average monthly profit = \$4,320.06

Cell G8: =STDEV(O4:O203)   Standard deviation of monthly profit = \$1,090.89

Note: Values in your file will be different if you recalculate the model because the random numbers will change, and we are using only 200 replications.

Excel's Descriptive Statistics procedure can also be used to compute summary statistics.

Alternatively, if the Analysis ToolPak add-in is installed and enabled, we can use Excel's Descriptive Statistics procedure to compute these and other statistics, such as confidence intervals. We invoke this procedure by clicking Data Analysis | Descriptive Statistics, found within the Data tab. The window shown in Screenshot 2D(a) appears. We enter the information as shown and press OK. The summary statistics shown in Screenshot 2D(b) are then displayed. The results indicate, for example, that the 95% confidence interval for the average monthly profit would extend from \$4,167.95 to \$4,472.17 (=\$4,320.06 ± \$152.11).

The simulation results can be used to compute several performance measures.

We can also calculate several other measures of performance. For example, suppose Harry estimates that in order for tire sales to be financially viable, he needs to get a monthly profit of at least \$4,000 from tires. What is the probability that Harry will get this amount of profit? To

SCREENSHOT 2D Descriptive Statistics for Harry's Auto Shop

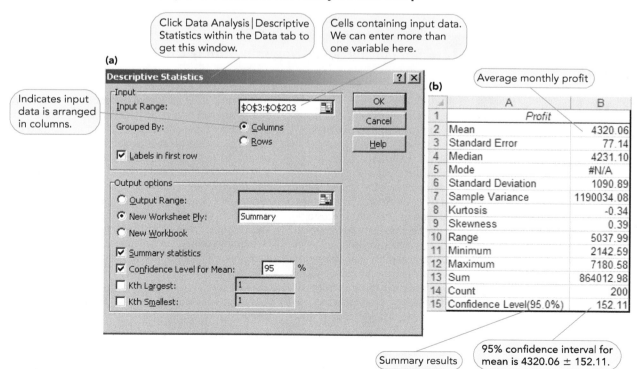

answer this question, we first need to count the number of months (of the 200 months) in which Harry's profit exceeds $4,000. We can use Excel's COUNTIF function to do this, as shown in cell G9 of Screenshot 2C. The relevant formula is

Cell G9:   =COUNTIF(O4:O203,">=4000")   Number of months with
profit $\geq$ \$4,000 = 113

Then, we divide this count by 200 to get the probability value (shown in cell G10). Screenshot 2C shows that Harry has a 56.5% chance of getting a monthly profit in excess of $4,000. Here again, the values will be different if you recalculate the model because the random numbers will change, and we are using only 200 replications.

Now suppose Harry decides that if his profit from tire sales is below $3,000 per month, he will stop selling tires. Using an approach similar to the one discussed here, see if you can calculate the probability of this event.

5   Simulation Model of an Inventory Problem

Factors in inventory problems include (1) how much to order and (2) when to order.

There are two main factors to consider in most inventory problems: (1) how much to order and (2) when to order. Under specific assumptions, it is possible to develop precise analytical models to answer these questions.[5]

In many real-world inventory situations, though, several inventory parameters are random variables. For example, the demand for an item could be random, implying that the rate at which its inventory is depleted is uncertain. Likewise, the time between when we place an order for an item with our supplier and when we receive it (known as the *lead time*) could be random. This implies that we may run out of inventory for the item before we receive the next consignment, causing a *stockout*.

Although it may be possible for us to express the behavior of parameters such as demand and lead time by using probability distributions, developing analytical models becomes extremely difficult. In such situations, the best means to answer the kind of inventory questions noted here is simulation.

Simulation is useful when demand and lead time are probabilistic.

In Solved Problem 1 at the end of this chapter, we simulate a fairly simple inventory problem in which only the demand is random. In the following pages, we illustrate a more comprehensive inventory problem in which both the demand and lead time are random variables.

DM IN ACTION   Simulating Volkswagen's Supply Chain

Volkswagen (VW) of America imports, markets, and distributes Volkswagens and Audis in the United States from its parent company in Germany. As part of a reengineering effort, VW developed a computer simulation model, using ProModel software, to analyze how to save money in its huge supply chain.

Since the early 1900s, vehicle distribution in the United States has followed the system introduced by Ford Motor. This structure, in which manufacturers view auto dealers as their primary customers, is so old that its original performance intentions are rarely examined. Dealers and auto manufacturers are loosely coupled, with each managing its own inventory costs. Like other manufacturers, VW encourages dealers to carry as much stock as possible but understands that having too much inventory could force a dealer out of business. Dealers recognize the threatening inventory costs but know that if they don't purchase enough cars, VW may restrict supply or appoint additional dealers. The average VW dealer sells 30 cars per month and stocks fewer than 100 in inventory.

To better the chances of a customer getting his or her first choice of car, to be able to deliver that car in 48 hours, and to be able to reduce total system (dealers and VW) costs for transportation, financing, and storage, VW considered a new strategy: pooling vehicles in regional depots. Rather than opening these centers and observing how well the concept worked, VW focused on simulating the flow of cars from plants to dealers. The model showed that there would be significant savings by opening its distribution centers. VW managers also learned that supply-chain performance must be viewed from the system level.

Source: Based on N. Karabakal, A. Gunal, and W. Ritchie. "Supply-Chain Analysis at Volkswagen of America," *Interfaces* 30, 4 (July–August 2000): 46–55.

---

[5] We discuss some of these models.

Simkin's Hardware Store

Simkin's Hardware Store sells the Ace model electric drill. Daily demand for the drill is relatively low but subject to some variability. Over the past 300 days, Barry Simkin has observed the demand frequency shown in column 2 of Table 5. He converts this historical frequency into a probability distribution for the variable daily demand (column 3).

When Simkin places an order to replenish his inventory of drills, the time between when he places an order and when it is received (i.e., the *lead time*) is a probabilistic variable. Based on the past 100 orders, Simkin has found that lead time follows a discrete uniform distribution between one and three days. He currently has seven Ace electric drills in stock, and there are no orders due.

Simkin wants to identify the order quantity, Q, and reorder point, R, that will help him reduce his total monthly costs. The *order quantity* is the fixed size of each order that is placed. The *reorder point* specifies the inventory level at which an order is triggered. That is, if the inventory level at the end of a day is at or below the reorder point, an order is placed. The total cost includes the following three components:

There are three components of the total cost.

- A fixed order cost that is incurred each time an order is placed
- A holding cost for each drill held in inventory from one period to the next
- A stockout cost for each drill that is not available to satisfy demand

Simkin estimates that the fixed cost of placing an order with his Ace drill supplier is $20. The cost of holding a drill in stock is $0.02 per drill per day. Each time Simkin is unable to satisfy a demand (i.e., he has a stockout), the customer buys the drill elsewhere, and Simkin loses the sale. He estimates that the cost of a stockout is $8 per drill. Assume that the shop operates 25 days each month on average.

Note that there are two decision variables (order quantity, Q, and reorder point, R) and two probabilistic components (demand and lead time) in Simkin's inventory problem. Using simulation, we can try different (Q, R) combinations to see which combination yields the lowest total cost. As an illustration, let us first examine a policy that has $Q = 10$ and $R = 5$; that is, each time the inventory at the end of a day drops to 5 or less, we place an order for 10 drills with the supplier.

There are two decision variables: order quantity (Q) and reorder point (R).

Setting Up the Model

A replication here corresponds to one month of operations at Simkin's store.

In Simkin's problem, each replication corresponds to tracking the inventory position and orders for electric drills over a month (i.e., 25 days), on a day-by-day basis. Hence, unlike Harry's Auto Shop problem in section 4, where we could model each replication by using just a single row in Excel, Simkin's simulation model will be much larger. If we represent the inventory operations of each day as a single row, the model will consist of 25 rows.

The Excel layout for Simkin's problem is shown in Screenshot 3A. Wherever necessary, we have shown the Excel formula used in a column.

In Screenshot 3A, all input parameters for the simulation model (e.g., the order quantity, reorder point, lead time range, all unit costs) are shown in separate cells (in column T). All formulas in the model use these cell references, rather than the values directly. This is a good

File: 10-3.xls, sheet: 10-3A

TABLE 5
Distribution of Daily Demand for Ace Electric Drills

DEMAND	FREQUENCY	PROBABILITY
0	15	$15/300 = 0.05$
1	30	$30/300 = 0.10$
2	60	$60/300 = 0.20$
3	120	$120/300 = 0.40$
4	45	$45/300 = 0.15$
5	30	$30/300 = 0.10$

SCREENSHOT 3A   Excel Layout and Results for Simkin's Hardware Store

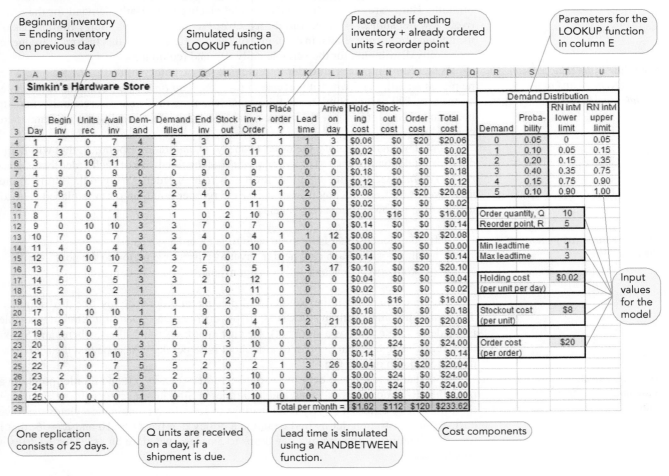

Beginning inventory = Ending inventory on previous day

Simulated using a LOOKUP function

Place order if ending inventory + already ordered units ≤ reorder point

Parameters for the LOOKUP function in column E

One replication consists of 25 days.

Q units are received on a day, if a shipment is due.

Lead time is simulated using a RANDBETWEEN function.

Cost components

To run several what-if scenarios using the same model, it is good to make parameter values cell references in all formulas.

practice to follow, especially if we want to use the simulation model to run several what-if scenarios using different values for these parameters (as we shall see shortly). The model in Screenshot 3A is organized as follows:

- Column A shows the day number (1 to 25).
- Column B shows the beginning inventory at the start of a day. On day 1, this equals 7 (given). On all other days, the beginning inventory equals the ending inventory of the previous day. For example, cell B5 = cell G4, cell B6 = cell G5, and so on.
- Column C shows the units received (if any) that day from a prior order. Because there are no outstanding orders on day 1, cell C4 shows a value of 0. The formula for the remaining cells in this column uses Excel's COUNTIF function. In column L (discussed shortly), we simulate the arrival day for each order that is placed. We use the COUNTIF formula to check the number of times the current day number matches the arrival day number. The formula used to calculate the number of units arriving each day is then as follows:

Here is how we simulate the inventory example.

$$\text{Units received} = \text{Number of orders due that day} \times \text{Order size}$$

For example, the formula in cell C5 is

$$=\text{COUNTIF}(\$L\$4:L4,A5)*\$T\$11$$

We use a $ symbol to anchor cell references while copying formulas in Excel.

The COUNTIF portion of the formula checks to see how many orders are due for arrival on day 2 (specified by cell A5). This number is then multiplied by the order quantity, Q, specified in cell T11. Note that the use of a $ to anchor cell references in this formula allows us to directly copy it to cells C6:C28.

- The total *available* inventory each day, shown in column D, is then the sum of the values in columns B and C:

$$\text{Column D} = \text{Column B} + \text{Column C}$$

Demand is simulated by using a LOOKUP function.

- Column E shows the demand each day. These values are simulated from a discrete general probability distribution shown in Table 5, using Excel's LOOKUP function. The parameters (demands, probabilities, and random number intervals) of the LOOKUP function are shown in cells R4:U9. Hence, the formula in cells E4:E28 is

$$=\text{LOOKUP(RAND( ),\$T\$4:\$T\$9,\$R\$4:\$R\$9)}$$

Here again, the use of $ to anchor cell references in the formula allows us to create it in cell E4 and then copy it to cells E5:E28.

- Column F shows the actual demand filled. If the demand is less than or equal to the available inventory, the entire demand is satisfied. In contrast, if the demand exceeds the available inventory, then only the demand up to the inventory level is satisfied. We can use Excel's MIN function to model this, as follows:

$$\text{Demand satisfied} = \text{MIN (Available inventory, Demand)}$$

Hence, column F = MIN(column D, column E).

If demand is less than available inventory, there is some ending inventory.

- Column G calculates the ending inventory. If the demand is less than the available inventory, there is some ending inventory. However, if the demand is greater than or equal to the available inventory, the ending inventory is zero. We can use Excel's MAX function to model this, as follows:

$$\text{Ending inventory} = \text{MAX (Available inventory} - \text{Demand, 0)}$$

Hence, column G = MAX(column D − column E, 0).

A stockout occurs when demand exceeds available inventory.

- We now calculate the stockout (or lost sales) in column H. If the demand exceeds the available inventory, there is a stockout. However, if the demand is less than or equal to the available inventory, there is no stockout. Once again, we can use the MAX function to model this, as follows:

$$\text{Stockout} = \text{MAX (Demand} - \text{Available inventory, 0)}$$

Hence, column H = MAX(column E − column D, 0).

We need to check for outstanding orders before placing a new order.

- If the ending inventory is at or below the reorder point, an order needs to be placed with the supplier. Before we place an order, however, we need to check whether there are outstanding orders. The reason for this is as follows. If the ending inventory level has already triggered an order on an earlier day, but that order has not yet been received due to the delivery lead time, a duplicate order should not be placed. Hence, in column I, we calculate the *apparent* ending inventory; that is, we add the *actual* ending inventory (shown in column G) and any orders that have already been placed. The logic behind the formula in column I is as follows:

$$\text{Apparent inventory at end of period } t =$$
$$\text{Apparent inventory at end of period } (t - 1)$$
$$- \text{Demand satisfied in period } t + \text{Order size, if}$$
$$\text{an order was placed at the end of period } (t - 1)$$

For example, the formula in cell I5 is

$$=\text{I4}-\text{F5}+\text{IF(J4}=1,\$T\$11,0)$$

- If the apparent inventory at the end of any day is at or below the reorder point (cell T12), an order is to be placed that day. We denote this event in column J by using an IF function (1 implies place an order, 0 implies don't place an order). For example, the formula in cell J5 is

$$=\text{IF(I5}<=\$T\$12,1,0)$$

Lead time is simulated by using a RANDBETWEEN function.

- If an order is placed, the delivery lead time for this order is simulated in column K by using a RANDBETWEEN function (between 1 and 3). For example, the formula in cell K5 is

$$=IF(J5=1,RANDBETWEEN(\$T\$14,\$T\$15),0)$$

- Finally, in column L, we calculate the arrival day of this order as follows:

$$\text{Arrive on day} = \text{Current day} + \text{Lead time} + 1$$

For example, the formula in cell L5 is

$$=IF(J5=1,A5+K5+1,0)$$

Note that this formula includes +1 because the order is actually placed at the end of the current day (or, equivalently, the start of the next day).

Computation of Costs

Columns M through P show the cost computations for Simkin's inventory model each day of the month. The relevant formulas are as follows:

We compute the costs.

Column M:	Holding Cost	$= \$T\$17 \times$ Ending inventory in column G
Column N:	Stockout Cost	$= \$T\$20 \times$ Shortage in Column H
Column O:	Order Cost	$= \$T\$23$ (if value in Column J $= 1$)
Column P:	Total Cost	$=$ Column M $+$ Column N $+$ Column O

The totals for each cost component for the entire month are shown in row 29 (cells M29:P29). For instance, the replication in Screenshot 3A shows a holding cost of $1.62 (cell M29), stockout cost of $112 (cell N29), order cost of $120 (cell O29), and total cost of $233.62 (cell P29).

Replication Using Data Table

To compute Simkin's average monthly cost, we need to replicate the model as many times as possible. Each time, due to the presence of random variables, all simulated values in the spreadsheet will change. Hence, the inventory costs will change.

   We have already seen how we can use Data Table to easily replicate a simulation model multiple times. In Harry's Auto Shop example, we replicated only a single output measure (i.e., monthly profit) by using Data Table (see Screenshot 2C). In contrast, suppose we would like to replicate each of the four costs—holding cost, stockout cost, order cost, and total cost—in Simkin's example. It turns out that we can expand the use of Data Table to replicate all four measures at the same time. The procedure, illustrated in Screenshot 3B, is as follows:

File: 10-3.xls, sheet: 10-3B

This is how we set up Data Table to replicate more than one output measure.

1. Here again, we illustrate only 200 replications of the model. We first enter numbers 1 to 200 in cells W4:W203, corresponding to these 200 replications.
2. In cells X4 to AA4 (i.e., adjacent to the *first* cell in the range W4:W203), we specify the cell references for the four output measures we want replicated. Hence, the formula in cell X4 is =M29, in cell Y4 is =N29, in cell Z4 is =O29, and in cell AA4 is =P29. We leave cells X5:AA203 blank. As before, Data Table will fill in these cells when we run it.
3. We now use the mouse or keyboard to select the entire range W4:AA203 (i.e., all five columns). *After* selecting this range, we choose Data | What-If Analysis | Data Table from Excel's menu.
4. We leave the row input cell box blank and enter some arbitrary cell reference in the column input box. As before, we need to make sure the selected cell (AA1, in this case) is not used anywhere in the simulation model.
5. Finally, we click OK to run Data Table. The procedure computes and displays 200 simulated values of the monthly holding, stockout, order, and total costs in columns X, Y, Z, and AA, respectively.

SCREENSHOT 3B   Data Table for Simkin's Hardware Store

Columns A through P are the same as in Screenshot 3A.

Values in cells W5:AA203 are automatically filled in by Data Table.

Formula in cell AA4: =P29

Simkin's Hardware Store

Day	Begin inv	Units rec	Avail inv	Dem-and	Demand filled	End inv	Stock out	End inv + Order	Place order?	Lead time	Arrive on day	Hold-ing cost	Stock-out cost	Order cost	Total cost
1	7	0	7	0	0	7	0	7	0	0	0	$0.14	$0	$0	$0.14
2	7	0	7	5	5	2	0	2	1	1	4	$0.04	$0	$20	$20.04
3	2	0	2	4	2	0	2	10	0	0	0	$0.00	$16	$0	$16.00
4	0	10	10	3	3	7	0	7	0	0	0	$0.14	$0	$0	$0.14
5	7	0	7	4	4	3	0	3	1	3	9	$0.06	$0	$20	$20.06
6	3	0	3	0	0	3	0	13	0	0	0	$0.06	$0	$0	$0.06
7	3	0	3	2	2	1	0	11	0	0	0	$0.02	$0	$0	$0.02
8	1	0	1	4	1	0	3	10	0	0	0	$0.00	$24	$0	$24.00
9	0	10	10	5	5	5	0	5	1	3	13	$0.10	$0	$20	$20.10
10	5	0	5	3	3	2	0	12	0	0	0	$0.04	$0	$0	$0.04
11	2	0	2	2	2	0	0	10	0	0	0	$0.00	$0	$0	$0.00
12	0	0	0	3	0	0	3	10	0	0	0	$0.00	$24	$0	$24.00
13	0	10	10	2	2	8	0	8	0	0	0	$0.16	$0	$0	$0.16
14	8	0	8	3	3	5	0	5	1	2	17	$0.10	$0	$20	$20.10
15	5	0	5	5	5	0	0	10	0	0	0	$0.00	$0	$0	$0.00
16	0	0	0	2	0	0	2	10	0	0	0	$0.00	$16	$0	$16.00
17	0	10	10	4	4	6	0	6	0	0	0	$0.12	$0	$0	$0.12
18	6	0	6	5	5	1	0	1	1	1	20	$0.02	$0	$20	$20.02
19	1	0	1	4	1	0	3	10	0	0	0	$0.00	$24	$0	$24.00
20	0	10	10	5	5	5	0	5	1	1	22	$0.10	$0	$20	$20.10
21	5	0	5	4	4	1	0	11	0	0	0	$0.02	$0	$0	$0.02
22	1	10	11	3	3	8	0	8	0	0	0	$0.16	$0	$0	$0.16
23	8	0	8	2	2	6	0	6	0	0	0	$0.12	$0	$0	$0.12
24	6	0	6	3	3	3	0	3	1	3	28	$0.06	$0	$20	$20.06
25	3	0	3	3	3	0	0	10	0	0	0	$0.00	$0	$0	$0.00
										Total per month =		$1.46	$104	$140	$245.46

Hidden rows

Demand Distribution

Demand	Proba-bility	RN intvl lower limit	RN intvl upper limit
0	0.05	0	0.05
1	0.10	0.05	0.15
2	0.20	0.15	0.35
3	0.40	0.35	0.75
4	0.15	0.75	0.90
5	0.10	0.90	1.00

Order quantity, Q	10
Reorder point, R	5
Min leadtime	1
Max leadtime	3
Holding cost (per unit per day)	$0.02
Stockout cost (per unit)	$8
Order cost (per order)	$20

Based on 200 replications:

Average holding cost =	$1.79
Average stockout cost =	$98.64
Average order cost =	$122.20
Average total cost =	$222.63

Results based on current replication

Results based on 200 replications

Select cells W4:AA203 before clicking Data | What-If Analysis | Data Table.

Data Table

Run	Hold-ing cost	Stock-out cost	Order cost	Total cost
1	$1.46	$104	$140	$245.46
2	$2.46	$16	$140	$158.46
3	$1.28	$128	$120	$249.28
4	$1.90	$56	$140	$197.90
5	$1.46	$120	$120	$241.46
6	$1.72	$88	$120	$209.72
7	$1.58	$96	$120	$217.58
8	$1.88	$96	$120	$217.88
9	$1.58	$128	$120	$249.58
10	$2.18	$48	$140	$190.18
11	$1.90	$88	$120	$209.90
12	$1.76	$136	$120	$257.76
13	$1.70	$112	$120	$233.70
14	$1.90	$24	$120	$145.90
15	$1.12	$168	$140	$309.12
16	$1.74	$40	$140	$181.74
17	$1.88	$80	$120	$201.88
18	$1.44	$152	$120	$273.44
19	$1.40	$104	$140	$245.40
20	$1.46	$168	$120	$289.46
21	$1.78	$112	$120	$233.78
22	$1.80	$96	$140	$237.80
23	$2.04	$80	$120	$202.04
24	$1.94	$56	$120	$177.94
25	$1.84	$168	$120	$289.84
26	$2.00	$80	$120	$202.00
27	$1.86	$64	$120	$185.86
199	$1.56	$152	$100	$253.56
200	$1.84	$80	$140	$221.84

Analyzing the Results

We can conduct statistical analyses on the replicated values.

We can now use the 200 cost values to conduct statistical analyses, as before. For example, if $Q = 10$ and $R = 5$, Screenshot 3B indicates that Simkin's average monthly costs of holding, stockout, and order are $1.79 (cell U27), $98.64 (cell U28), and $122.20 (cell U29), respectively. The average total cost, shown in cell U30, is $222.63.

As an exercise, see if you can set up Data Table to calculate Simkin's average demand fill rate per month. That is, what percentage of monthly demand received does Simkin satisfy on average? *Hint:* The fill rate for each replication is the ratio of demand satisfied (sum of entries in column F) to demand received (sum of entries in column E).

Using Scenario Manager to Include Decisions in a Simulation Model

In simulating Simkin's inventory model so far, we have assumed a fixed order quantity, Q, of 10, and a fixed reorder point, R, of 5. Recall, however, that Simkin's objective was to identify the Q and R values that will help him reduce his total monthly costs. To achieve this objective, suppose Simkin wants to try four different values for Q (i.e., 8, 10, 12, and 14) and two different values for R (i.e., 5 and 8). One approach to run this extended simulation would be to run the model and Data Table (see Screenshot 3B) eight times—once for each combination of Q and R values. We could then compare the average total cost (cell U30) in each case to determine which combination of Q and R is best. This approach, of course, could become quite cumbersome, especially if we wanted to vary several different input parameters and try multiple values for each parameter.

We use Scenario Manager when we want to try several values for one or more input parameters in a model.

It turns out that we can use an Excel procedure called Scenario Manager to automatically run a simulation model for several combinations of input parameter values. To do so, we first assume *any* combination of values for the input parameters and set up the complete simulation model (including Data Table) to replicate the desired output measures. After we have done so, we next define multiple scenarios—one for each combination of input parameter values. When we then run Scenario Manager, Excel will automatically run the model and the Data Table replications for each scenario and report the desired results.

We illustrate the construction and use of Scenario Manager by using the simulation model we have already constructed for Simkin (shown in Screenshot 3B for $Q = 10$ and $R = 5$). The procedure is as follows:

This is how we set up Scenario Manager.

1. Invoke Scenario Manager by clicking What-If Analysis | Scenario Manager, found within the Data tab. The window shown in Screenshot 3C(a) is displayed.
2. Click Add to create a new scenario. The Add Scenario window shown in Screenshot 3C(b) is displayed. In the box titled Scenario name, enter any name of your choice for the scenario. (In Simkin's model, we have used names such as Q8R5, Q8R8, and Q12R5 to make the scenarios self-explanatory.) In the Changing cells box, enter the cell references for the cells whose values you wish to change. In Simkin's model, these would be cells T11 and T12, corresponding to the input parameters Q and R, respectively. If the changing cells are not contiguous in the model, separate the cell references with commas. Next, if desired, enter a comment to describe the scenario. Checking the Prevent changes option protects the scenario from being accidentally edited or deleted, while the Hide option hides the scenario.

SCREENSHOT 3C   Setting Up Scenario Manager in Excel

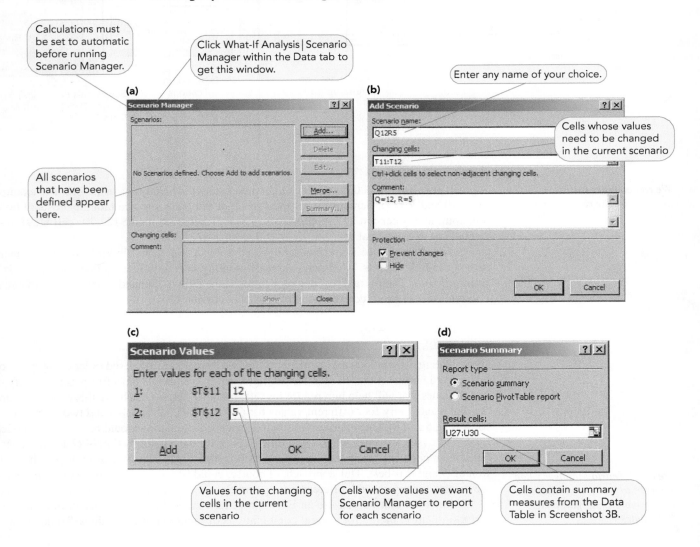

Click OK to get the Scenario Values window, as shown in Screenshot 3C(c). For each changing cell, enter the appropriate value. For example, for the scenario shown in Screenshot 3C(c), the values of Q and R are 12 and 5, respectively.

3. Repeat step 2 for as many scenarios as desired. In Simkin's model, you define eight scenarios corresponding to the eight combinations
$(Q, R) - (8, 5), (8, 8), (10, 5), (10, 8), (12, 5), (12, 8), (14, 5),$ and $(14, 8)$. You can also edit or delete a scenario after it has been created (assuming that the Prevent changes option is unchecked).

Scenario Manager's results can be shown either as a scenario summary table or as a PivotTable.

4. When all scenarios have been defined, click Summary (see Screenshot 3C(a)) to run Scenario Manager. The Scenario Summary window shown in Screenshot 3C(d) appears. In the box titled Result cells, enter the cell references for the output measures you would like Scenario Manager to report for each scenario. In Simkin's model, these would be cells U27:U30, corresponding to the four average cost measures—holding cost, stockout cost, order cost, and total cost (see Screenshot 3B). Here again, use commas to separate cell references that are not contiguous.

The results can be shown either as a Scenario summary table (preferred in most cases) or as a PivotTable report. (Choose the latter option if there are many changing cells and scenarios, and if you are comfortable analyzing results using PivotTables in Excel.)

5. Click OK. Scenario Manager runs the simulation model (including Data Table) for each scenario and presents the results in a separate worksheet, as shown in Screenshot 3D. (We have added grid lines to the summary table to make it clearer.)

File: 10-3.xls, sheet: 10-3D

Excel Notes

- The Calculation Options in Excel must not be set to Manual *before* you run Scenario Manager. If this option is set to Manual, Scenario Manager will report the same summary results for all scenarios.
- The standard version of Excel can accommodate up to 32 changing cells for each scenario.
- Although the number of scenarios allowed in Excel is limited only by your computer's memory, note that Scenario Manager may take a long time to execute if you include too many scenarios, especially if running each scenario involves running Data Table with many replications.

Analyzing the Results

For each combination of order quantity and reorder point, Screenshot 3D shows the average monthly holding, stockout, order, and total costs. Note that because all these values are based on only 200 replications of the simulation model, they could change each time we run Scenario Manager.

SCREENSHOT 3D Scenario Manager Results for Simkin's Hardware Store

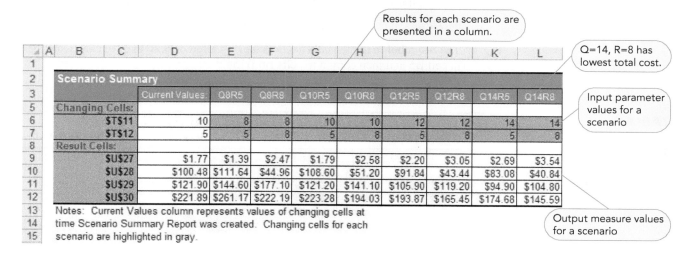

		Current Values	Q8R5	Q8R8	Q10R5	Q10R8	Q12R5	Q12R8	Q14R5	Q14R8
Scenario Summary										
Changing Cells:										
	$T$11	10	8	8	10	10	12	12	14	14
	$T$12	5	5	8	5	8	5	8	5	8
Result Cells:										
	$U$27	$1.77	$1.39	$2.47	$1.79	$2.58	$2.20	$3.05	$2.69	$3.54
	$U$28	$100.48	$111.64	$44.96	$108.60	$51.20	$91.84	$43.44	$83.08	$40.84
	$U$29	$121.90	$144.60	$177.10	$121.20	$141.10	$105.90	$119.20	$94.90	$104.80
	$U$30	$221.89	$261.17	$222.19	$223.28	$194.03	$193.87	$165.45	$174.68	$145.59

Notes: Current Values column represents values of changing cells at time Scenario Summary Report was created. Changing cells for each scenario are highlighted in gray.

Results for each scenario are presented in a column.

Q=14, R=8 has lowest total cost.

Input parameter values for a scenario

Output measure values for a scenario

Looking at the values in Screenshot 3D, it appears that Simkin's lowest total cost of $145.59 per month is obtained when he uses an order quantity of 14 units and a reorder point of 8 units.

As an exercise, see if you can compute other output measures (e.g., demand fill rate, probability that total monthly cost exceeds $200) in the simulation model. Then, include these measures also in the Results cell for each scenario and run Scenario Manager. Likewise, see if you can analyze the impact on total cost when you vary the values of other input parameters, such as the minimum and maximum delivery lead times.

6 Simulation Model of a Queuing Problem

Many real-world queuing systems can be difficult to model analytically. In such cases, we usually turn to simulation to analyze the performance of these systems. To study this issue, in this section we illustrate an example of a queuing model in which both the arrival times of customers and the service times at the facility follow discrete general distributions. Then, in Solved Problem 2 at the end of this chapter, we discuss the simulation of another queuing model in which arrival times are exponentially distributed and service times are normally distributed.

Denton Savings Bank

Sanjay Krishnan, manager at the Denton Savings Bank, is attempting to improve customer satisfaction by offering service such that (1) the average customer waiting time does not exceed 2 minutes and (2) the average queue length is 2 or fewer customers. The bank gets an average of 150 customers each day. Given the existing situation for service and arrival times, as shown in Table 6, does the bank meet Sanjay's criteria?

In discrete-event simulation models, we need to keep track of the passage of time by using a simulation clock.

Note that in simulating this queuing model, we need to keep track of the passage of time to record the specific arrival and departure times of customers. We refer to such models, in which events (e.g., customer arrivals and departures) occur at discrete points in time, as **discrete-event simulation** models.

Setting Up the Model

File: 10-4.xls

Each replication of this simulation model corresponds to a day's operation at the bank (i.e., the arrival and service of 150 customers). The Excel layout for this problem is presented in Screenshot 4. To keep track of the passage of time in this model, we monitor a clock that starts at zero and continually counts time (in minutes, in Denton's model). Observe that in row 4, we have included customer number 0, with zero values for all columns, to *initialize* this simulation clock. This is a good practice in all discrete-event simulation models. Rows 5 through 154 in the spreadsheet are organized as follows:

Time between successive arrivals follows a discrete general distribution.

- Column A lists the customer number (1 through 150).
- Column B shows the time between arrivals of successive customers, simulated using a LOOKUP function. The parameters (i.e., arrival times, probabilities, and random number intervals) for this LOOKUP function are shown in cells J6:M11. The formula in cells B5:B154 is

$$=LOOKUP(RAND(),\$L\$6:\$L\$11,\$J\$6:\$J\$11)$$

The $ symbol in the formula anchors the cell references so that we can create the formula in cell B5 and then copy it to cells B6:B154.

				TIME BETWEEN	
SERVICE TIME	**PROBABILITY**			**ARRIVALS**	**PROBABILITY**
1	0.25			0	0.10
2	0.20			1	0.15
3	0.40			2	0.10
4	0.15			3	0.35
				4	0.25
				5	0.05

TABLE 6
Distribution of Service Times and Time between Arrivals at Denton Savings Bank

SCREENSHOT 4 Excel Layout and Results for Denton Savings Bank

Simulated using a LOOKUP function

= Start time + Service time

Length of queue, including current patient

Denton Savings Bank

Custo-mer #	Time between arrivals	Arrival time	Start service	Service time	End service	Wait time	Queue length
0	0	0	0	0	0	0	0
1	3	3	3	2	5	0	0
2	2	5	5	3	8	0	0
3	4	9	9	2	11	0	0
4	3	12	12	3	15	0	0
5	3	15	15	3	18	0	0
6	4	19	19	3	22	0	0
7	4	23	23	3	26	0	0
8	2	25	26	1	27	1	1
9	4	29	29	3	32	0	0
10	0	29	32	3	35	3	1
11	5	34	35	3	38	1	1
12	3	37	38	4	42	1	1
13	3	40	42	2	44	2	1
14	1	41	44	1	45	3	2
15	4	45	45	3	48	0	0
16	3	48	48	1	49	0	0
17	3	51	51	3	54	0	0
18	3	54	54	4	58	0	0
19	3	57	58	3	61	1	1
20	4	61	61	3	64	0	0
21	3	64	64	4	68	0	0
22	1	65	68	1	69	3	1
149	4	413	413	2	415	0	0
150	3	416	416	1	417	0	0

Hidden rows

= Start time – Arrival time

Middle section:

Time	Proba-bility	RN intvl lower limit	RN intvl upper limit
	Arrival Distribution		
0	0.10	0.00	0.10
1	0.15	0.10	0.25
2	0.10	0.25	0.35
3	0.35	0.35	0.70
4	0.25	0.70	0.95
5	0.05	0.95	1.00
	Service Time Distribution		
1	0.25	0.00	0.25
2	0.20	0.25	0.45
3	0.40	0.45	0.85
4	0.15	0.85	1.00

Based on 1 replication:

Average wait time =	1.64
Average queue length =	0.86

Based on 200 replications:

Average wait time =	4.82
Average queue length =	2.14

Data Table

Run	Avg wait time	Avg queue length
1	1.64	0.86
2	1.37	0.71
3	3.86	1.76
4	4.94	2.20
5	2.53	1.18
6	2.53	1.24
7	3.09	1.47
8	3.45	1.56
9	3.60	1.66
10	13.33	5.57
11	6.66	2.85
12	1.83	0.96
13	2.42	1.27
14	3.88	1.82
15	2.73	1.28
16	1.31	0.65
17	6.99	2.87
18	1.99	0.93
19	3.11	1.49
20	1.34	0.72
21	3.21	1.49
22	3.61	1.59
23	4.21	1.82
150	7.88	3.29
151	5.46	2.47
152	17.02	6.70
199	5.31	2.41
200	4.82	2.11

=M20

=M21

Data Table replicates both output measures 200 times each.

Summary measures from Data Table

- Column C calculates the actual arrival time of the current customer as the sum of the arrival time of the previous customer and the time between arrivals (simulated in column B). This type of computation is an example of the use of the simulation clock, which records the actual elapsed clock time in a simulation model. For example, the formula in cell C5 is

$$=C4+B5$$

- The actual time at which this customer starts service is calculated in column D as the maximum of the customer's arrival time and the time the previous customer finishes service. For example, the formula in cell D5 is

$$=MAX(C5,F4)$$

Service time also follows a discrete general distribution.

- Column E shows the service time for this customer, simulated using a LOOKUP function. The parameters of this LOOKUP function are shown in cells J14:M17. The formula in cells E5:E154 is

$$=LOOKUP(RAND( ),\$L\$14:\$L\$17,\$J\$14:\$J\$17)$$

- The clock time at which this customer ends service is shown in column F as the sum of the start time (shown in column D) and the service time (shown in column E). For example, the formula in cell F5 is

$$=D5+E5$$

- Column G calculates the wait time of this customer as the difference between the customer's start time (shown in column D) and arrival time (shown in column C). For example, the formula in cell G5 is

$$=D5\ \ C5$$

385

We use Excel's MATCH function to calculate the queue length.

- Finally, column H calculates the queue length by using Excel's MATCH function. The MATCH function is used to determine how many customers (up to the current customer) have start times that are smaller than the arrival time of the current customer. Clearly, all customers (including the current one) who do not meet this criterion are in the queue. For example, the formula in cell H5 is

$$=A5-MATCH(C5,\$D\$5:D5,1)$$

Using the wait times and queue lengths shown in cells G5:H154 for the 150 customers, we can determine the following two performance measures for the bank each day: (1) average wait time per customer (shown in cell M20) and (2) average queue length (shown in cell M21).

Replication Using Data Table

Data Table is used here to replicate both performance measures.

Based on the average wait time and queue length values in cells M20 and M21, respectively, of Screenshot 4, it may seem to appear that Denton is meeting both of Sanjay's desired targets. The average wait time is only 1.64 minutes, and there are only 0.86 customers on average in the queue. However, note that these values are based on just one replication and will change each time we recalculate the model. Hence, to determine more precise values for these averages, we now replicate each performance measure 200 times. Screenshot 4 shows how we can use Data Table to do so, in columns O through Q. Note that Data Table has been used here to replicate both performance measures at the same time.

Analyzing the Results

Based on the average values computed from 200 replications in Screenshot 4, it appears that the system does *not* meet either criterion. The average wait time of 4.82 minutes per customer (cell M24) is more than double Sanjay's desired target of 2 minutes per customer. The average queue length of 2.14 customers (cell M25) is, however, close to Sanjay's desired target of 2 customers. Sanjay should, perhaps, focus on initiating training programs to improve the average service rate of his tellers.

IN ACTION **Using Simulation to Facilitate Better Healthcare**

A healthcare–associated infection (HAI) occurs when there is no evidence of patient infection at the time of hospital admission. There are about 2 million annual incidents of HAIs in the United States, resulting in over 100,000 deaths. Although HAIs cost hospitals more than $30 billion per year, hospitals typically have a financial and legal incentive to conceal HAIs, making it difficult to study the problem. Hospitals, however, are very interested in studying various issues such as whether greater compliance with hand-hygiene measures reduce costs, the relative merits of isolation versus hand hygiene, and how infection-control measures impact costs.

To address these questions, researchers developed a simulation model to track HAIs in an intensive care unit (ICU). The

discrete-event simulation model used data from Cook County Hospital in Chicago, Illinois, to model the entire process and its associated costs. The process includes the following steps: pathogens, patients, and visitors enter an ICU, interact with health care workers and with each other, infect or become infected, get cured of both primary disease and additional infections, and are finally discharged.

A Cook County Hospital spokesperson notes that the "model was useful and has caused us to develop two more infection control interventions."

Source: Based on R. Hagtvedt et al. "A Simulation Model to Compare Strategies for the Reduction of Health-Care–Associated Infections," *Interfaces* 39, 3 (May-June 2009): 256–270.

---

7 Simulation Model of a Revenue Management Problem

Revenue management problems are popular in the airline and hotel industries.

Another popular application of simulation is in *revenue management* problems, first introduced by the airline and hotel industries as *yield management* problems. This type of problem focuses on trying to identify the most efficient way of using an existing capacity (usually fixed) to manage revenues in situations where customer demand and behavior are uncertain.[6] To study this type of problem, in this section we consider an example in which the owner of a limousine service wants to find the optimal number of reservations she should accept for a trip. Then, in Solved Problem 3 at the end of this chapter, we illustrate the simulation of another revenue management problem, involving room reservations at a hotel.

Judith's Airport Limousine Service

Judith McKnew is always on the lookout for entrepreneurial opportunities. Living in Six Mile, South Carolina, she recognizes that the nearest airport is 50 miles away. Judith estimates that, on average, there are about 45 people from Six Mile (and its vicinity) who need rides to or from the airport each day. To help them, Judith is considering leasing a 10-passenger van and offering a limousine service between Six Mile and the airport. There would be four trips per day: a morning trip and an evening trip to the airport, and a morning trip and an evening trip from the airport.

After researching the issue carefully, Judith sets some operating guidelines for her problem and estimates the following parameters for each trip:

The number of reservations is probabilistic.

- Reservations for a trip can be made up to 12 hours in advance, by paying a nonrefundable $10 deposit. Judith will accept reservations up to her reservation limit (which this simulation model will help her decide).
- The ticket price is $35 per passenger per trip. Passengers with reservations must pay the $25 balance at the start of the trip.

The number of show-ups is also probabilistic.

- The number of reservations requested each trip follows a discrete uniform distribution between 7 and 14. Judith will, of course, reject a reservation request if she has reached her reservation limit.
- The probability that a person with a reservation shows up for the trip is 0.80. In other words, 20% of people with reservations do not show up. Anyone who does not show up forfeits the $10 deposit.
- If the number of passengers who show up exceeds 10 (the passenger capacity of the van), alternate arrangements must be made to get these extra people to the airport. This will cost Judith $75 per person. That is, Judith will lose $40 (= $75 − $35) per overbooked person.

Finally, the number of walk-ups is also probabilistic.

- The number of walk-up passengers (i.e., passengers without reservations) for a trip has the following discrete general distribution: probability of zero walk-ups is 0.30, probability of one walk-up is 0.45, and probability of two walk-ups is 0.25. Judith does not anticipate that there will ever be more than two walk-ups per trip.
- Walk-up passengers pay $50 per trip. However, Judith does not have to make alternate arrangements for these passengers if her van is full.
- The total cost per trip (to or from the airport) to Judith is $100. Note that due to the possibility of walk-up passengers on the return trip, Judith has to make a trip to the airport even if she has no passengers on that trip.

Judith wants to find out how many reservations she should accept in order to maximize her average profit per trip. Specifically, she is considering accepting 10, 11, 12, 13, or 14 reservations.

Setting Up the Model

File: 10-5.xls, sheet: 10-5A

Each replication here corresponds to one trip.

Each replication in Judith's problem corresponds to one trip. The Excel layout for this problem, shown in Screenshot 5A, is organized as follows:

- Cell B3 shows the number of reservations accepted for the trip. Note that this is a decision that is specified by Judith. Let us first set up the model assuming that Judith accepts 14 reservations for each trip. Later, we will use Scenario Manager to run this model automatically for all reservation limits (i.e., 10 to 14).

---

[6] A good description of *yield management* can be found in B. C. Smith, J. F. Leimkuhler, and R. M. Darrow. "Yield Management at American Airlines," *Interfaces* 22, 1 (January-February 1992): 8–31.

SCREENSHOT 5A   Excel Layout and Results for Judith's Limousine Service

Computed using the CRITBINOM function.

=RANDBETWEEN(G4,G5).

=B14

=B15

	A	B	C	D	E	F	G	H	I	J	K
1	**Judith's Limousine Service**								**Data Table**		
2											
3	Judith's reservation limit	14		Van's passenger capacity =			10		Run	Profit	Occ rate
4	Reservations requested	7		Minimum reservation request =			7		1	$220	80.0%
5	Reservations accepted	7		Maximum reservation request =			14		2	$180	100.0%
6	Number show up	6		Probability person shows up			0.80		3	$180	100.0%
7	Number overbook	0		Reservation deposit amount =			$10		4	$170	60.0%
8	Seats remaining	4		Balance of ticket price =			$25		5	$170	60.0%
9	Number walk-up	2		Walk-up ticket price =			$50		6	$180	70.0%
10	Walk-up accepted	2		Cost per overbooked person =			$75		7	$305	100.0%
11	Total seats occupied	8		Fixed cost per trip =			$100		8	$170	70.0%
12	Revenue	$320							9	$140	100.0%
13	Cost	$100			Walk-up Distribution				10	$200	80.0%
14	Profit	$220		Number	Probability	RN intvl LL	RN intvl UL		11	$265	90.0%
15	Occupancy rate	80.0%		0	0.30	0.00	0.30		12	$240	90.0%
16				1	0.45	0.30	0.75		13	$275	100.0%
17				2	0.25	0.75	1.00		14	$145	60.0%
18									15	$250	100.0%
19				Based on 200 replications:					16	$230	100.0%
20				Average profit =			$221.53		17	$275	100.0%
21				Average occupancy rate =			89.1%		18	$295	90.0%
22									19	$275	100.0%
202									199	$275	100.0%
203									200	$220	80.0%

=B11/G3

Hidden rows.

Parameters for LOOKUP function in cell B9.

Summary measures from Data Table.

Data Table replicates both output measures 200 times each.

- Cell B4 shows the number of reservations requested for a trip. We simulate this value from a discrete uniform distribution by using the RANDBETWEEN function with parameters $a = 7$ (specified in cell G4) and $b = 14$ (specified in cell G5). The formula in cell B4 is

$$=\text{RANDBETWEEN}(G4,G5)$$

- In cell B5, we set the actual number of reservations accepted by Judith for the trip as the *smaller* of Judith's reservation limit (cell B3) and the number of reservations requested (cell B4). The formula in cell B5 is

$$=\text{MIN}(B3,B4)$$

The number of people showing up is simulated using a CRITBINOM function.

- Next, we simulate the number of people with reservations who actually show up. This can be modeled as a binomial distribution where the number of independent events (n) corresponds to the number of people with reservations (i.e., cell B5), and the probability of success in each event (p) is the probability the person will actually show up (0.80 here, shown in cell G6). The relevant formula in cell B6 is[7]

$$=\text{CRITBINOM}(B5,G6,\text{RAND}())$$

- If the number of passengers showing up (cell B6) exceeds the van's passenger capacity (specified in cell G3), we have overbooked passengers. Otherwise, we have no overbooked passengers. In cell B7, we calculate the number of overbooked passengers by using the MAX function, as follows:

$$=\text{MAX}(B6-G3,0)$$

---

[7] As noted previously, we can use either the CRITBINOM function or the BINOM.INV function in Excel 2010.

- Likewise, if the van capacity exceeds the number of passengers showing up, we have some seats remaining. Otherwise, we are full. In cell B8, we calculate this number as follows:

$$=MAX(G3-B6,0)$$

- Next, in cell B9, we simulate the number of walk-up passengers by using a LOOKUP function. The parameter values for this function are specified in cells D15:G17. The formula in cell B9 is

$$=LOOKUP(RAND(),F15:F17,D15:D17)$$

- The number of walk-ups who can be accommodated in the van is obviously limited by the seats remaining (cell B8). Hence, in cell B10, we calculate the number of walk-ups accepted by using a MIN function, as follows:

$$=MIN(B8,B9)$$

- In cell B11, we compute the total number of seats occupied for the trip. The formula is

$$=G3-B8+B10$$

- The total revenue and cost for the trip are now calculated in cells B12 and B13, respectively, as

Revenue = \$10 × Reservations accepted + \$25 × Number of people who show up + \$50 × Walk-ups accepted

= G7*B5 + G8*B6 + G9*B10

Cost = \$75 × Number overbooked + \$100

= G10*B7 + G11

- In cell B14, we calculate the trip profit as (Revenue − Cost).
- Another performance measure that is popular in many revenue management problems is the percentage of capacity that has been actually utilized. Airlines and hotels refer to this measure as the *load factor*. To illustrate this measure, we compute Judith's occupancy rate for the trip in cell B15 as

$$=B11/G3$$

Replicating the Model Using Data Table and Scenario Manager

The profit of \$220 (shown in cell B14) and occupancy rate of 80% (shown in cell B15) in Screenshot 5A are based on just one replication of the model. Hence, they should not be used to make any conclusive statements about Judith's problem. To determine more precise values, we now replicate each performance measure 200 times. Columns I through K show how we can use Data Table to do so. The formula in cell J4 is =B14, while the formula in cell K4 is =B15. Cells J5:K203 are left blank and will be automatically filled in by the Data Table procedure when it is run. Based on these 200 replicated values, we calculate the average values of both measures (shown in cells G20 and G21, respectively). With a reservation limit of 14, Screenshot 5A indicates that Judith can expect a profit of \$221.53 per trip and an occupancy rate of 89.1%.

Now that we have set up Judith's simulation model and Data Table for a specific reservation limit, we can use Scenario Manager to try different values for this parameter. The procedure is as follows (here again, remember to make sure that the Calculations Options is set to Automatic in Excel before running Scenario Manager):

1. Invoke Scenario Manager by clicking Data | What-If Analysis | Scenario Manager.
2. Define five scenarios, corresponding to the five reservation limits that Judith wants to try (i.e., 10 to 14). For each scenario, specify cell B3 as the cell reference in the Changing cells box and enter the appropriate reservation limit in the Scenario Values window.
3. Once all scenarios have been defined, click Summary. In the box titled Result cells, specify cells G20 and G21 as the cells to track.
4. Click OK to run Scenario Manager. The results appear in a separate worksheet, as shown in Screenshot 5B.

SCREENSHOT 5B Scenario Manager Results for Judith's Limousine Service

Cell showing reservation limit in model

	A	B	C	D	E	F	G	H	I
1									
2		Scenario Summary							
3				Current Values	R10	R11	R12	R13	R14
5		Changing Cells:							
6		$B$3		14	10	11	12	13	14
7		Result Cells:							
8		$G$20		$224.08	$222.95	$228.20	$230.98	$220.88	$222.20
9		$G$21		86.1%	82.0%	83.8%	85.6%	85.3%	87.6%
10				Notes: Current Values column represents values of changing cells at					
11				time Scenario Summary Report was created. Changing cells for each					
12				scenario are highlighted in gray.					

Values for reservation limit

Profit

Occupancy rate

Limit of 12 yields highest profit here, based on 200 replications.

Analyzing the Results

Comparing the profit values in Screenshot 5B, it appears that Judith's best choice would be to accept 12 reservations per trip. (Remember that this result is based on only 200 replications.) The resulting average profit is $230.98 per trip. Not surprisingly, the occupancy rate is highest when Judith accepts 14 reservations, even though the rate does not seem to exceed 90% in any scenario.

So far, we have developed four simulation models using only Excel's built-in functions. We have also used Data Table to replicate the output measures in each model and Scenario Manager to automatically try different values for one or more input parameters. Solved Problems 1 to 3 at the end of this chapter discuss three additional simulation models using only Excel's built-in functions.

There are, however, several add-in programs available that make it even easier to develop and replicate simulation models using Excel. Hence, in the next two sections (and in Solved Problem 4 at the end of this chapter, in which we simulate a project management problem), we illustrate the use of one of the more powerful Excel add-ins for simulation, Crystal Ball.

8 Simulation Model of an Inventory Problem Using Crystal Ball

Crystal Ball is an Excel add-in used for simulation.

Crystal Ball, an add-in for Excel, is published by Oracle, Inc. (For more information, please refer to www.oracle.com.)

Reasons for Using Add-in Programs

From a logic and appearance point of view, a simulation model that is set up in Excel with Crystal Ball (or any other add-in) will look very similar to one that is set up without an add-in. Hence, any of the simulation models that we have created so far (using only Excel's built-in functions) can also be used with Crystal Ball. There are, however, three main features that add-ins such as Crystal Ball offer over Excel's built-in functions and procedures. As we will see shortly, these features are worthwhile enough to make the use of such add-in programs very useful in simulation modeling. The three features that add-ins such as Crystal Ball offer are as follows:

These three features of add-ins make them useful tools for developing simulation models on spreadsheets.

1. They have built-in functions to simulate not only from the simple probability distributions discussed so far but also from many other distributions that are commonly encountered in practice (e.g., binomial, triangular, lognormal). Further, the formulas to simulate from these distributions are simple, intuitive, and easy to use. For example, to simulate a random value in Crystal Ball from a normal distribution with mean and standard deviation σ, we use the following formula $=CB.NORMAL(\mu,\sigma)$. As you can see, this formula is much more intuitive than the formula we used earlier for simulating from a normal distribution: $=NORMINV(RAND(),\mu,\sigma)$.

2. They have built-in procedures that make it very easy to replicate the simulation model several hundred (or even several thousand) times. This means we will not have to set up and use Data Table.

3. They have built-in procedures that make it easy to collect and present information on various output measures. These measures can also be displayed graphically, if desired.

We should note that our intent here is to only provide a brief introduction to Crystal Ball and not to describe every aspect or capability of this add-in program. Once you have completed this section and the next, however, you should have sufficient knowledge about this add-in to explore some of its other options and procedures. Many of these are self-explanatory, and we strongly encourage you to try these out on your own.

Simulation of Simkin's Hardware Store Using Crystal Ball

Here we revisit Simkin's Hardware Store example.

To illustrate the use of Crystal Ball, let us revisit the inventory problem of Simkin's Hardware Store. Recall from section 5 that Simkin wants to test four different values (8, 10, 12, and 14) for the order quantity, Q, and two different values (5 and 8) for the reorder point, R, to see which combination of values for these two input parameters minimizes his monthly total cost. The total cost includes the following components: holding cost, stockout cost, and order cost. (At this time, we recommend that you refer to section 5 for a quick refresher on this problem and the simulation model we developed for it.)

File: 10-6.xls

STARTING CRYSTAL BALL If you have installed Crystal Ball on your PC, you can start the program (and Excel) by clicking Crystal Ball in the Windows Start menu.

Once the add-in has been loaded in Excel, you will see a new tab called Crystal Ball in Excel, with several menu commands, as shown in the top part of Screenshot 6A.

SCREENSHOT 6A   Excel Layout and Results Using Crystal Ball for Simkin's Hardware Store

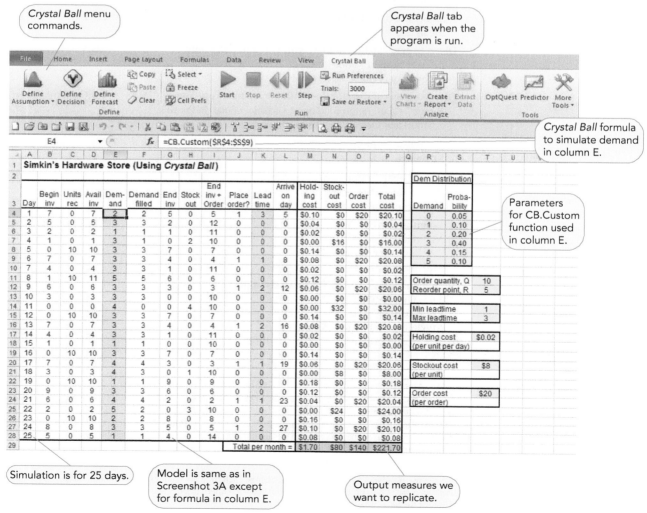

The Crystal Ball menus and toolbar are shown when the program is run.

The model with Crystal Ball looks very similar to the model that uses only Excel's built-in functions.

As noted earlier, add-ins such as Crystal Ball include an extensive set of built-in functions to simulate from many probability distributions. For your convenience, Table 7 presents a list of some of the functions available in Crystal Ball to generate random values from some of the distributions commonly used in simulation.[8, 9]

EXCEL LAYOUT USING CRYSTAL BALL FOR SIMKIN'S HARDWARE STORE We begin by setting up Simkin's inventory simulation model for any combination of Q and R values. (Let's use $Q = 10$ and $R = 5$, as we did in section 5.) Notice that the Excel layout in Screenshot 6A is very similar to the one we developed in section 5 for this problem using only Excel's built-in functions (refer to Screenshot 3A). In fact, the only change here is in column E, where we simulate the demand each day. Recall that we simulated these values in Screenshot 3A by using Excel's LOOKUP function. In Screenshot 6A, however, we use the CB.Custom function that is available in Crystal Ball to simulate from discrete general distributions (see Table 7 for details). The parameters for this function are shown in cells R4:S9 in Screenshot 6A. The formula for the demand in cells E4:E28 is[10]

We use the CB.Custom function to simulate demand here.

$$=\text{CB.Custom}(\$R\$4:\$S\$9)$$

TABLE 7
Simulating from Various Probability Distributions Using Crystal Ball

TO SIMULATE FROM	CRYSTAL BALL FORMULA
Continuous uniform distribution Between a and b	$=\text{CB.Uniform}(a,b)$
Discrete uniform distribution Between a and b	$=\text{CB.DiscreteUniform}(a,b)$
Normal distribution Mean $= \mu$; standard deviation $= \sigma$	$=\text{CB.Normal}(\mu,\sigma)$
Exponential distribution Mean rate $= \mu$	$=\text{CB.Exponential}(\mu)$
Discrete general distribution with two outcomes only A (code 1) and B (code 0) Probability of outcome $A = p$	$=\text{CB.YesNo}(p)$
Discrete general distribution with two or more outcomes $Range$ = Cell range containing variable values (in the first column) and their probabilities (in the second column)	$=\text{CB.Custom}(Range)$
Poisson distribution Mean rate $= \mu$	$=\text{CB.Poisson}(\mu)$
Binomial distribution Probability of success $= p$ Number of trials $= n$	$=\text{CB.Binomial}(p,n)$
Triangular distribution Minimum value $= a$ Likeliest value $= b$ Maximum value $= c$	$=\text{CB.Triangular}(a,b,c)$
Beta distribution (for PERT analysis in projects) Minimum (or Optimistic) time $= a$ Likeliest time $= b$ Maximum (or Pessimistic) time $= c$	$=\text{CB.BetaPert}(a,b,c)$

---

[8] You can see a list of all the functions available in Crystal Ball by clicking f_x in Excel's standard toolbar and selecting Crystal Ball in the function category.

[9] Instead of using the formulas shown in Table 7 to define probability distributions in Crystal Ball, we could have used the Define Assumption menu command. Using this option opens a graphical template of all the probability distributions available, from which we select the distribution we want. We have, however, chosen to use the formulas here because we find them to be more convenient.

[10] To see the simulated value for a variable change each time the model is recomputed, make sure the Set cell value to distribution mean box under Cell Prefs is unchecked. Otherwise, Crystal Ball will always show the mean of the distribution for the variable.

The rest of the formulas in Screenshot 6A are the same as in Screenshot 3A. Cells M29:P29 show the four total monthly cost measures—holding cost, stockout cost, order cost, and total cost.

Replicating the Model

Once we have set up Simkin's simulation model, we want to replicate it several thousand times and keep track of the cost measures (cells M29:P29) each time. Instead of using Data Table (as we did in Screenshot 3B), we replicate the model in Crystal Ball, using the following two-step procedure: (1) define forecasts and (2) run replications.

Output measures are called forecasts in Crystal Ball.

DEFINING FORECASTS First, we define the cells that we want to replicate. This is done as follows:

We can track several forecasts at the same time.

1. Select cell M29. This cell *must* contain the formula for an output measure (forecast) we want to replicate.
2. Click Define Forecast, found within the Crystal Ball tab. The window shown in Screenshot 6B is displayed.
3. If desired, specify the name and units of the output measure, as shown in Screenshot 6B. Click OK.
4. Repeat this procedure for the other three output measures (forecasts) in cells N29, O29, and P29.

RUNNING REPLICATIONS Once all forecasts have been defined, click Run Preferences, found within the Crystal Ball tab. The Run Preferences window shown in Screenshot 6C is displayed.

SCREENSHOT 6B
Defining a Forecast Cell in Crystal Ball

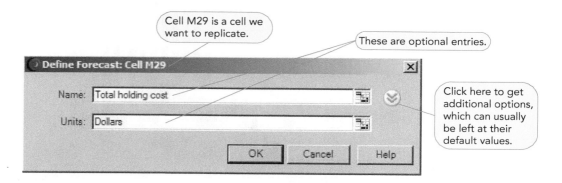

SCREENSHOT 6C
Setting Run Preferences in Crystal Ball

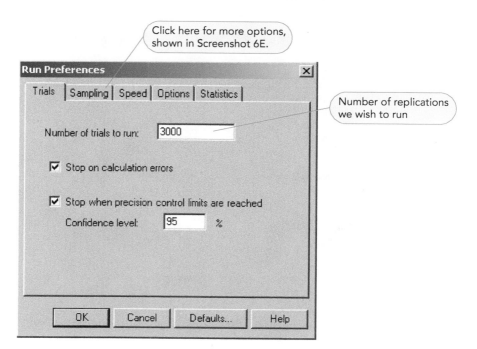

We can specify a larger number of replications here without worrying about the Excel file becoming too large.

Specify the number of trials (replications) desired and click OK. Note that because Crystal Ball is not going to show each replication's cost values in the spreadsheet (unlike Data Table in section 5), we do not have to be concerned about the Excel file getting too large. Hence, we can ask for a much larger number of replications here. For our discussion here, let us simulate the model 3,000 times. All other options in the window can be left at their defaults.

To now run the model, click Start, found within the Crystal Ball tab.[11] Crystal Ball runs the model for the specified number of replications, keeping track of forecast cells M29:P29 for each replication. When finished, the results of the simulation are presented in a separate window for each output measure. As shown in Screenshot 6D for the total cost (cell P29), we can view the results for each output measure either in graphical form or as a summary statistics table. To switch from the graphical view to the table, click View | Statistics on the window shown in Screenshot 6D.

The results can be viewed in either graphical or tabular form.

SCREENSHOT 6D **Graphical and Tabular Results from Crystal Ball for Simkin's Hardware Store**

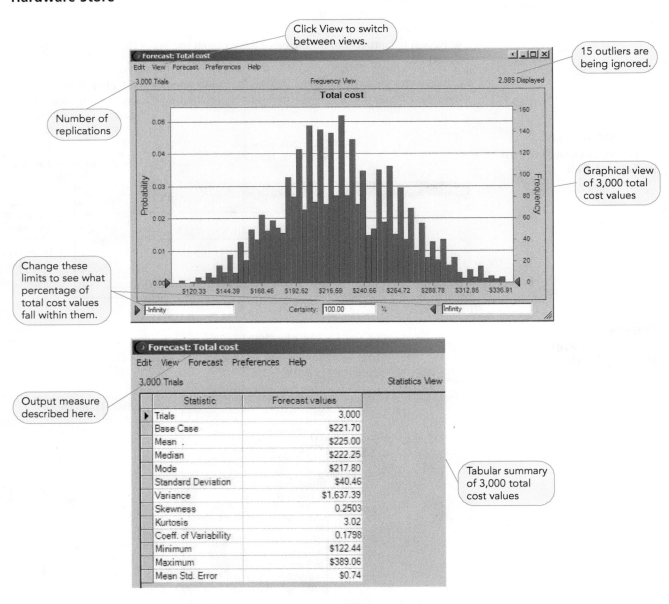

---

[11] After completing a simulation run, you may need to reset the run count (click Reset, found with the Crystal Ball tab) before running the model again.

Screenshot 6D indicates that if $Q = 10$ and $R = 5$, Simkin's average monthly total cost is $225. Note that this value is a more precise estimate of the average cost than the $222.63 value we computed in section 5 using 200 replications with Data Table. Can you see why?

As an exercise, see if you can set up Crystal Ball to run 3,000 replications and compute Simkin's average fill rate per month with $Q = 10$. *Hint:* The answer should be around 82%.

Using Decision Table in Crystal Ball

We use Decision Table in Crystal Ball to try several values automatically for an input parameter.

The model discussed so far allows us to determine Simkin's average monthly cost for an inventory policy with $Q = 10$, and $R = 5$. However, recall that Simkin wants to test four different values (8, 10, 12, and 14) for Q and two different values (5 and 8) for R to see which combination of values is best for his inventory system. Just as we used Scenario Manager in section 5 to get Excel to try these values of Q and R automatically in the simulation model, we use a procedure called Decision Table in Crystal Ball for this purpose.

Crystal Ball also includes a procedure called OptQuest that can be used to automatically search for the best combination of decision variable values (within preset bounds) that optimizes a defined output measure.

It is a good idea to use the same series of random numbers each time we run a simulation model with different values for input parameters.

USING THE SAME SEQUENCE OF RANDOM NUMBERS Before we describe the Decision Table and OptQuest procedures, we note an important issue. Whenever we run a simulation model multiple times with different values for input parameters, and then compare the results, it is a good idea to run the model using the same series of random numbers. By doing so, we are sure that any observed differences in output measures are due to differences in the input parameter values and not due to the randomness of the simulation process. Although Excel's RAND function does not allow us to fix the sequence of random numbers generated in the examples we discussed in sections 4 to 7, Crystal Ball permits us to do so here. To enable this feature, we first click Run Preferences to get the window shown in Screenshot 6C. We then click the tab titled Sampling on this window to get the window shown in Screenshot 6E. Finally, we check the Use same sequence of random numbers option and specify any number of our choice for the Initial seed value. (We use the same number each time.)

This is how we set up the Decision Table procedure.

SETTING UP THE DECISION TABLE PROCEDURE IN CRYSTAL BALL The steps to set up and run the Decision Table procedure for Simkin's simulation model are as follows:

1. As before, define cells M29:P29 as forecast cells by using the Define Forecast menu command.
2. Select cell T11 (i.e., a cell in which we want different values to be plugged in). Click Define Decision, found within the Crystal Ball tab. The Define Decision Variable window

SCREENSHOT 6E
Using the Same Sequence of Random Numbers in Crystal Ball

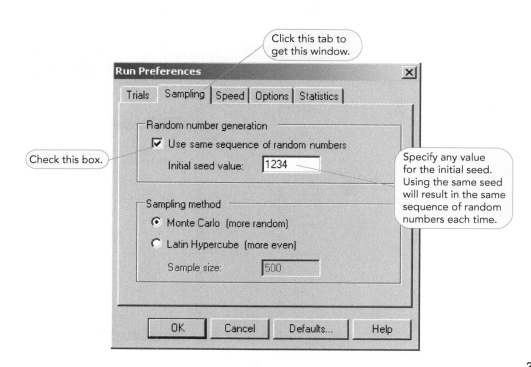

SCREENSHOT 6F
Defining a Decision Variable Cell in Crystal Ball

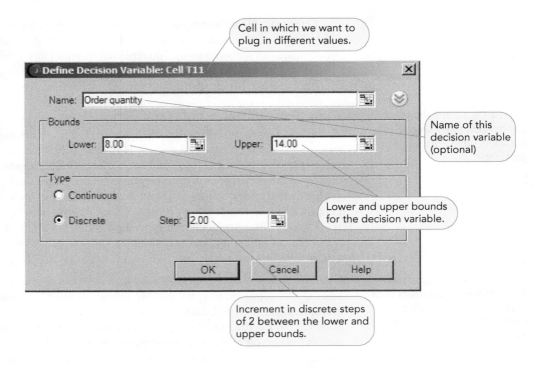

SCREENSHOT 6G
Setting Up Decision Table in Crystal Ball—Step 1 of 3

We should run Decision Table separately for each output measure that we wish to analyze.

shown in Screenshot 6F is displayed. Name the decision variable (if desired). Enter the lower and upper bounds (i.e., 8 and 14, respectively) for the order quantity. Specify a discrete step size of 2 to analyze Q values of 8, 10, 12, and 14 only. Click OK.

Repeat this step after selecting cell T12. In this case, the lower and upper bounds are 5 and 8, respectively, and the discrete step size is 3 (because we want to analyze R values of 5 and 8 only).

3. Click More Tools, found within the Crystal Ball tab, and then select Decision Table from the choices that are presented. The window shown in Screenshot 6G is displayed. From the list of defined forecasts, select the forecast that you want Decision Table to track. In Screenshot 6G, we have selected the total cost (cell P29) as the target cell. *Note:* Because Decision Table presents detailed results for each combination of decision values, it should be run separately for each forecast. Hence, if we wish to also analyze holding cost, stock-out cost, and order cost, we should run Decision Table separately for each forecast.

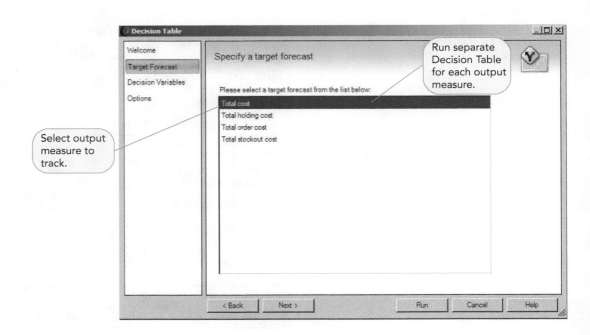

SCREENSHOT 6H
Setting Up Decision
Table in Crystal
Ball—Step 2 of 3

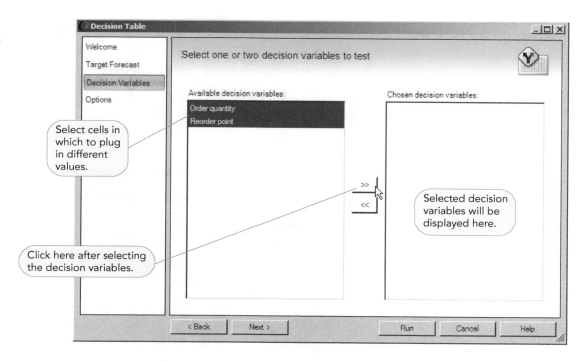

4. Click Next. The window shown in Screenshot 6H is displayed. From the window on the left, select the one or two decision variables (input parameters) whose values you wish to vary. In Simkin's model, these are the order quantity (cell T11) and reorder point (cell T12). Click the button marked >>. The selected decision variables are now displayed in the window on the right.
5. Click Next. The window shown in Screenshot 6I is displayed. Make sure the appropriate number of values are shown for the order quantity (four values) and reorder point (two values). Enter the desired number of replications. Although we have specified 3,000 replications in Screenshot 6I, it is a good idea to run Decision Table with just a few replications first to verify that everything has been set up properly before running it with a larger number. Click Run.

SCREENSHOT 6I **Setting Up Decision Table in Crystal Ball—Step 3 of 3**

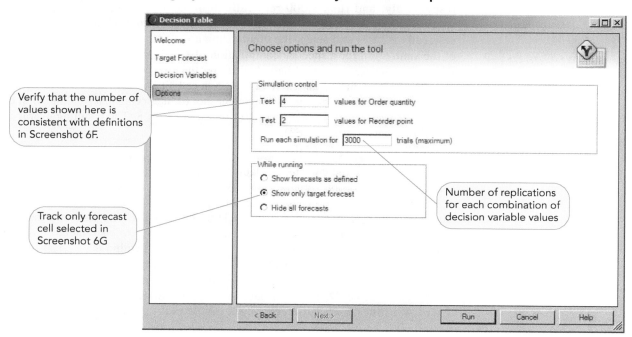

SCREENSHOT 6J **Results from Decision Table in Crystal Ball for Simkin's Hardware Store**

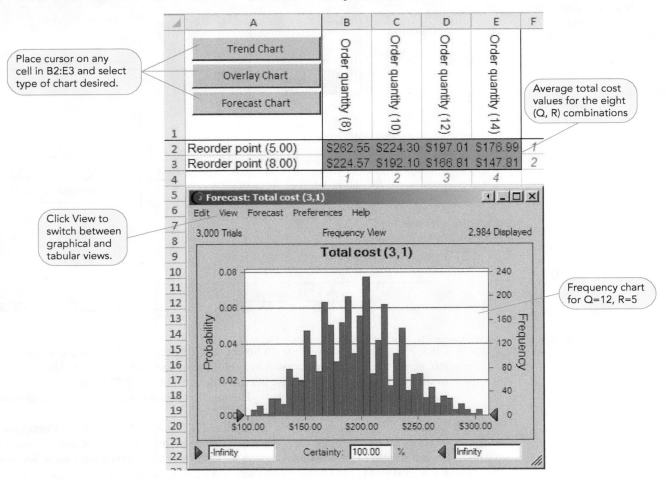

Decision Table plugs in each value of Q and R in cells T11 and T12 (see Screenshot 6A), respectively, and runs 3,000 replications in each case. The results, shown in Screenshot 6J, are displayed in a separate workbook. We can click any of these total cost values (cells B2:E3) and select the charts shown (Trend, Overlay, or Forecast) to see details of the simulation for a specific combination of Q and R values. For example, Screenshot 6J shows the forecast frequency chart obtained for the total cost in cell D2, which corresponds to a Q value of 12 in cell T11 and an R value of 5 in cell T12.

Comparing the average values in Screenshot 6J, it appears that Simkin's best choice, based on 3,000 replications, would be to set $Q = 14$ and $R = 8$. The resulting average total cost is $147.81 per month (see cell E3).

USING THE OPTQUEST PROCEDURE IN CRYSTAL BALL If we are unsure of the specific values we want to try for the decision variables, or if we want to automatically search for the best combination of decision variable values (within preset bounds) that optimizes a defined output measure, we can use a procedure called OptQuest that is included in Crystal Ball. As with the Decision Table procedure, we need to first define our model's forecasts (using the Define Forecast menu command) and decision variables (using the Define Decision menu command). We then run the OptQuest procedure by clicking OptQuest, found within the Crystal Ball tab to get the window shown in Screenshot 6K. We select Objectives from the choices in the left window, and then click Add Objective to specify our desired objective as illustrated in the screenshot.

Next, we select Decision Variables from the choices in the left window to get the Op-tQuest window shown in Screenshot 6L. Note that this window automatically shows the

SCREENSHOT 6K   Setting Up the Objective in Crystal Ball's OptQuest Procedure

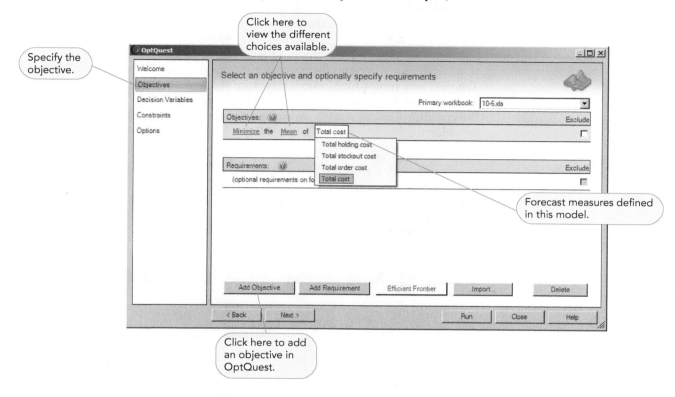

SCREENSHOT 6L   Setting Up the Decision Variables in Crystal Ball's OptQuest Procedure

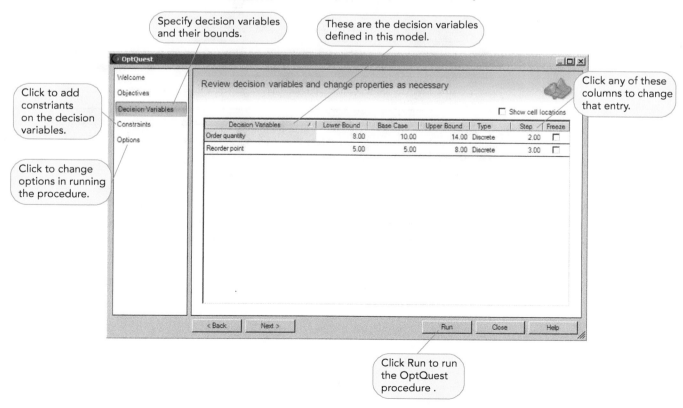

decision variables that have already been defined for this model. We can click on any of the columns (e.g., Lower Bound, Upper Bound, Step, etc.) to modify that parameter. If desired, we can add constraints on the decision variables as well as change the default options in OptQuest.

When we click Run, the procedure automatically tries different possible values for the decision variables and presents the results for the optimal combination of decision variable values. The OptQuest results for Simkin's inventory problem, shown in Screenshot 6M, indicate once again that the best choice, based on 3,000 replications, would be to set $Q = 14$ and $R = 8$. We can click View or Analyze in the results window to see additional results of the OptQuest procedure.

SCREENSHOT 6M   Results Window in Crystal Ball's OptQuest Procedure

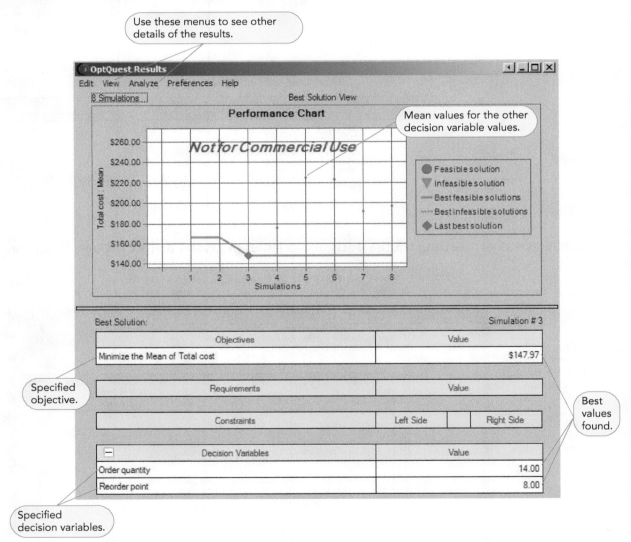

IN ACTION   **Simulating Taco Bell's Restaurant Operation**

Determining how many employees to schedule each 15 minutes to perform each function in a Taco Bell restaurant is a complex and vexing problem. So Taco Bell, the $5 billion giant with 6,500 U.S. and foreign locations, decided to build a simulation model. In selected MODSIM as its software to develop a new labor-management system called LMS.

To develop and use a simulation model, Taco Bell had to collect quite a bit of data. Almost everything that takes place in a restaurant, from customer arrival patterns to the time it takes to wrap a taco, had to be translated into reliable, accurate data. Just as an example, analysts had to conduct time studies and data analysis for every task that is part of preparing every item on the menu.

To the researchers' surprise, the hours devoted to collecting data greatly exceeded those it took to actually build the LMS model.

Inputs to LMS include staffing, such as the number of people and positions. Outputs are performance measures, such as mean time in the system, mean time at the counter, people utilization, and equipment utilization. The model paid off. More than $53 million in labor costs were saved in LMS's first four years of use.

Sources: Based on J. Hueter and W. Swart. "An Integrated Labor-Management System for Taco Bell," *Interfaces* 28, 1 (January–February 1998): 75–91 and L. Pringle. "Productivity Engine," *OR/MS Today* 27, 3 (June 2000): 30.

9   Simulation Model of a Revenue Management Problem Using Crystal Ball

We revisit the Judith's Limousine Service example.

In this section, we illustrate the use of Crystal Ball to simulate the revenue management problem we discussed in section 7. Recall that the problem involves an entrepreneur, Judith McKnew, who is trying to decide how many reservations (10, 11, 12, 13, or 14) she should accept per trip for her 10-passenger airport limousine service. (At this time, we recommend that you refer to section 7 for a quick refresher on this problem and the simulation model we developed for it.)

Setting Up the Model

File: 10-7.xls

The number of people showing up is simulated here using Crystal Ball's CB.Binomial function.

We begin by setting up Judith's model for a specific reservation limit (let's use 14, just as we did in section 7). Notice that the Excel layout in Screenshot 7A is very similar to the one we developed in section 7 for this problem (refer to Screenshot 5A). The only differences are in the formulas used in cells B6 and B9, as follows:

- Cell B6 simulates the number of passengers with reservations who actually show up for the trip. In section 7, we simulated this using Excel's CRITBINOM function. In Crystal Ball, we can simulate this using the CB.BINOMIAL function with parameters $p = 0.8$ (specified in cell G6) and $n =$ number of reservations accepted (cell B5). The formula in cell B6 (refer to Table 7 for details if necessary) is

$$=CB.BINOMIAL(G6,B5)$$

- In cell B9, we simulate the number of walk-up passengers. In section 7, we simulated this using Excel's LOOKUP function. In Crystal Ball, we can simulate this using the custom distribution function. The range of values and probabilities has been specified in cells D15:E17 in Screenshot 7A. The formula in cell B9 is

$$=CB.Custom(D15:E17)$$

The two desired output measures—profit and occupancy rate—are computed in cells B14 and B15, respectively.

We use Decision Table to test different values for the reservation limit.

USING DECISION TABLE TO IDENTIFY THE BEST RESERVATION LIMIT   In Judith's problem, we want to try out five different values (10, 11, 12, 13, and 14) for the reservation limit. To do so using Decision Table in Crystal Ball, we use the following steps, just as we did in section 8 for Simkin's inventory model. Let us run Decision Table to track the profit (cell B14):

1. Specify that Crystal Ball should use the same sequence of random numbers in each case (refer to Screenshot 6E for details).

SCREENSHOT 7A   Excel Layout and Results Using Crystal Ball for Judith's Limousine Service

We want to try different values for this limit.

CB.Binomial function is used to simulate number showing up in cell B6.

Input values for the model

Range for CB.Custom function used to simulate walk-ups in cell B9

Output measures that we want to replicate

Model is same as in Screenshot 5A except for formulas in cells B6 and B9.

B6 = =CB.Binomial(G6,B5)

	A	B	C	D	E	F
1	Judith's Limousine Service (Using *Crystal Ball*)					
2						
3	Judith's reservation limit	14		Van's passenger capacity =		10
4	Reservations requested	11		Minimum reservation request =		7
5	Reservations accepted	11		Maximum reservation request =		14
6	Number show up	8		Probability person shows up		0.80
7	Number overbook	0		Reservation deposit amount =		$10
8	Seats remaining	2		Balance of ticket price =		$25
9	Number walk-up	1		Walk-up ticket price =		$50
10	Walk-up accepted	1		Cost per overbooked person =		$75
11	Total seats occupied	9		Fixed cost per trip =		$100
12	Revenue	$360				
13	Cost	$100		Walk-up Distribution		
14	Profit	$260		Number	Probability	
15	Occupancy rate	90.0%		0	0.30	
16				1	0.45	
17				2	0.25	

We define the forecast cells that we want to track.

2. Select cell B14, which contains the formula for the output measure (i.e., profit) that we want to track. Click Define Forecast, found within the Crystal Ball tab. If desired, specify the name and units of the output measure in the window that is displayed (refer to Screenshot 6B for a sample view of this window). Click OK.

We define the input parameter cells that we want to vary automatically.

3. Select cell B3 (the cell in which you want the reservation limit values to be plugged in). Click Define Decision, found within the Crystal Ball tab. In the window that is displayed (refer to Screenshot 6F for a sample view of this window), enter a lower value of 10 and an upper value of 14. The discrete step size is 1 because we want to study all reservations limits between 10 and 14. Click OK.

4. Click More Tools, found within the Crystal Ball tab, and then select Decision Table from the choices that are presented. Make sure the desired forecast cell (cell B14, in Judith's problem) is shown as the target cell in the window that is displayed. Click Next.

5. Select the decision variable cell (B3) and click the button marked >>> in the window that is displayed. Click Next.

6. In the final window (refer to Screenshot 6I for a sample view of this window), make sure the appropriate number of values is shown for cell B3 (five values in Judith's problem). Enter the desired number of replications (such as 3,000) for each choice. Click Run.

We can see details for any of the simulation results.

Decision Table plugs in each value (i.e., 10 to 14) of the decision variable (reservation limit) in cell B3 (see Screenshot 7A) and runs 3,000 replications in each case. The results, shown in Screenshot 7B, are displayed in a separate workbook. We can click on any of these profit values (in cells B2:F2) and select the charts shown to see details for that simulation. For example, Screenshot 7B shows the tabular summary obtained for the profit when the reservation limit is 11.

Comparing the profit values in Screenshot 7B, it appears that based on 3,000 replications, Judith's best choice would be to accept 12 reservations per trip. The resulting average profit is $226.69 per trip.

At this stage, see if you can set up and run Decision Table to track the occupancy rate (cell B15) for the five reservation limits. For your reference, Screenshot 7C shows a tabular summary of the occupancy rates obtained by running the OptQuest procedure in Crystal Ball (click

SCREENSHOT 7B   Results from Decision Table in Crystal Ball for Judith's Limousine Service

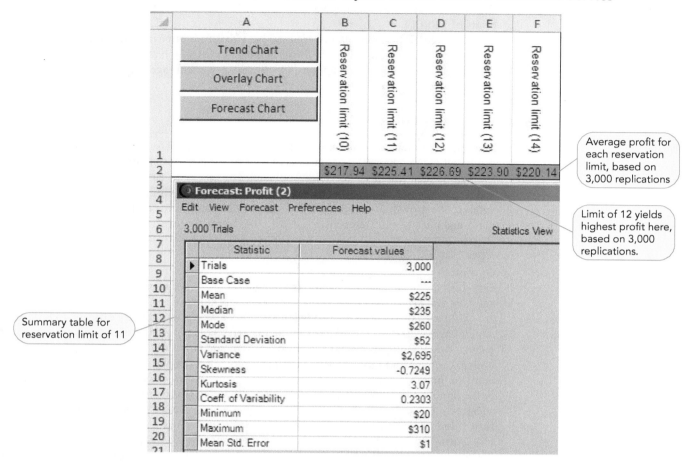

	A	B	C	D	E	F
	Trend Chart	Reservation limit (10)	Reservation limit (11)	Reservation limit (12)	Reservation limit (13)	Reservation limit (14)
	Overlay Chart					
	Forecast Chart					
1						
2		$217.94	$225.41	$226.69	$223.90	$220.14

Average profit for each reservation limit, based on 3,000 replications

Limit of 12 yields highest profit here, based on 3,000 replications.

Forecast: Profit (2)

Edit   View   Forecast   Preferences   Help

3,000 Trials   Statistics View

Summary table for reservation limit of 11

Statistic	Forecast values
Trials	3,000
Base Case	---
Mean	$225
Median	$235
Mode	$260
Standard Deviation	$52
Variance	$2,695
Skewness	-0.7249
Kurtosis	3.07
Coeff. of Variability	0.2303
Minimum	$20
Maximum	$310
Mean Std. Error	$1

SCREENSHOT 7C
Results from OptQuest in Crystal Ball for Judith's Limousine Service

Click View | Solution Analysis to get this table.

OptQuest Results

Edit   View   Analyze   Preferences   Help

5 Total Solutions   Solution Analysis View

Rank	Solution #	Objective Maximize Mean Occupancy rate	Decision Variables Reservation limit
1	5	86.7%	13.00
2	1	86.6%	12.00
3	3	86.4%	14.00
4	4	85.3%	11.00
5	2	81.9%	10.00

Objective specified in OptQuest.

Rank order of the five reservation limits with respect to occupancy rates.

View│Solution Analysis in the OptQuest Results window to get this table). The results seem to indicate that the average occupancy rate does not change appreciably between reservation limits of 12 to 14.

As noted earlier, our intent here is to provide just a brief introduction to Crystal Ball. As you navigate the various menus in the package (some of which are discussed here), you may notice several other choices and options. Once again, we encourage you to try out these procedures on your own.

10   Other Types of Simulation Models

Simulation models are often broken into three categories. The first, the Monte Carlo method discussed in this chapter, uses the concepts of probability distribution and random numbers to evaluate system responses to various policies. The other two categories are operational gaming and systems simulation. Although in theory the three methods are distinctly different from one another, the growth of computerized simulation has tended to create a common basis in procedures and blur these differences.[12]

Operational Gaming

Operational gaming refers to simulation involving two or more competing players. The best examples are military games and business games. Both allow participants to match their management and decision-making skills in hypothetical situations of conflict.

Business simulation games are popular educational tools in many colleges.

Military games are used worldwide to train a nation's top military officers, to test offensive and defensive strategies, and to examine the effectiveness of equipment and armies. Business games, first developed by the firm Booz, Allen, and Hamilton in the 1950s, are popular with both executives and business students. They provide an opportunity to test business skills and decision-making ability in a competitive environment. The person or team that performs best in the simulated environment is rewarded by knowing that his or her company has been most successful in earning the largest profit, grabbing a high market share, or perhaps increasing the firm's trading value on the stock exchange.

During each period of competition, be it a week, month, or quarter, teams respond to market conditions by coding their latest management decisions with respect to inventory, production, financing, investment, marketing, and research. The competitive business environment is simulated using a computer, and a new printout summarizing current market conditions is presented to players. This allows teams to simulate years of operating conditions in a matter of days, weeks, or a semester.

Systems Simulation

Systems simulation is similar to business gaming in that it allows users to test various managerial policies and decisions to evaluate their effect on the operating environment. This variation of simulation models the dynamics of large systems. Such systems are corporate operations,[13] the national economy, a hospital, or a city government system.

In a corporate operating system, sales, production levels, marketing policies, investments, union contracts, utility rates, financing, and other factors are all related in a series of mathematical equations that are examined through simulation. In a simulation of an urban government, systems simulation could be employed to evaluate the impact of tax increases, capital expenditures for roads and buildings, housing availability, new garbage routes, immigration and outmigration, locations of new schools or senior citizen centers, birth and death rates, and many more vital issues. Simulations of *economic systems*, often called *econometric* models, are used by government agencies, bankers, and large organizations to predict inflation rates, domestic and foreign money supplies, and unemployment levels. Inputs and outputs of a typical economic system simulation are illustrated in Figure 3.

---

[12] Theoretically, random numbers are used only in Monte Carlo simulation. However, in some complex gaming or systems simulation problems in which relationships cannot be defined exactly, it may be necessary to use the probability concepts of the Monte Carlo method.

[13] This is sometimes referred to as *industrial dynamics*, a term coined by Jay Forrester. Forrester's goal was to find a way "to show how policies, decisions, structure, and delays are interrelated to influence growth and stability" in industrial systems. See J. W. Forrester. *Industrial Dynamics*. Cambridge, MA: MIT Press, 1961.

FIGURE 3

Inputs and Outputs of a Typical Economic System Simulation

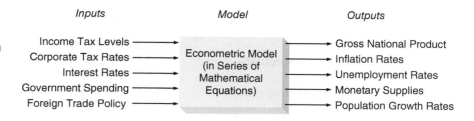

Econometric models are huge simulations involving thousands of regression equations tied together by economic factors. They use what-if questions to test various policies.

The value of systems simulation lies in its allowance of what-if questions to test the effects of various policies. A corporate planning group, for example, can change the value of any input, such as an advertising budget, and examine the impact on sales, market share, or short-term costs. Simulation can also be used to evaluate different research and development projects or to determine long-range planning horizons.

Summary

This chapter discusses the concept and approach of simulation as a problem-solving tool. Simulation involves building a mathematical model that attempts to describe a real-world situation. The model's goal is to incorporate important variables and their interrelationships in such a way that we can study the impact of managerial changes on the total system. The approach has many advantages over other decision modeling techniques and is especially useful when a problem is too complex or difficult to solve by other means.

The Monte Carlo method of simulation uses random numbers to generate random variable values from probability distributions. The simulation procedure is conducted for many time periods to evaluate the long-term impact of each policy value being studied.

We first illustrate how to set up Monte Carlo simulations by using Excel's built-in functions. We also show how Excel's Data Table can be used to run several replications of simulation models and how Scenario Manager can be used to try different values for input parameters. Then, we show how Crystal Ball, an Excel add-in for simulation, can be used to develop and run simulation models. The major advantages of using add-ins are (1) the availability of easy formulas for many common probability distributions, (2) the ability to quickly set up and run many replications of the model, and (3) the ability to easily collect statistical information on many different output measure.

We conclude this chapter with a brief discussion of operational gaming and systems simulation, two other categories of simulation.

Glossary

CRITBINOM   An Excel function that can be used to randomly generate values from binomial probability distributions. Excel 2010 includes an improved version of this function, called BINOM.INV.

Crystal Ball   An add-in for Excel that simplifies the implementation and solution of simulation models.

Data Table   A procedure in Excel that allows simulation models to be replicated several times.

Decision Table   A procedure in Crystal Ball that is used to automatically try different values for a decision variable in the simulation model.

Discrete-Event Simulation   A simulation model in which we need to keep track of the passage of time by using a simulation clock.

Discrete General Distribution   A distribution in which a variable can take on one of several discrete values, each with its own probability.

Flow Diagram, or Flowchart   A graphical means of presenting the logic of a simulation model. It is a tool that helps in writing a simulation computer program.

LOOKUP   An Excel function that can be used to randomly generate values from discrete general probability distributions.

Monte Carlo simulation   A simulation that experiments with probabilistic elements of a system by generating random numbers to create values for those elements.

NORMINV   An Excel function that can be used to randomly generate values from normal probability distributions.

Operational Gaming   The use of simulation in competitive situations such as military games and business or management games.

OptQuest   A procedure in Crystal Ball that is used to automatically identify the best combination of values for decision variables that optimizes a desired output measure in the simulation model.

RAND   An Excel function that generates a random number between 0 and 1 each time it is computed.

RANDBETWEEN   An Excel function that can be used to randomly generate values from discrete uniform probability distributions.

Random Number   A number (typically between zero and one in most computer programs) whose value is selected completely at random.

Replication   A single run of a simulation model. Also known as a *run* or *trial*.

Simulation   A technique that involves building a mathematical model to represent a real-world situation. The model is then experimented with to estimate the effects of various actions and decisions.

Systems Simulation   A simulation model that deals with the dynamics of large organizational or governmental systems.

Solved Problems

Solved Problem 1

Higgins Plumbing and Heating maintains a supply of eight water heaters in any given week. Owner Jerry Higgins likes the idea of having this large supply on hand to meet customer demand but also recognizes that it is expensive to do so. He examines water heater sales over the past 50 weeks and notes the following data:

WATER HEATER SALES PER WEEK	NUMBER OF WEEKS THIS NUMBER WAS SOLD
4	6
5	5
6	9
7	12
8	8
9	7
10	3

a. Set up a model to simulate Higgins' weekly sales over a 2-year (104-week) period and compute the following measures (based on a single replication):

- Average weekly sales
- Number of weeks with stockouts over a two-year period

Replicate your model 200 times, using Data Table, to determine the (1) average weekly sales and (2) probability that Higgins will have more than 20 weeks with stockouts over a 2-year period.

b. Use the probability distribution for sales to determine the expected value of sales. Explain any differences between this value and the average value computed using Data Table in part (a).

File: 10-8.xls

Solution

The Excel layout to answer all the questions in this problem is presented in Screenshot 8. The spreadsheet is organized as follows:

- Column A shows the week number.
- We use a LOOKUP function to simulate the weekly sales in column B. The parameters (random number intervals, sales, and probabilities) for the LOOKUP function are shown in cells E4:H10.
- In column C, we use an IF function to determine the occurrence of a stockout ($0 = $ no stockout, $1 = $ stockout). For example, the formula in cell C4 is $=IF(B4>\$H\$12,1,0)$.

a. The average sales over the 2-year period is the average of the sales values in cells B4:B107. This value, shown in cell H16 in Screenshot 8, is 7.14 units per week. Next, we can add the 104 stockout indicators in cells C4:C107 to determine the number of

SCREENSHOT 8   **Excel Layout and Results for Higgins Plumbing and Heating**

Parameters for LOOKUP function used to simulate sales

	A	B	C	D	E	F	G	H	I	J	K	L
1	**Higgins Plumbing and Heating**									**Data Table**		
2						Sales Distribution						
3	Week	Sales	Stockout? (1 = Yes)		Sales	Prob-ability	RN intvl lower limit	RN intvl upper limit		Run	Avg sales	Stockout weeks
4	1	8	0		4	0.12	0.00	0.12		1	7.14	24
5	2	8	0		5	0.10	0.12	0.22		2	6.81	21
6	3	4	0		6	0.18	0.22	0.40		3	7.14	23
7	4	9	1		7	0.24	0.40	0.64		4	6.94	22
8	5	6	0		8	0.16	0.64	0.80		5	6.75	21
9	6	7	0		9	0.14	0.80	0.94		6	6.88	23
10	7	8	0		10	0.06	0.94	1.00		7	6.83	21
11	8	7	0							8	7.03	23
12	9	7	0		Supply each week =			8		9	6.84	17
13	10	7	0							10	6.76	23
14	11	9	1		(a)					11	6.76	18
15	12	9	1		Based on 1 replication:					12	6.76	21
16	13	8	0		Average sales =			7.14		13	6.95	23
17	14	9	1		No. of stockout weeks =			24		14	6.80	18
18	15	8	0							15	6.77	21
19	16	8	0		Based on 200 replications:					16	7.12	25
20	17	9	1		Average sales =			6.90		17	6.93	20
21	18	9	1		P(>20 stockout weeks) =			54.5%		18	6.77	22
22	19	7	0							19	7.01	20
23	20	9	1		(b)					20	6.65	19
24	21	8	0		Expected sales =			6.88		21	6.95	27
25	22	7	0							22	6.88	20
106	103	7	0							103	6.99	22
107	104	6	0							104	6.92	26
108										105	7.08	21
202										199	6.84	19
203										200	6.94	23

=H16

=H17

Hidden rows

COUNTIF function is used to count number of weeks with >20 stockouts.

Data Table used to replicate both output measures 200 times each.

stockouts over the 2-year period. This value, shown in cell H17, is 24 stockout weeks. (Remember that these values will change each time you recalculate the model.)

We now set up Data Table to run 200 replications of the values in cells H16 and H17. The table is shown in columns J to L in Screenshot 8. From the 200 replicated values in cells K4:K203, we compute the average sales to be 6.90 units per week (shown in cell H20). We then use Excel's COUNTIF function on the 200 replicated values in cells L4:L203 to compute the probability that Higgins will have more than 20 weeks with stockouts over a 2-year period. The formula used is =COUNTIF(L4:L203,">20")/200. The value, shown in cell H21, indicates that there is a 54.5% chance that this event will occur.

b. Using expected values, we find the following:

$$\text{Expected heater sales} = 0.12 \times 4 + 0.10 \times 5 + 0.18 \times 6 + 0.24 \times 7$$
$$+ 0.16 \times 8 + 0.14 \times 9 + 0.06 \times 10$$

$$= 6.88 \text{ heaters}$$

We can compute this value by using the following formula:

$$=\text{SUMPRODUCT(E4:E10,F4:F10)}$$

This value is shown in cell H24 in Screenshot 8. The simulated average (6.90 in Screenshot 8) is based on just 200 replications of the model. Hence, although this value is close to the expected value of 6.88, the two values need not necessarily be the same. With a longer simulation, the two values will become even closer.

Solved Problem 2

Norris Medical Clinic is staffed by a single physician who, on average, requires 15 minutes to treat a patient. The distribution of this service time follows a truncated normal distribution with a standard deviation of 4 minutes and a minimum value of 5 minutes. Patients arrive at an average rate of 2.5 customers per hour, according to the exponential distribution. Simulate 100 patient arrivals and replicate the model 200 times, using Data Table, to answer the following questions:

a. What percentage of time is the queue empty?
b. How many patients, on average, are in the queue?
c. What is the average wait time per patient in the queue?

Solution

File: 10-9.xls

This is an example of a discrete-event simulation model. The model simulates a queuing system in which arrival times follow an exponential distribution and service times follow a normal distribution. Each replication of the model corresponds to the arrival and service of 100 patients at the clinic. The Excel layout for this problem is presented in Screenshot 9.

SCREENSHOT 9   Excel Layout and Results for Norris Medical Clinic

Simulated using LN function

Simulated using NORMINV function. Set to minimum of 5 minutes.

=K15 =K16 =K17

Pati-ent #	Time between arrivals	Arrival time	Start service	Service time	End service	Wait time	Queue length			Data Table			
									Run	% empty queue	Avg # patients	Avg wait time
0	0.0	0	0	0.0	0	0	0		1	0.21	1.90	23.71
1	4.0	4.0	4.0	18.0	22.0	0.0	0		2	0.22	2.32	30.05
2	49.6	53.5	53.5	6.2	59.7	0.0	0		3	0.46	0.66	5.50
3	5.1	58.7	59.7	20.7	80.5	1.1	1		4	0.51	0.87	9.72
4	8.0	66.7	80.5	13.8	94.3	13.8	1		5	0.41	1.17	13.39
5	6.9	73.6	94.3	21.0	115.3	20.7	2		6	0.45	0.72	6.21
6	5.0	78.6	115.3	17.1	132.4	36.7	3		7	0.53	0.65	6.71
7	41.7	120.3	132.4	14.6	146.9	12.1	1		8	0.37	0.90	9.55
8	8.5	128.8	146.9	15.8	162.8	18.2	2		9	0.51	0.70	6.60
9	28.7	157.4	162.8	16.4	179.2	5.4	1		10	0.29	1.48	17.16
10	12.6	170.0	179.2	16.4	195.6	9.2	1		11	0.34	1.01	11.13
11	3.5	173.5	195.6	17.9	213.5	22.1	2		12	0.54	0.53	4.36
12	90.5	264.0	264.0	17.8	281.8	0.0	0		13	0.43	0.95	10.83
13	36.2	300.2	300.2	10.4	310.7	0.0	0		14	0.42	1.05	12.79
14	2.0	302.2	310.7	16.8	327.5	8.5	1		15	0.30	1.71	20.56
15	1.9	304.1	327.5	18.3	345.8	23.4	2		16	0.40	0.90	9.31
16	20.9	325.0	345.8	13.5	359.3	20.8	2		17	0.38	1.03	11.20
17	1.9	326.9	359.3	13.9	373.3	32.4	3		18	0.41	0.86	8.82
18	19.2	346.1	373.3	18.7	392.0	27.1	2		19	0.38	1.13	12.94
19	15.5	361.6	392.0	12.0	404.0	30.3	2		20	0.37	0.88	8.15
20	19.7	381.3	404.0	12.2	416.2	22.7	2		21	0.41	1.03	11.35
99	24.6	1965.7	2054.4	17.1	2,071.4	88.6	6		100	0.40	1.30	15.94
100	1.3	1967.0	2071.4	14.1	2,085.6	104.4	7		101	0.46	0.77	7.55
									102	0.51	0.85	10.72
									103	0.37	1.01	10.12
									199	0.23	2.62	35.11
									200	0.30	1.49	16.96

Norris Medical Clinic

Arrival Distribution	
Exponential	
Average arrival rate (per hour)	2.5

Service Time Distribution	
Normal	
Mean service time (minutes)	15
Std dev of service time (minutes)	4
Minimum service time (minutes)	5

Based on 1 replication:	
Percent of time the queue is empty =	21.0%
Average number of patients in the queue =	1.90
Average wait time per patient in the queue =	23.71

Based on 200 replications:	
Percent of time the queue is empty =	38.7%
Average number of patients in the queue =	1.13
Average wait time per patient in the queue =	12.66

Hidden rows

= Start time + Service time

Summary results from Data Table

Data Table used to replicate all three output measures 200 times each.

We have included patient number 0, with zero values for all columns, to *initialize* the simulation clock that keeps track of the passage of time. Rows 5 through 104 in the spreadsheet are organized as follows:

- Column A shows the patient number (1 through 100).
- Column B shows the time between arrivals of successive patients, simulated from an exponential distribution by using the LN function. From Table 4, the Excel formula is $=-(1/\mu)*LN(RAND())$. Note that the average arrival rate, μ, in this case is 2.5 patients per hour. However, because all other times in this problem are counted in minutes, we convert the interarrival time between successive patients to minutes also. The formula in cells B5:B104 is therefore

$$=-60*(1/\$K\$6)*(LN(RAND()))$$

- In column C, we calculate the arrival time of the current patient as the sum of the arrival time of the previous patient and the time between arrivals (column B). For example, the formula in cell C5 is

$$=C4+B5$$

- The time this patient actually starts service is calculated in column D as the maximum of the arrival time and the time the previous patient finishes service. For example, the formula in cell D5 is

$$=MAX(C5,F4)$$

- Column E shows the service time for this patient, simulated using a NORMINV function. The parameters of this NORMINV function are shown in cells K10:K11. We use a MAX function to ensure that the minimum service time per patient is 5 minutes. The formula in cells E5:E104 is

$$=MAX(\$K\$12,NORMINV(RAND(),\$K\$10,\$K\$11))$$

- The time at which this patient ends service is shown in column F as the sum of the start time (shown in column D) and the service time (shown in column E).
- In column G, we calculate the wait time of this patient as the difference between the patient's start time (shown in column D) and arrival time (shown in column C).
- Finally, in column H, we calculate the queue length, using Excel's MATCH function. For example, the formula in cell H5 is

$$=A5-MATCH(C5,\$D\$5:D5,1)$$

Using the 100 wait time and queue length values in cells G5:H104, we determine the following three performance measures for the queuing system each day:

a. Percentage of time the queue is empty (cell K15) $=COUNTIF(H5:H104,"=0")/100 = 21\%$

b. Average number of patients in the queue (cell K16) $=AVERAGE(H5:H104) = 1.90$

c. Average wait time per patient in the queue (cell K17) $=AVERAGE(G5:G104) = 23.71$ minutes

The values in cells K15:K17 represent results from just one replication of the model. To determine more precise values for these measures, we now replicate all three measures 200 times each. The Data Table procedure to do so is shown in columns M through P in Screenshot 9. Based on the 200 replicated values in this Data Table procedure, the queue at the clinic is empty 36.7% of the time, there are 1.13 patients on average in the queue at any time, and each patient in the queue waits for an average of 12.66 minutes.

Solved Problem 3

Heartbreak Hotel routinely experiences no-shows (people who make reservations for a room and don't show up) during the peak season when the hotel is always full. No-shows follow the distribution shown in the following table:

NO-SHOWS	PROBABILITY
0	0.10
1	0.13
2	0.31
3	0.16
4	0.21
5	0.09

To reduce the number of vacant rooms, the hotel overbooks three rooms; that is, the hotel accepts three more reservations than the number of rooms available. On a day when the hotel experiences fewer than three no-shows, there are not enough rooms for those who have reservations. The hotel's policy is to send these guests to a competing hotel down the street, at Heartbreak's expense of $125. If the number of no-shows is more than three, the hotel has vacant rooms, resulting in an opportunity cost of $50 per room.

a. Simulate 1 month (30 days) of operation to calculate the hotel's total monthly cost due to overbooking and opportunity loss. Replicate this cost 200 times to compute the average monthly cost.

b. Heartbreak Hotel would like to determine the most desirable number of rooms to overbook. Of these six choices—0, 1, 2, 3, 4, or 5 rooms—what is your recommendation? Why?

Solution

File: 10-10.xls, sheet: 10-10A

This is an example of a revenue management problem where the number of no-shows follows a discrete general distribution. Each replication of the simulation model corresponds to 30 days of operations at the hotel. The Excel layout for this model is presented in Screenshot 10A. The spreadsheet is organized as follows:

- Column A shows the day number (1 through 30).
- In column B, we use a LOOKUP function to simulate the number of no-shows. The parameters for this LOOKUP function are shown in cells I4:L9.
- In column C, we compute the number of short rooms (i.e., rooms that are unavailable for guests) by comparing the number of no-shows with the number of rooms we decide to overbook (shown in cell K11). For example, the formula in cell C4 is

$$=MAX(\$K\$11-B4,0)$$

- Short cost in column D = $K$13 × column C.
- In column E, we compute the number of vacant rooms by once again comparing the number of no-shows with the number of rooms we decide to overbook (shown in cell K11). For example, the formula in cell E4 is

$$=MAX(B4-\$K11,0)$$

- Vacant cost in column F = $K$14 × column E.
- Total cost in column G = column D + column E.

SCREENSHOT 10A Excel Layout and Results for Heartbreak Hotel

Parameters for LOOKUP function in column B

Day	No-shows	Short rooms	Short cost	Vacant rooms	Vacant cost	Total cost
1	5	0	$0.00	2	$100.00	$100.00
2	4	0	$0.00	1	$50.00	$50.00
3	4	0	$0.00	1	$50.00	$50.00
4	2	1	$125.00	0	$0.00	$125.00
5	1	2	$250.00	0	$0.00	$250.00
6	4	0	$0.00	1	$50.00	$50.00
7	1	2	$250.00	0	$0.00	$250.00
8	3	0	$0.00	0	$0.00	$0.00
9	2	1	$125.00	0	$0.00	$125.00
10	2	1	$125.00	0	$0.00	$125.00
11	5	0	$0.00	2	$100.00	$100.00
12	1	2	$250.00	0	$0.00	$250.00
13	2	1	$125.00	0	$0.00	$125.00
14	5	0	$0.00	2	$100.00	$100.00
15	2	1	$125.00	0	$0.00	$125.00
16	3	0	$0.00	0	$0.00	$0.00
17	0	3	$375.00	0	$0.00	$375.00
18	2	1	$125.00	0	$0.00	$125.00
19	4	0	$0.00	1	$50.00	$50.00
20	2	1	$125.00	0	$0.00	$125.00
21	1	2	$250.00	0	$0.00	$250.00
22	2	1	$125.00	0	$0.00	$125.00
23	4	0	$0.00	1	$50.00	$50.00
24	0	3	$375.00	0	$0.00	$375.00
25	5	0	$0.00	2	$100.00	$100.00
26	3	0	$0.00	0	$0.00	$0.00
27	1	2	$250.00	0	$0.00	$250.00
28	0	3	$375.00	0	$0.00	$375.00
29	4	0	$0.00	1	$50.00	$50.00
30	2	1	$125.00	0	$0.00	$125.00

No-Shows Distribution

No-shows	Probability	RN intvl lower limit	RN intvl upper limit
0	0.10	0.00	0.10
1	0.13	0.10	0.23
2	0.31	0.23	0.54
3	0.16	0.54	0.70
4	0.21	0.70	0.91
5	0.09	0.91	1.00

Rooms overbooked	3

| Cost per room short | $125 |
| Cost per room vacant | $50 |

| Based on 1 replication: | |
| Average daily cost = | $140.00 |

| Based on 200 replications: | |
| Average daily cost = | $130.35 |

Data Table

Run	Cost
1	$140.00
2	$122.50
3	$94.17
4	$140.00
5	$101.67
6	$103.33
7	$79.17
8	$135.83
9	$104.17
10	$125.00
11	$108.33
12	$126.67
13	$142.50
14	$137.50
15	$115.00
16	$134.17
17	$94.17
18	$100.00
19	$133.33
20	$134.17
21	$143.33
22	$120.83
23	$152.50
24	$131.67
25	$121.67
26	$125.83
27	$140.83
28	$145.00
29	$109.17
30	$129.17
31	$148.33
199	$141.67
200	$154.17

=K17

We want to try different values here.

Simulated using LOOKUP function

Total cost is sum of short cost and vacant cost.

a. The average total cost of $140 per day shown in cell K17 is based on only 1 replication. Hence, to get a more precise estimate of this average, we replicate this measure by using Data Table, as shown in column N and O in Screenshot 10A. Based on 200 replications, the average total cost at Heartbreak Hotel appears to be $130.35 per day (shown in cell K20).

b. To determine the number of rooms that Heartbreak Hotel should overbook each day, we set up Scenario Manager to automatically try the six choices—0, 1, 2, 3, 4, and 5. For each scenario, cell K11 is the changing cell and cell K20 is the result cell. The results of the Scenario Manager procedure, shown in Screenshot 10B, indicate that Heartbreak Hotel should overbook two rooms each day. The total cost of $83.55 at this level is the lowest among all scenarios.

411

SCREENSHOT 10B   Scenario Manager Results for Heartbreak Hotel

Changing cell is the number of rooms overbooked.

⊿	A	B	C	D	E	F	G	H	I	J
1										
2	Scenario Summary									
3				Current Values	OB0	OB1	OB2	OB3	OB4	OB5
5	Changing Cells:									
6	$K$11			3	0	1	2	3	4	5
7	Result Cells:									
8	$K$20			$128.42	$125.79	$93.38	$83.55	$128.30	$204.38	$304.69
9	Notes: Current Values column represents values of changing cells at									
10	time Scenario Summary Report was created. Changing cells for each									
11	scenario are highlighted in gray.									

Result cell is the total cost.

Overbooking two rooms yields the lowest total cost.

Different values we want to try for the number of rooms overbooked

Solved Problem 4

General Foundry, Inc., a metalworks plant in Milwaukee, has long been trying to avoid the expense of installing air pollution control equipment. The local environmental protection agency (EPA) has recently given the foundry 16 weeks to install a complex air filter system on its main smokestack. General Foundry has been warned that it may be forced to close unless the device is installed in the allotted period. Lester Harky, the managing partner, wants to make sure that installation of the filtering system progresses smoothly and on time. General Foundry has identified the eight activities that need to be performed in order for the project to be completed. For each activity, the following table shows the immediate predecessors and three times estimates—optimistic, most likely, and pessimistic:

ACTIVITY	DESCRIPTION	IMMEDIATE PREDECESSORS	OPTIMISTIC TIME (a)	MOST LIKELY TIME (m)	PESSIMISTIC TIME (b)
A	Build internal components	—	1	2	3
B	Modify roof and floor	—	2	3	4
C	Construct collection stack	A	1	2	3
D	Pour concrete and install frame	A, B	2	4	6
E	Build high-temperature burner	C	1	4	7
F	Install pollution control system	C	1	2	9
G	Install air pollution device	D, E	3	4	11
H	Inspect and test	F, G	1	2	3

Lester wants to find the probability that the project will meet the EPA's 16-week deadline. Round off all activity times to two decimal places.[14]

---

[14] Current versions of Crystal Ball include a function called CB.BetaPert that can be used to simulate activity times using a beta distribution and the three time estimates. Prior versions did not include this function and the easy option there is to use a triangular distribution, which also uses three time estimates and is commonly used to model project activity times.

FIGURE 4   Project Network for General Foundry

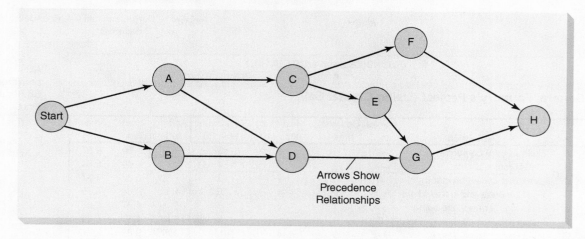

Arrows Show
Precedence
Relationships

Solution

This is an example of analyzing uncertainty in a project management problem. A popular way to analyze uncertainty in projects is by using simulation. Let us simulate General Foundry's project here.

It is convenient to first express the activities in the project as a project network. We show this in Figure 4, where the nodes represent the activities and the arcs represent the precedence relationships between activities.

The Excel layout for this simulation model is presented in Screenshot 11. The spreadsheet is organized as follows:

- Columns A through F show the name, description, immediate predecessors, and three time estimates for each activity (activities A through H).

- In column G, we simulate the actual duration of each activity by using the CB.BetaPert function in Crystal Ball. We then round this value to two decimal places, using the ROUND function. For example, the formula in cell G4 is

$$=\text{ROUND(CB.BetaPert(D4,E4,F4),2)}$$

- In column H, we calculate the actual start time for each activity. In computing this time, we need to ensure that all predecessors for an activity have been completed before that activity can begin. For example, both activities A and B have to finish before activity D can start. Hence, the start time for activity D is set equal to the maximum of the finish times of activities A and B. That is, the formula in cell H7 is

$$=\text{MAX(I4,I5)}$$

- In column I, we compute the finish time of each activity as the sum of the start time of that activity (column H) and the actual duration of that activity (column G).

In General Foundry's project, the project completion time is the completion time of activity H, shown in cell I11. Based on the single replication shown in Screenshot 11, it appears that the project will finish in only 15.26 weeks. However, in order to get a more precise value of this output measure, we use Crystal Ball to replicate the model 3,000 times. Cell I11 is defined as the forecast cell.

SCREENSHOT 11 Excel Layout and Results Using Crystal Ball for General Foundry

Formula in cell G4. Rounded off to 2 decimals using the ROUND function.

| G4 | fx =ROUND(CB.BetaPert(D4,E4,F4),2) |

Activity times simulated using CB.BetaPert function.

	A	B	C	D	E	F	G	H	I
1	**General Foundry's Project (Using Crystal Ball)**								
2									
3	Activity	Description	Immed. pred.	Optimistic time (a)	Most likely time (m)	Pessimistic time (b)	Activity time	Start time	Finish time
4	A	Build internal components	—	1	2	3	2.07	0.00	2.07
5	B	Modify roof and floor	—	2	3	4	2.64	0.00	2.64
6	C	Construct collection stack	A	1	2	3	2.30	2.07	4.37
7	D	Pour concrete and install frame	A, B	2	4	6	4.15	2.64	6.79
8	E	Build high-temperature burner	C	1	4	7	5.48	4.37	9.85
9	F	Install pollution control system	C	1	2	9	1.81	4.37	6.18
10	G	Install air pollution device	D, E	3	4	11	3.07	9.85	12.92
11	H	Inspect and test	F, G	1	2	3	2.34	12.92	15.26

= Start time + Activity time

Start time of an activity must satisfy all precedence relationships.

Forecast: Project completion time

Frequency chart based on 3,000 replications.

Edit View Forecast Preferences Help

3,000 Trials   Frequency View   2,991 Displayed

Project completion time

Not for Commercial Use

Mean = 15.20

Certainty: 70.03 %   -Infinity   16.00

Project has 70.03% chance of meeting deadline.

Upper limit changed to 16 to show P(completion time) ≤ 16

The frequency chart obtained from Crystal Ball is also shown in Screenshot 11. Based on this chart, it appears that the average completion time of the project is 15.20 weeks. (To show the mean, click on the graph to get an options window where you can enable this feature.) More importantly for General Foundry, the chart indicates that there is a 70.03% chance that the project will finish in less than 16 weeks.

Discussion Questions and Problems

Discussion Questions

1 What are the advantages and limitations of simulation models?

2 Why might a manager be forced to use simulation instead of an analytical model in dealing with a problem of
   (a) inventory ordering policy?
   (b) ships docking in a port to unload?
   (c) bank teller service windows?
   (d) the U.S. economy?

3 What types of management problems can be solved more easily by using decision modeling techniques other than simulation?

4 What are the major steps in the simulation process?

5 What is Monte Carlo simulation? What principles underlie its use, and what steps are followed in applying it?

6 Why is a computer necessary in conducting a real-world simulation?

7 What is operational gaming? What is systems simulation? Give examples of how each may be applied.

8 Do you think the application of simulation will increase strongly in the next 10 years? Why or why not?

9 Would the average output value in a simulation problem change appreciably if a longer period were simulated? Why or why not?

10 How might drawing a flow diagram help in developing a simulation model?

11 List the advantages of using an Excel add-in program rather than using Excel's built-in functions to develop a simulation model.

12 What does Scenario Manager allow you to accomplish in an Excel-based simulation model?

13 Do you think we can use Excel's Solver to solve simulation models? Why or why not?

Problems

Notes:

- *Simulation models for all the following problems can be set up by using Excel.*

- *Wherever necessary, replications can be done either using Data Table or using Crystal Ball.*

- *In all problems, we have specified the number of replications to use simply as **N**. Your instructor may specify the actual value of **N** that he or she wants you to use. If not, we recommend that you try to replicate each simulation model as many times as is convenient. If you are using Data Table, 200 to 300 replications should be appropriate to keep the computation time*

reasonable and the resulting Excel file relatively small (even though the average values may vary from simulation to simulation). However, if you are using Crystal Ball, you should try 3,000 or more replications.

- *Wherever a decision is involved, you can use Scenario Manager in Excel and Decision Table or OptQuest if you are using Crystal Ball.*

14 Weekly demand for tennis balls at The Racquet Club is normally distributed, with a mean of 35 cases and a standard deviation of 5 cases. The club gets a profit of $50 per case.
   (a) Simulate 52 weeks of demand and calculate the average weekly profit. Make all demand values integers in your model.
   (b) What is the probability that weekly profit will be $2,000 or more?

15 Edward Owen is responsible for the maintenance, rental, and day-to-day operation of several large apartment complexes on the upper-east side of New York City. Owen is especially concerned about the cost projections for replacing air conditioner (A/C) compressors. He would like to simulate the number of A/C failures each month. Using data from similar apartment buildings he manages in a New York City suburb, Clark establishes the probability of failures during a month as follows:

NUMBER OF A/C FAILURES	PROBABILITY
0	0.10
1	0.17
2	0.21
3	0.28
4	0.16
5	0.07
6	0.01

   (a) Simulate Owen's monthly A/C failures for a period of three years. Compute the average number of failures per month.
   (b) Explain any difference between the simulated average failures and the expected value of failures computed by using the probability distribution.

16 Jay's Appliances sells micro-fridges according to the monthly demand distribution shown in the table at the top of the next page. Simulate 6 years of demand and compare theoretical and simulated results for the following measures:
   (a) Average demand.
   (b) Probability that demand will be less than or equal to 30 micro-fridges.

Table for Problem 16

DEMAND	PROBABILITY
10	0.02
15	0.07
20	0.11
25	0.12
30	0.21
35	0.18
40	0.21
45	0.06
50	0.02

17 Shawn Bishop, a neuroscience PhD student at Clarksville University, has been having problems balancing his checkbook. His monthly income is derived from a graduate research assistantship; however, he also makes extra money in most months by tutoring undergraduates in their introductory neurobiology course. His chances of various income levels are shown here (assume that this income is received at the beginning of each month):

MONTHLY INCOME	PROBABILITY
$ 850	0.35
$ 900	0.25
$ 950	0.25
$1,000	0.15

Bishop has expenditures that vary from month to month, and he estimates that they will follow this distribution:

MONTHLY EXPENSES	PROBABILITY
$ 800	0.05
$ 900	0.20
$1,000	0.40
$1,100	0.35

Bishop begins his final year with $1,500 in his checking account. Simulate the cash flow for 12 months and replicate your model N times to identify Bishop's (a) ending balance at the end of the year and (b) probability that he will have a negative balance in any month.

18 Chelsea Truman sells celebrity magazines on Sunday morning in an area surrounded by three busy shopping centers. Demand for the magazines is distributed as shown in the following table:

DEMAND	PROBABILITY
50	0.05
75	0.10
100	0.25
125	0.30
150	0.20
175	0.10

Chelsea has decided to order 100 magazines from her supplier. Chelsea pays $2 for each magazine she orders and sells each magazine for $3. Unsold magazines can be returned to the supplier for $0.75.

(a) Simulate 1 year (52 Sundays) of operation to calculate Chelsea's total yearly profit. Replicate this calculation N times. What is the average yearly profit?

(b) Chelsea would like to investigate the profitability of ordering 50, 100, 150, and 175 magazines at the start of each Sunday. Which order quantity would you recommend? Why?

19 The Paris Bakery has decided to bake 30 batches of its famous beignets at the beginning of the day. The store has determined that daily demand will follow the distribution shown in the following table:

DAILY DEMAND	PROBABILITY
15	0.08
20	0.12
25	0.25
30	0.20
35	0.20
40	0.15

Each batch costs the Paris Bakery $50 and can be sold for $100. The Paris Bakery can sell any unsold batches for $25 the next day.

(a) Simulate 1 month (25 days) of operation to calculate the bakery's total monthly profit. Replicate this calculation N times to compute the average total monthly profit.

(b) The Paris Bakery would like to investigate the profitability of baking 25, 30, 35, or 40 batches at the start of the day. Which quantity would you recommend? Why?

20 Lionel's Life Jacket Rentals leases life jackets each day from a supplier and rents them to customers who use them when they raft down the Delaware River. Each day, Lionel leases 30 life jackets from his supplier, at a cost of $4 per life jacket. He rents them to his customers for $15 per day. Rental demand follows the normal distribution, with a mean of 30 life

jackets and a standard deviation of 6 life jackets. (In your model use integers for all demands.)

(a) Simulate this leasing policy for a month (30 days) of operation to calculate the total monthly profit. Replicate this calculation N times. What is the average monthly profit?

(b) Lionel would like to evaluate the average monthly profit if he leases 25, 30, 35, and 40 life jackets. What is your recommendation? Why?

21 Kirkpatrick Aircrafts operates a large number of computerized plotting machines. For the most part, the plotting devices are used to create line drawings of complex wing airfoils and fuselage part dimensions. The engineers operating the automated plotters are called loft lines engineers.

The computerized plotters consist of a mini-computer system connected to a 4- by 5-foot flat table with a series of ink pens suspended above it. When a sheet of clear plastic or paper is properly placed on the table, the computer directs a series of horizontal and vertical pen movements until the desired figure is drawn.

The plotting machines are highly reliable, with the exception of the four sophisticated ink pens that are built in. The pens constantly clog and jam in a raised or lowered position. When this occurs, the plotter is unusable.

Currently, Kirkpatrick Aircrafts replaces each pen as it fails. The service manager has, however, proposed replacing all four pens every time one fails. This should cut down the frequency of plotter failures. At present, it takes one hour to replace one pen. All four pens could be replaced in two hours. The total cost of a plotter being unusable is $500 per hour. Each pen costs $80. The following breakdown data are thought to be valid:

ONE PEN REPLACED		FOUR PENS REPLACED	
HOURS BETWEEN FAILURES	PROBABILITY	HOURS BETWEEN FAILURES	PROBABILITY
10	0.05	70	0.10
20	0.15	100	0.15
30	0.15	110	0.25
40	0.20	120	0.35
50	0.20	130	0.20
60	0.15	140	0.05

(a) For each option (replacing one pen at a time and replacing all four pens at a time), simulate the average total time a plotter would operate

before it would have 20 failures. Then compute the total cost per hour for each option to determine which option Kirkpatrick Aircrafts should use. Use N replications.

(b) Compute the total cost per hour analytically for each option. How do these results compare to the simulation results?

22 A high school guidance counselor has scheduled one-on-one meetings today with 10 seniors to discuss their college plans. Each meeting is scheduled for 20 minutes, with the first meeting set to start at 9:00 A.M. Due to their hectic class and extra-curricular schedules, not every student arrives on time, and not every meeting lasts exactly 20 minutes. The counselor knows the following from past experience: A student will be 10 minutes early 5% of the time, 5 minutes early 20% of the time, exactly on time 35% of the time, 5 minutes late 30% of the time, and 10 minutes late 10% of the time. The counselor further estimates that there is a 15% chance that a meeting will take only 15 minutes, 50% chance it will take exactly the planned time, 25% chance it will take 25 minutes, and 10% chance it will take 30 minutes.

Students are seen in the order in which they have been scheduled, regardless of when they arrive. However, a student arriving early can see the counselor as soon as the previous meeting ends. Use N replications to determine when the counselor will complete the last meeting.

23 Dr. Carter Logue practices dentistry in Santa Fe, New Mexico. Logue tries hard to schedule appointments so that patients do not have to wait beyond their appointment time. His October 20 schedule is shown in the following table:

PATIENT	SCHEDULED APPOINTMENT	TIME NEEDED (MIN.)
Adams	9:30 A.M.	20
Brown	9:45 A.M.	15
Crawford	10:15 A.M.	15
Dannon	10:30 A.M.	10
Erving	10:45 A.M.	20
Fink	11:15 A.M.	15
Graham	11:30 A.M.	30
Hinkel	11:45 A.M.	15

Unfortunately, not every patient arrives exactly on schedule. Also, some examinations take longer than planned, and some take less time than planned. Logue's experience dictates the following: 20% of the patients will be 20 minutes early, 10% of the patients will be 10 minutes early, 40% of the patients will be on time, 25% of the patients will be 10 minutes late, and 5% of the patients will be 20 minutes late.

He further estimates that there is a 15% chance that an appointment will take 20% less time than planned, 50% chance it will take exactly the planned time, 25% chance it will take 20% more time than planned, and 10% chance it will take 40% more time than planned.

Dr. Logue has to leave at 12:15 P.M. on October 20 to catch a flight to a dental convention in Rio de Janerio. Assuming that he is ready to start his workday at 9:30 A.M. and that patients are treated in order of their scheduled exam (even if one late patient arrives after an early one), will he be able to make the flight? Use *N* replications.

24 Lee Appliances knows that weekly demand for high-end microwaves is normally distributed, with a mean of 25 units and a standard deviation of 7 units. (In your model use integers for all demands.) Lee replenishes its inventory by ordering 300 units from the distributor whenever its current inventory reaches 70 units. The lead time (in weeks) to receive an order from the distributor follows the distribution shown in the following table:

LEAD TIME	PROBABILITY
1	0.15
2	0.25
3	0.30
4	0.15
5	0.10
6	0.10

The cost to hold 1 unit in inventory for 1 week is $20. The cost to place an order with the factory is $300. Stockout costs are estimated at $100 per unit. The initial inventory level is 140 units.

(a) Simulate 52 weeks of operation to calculate the total semiannual cost and the percentage of stockouts for the period. Replicate these calculations *N* times each to calculate the average values for these measures.

(b) Lee would like to evaluate the economics of ordering 250, 275, 300, 325, and 350 units, with a reorder point of 70 units. Based on the average total semiannual cost, which order quantity would you recommend?

(c) Lee would like to evaluate the economics of ordering 300 units, with reorder points of 60, 70, 80, 90, and 100 tires. Based on the average total semiannual cost, which reorder point would you recommend?

25 Mattress Heaven orders a certain brand of mattress from its supplier and sells the mattresses at its retail location. The store currently orders 400 mattresses whenever the inventory level drops to 200. The cost to hold 1 mattress in inventory for one day is $0.75. The cost to place an order with the supplier is $75, and stockout costs are $150 per mattress. Beginning inventory is 150 mattresses. The daily demand probabilities are shown in the following table:

DAILY DEMAND	PROBABILITY
20	0.08
30	0.14
40	0.20
50	0.26
60	0.22
70	0.10

Lead time follows a discrete uniform distribution between 2 and 5 days (both inclusive). Simulate this inventory policy for a quarter (90 days) and calculate the total quarterly cost. Also calculate the percentage of stockouts for the quarter. Replicate these calculations *N* times each to calculate the average values for these measures.

26 Consider the Mattress Heaven problem described in Problem 25.
(a) Mattress Heaven would like to evaluate ordering 350, 400, 450, and 500 mattresses when the reorder point of 200 is reached. Based on the average total quarterly cost, which order quantity would you recommend?
(b) Mattress Heaven would like to evaluate reorder points of 150, 200, 250, and 300 mattresses, with an order quantity of 400 mattresses. Based on the average total quarterly cost, which reorder point would you recommend?

27 Music Mania sells MP3 players to its customers. Music Mania orders 300 MP3 players from its supplier when its inventory reaches 80 units. Daily demand for MP3 players is discrete, uniformly distributed between 30 and 60 (both inclusive). The lead time from the supplier also varies for each order and is discrete, uniformly distributed between 1 and 3 days (both inclusive). The cost to hold 1 unit in inventory for one day is $0.50. The cost to place an order is $100. Stockout cost per unit is estimated at $20. Initial inventory is 300 units.

Simulate this inventory policy for a quarter (90 days) and calculate the total quarterly cost. Also calculate the percentage of stockouts for the quarter. Replicate these calculations *N* times each to calculate the average values for these measures.

28 Consider the Music Mania problem described in Problem 27.

   (a) Music Mania would like to evaluate ordering 250, 300, 350, and 400 MP3 players when the reorder point of 80 is reached. Based on the average total quarterly cost, which order quantity would you recommend?

   (b) Music Mania would like to evaluate reorder points of 60, 80, and 100 MP3 players, with an order quantity of 300 players. Based on the average total cost for the quarter, which reorder point would you recommend?

29 Troy's Tires sells a certain brand tire which has a daily demand that is normally distributed, with a mean of 15 tires and a standard deviation of 4 tires. (In your model use integers for all demands.) Troy's Tires replenishes its inventory by ordering 250 tires from the factory whenever its current inventory reaches 40 tires. The lead time (in days) to receive an order from the factory follows the distribution shown in the following table:

LEAD TIME	PROBABILITY
1	0.10
2	0.22
3	0.28
4	0.15
5	0.15
6	0.10

The cost to hold 1 tire in inventory for one day is $0.20. The cost to place an order with the factory is $100. Stockout costs are estimated at $10 per tire. The initial inventory level is 100 tires.

   (a) Simulate 6 months (180 days) of operation to calculate the total semiannual cost and the percentage of stockouts for the period. Replicate these calculations N times each to calculate the average values for these measures.

   (b) Troy's Tires would like to evaluate the economics of ordering 150, 200, 250, 300, and 350 tires, with a reorder point of 40 tires. Based on the average total semiannual cost, which order quantity would you recommend?

   (c) Troy's Tires would like to evaluate the economics of ordering 250 tires, with reorder points of 40, 50, 60, 70, and 80 tires. Based on the average total semiannual cost, which reorder point would you recommend?

30 Ashcroft Airlines flies a six-passenger commuter fight once a day to Gainesville, Florida. A non-refundable one-way fare with a reservation costs $129. The daily demand for this flight is given in the following table, along with the probability distribution of no-shows (where a no-show has a reservation but does not arrive at the gate and forfeits the fare):

DEMAND	PROBABILITY	NO-SHOWS	PROBABILITY
5	0.05	0	0.15
6	0.11	1	0.25
7	0.20	2	0.26
8	0.18	3	0.23
9	0.16	4	0.11
10	0.12		
11	0.10		
12	0.08		

Ashcroft currently overbooks three passengers per flight. If there are not enough seats for a passenger at the gate, Ashcroft Airlines refunds his or her fare and also provides a $150 voucher good on any other trip. The fixed cost for each flight is $450, regardless of the number of passengers.

   (a) Set up a simulation model and calculate Ashcroft's profit per flight. Replicate the calculation N times each to calculate the average profit per flight.

   (b) Ashcroft Airlines would like to investigate the profitability of overbooking 0, 1, 2, 3, 4, and 5 passengers. What is your recommendation? Why?

31 Winston-Salem's general hospital has an emergency room that is divided into six departments: (1) the initial exam station, to treat minor problems and make diagnoses; (2) an x-ray department; (3) an operating room; (4) a cast-fitting room; (5) an observation room for recovery and general observation before final diagnosis or release; and (6) an out-processing department, where clerks check out patients and arrange for payment or insurance forms. The probabilities that a patient will go from one department to another are presented in the following table. (See Table for Problem 31.)

   Simulate the trail followed by 200 emergency room patients. Process 1 patient at a time, from entry at the initial exam station until leaving through out-processing. Note that a patient can enter the same department more than once. Based on your simulation, what is the probability that a patient enters the x-ray department more than once?

32 Management of Charlottesville Bank is concerned about a loss of customers at its main office downtown. One solution that has been proposed is to add one or more drive-through teller windows to make it easier for customers in cars to obtain quick service without parking. Neha Patel, the bank president, thinks the bank should only risk the cost of installing one drive-through window. She is

Table for Problem 31

FROM	TO	PROBABILITY
Initial exam station	X-ray department	0.45
	Operating room	0.15
	Observation room	0.10
	Out-processing clerk	0.30
X-ray department	Operating room	0.10
	Cast-fitting room	0.25
	Observation room	0.35
	Out-processing clerk	0.30
Operating room	Cast-fitting room	0.25
	Observation room	0.70
	Out-processing clerk	0.05
Cast-fitting room	Observation room	0.55
	X-ray department	0.05
	Out-processing clerk	0.40
Observation room	Operating room	0.15
	X-ray department	0.15
	Out-processing clerk	0.70

informed by her staff that the cost (amortized over a 20-year period) of building a drive-through window is $36,000 per year. It also costs $48,000 per year in wages and benefits to staff each new drive-through window.

The director of management analysis, Robyn Lyon, believes that two factors encourage the immediate construction of two drive-through windows, however. According to a recent article in *Banking Research* magazine, customers who wait in long lines for drive-through service will cost banks an average of $3 per minute in loss of goodwill. Also, adding a second drive-through window will cost an additional $48,000 in staffing, but amortized construction costs can be cut to a total of $60,000 per year if the two drive-through windows are installed together instead of one at a time. To complete her analysis, Lyon collected arrival and service rates at a competing downtown bank's drive-through windows for one month. These data are shown in the following table:

TIME BETWEEN ARRIVALS (MIN.)	OCCURRENCES	SERVICE TIME (MIN.)	OCCURRENCES
1	200	1	100
2	250	2	150
3	300	3	350
4	150	4	150
5	100	5	150
		6	100

(a) Simulate a 1-hour time period for a system with one drive-through window. Replicate the model N times.

(b) Simulate a 1-hour time period for a system with two drive-through windows. Replicate the model N times.

(c) Conduct a cost analysis of the two options. Assume that the bank is open 7 hours per day and 200 days per year.

33 Erik Marshall owns and operates one of the largest BMW auto dealerships in St. Louis. In the past 36 months, his weekly sales of Z3s have ranged from a low of 6 to a high of 12, as reflected in the following table:

Z3 SALES PER WEEK	FREQUENCY
6	3
7	4
8	6
9	12
10	9
11	1
12	1

Erik believes that sales will continue during the next 24 months at about the same rate and that delivery lead times will also continue to follow this pace (stated in probability form):

DELIVERY TIME (WEEKS)	PROBABILITY
1	0.44
2	0.33
3	0.16
4	0.07

Erik's current policy is to order 14 autos at a time (two full truckloads, with 7 autos on each truck) and to place a new order whenever the stock on hand reaches 12 autos. Beginning inventory is 14 autos. Erik establishes the following relevant costs: (i) The carrying cost per Z3 per week is $400, (ii) the cost of a lost sale averages $7,500, and (iii) the cost of placing an order is $1,000.

(a) Simulate Erik's inventory policy for the next two years. What is the total weekly cost of this policy? Also, what is the average number of stockouts per week? Use N replications of your model.

(b) Erik wishes to evaluate several different ordering quantities—12, 14, 16, 18, and 20. Based on the total weekly cost, what would you recommend? Why? Set $R = 12$ in each case.

34 Jesse's Plumbing Service's monthly demand follows a discrete uniform distribution between 40 and 55 jobs. The probability that a specific job will be for minor service (e.g., clogged sink) is 0.65, and the probability that it will be for a major service (e.g., flooded basement) is 0.35. Revenues for minor service follow a normal distribution, with a mean of $100 and a standard deviation of $15. For major projects, Jesse estimates that revenues will be $600 with 30% chance, $900 with 40% chance, or $1,200 with 30% chance. Set up a simulation model for Jesse's problem and replicate it N times to calculate his average monthly revenue.

35 Sydney Garner is considering building a 300-seat amphitheater in a popular park. After studying the market, Sydney has drawn the following conclusions:

- There will be one show every night during summer months
- The theater will make a profit of $1 on each occupied seat and suffer a loss of $0.25 on each unoccupied seat.
- The probability that it rains on any given night is 0.2.
- The number of customers on a dry night is normally distributed, with a mean of 275 and a standard deviation of 30.
- The number of customers on a cold night is normally distributed, with a mean of 200 and a standard deviation of 50.

Set up Sydney's problem and simulate total profit for 1 month (30 days). In your model use integers for all demands. Replicate your model N times and calculate Sydney's average monthly profit.

36 Wang's Concrete Service notes that the number of jobs each month follows the following distribution: 10 with probability 0.15, 11 with probability 0.20, 12 with probability 0.20, 13 with probability 0.20, 14 with probability 0.15, and 15 with probability 0.10. The probability that a specific job will be for a residential driveway is 70%, and the probability that it will be for a commercial project is 30%. Revenues for residential driveways follow a normal distribution, with a mean of $500 and a standard deviation of $50. Commercial projects, although more lucrative, also have larger variability. Wang estimates that revenues here follow a normal distribution, with a mean of $1,500 and a standard deviation of $400. Set up a simulation model for Wang's problem and replicate it N times to calculate the average monthly revenue.

37 The Decatur Fire Department makes annual door-to-door solicitations for funds. Residents of each visited house are asked to contribute $15 (and receive a free family portrait package), $25 (and receive two free family portrait packages), or $35 (and receive three free family portrait packages). An analysis from previous years' solicitations indicates that the following:

- Only 80% of the homes visited have someone at home.
- When someone is at home, there is only a 40% chance that he or she will make a donation.
- Of the people making donations, there is a 50% chance they will contribute $15, a 25% chance they will contribute $25, and a 15% chance they will contribute $35. Occasionally (10% chance), a person makes a donation in excess of $35. Such distributions follow a discrete uniform distribution between $40 and $50 (in increments of $1).

The fire chief plans to visit 30 houses tomorrow. Set up a simulation model and replicate it N times to determine the probability that the chief will receive more than $300 in donations from these 30 houses.

38 A local bank has a single drive-through window with arrival times and service times that follow the distributions from the following table:

TIME BETWEEN ARRIVALS (MIN.)	PROBABILITY	SERVICE TIME (MIN.)	PROBABILITY
1	0.15	1	0.15
2	0.24	2	0.35
3	0.27	3	0.22
4	0.22	4	0.28
5	0.12		

Simulate the arrival of 200 customers to compute each of the following measures: (a) average time a customer waits for service, (b) average time a customer is in the system (wait plus service time), and (c) percentage of time the server is busy with customers. Replicate each measure N times to compute the average.

39 Colin sells pretzels at the local high school basketball games. For an upcoming game, Colin has to decide how many pretzels to order (170, 190, or 210), at a cost of $0.50 each. Colin sells pretzels for $1.50 each. However, any unsold pretzels must be thrown away.

If the game is interesting, Colin thinks that fewer people will visit his stand. In such a case, Colin estimates that demand will be normally distributed, with a mean of 140 and a standard deviation of 20. However, if the game is a blowout, he expects more people to visit the stand. Demand in this case follows a discrete uniform distribution between 180 and 200. Based on his familiarity with the two teams, he estimates that there is only a 40% chance that the game will be a blowout.

Set up a simulation model and replicate it N times for each order size to determine Colin's expected profit and expected percentage of unsold pretzels. What do you recommend that Colin do?

40 The Diego Street Convenience Store has a single checkout register, with customer arrival distribution shown in the following table:

TIME BETWEEN ARRIVALS (MIN.)	PROBABILITY
1	0.18
2	0.20
3	0.22
4	0.25
5	0.15

Service time follows a discrete uniform distribution between 1 and 4 minutes. Simulate the arrival of 200 customers to compute the average time a customer waits for service and the probability that a customer waits 3 minutes or longer for service.

Replicate each measure N times to compute its average.

41 Zodiac Chemical manufactures chlorine gas by passing electricity through saltwater in a diaphragm cell. The plant has 88 diaphragm cells that operate in parallel. Each cell can produce 5 tons of chlorine gas per day, and each ton of chlorine gas has a profit contribution of $15. Due to the harsh environment, cell failures occur, causing the cell to be taken offline for maintenance. A cell fails, on average, every 30 hours, according to the exponential probability distribution. Only one cell can be repaired at any given time. Using the current maintenance procedure, the repair time follows a truncated normal probability distribution, with a mean of 21 hours, a standard deviation of 6 hours, and a minimum value of 5 hours. A new maintenance procedure is being considered that will require a significant capital investment. If this new procedure is implemented, the repair time will still follow a truncated normal distribution, but the mean time will be 14 hours, the standard deviation will be 4 hours, and the minimum time will be 3 hours. Simulate 200 failures to determine the annual savings in downtime with the new method.

42 Make a Splash T-Shirts is planning to print and sell specially designed tee shirts for the upcoming World Series. The shirts will cost $12 each to produce and can be sold for $30 each until the World Series. After the World Series, the price will be reduced to $20 per shirt. The demand at the $30 price is expected to be normally distributed, with a mean

of 12,000 shirts and a standard deviation of 2,500 shirts. The demand for the $20 price is expected to be normally distributed, with a mean of 5,000 shirts and a standard deviation of 1,000 shirts. Any shirts left over will be discarded. Because of the high setup costs, Make a Splash T-Shirts is planning on producing one run of 17,000 shirts. In your model use integers for all demands.

(a) Simulate N setups to calculate the average profit for this quantity of shirts.

(b) Make a Splash T-Shirts would like to evaluate producing 16,000, 17,000, 18,000, 19,000, and 20,000 shirts. Which would you recommend? Why?

43 Phillip Florrick is responsible for the warehouse operation for a local discount department store chain. The warehouse has only one unloading dock that is currently operated by a single three-person crew. Trucks arrive at an average rate of five per hour and follow the exponential probability distribution. The average time for one of the crews to unload a truck tends to follow a normal distribution, with a mean of 9 minutes and standard deviation of 3 minutes (minimum time is 1 minute). Phillip has estimated the cost of operating a truck at $40 per hour. Phillip pays each person on the unloading crew $11 per hour. The unloading dock operates 8 hours each day. Simulate 100 days of this operation to calculate the total daily cost. Replicate this calculation N times to compute the expected total cost per day of this operation.

44 A customer service counter at a local bookstore is normally staffed by a single employee. The probabilities of arrival times and service times are shown in the following table:

TIME BETWEEN ARRIVALS (MIN.)	PROBABILITY	SERVICE TIME (MIN.)	PROBABILITY
1	0.07	1	0.07
2	0.25	2	0.24
3	0.23	3	0.28
4	0.26	4	0.28
5	0.19	5	0.13

Simulate the arrival of 100 customers to compute the average number of customers in line and the probability that a customer will have to wait 3 or more minutes for service to begin. Replicate each measure N times to compute its average.

45 Timberwolves Electric and Wiring Company installs wiring and electrical fixtures in residential construction. Andrew Dickel, the owner of Timberwolves, has been concerned with the amount of time it takes to complete wiring jobs because some

of his workers are very unreliable. For each wiring job, a list of activities, their mean duration times, standard deviation of duration times, and immediate predecessors are given in the following table:

	DAYS		
ACTIVITY	MEAN	STANDARD DEVIATION	IMMEDIATE PREDECESSORS
A	5.83	0.83	—
B	3.67	0.33	—
C	2.00	0.33	—
D	7.00	0.33	C
E	4.00	0.67	B, D
F	10.00	1.33	A, E
G	2.17	0.50	A, E
H	6.00	1.00	F
I	11.00	0.33	G
J	16.33	1.00	G
K	7.33	1.33	H, I

Assume that all activity durations follow a normal distribution, with the means and standard deviations shown. Use simulation to determine the probability that Timberwolves will finish the project in 40 days or less.

46 A plant engineering group needs to set up an assembly line to produce a new product. The following table describes the relationships between the activities that need to be completed for this product to be manufactured:

	DAYS			IMMEDIATE
ACTIVITY	a	m	b	PREDECESSORS
A	3	6	8	—
B	5	8	10	A
C	5	6	8	A
D	1	2	4	B, C
E	7	11	17	D
F	7	9	12	D
G	6	8	9	D
H	3	4	7	F, G
I	3	5	7	E, F, H

If using Crystal Ball, assume that the duration of each activity follows a BetaPert distribution, with the three time estimates shown for that activity. Otherwise, assume that each activity time is normally distributed with expected time and standard deviation. Round off all activity times to two decimal places.

(a) Use simulation to determine the probability that the project will finish in 37 days or less.
(b) Use simulation to determine the probability that the project will take more than 32 days.

47 Luna Martinez, director of personnel at Management Resources, Inc., is in the process of designing a program that its customers can use in the job-finding process. Some of the activities include preparing résumés, writing letters, making appointments to see prospective employers, researching companies and industries, and so on. Information on the activities is shown in the following table:

	DAYS		
ACTIVITY	MEAN	STANDARD DEVIATION	IMMEDIATE PREDECESSORS
A	10.00	0.67	—
B	7.17	0.50	—
C	3.17	0.17	—
D	20.00	3.33	A
E	7.00	0.33	C
F	10.00	0.33	B, D, E
G	7.33	0.67	B, D, E
H	15.00	0.33	F
I	11.17	0.50	F
J	7.00	0.33	G, H
K	6.67	0.67	I, J
L	2.17	0.50	G, H

Assume that all activity durations follow a normal distribution, with the means and standard deviations shown. Round off all activity times to two decimal places. Use simulation to determine the average project completion time and the probability that the project will take at least 75 days.

48 Lamont Henri needs to plan and manage a local construction project. The following table describes the relationships between the activities that need to be completed:

	DAYS			IMMEDIATE
ACTIVITY	a	m	b	PREDECESSORS
A	4	8	13	—
B	4	10	15	A
C	7	14	20	B
D	9	16	19	B
E	6	9	11	B
F	2	4	5	D, E
G	4	7	11	C, F
H	3	5	9	G
I	2	3	4	G, H

If using Crystal Ball, assume that the actual duration of each activity follows a BetaPert distribution, with the three time estimates shown for that activity. Otherwise, assume that each activity time is normally distributed with expected time and standard deviation. Round off all activity times to one decimal place. Use simulation to determine the probability that the project will take at least 50 days.

49 Elena Wilhelm is responsible for developing a comprehensive sales training program for her organization. The following table describes the relationships between the activities that need to be completed:

ACTIVITY	DAYS MINIMUM	MAXIMUM	IMMEDIATE PREDECESSORS
A	7	13	—
B	5	11	—
C	3	8	A, B
D	5	9	C
E	2	9	C
F	3	5	E
G	5	12	F
H	9	12	D
I	6	8	F, H
J	7	10	G, I

Assume that the actual duration of each activity follows a discrete uniform distribution between the minimum and maximum times shown for that activity. Use simulation to determine the probability that the project will be finished in less than 49 days. Round off each activity time to the nearest whole number.

50 Lynn Rogers (who just turned 30) currently earns $60,000 per year. At the end of each calendar year, she plans to invest 10% of her annual income in a tax-deferred retirement account. Lynn expects her salary to grow between 0% and 8% each year, following a discrete uniform distribution between these two rates. Based on historical market returns, she expects the tax-deferred account to return between −5% and 20% in any given year, following a continuous uniform distribution between these two rates. Use N replications of a simulation model to answer each of the following questions.
(a) What is the probability that Lynn will have in excess of $1 million in this account when she turns 60 (i.e., in 30 years)?
(b) If Lynn wants this probability to be over 95%, what should be her savings rate each year?

51 Adams College has a self-insured employee health care plan. Each employee pays a monthly premium of $100. Adams pays the rest of the health care costs. The number of covered employees is 1,000 this year. Each year, the number of employees who have major health claims follows a continuous uniform distribution between 10% and 15%, and the number of employees who have minor health claims follows a continuous uniform distribution between 60% and 65%. The rest have no health claims. Round off all numbers of claims to integers.

For this year, major health claims are expected to follow a normal distribution, with a mean of $5,000 and a standard deviation of $1,000. Minor health claims are expected to follow a normal distribution, with a mean of $1,500 and a standard deviation of $300. For purposes of simulating this model, assume that every minor health claim is the same amount simulated above. Assume likewise for major health clams. Use N replications of a simulation model to answer each of the following questions.
(a) What is the probability that Adams College's total out-of-pocket cost will exceed $300,000 this year?
(b) The number of employees from year to year follows a continuous uniform distribution between a 3% decrease and a 4% increase. Round off all numbers of employees to integers. Also, due to rising health costs, the mean of minor health claims is expected to rise in a discrete uniform manner between 2% and 5% each year, and the mean of major health claims is expected to rise in a discrete uniform manner between 4% and 7% each year. What is the probability that Adams College's total out-of-pocket cost will exceed $2,000,000 over the next five years?

Case Study

Alabama Airlines

Alabama Airlines opened its doors in June 2011 as a commuter service, with its headquarters and only hub located in Birmingham. A product of airline deregulation, Alabama Air joined the growing number of successful short-haul, point-to-point airlines, including Lone Star, Comair, Atlantic Southeast, Skywest, and Business Express.

Alabama Air was started and managed by two former pilots, David Douglas (formerly with the defunct Eastern Airlines) and Michael Hanna (formerly with Pan Am). It acquired a fleet of 12 used prop-jet planes and the airport gates vacated by Sprint Airlines when it downsized in 2010.

With business growing quickly, Douglas turned his attention to Alabama Air's toll-free reservations system. Between midnight and 6:00 A.M., only one telephone reservations agent had been on duty. The time between incoming calls during this period is distributed as shown in Table 8. Douglas carefully observed and timed the agent and estimated that the time taken to process passenger inquiries is distributed as shown in Table 9.

TABLE 8   Current Incoming Call Distribution

TIME BETWEEN CALLS (MIN.)	PROBABILITY
1	0.11
2	0.21
3	0.22
4	0.20
5	0.16
6	0.10

TABLE 9   Service Time Distribution

TIME TO PROCESS ENQUIRIES (MIN.)	PROBABILITY
1	0.20
2	0.19
3	0.18
4	0.17
5	0.13
6	0.10
7	0.03

All customers calling Alabama Air go on hold and are served in the order of the calls unless the reservations agent is available for immediate service. Douglas is deciding whether a second agent should be on duty to cope with customer demand. To maintain customer satisfaction, Alabama Air does not want a customer on hold for more than three to four minutes and also wants to maintain a "high" operator utilization.

Further, the airline is planning a new TV advertising campaign. As a result, it expects an increase in toll-free line phone enquiries. Based on similar campaigns in the past, the incoming call distribution from midnight to 6 A.M. is expected to be as shown in Table 10. (The same service time distribution will apply.)

TABLE 10   Revised Incoming Call Distribution

TIME BETWEEN CALLS (MIN.)	PROBABILITY
1	0.22
2	0.25
3	0.19
4	0.15
5	0.12
6	0.07

Discussion Questions

1. What would you advise Alabama Air to do for the current reservation system, based on the original call distribution? Create a simulation model to investigate the scenario. Describe the model carefully and justify the duration of the simulation, assumptions, and measures of performance.
2. What are your recommendations regarding operator utilization and customer satisfaction if the airline proceeds with the advertising campaign?

Source: © Zbigniew H. Przasnyski. Used with permission.

Case Study

Abjar Transport Company

In 2011, Samir Khaldoun, after receiving an MBA degree from a leading university in the United States, returned to Jeddah, Saudi Arabia, where his family has extensive business holdings. Samir's first assignment was to stabilize and develop a newly formed, family-owned transport company—Abjar Transport.

An immediate problem Samir faces is the determination of the number of trucks needed to handle the forecasted freight volume. Before now, trucks were added to the fleet on an "as-needed" basis, without comprehensive capacity planning. This approach has created problems of driver recruitment, truck service and maintenance, and excessive demurrage (i.e., port fees) because of delays at unloading docks and retention of cargo containers.

Samir forecasts that Abjar's freight volume should average 160,000 tons per month, with a standard deviation of 30,000 tons. Freight is unloaded on a uniform basis throughout the month. Based on past experience, the amount handled per month is assumed to be normally distributed.

After extensive investigation, Samir concludes that the fleet should be standardized to 40-foot Mercedes 2624 2 × 4 tractor-trailer rigs, which are each suitable for carrying two 20-foot containers, or one 40-foot container cargo capacity is approximately 60 tons per rig. Each tractor-trailer unit is estimated to cost 240,000 riyals. Moreover, they must meet Saudi Arabian specifications—double cooling fans, oversized radiators, and special high-temperature tires. Historical evidence suggests that these Mercedes rigs will operate 96% of the time.

Approximately 25% of the freight handled by these tractor-trailer rigs is containerized in container lengths of 20, 30, and 40 feet. (The balance of the freight—75%—is not containerized.) The 20-foot containers hold approximately 20 tons of cargo, the 30-foot containers hold 45 tons, and the 40-foot containers hold 60 tons of freight. Approximately 60% of the containerized freight is shipped in 40-foot units, 20% is shipped in 30-foot units, and 20% is transported in 20-foot units.

Abjar Transport picks up freight at the dock and delivers it directly to customers or to warehouses for later delivery. Based on his study of truck routing and scheduling patterns, Samir concludes that each rig should pick up freight at the dock three times each day.

Discussion Questions

1. How many tractor-trailer rigs should make up the Abjar Transport fleet?

 Internet Case Studies

See the Companion Website for this text, at www.pearsonhighered.com/balakrishnan, for additional case studies

Brief Solutions to Odd-Numbered End-of-Chapter Problems

Note: **All answers given here are based on only 200 replications of the simulation model and are, hence, rather approximate. Your answers may therefore vary.**

15 Expected failures = 2.48 per month. Simulation average is around the same value. Difference is due to small number of replications in simulation.

17 (a) $359. (b) 0.0204.

19 (a) $30,649. (b) Order 35.

21 (a) 1 pen = $14 per hour; 4 pens = $11.25 per hour. (b) 1 pen = $13.81 per hour; 4 pens = $11.23 per hour. Compares very favorably.

23 Average time needed = 175 minutes, Probability finish in ≤ 165 minutes = 0.135.

25 $49,229; 5.51%.

27 $15,271; 10.67%.

29 (a) $6,899; 7.15%. (b) 200. (c) 70.

31 0.056.

33 $28,664 per month; 3.67 cars. (b) 20 cars.

35 $7,368.

37 0.14.

39 Order 190 pretzels. Profit = $145. Unsold = 16%.

41 $23,960.

43 $1,054.

45 0.94.

47 0.035.

49 0.45.

51 (a) 0.62. (b) 0.88.

MODULE

Game Theory

After completing this supplement, students will be able to:

1. Understand the principles of zero-sum, two-person games.
2. Analyze pure strategy games and use dominance to reduce the size of a game.
3. Solve mixed strategy games when there is no saddle point.

1 Introduction

Competition can be an important decision-making factor. The strategies taken by other organizations or individuals can dramatically affect the outcome of our decisions. In the automobile industry, for example, the strategies of competitors to introduce certain models with certain features can dramatically affect the profitability of other carmakers. Today, business cannot make important decisions without considering what other organizations or individuals are doing or might do.

Game theory is one way to consider the impact of the strategies of others on our strategies and outcomes. A *game* is a contest involving two or more decision makers, each of whom wants to win. *Game theory is* the study of how optimal strategies are formulated in conflict.

The study of game theory dates back to 1944, when John von Neumann and Oscar Morgenstern published their classic book, *Theory of Games and Economic Behavior.*[1] Since then, game theory has been used by army generals to plan war strategies, by union negotiators and managers in collective bargaining, and by businesses of all types to determine the best strategies given a competitive business environment.

Game theory continues to be important today. In 1994, John Harsanui, John Nash, and Reinhard Selten jointly received the Nobel Prize in Economics from the Royal Swedish Academy of Sciences.[2] In their classic work, these individuals developed the notion of *noncooperative game theory.* After the work of John von Neumann, Nash developed the concepts of the Nash equilibrium and the Nash bargaining problem, which are the cornerstones of modern game theory.

Game models are classified by the *number of players,* the *sum of all payoffs,* and the *number of strategies* employed. Due to the mathematical complexity of game theory, we limit the analysis in this module to games that are two person and zero sum. A *two-person game* is one in which only two parties can play—as in the case of a union and a company in a bargaining session. For simplicity, *X* and *Y* represent the two game players. *Zero sum* means that the sum of losses for one player must equal the sum of gains for the other player. Thus, if *X* wins 20 points or dollars, *Y* loses 20 points or dollars. With any zero-sum game, the sum of the gains for one player is always equal to the sum of the losses for the other player. When you sum the gains and losses for both players, the result is zero—hence the name *zero-sum games.*

In a zero-sum game, what is gained by one player is lost by the other.

2 Language of Games

To introduce the notation used in game theory, let us consider a simple game. Suppose there are only two lighting fixture stores, *X* and *Y*, in Urbana, Illinois. (This is called a *duopoly*.) The respective market shares have been stable up until now, but the situation may change. The daughter of the owner of store *X* has just completed her MBA and has developed two distinct advertising strategies, one using radio spots and the other newspaper ads. Upon hearing this, the owner of store *Y* also proceeds to prepare radio and newspaper ads.

The 2 × 2 payoff matrix in Table 1 shows what will happen to current market shares if both stores begin advertising. By convention, payoffs are shown only for the first game player, *X* in this case. *Y*'s payoffs will just be the negative of each number. For this game, there are only two strategies being used by each player. If store *Y* had a third strategy, we would be dealing with a 2 × 3 payoff matrix.

[1]J. von Neumann and O. Morgenstern. *Theory of Games and Economic Behavior.* Princeton, NJ: Princeton University Press, 1944.
[2]Rita Koselka. "The Games Businesses Play," *Forbes* (November 7, 1994): 12.

TABLE 1
Store X's Payoff Matrix

		GAME PLAYER Y's STRATEGIES	
		Y_1 (Use radio)	Y_2 (Use newspaper)
GAME PLAYER X'S STRATEGIES	X_1 (Use radio)	3	5
	X_2 (Use newspaper)	1	−2

A positive number in Table 1 means that X wins and Y loses. A negative number means that Y wins and X loses. It is obvious from the table that the game favors competitor X, since all values are positive except one. If the game had favored player Y, the values in the table would have been negative. In other words, the game in Table 1 is biased against Y. However, since Y must play the game, he or she will play to minimize total losses. To do this, Player Y would use the minimax criterion, our next topic.

Game Outcomes

STORE X's STRATEGY	STORE Y's STRATEGY	OUTCOME (% CHANGE IN MARKET SHARE)
X_1 (use radio)	Y_1 (use radio)	X wins 3 and Y loses 3
X_1 (use radio)	Y_2 (use newspaper)	X wins 5 and Y loses 5
X_2 (use newspaper)	Y_1 (use radio)	X wins 1 and Y loses 1
X_2 (use newspaper)	Y_2 (use newspaper)	X loses 2 and Y wins 2

3   The Minimax Criterion

A player using the minimax criterion will select the strategy that minimizes the maximum possible loss.

The upper value of the game is equal to the minimum of the maximum values in the columns.

The lower value of the game is equal to the maximum of the minimum values in the rows.

For two-person, zero-sum games, there is a logical approach to finding the solution: In a zero-sum game, each person should choose the strategy that minimizes the maximum loss, called the *minimax criterion*. This is identical to maximizing one's minimum gains, so for one player, this could be called the maximin criterion.

Let us use the example in Table 1 to illustrate the minimax criterion. This is a two-person zero-sum game with the strategies for player Y given as the columns of the table. The values are gains for player X and losses for player Y. Player Y is looking at a maximum loss of 3 if strategy Y_1 is selected and a maximum loss of 5 if strategy Y_2 is selected. Thus, Player Y should select strategy Y_1, which results in a maximum loss of 3 (the minimum of the maximum possible losses). This is called the *upper value of the game.* Table 2 illustrates this minimax approach.

In considering the maximin strategy for player X (whose strategies correspond to the rows of the table), let us look at the minimum payoff for each row. The payoffs are +3 for strategy X_1 and −2 for strategy X_2. The maximum of these minimums is +3, which means strategy X_1, will be selected. This value (+3) is called the *lower value of the game.*

If the upper and lower values of a game are the same, this number is called the *value of the game,* and an equilibrium or *saddle point* condition exists. For the game presented in

TABLE 2
Minimax Solution

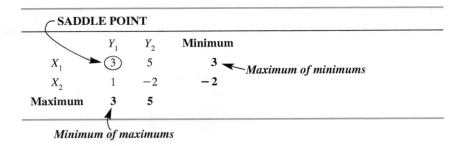

An equilibrium or saddle point condition exists if the upper value of the game is equal to the lower value of the game. This is called the value of the game.

Table 2, the value of the game is 3 because this is the value for both the upper and lower values. The value of the game is the average or expected game outcome if the game is played an infinite number of times.

In implementing the minimax strategy, player Y will find the maximum value in each column and select the minimum of these maximums. In implementing the maximin strategy, player X will find the minimum value in each row and select the maximum of these minimums. When a saddle point is present, this approach will result in pure strategies for each player. Otherwise, the solution to the game will involve mixed strategies. These concepts are discussed in the following sections.

4 Pure Strategy Games

A pure strategy exists whenever a saddle point is present.

When a saddle point is present, the strategy each player should follow will always be the same regardless of the other player's strategy. This is called a *pure strategy*. A saddle point is a situation in which both players are facing pure strategies.

Using minimax criterion, we saw that the game in Table 2 had a saddle point and thus is an example of a pure strategy game. It is beneficial for player X and for player Y to always choose one strategy. Simple logic would lead us to this same conclusion. Player X will always select X_1, since the payoffs for X_1 are better than the payoffs for X_2, regardless of what player Y does. Knowing that player X will select X_1, player Y will always select strategy Y_1 and only lose 3 rather than 5. Note that the saddle point in this example, 3, is the largest number in its column and the smallest number in its row. This is true of all saddle points.

Another example of a pure strategy game is shown in Table 3. Notice that the value 6 is the lowest number in its row and the highest number in its column. Thus, it is a saddle point and indicates that strategy X_1 will be selected by player X and strategy Y_2 will be selected by player Y. The value of this game is 6.

TABLE 3

Example of a Pure Strategy Game

		PLAYER Y's STRATEGIES		
				Minimum row number ↓
		Y_1	Y_2	
PLAYER X's STRATEGIES	X_1	10	6	⑥
	X_2	−12	2	−12
Maximum column number →		10	⑥	

430

IN ACTION Game Theory in the Brewing Business

Companies that understand the principles and importance of game theory can often select the best competitive strategies. Companies that don't can face financial loss or even bankruptcy. The successful and unsuccessful selection of competitive gaming strategies can be seen in most industries, including the brewing industry.

In the 1970s, Schlitz was the second-largest brewer in the United States. With its slogan "the beer that made Milwaukee famous," Schlitz was chasing after the leader in beer sales, Anheuser-Busch, maker of Budweiser. Schlitz could either keep its current production output or attempt to produce more beer to compete with Anheuser-Busch. It decided to get more beer to the market in a shorter amount of time. In order to accomplish this, Schlitz selected a strategy of distributing "immature" beer. The result was cloudy beer that often contained a slimy suspension. The beer and Schlitz's market share and profitability went down the drain. Anheuser-Busch, Miller, and Coors became the market leaders.

Similarly, when Miller first decided to market Miller Lite, with the slogan "tastes great—less filling," Anheuser-Busch had two possible gaming strategies: to develop its own low-calorie beer or to criticize Miller in its advertising for producing a watered-down beer. The strategy it selected was to criticize Miller in its advertising. The strategy didn't work, Miller gained significant market share, and Anheuser-Busch was forced to come out with its own low-calorie beer—Bud Light.

Today, Anheuser-Busch, Miller, Coors, and other large beer manufacturers face new games and new competitors that produce micro-brews, dry beer, and ice beer. Although it is too early to tell what the large beer makers will do and how successful their strategies will be, it appears that their strategy will be to duplicate what these smaller brewers are doing. What is clear, however, is that a knowledge of the fundamentals of game theory can make a big difference.

Source: Philip Van Munching. "American Brewing, Unreal," *The Economist* (September, 4, 1977): 24.

5 Mixed Strategy Games

In a mixed strategy game, each player should optimize the expected gain.

When there is no saddle point, players will play each strategy for a certain percentage of the time. This is called a *mixed strategy game.* The most common way to solve a mixed strategy game is to use the expected gain or loss approach. The goal of this approach is for a player to play each strategy a particular percentage of the time so that the expected value of the game does not depend upon what the opponent does. This will only occur if the expected value of each strategy is the same.

Consider the game shown in Table 4. There is no saddle point, so this will be a mixed strategy game. Player Y must determine the percentage of the time to play strategy Y_1 and the percentage of the time to play strategy Y_2. Let P be the percentage of time that player Y chooses strategy Y_1 and $1 - P$ be the percentage of the time that player Y chooses strategy Y_2. We must weight the payoffs by these percentages to compute the expected gain for each of the different strategies that player X may choose.

For example, if player X chooses strategy X_1, then P percent of the time the payoff for Y will be 4, and $1 - P$ percent of the time the payoff will be 2, as shown in Table 5. Similarly, if player X chooses strategy X_2, then P percent of the time the payoff for Y will be 1, and $1 - P$ percent of the time the payoff will be 10. If these expected values are the same,

TABLE 4
Game Table for Mixed Strategy Game

		PLAYER Y's STRATEGIES	
		Y_1	Y_2
PLAYER X's STRATEGIES	X_1	4	2
	X_2	1	10

TABLE 5

Game Table for Mixed Strategy Game with Percentages (P, Q) Shown

		Y_1	Y_2	
		P	$1 - P$	Expected gain
X_1	Q	4	2	$4P + 2(1 - P)$
X_2	$1 - Q$	1	10	$1P + 10(1 - P)$
Expected gain		$4Q + 1(1 - Q)$	$2Q + 10(1 - Q)$	

then the expected value for player Y will not depend on the strategy chosen by X. Therefore, to solve this, we set these two expected values equal, as follows:

$$4P + 2(1 - P) = 1P + 10(1 - P)$$

Solving this for P, we have

$$P = {}^8\!/_{11}$$

and

$$1 - P = 1 - {}^8\!/_{11} = {}^3\!/_{11}$$

Thus, ${}^8\!/_{11}$ and ${}^3\!/_{11}$ indicate how often player Y will choose strategies Y_1 and Y_2 respectively. The expected value computed with these percentages is

$$1P + 10(1 - P) = 1({}^8\!/_{11}) + 10({}^3\!/_{11}) = {}^{38}\!/_{11} = 3.46$$

Performing a similar analysis for player X, we let Q be the percentage of the time that strategy X_1 is played and $1 - Q$ be the percentage of the time that strategy X_2 is played. Using these, we compute the expected gain shown in Table 5. We set these equal, as follows:

$$4Q + 1(1 - Q) = 2Q + 10(1 - Q)$$

Solving for Q, we get

$$Q = {}^9\!/_{11}$$

and

$$1 - Q = {}^2\!/_{11}$$

Thus, ${}^9\!/_{11}$ and ${}^2\!/_{11}$ indicate how often player X will choose strategies X_1 and X_2 respectively. The expected gains with these probabilities will also be ${}^{38}\!/_{11}$, or 3.46.

 IN ACTION   **Using Game Theory to Shape Strategy at General Motors**

Game theory often assumes that one player or company must lose for another to win. In the auto industry, car companies typically compete by offering rebates and price cuts. This allows one company to gain market share at the expense of other car companies. Although this win–lose strategy works in the short term, competitors quickly follow the same strategy. The result is lower margins and profitability. Indeed, many customers wait until a rebate or price cut is offered before buying a new car. The short-term win–lose strategy turns into a long-term lose–lose result.

By changing the game itself, it is possible to find strategies that can benefit all competitors. This was the case when General Motors (GM) developed a new credit card that allowed people to apply 5% of their purchases to a new GM vehicle, up to $500 per year, with a maximum of $3,500. The credit card program replaced other incentive programs offered by GM. Changing the game helped bring profitability back to GM. In addition, it also helped other car manufacturers who no longer had to compete on price cuts and rebates. In this case, the new game resulted in a win–win situation with GM. Prices, margins, and profitability increased for GM and for some of its competitors.

Source: Adam Brandenburger, et al. "The Right Game: Use Game Theory to Shape Strategy," *Harvard Business Renew* (July-August 1995): 57.

6   Dominance

The principle of *dominance* can be used to reduce the size of games by eliminating strategies that would never be played. A strategy for a player is said to be dominated if the player can always do as well or better playing another strategy. Any dominated strategy can be eliminated from the game. In other words, a strategy can be eliminated if all its game's outcomes are the same or worse than the corresponding game outcomes of another strategy.

Using the principle of dominance, we reduce the size of the following game:

	Y_1	Y_2
X_1	4	3
X_2	2	20
X_3	1	1

In this game, X_3 will never be played because X can always do better by playing X_1 or X_2. The new game is

	Y_1	Y_2
X_1	4	3
X_2	2	20

Here is another example:

	Y_1	Y_2	Y_3	Y_4
X_1	−5	4	6	−3
X_2	−2	6	2	−20

In this game, Y would never play Y_2 and Y_3 because Y could *always* do better playing Y_1 or Y_4. The new game is

	Y_1	Y_4
X_1	−5	−3
X_2	−2	−20

Summary

Game theory is the study of how optimal strategies are formulated in conflict. Because of the mathematical complexities of game theory, this module is limited to two-person and zero-sum games. A two-person game allows only two people or two groups to be involved in the game. *Zero sum* means that the sum of the losses for one player must equal the sum of the gains for the other player. The overall sum of the losses and gains for both players, in other words, must be zero.

Depending on the actual payoffs in the game and the size of the game, a number of solution techniques can be used. In a pure strategy game, strategies for the players can be obtained without making any calculations. When there is *not* a pure strategy, also called a saddle point, for both players, it is necessary to use other techniques, such as the mixed strategy approach, dominance, and a computer solution for games larger than 2 × 2.

Glossary

Dominance   A procedure that is used to reduce the size of the game.

Minimax Criterion   A criterion that minimizes one's maximum losses. This is another way of solving a pure strategy game.

Mixed Strategy Game   A game in which the optimal strategy for both players involves playing more than one strategy over time. Each strategy is played a given percentage of the time.

Pure Strategy   A game in which both players will always play just one strategy.

Saddle Point Game   A game that has a pure strategy.

Two-Person Game   A game that has only two players.

Value of the Game   The expected winnings of the game if the game is played a large number of times.

Zero-Sum Game   A game in which the losses for one player equal the gains for the other player.

Solved Problems

Solved Problem 1

George Massic (player X) faces the following game. Using dominance, reduce the size of the game, if possible.

	Y_1	Y_2
X_1	6	5
X_2	20	23
X_3	15	11

Solution

After carefully analyzing the game, George realizes that he will never play strategy X_1. The best outcome for this strategy (6) is worse than the worst outcome for the other two strategies. In addition, George would never play strategy X_3, for the same reason. Thus, George will always play strategy X_2. Given this situation, player Y would always play strategy Y_1 to minimize her losses. This is a pure strategy game with George playing X_2 and person Y playing strategy Y_1. The value of the game for this problem is the outcome of these two strategies, which is 20.

Solved Problem 2

Using the solution procedure for a mixed strategy game, solve the following game:

	Y_1	Y_2
X_1	4	2
X_2	0	10

Solution

This game can be solved by setting up the mixed strategy table and developing the appropriate equations:

		Y_1	Y_2	
		P	$1 - P$	**Expected gain**
X_1	Q	4	2	$4P + 2(1 - P)$
X_1	$1 - Q$	1	10	$0P + 10(1 - P)$
Expected gain		$4Q + 0(1 - Q)$	$2Q + 10(1 - Q)$	

The equations for Q are

$$4Q + 0(1 - Q) = 2Q + 10(1 - Q)$$
$$4Q = 2Q + 10 - 10Q$$
$$12Q = 10 \text{ or } Q = {}^{10}/_{12} \text{ and } 1 - Q = {}^{2}/_{12}$$

The equations for P are

$$4P + 2(1 - P) = 0P + 10(1 - P)$$
$$4P + 2 - 2P = 10 - 10P$$
$$12P = 8 \text{ or } P = {}^{8}/_{12} \text{ and } 1 - P = {}^{4}/_{12}$$

Self-Test

- Before taking the self-test, refer back to the learning objectives at the beginning of the supplement and the glossary at the end of the supplement.
- Use the key at the back of the book to correct your answers.
- Restudy pages that correspond to any questions that you answered incorrectly or material you feel uncertain about.

1. In a two-person, zero-sum game,
   a. each person has two strategies.
   b. whatever is gained by one person is lost by the other.
   c. all payoffs are zero.
   d. a saddle point always exists.
2. A saddle point exists if
   a. the largest payoff in a column is also the smallest payoff in its row.
   b. the smallest payoff in a column is also the largest payoff in its row.
   c. there are only two strategies for each player.
   d. there is a dominated strategy in the game.
3. If the upper and lower values of the game are the same,
   a. there is no solution to the game.
   b. there is a mixed solution to the game.
   c. a saddle point exists.
   d. there is a dominated strategy in the game.
4. In a mixed strategy game,
   a. each player will always play just one strategy.
   b. there is no saddle point.
   c. each player will try to maximize the maximum of all possible payoffs.
   d. a player will play each of two strategies exactly 50% of the time.

5. In a two-person zero-sum game, it is determined that strategy X_1 dominates strategy X_2. This means
   a. strategy X_1 will never be chosen.
   b. the payoffs for strategy X_1 will be greater than or equal to the payoffs for X_2.
   c. a saddle point exists in the game.
   d. a mixed strategy must be used.
6. In a pure strategy game,
   a. each player will randomly choose the strategy to be used.
   b. each player will always select the same strategy, regardless of what the other person does.
   c. there will never be a saddle point.
   d. the value of the game must be computed using probabilities.
7. The solution to a mixed strategy game is based on the assumption that
   a. each player wishes to maximize the long-run average payoff.
   b. both players can be winners with no one experiencing any loss.
   c. players act irrationally.
   d. there is sometimes a better solution than a saddle point solution.

Discussion Questions and Problems

Discussion Questions

1   What is a two-person, zero-sum game?

2   How do you compute the value of the game?

3   What is a pure strategy?

4   Explain the concept of dominance. How is it used?

5   How is a saddle point found in a game?

6   How do you determine whether a game is a pure strategy game or a mixed strategy game?

7   What is a mixed game, and how is it solved?

Problems*

Q•8 Determine the strategies for X and Y, given the following game. What is the value of the game?

	Y_1	Y_2
X_1	2	−4
X_2	6	10

Q•9 What is the value of the following game and the strategies for A and B?

	B_1	B_2
A_1	19	20
A_2	5	−4

Q:10 Determine each player's strategy and the value of the game, given the following table:

	Y_1	Y_2
X_1	86	42
X_2	36	106

Q:11 What is the value of the following game?

	S_1	S_2
R_1	21	116
R_2	89	3

Q:12 Player A has a $1 bill and a $20 bill, and player B has a $5 bill and a $10 bill. Each player will select a bill from the other player without knowing what bill the other player selected. If the total of the bills selected is odd, player A gets both of the two bills that were selected, but if the total is even, player B gets both bills.
(a) Develop a payoff table for this game. (Place the sum of both bills in each cell.)
(b) What are the best strategies for each player?
(c) What is the value of the game? Which player would you like to be?

Q:13 Resolve Problem 12. If the total of the bills is even, player A gets both of the bills selected, but if the total is odd, player B gets both bills.

Q:14 Solve the following game:

	Y_1	Y_2
X_1	−5	−10
X_2	12	8
X_3	4	12
X_4	−40	−5

Q:15 Shoe Town and Fancy Foot are both vying for more share of the market. If Shoe Town does no advertising, it will not lose any share of the market if Fancy Foot does nothing. It will lose 2% of the market if Fancy Foot invests $10,000 in advertising, and it will lose 5% of the market if Fancy Foot invests $20,000 in advertising. On the other hand, if Shoe Town invests $15,000 in advertising, it will gain 3% of the market if Fancy Foot does nothing; it will gain 1% of the market if Fancy Foot invests $10,000 in advertising; and it will lose 1% if Fancy Foot invests $20,000 in advertising.
(a) Develop a payoff table for this problem.
(b) Determine the various strategies using the computer.
(c) How would you determine the value of the game?

Q:16 Assume that a 1% increase in the market means a profit of $1,000. Resolve Problem 15, using monetary value instead of market share.

Q:17 Solve for the optimal strategies and the value of the following game:

A \ B	STRATEGY B_1	STRATEGY B_2	STRATEGY B_3
STRATEGY A_1	−10	5	15
STRATEGY A_2	20	2	−20
STRATEGY A_3	6	2	6
STRATEGY A_4	−13	−10	44
STRATEGY A_5	−30	0	45
STRATEGY A_6	16	−20	6

Q:18 For the following two-person, zero-sum game, are there any dominated strategies? If so, eliminate any dominated strategy and find the value of the game.

	PLAYER Y's STRATEGIES		
		Y_1	Y_2	Y_3
PLAYER X's STRATEGIES	X_1	4	5	10
	X_2	3	4	2
	X_3	8	6	9

Q:19 Refer to Problem 8. There is a saddle point in this game, making it a pure strategy game. Ignore this and solve it as a mixed strategy game. What special condition in the solution indicates that this should not have been solved as a mixed strategy game?

---

*Note: ℚ means the problem may be solved with QM for Windows.

● : 20   Petroleum Research, Inc. (*A*), and Extraction International, Inc. (*B*), have each developed a new extraction procedure that will remove metal and other contaminants from used automotive engine oil. The equipment is expensive, and the extraction process is complex, but the approach provides an economical way to recycle used engine oil. Both companies have developed unique technical procedures. Both companies also believe that advertising and promotion are critical to their success. Petroleum Research, with the help of an advertising firm, has developed 15 possible strategies. Extraction International has developed 5 possible advertising strategies. The economic outcome in millions of dollars is shown in the following table. What strategy do you recommend for Petroleum Research? How much money can it expect from its approach?

A \ B	STRATEGY B_1	STRATEGY B_2	STRATEGY B_3	STRATEGY B_4	STRATEGY B_5
STRATEGY A_1	1	2	2	1	4
STRATEGY A_2	−1	3	−6	7	5
STRATEGY A_3	10	−3	−5	−20	12
STRATEGY A_4	6	−8	5	2	2
STRATEGY A_5	−5	3	3	7	5
STRATEGY A_6	−1	−1	−3	4	−2
STRATEGY A_7	−1	0	0	0	−1
STRATEGY A_8	3	6	−6	8	3
STRATEGY A_9	2	6	−5	4	−7
STRATEGY A_{10}	0	0	0	−5	7
STRATEGY A_{11}	4	8	−5	3	3
STRATEGY A_{12}	−3	−3	0	3	3
STRATEGY A_{13}	1	0	0	−2	2
STRATEGY A_{14}	4	3	3	5	7
STRATEGY A_{15}	4	−4	4	−5	5

Bibliography

Bierman, H., and L. Fernandez. *Game Theory with Economic Applications*, 2nd ed. New York: Addison-Wesley, 1998.

Bowen, Kenneth Credson, with contributions by Janet I. Harris. *Research Games: An Approach to the Study of Decision Process.* New York: Halstead Press, 1978.

Brandenburger, A., et al. "The Right Game: Use Game Theory to Shape Strategy," *Harvard Business Review* (July–August 1995): 57–71.

Bushko, David, et al. "Consulting's Future, Game Theory, and Storytelling," *Journal of Management Consulting* (November 1997): 3.

Davis, M. *Game Theory: A Nontechnical Introduction.* New York: Basic Books, Inc., 1970.

Dixit, A. K., and Susan Skeath. *Games of Strategy.* New York; WW Norton and Co., 1999.

Dutta, Prajit. *Strategies and Games: Theory and Practice.* Cambridge, MA: MIT Press, 1999.

Fudenberg, D., and D. K. Levine. *The Theory of Learning in Games.* Cambridge, MA: MIT Press, 1998.

Koselka, Rita. "Playing Poker with Craig McCaw," *Forbes* (July 3, 1995): 62–64.

Lan, Lim, et al. "Property Acquisition and Negotiation Styles," *Real Estate Finance* (Spring 1998): 72.

Lucas, W. "An Overview of the Mathematical Theory of Games," *Management Science* 8, 5, Part II (January 1972): 3–19.

Luce, R. D., and H. Raiffa. *Games and Decisions.* New York: John Wiley & Sons, Inc., 1957.

Shubik, M. *The Uses and Methods of Game Theory.* New York: American Elsevier Publishing Company, 1957.

Sinha, Arunava. "The Value Addition Game," *Business Today* (February 7, 1998): 143.

von Neumann, J., and O. Morgenstern. *Theory of Games and Economic Behavior.* Princeton, NJ: Princeton University Press, 1944.

Appendix 1: Game Theory with QM for Windows

In this module we show how to solve 2×2 games using a variety of techniques. In Section 5, for example, we discuss how a mixed strategy game could be solved using straightforward algebraic techniques. In this game, player X will receive 4 and 2 by playing strategy X_1 when player Y plays strategies Y_1 and Y_2, respectively. Values of 1 and 10 are the results when player X_1 plays strategy X_2.

To illustrate QM for Windows, let's use these data. Program 1 shows the mix that each player should play for each strategy. The value of the game, 3.45, is displayed at the bottom right of the decision table.

PROGRAM 1

QM for Windows Output for Game Theory

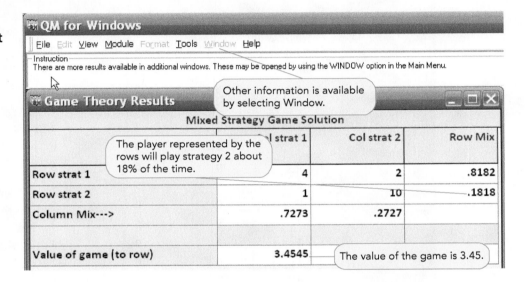

Linear Programming Models: Graphical and Computer Methods

LEARNING OBJECTIVES

After completing this chapter, students will be able to:

1. Understand the basic assumptions and properties of linear programming (LP).
2. Graphically solve any LP problem that has only two variables by both the corner point and isoprofit line methods.
3. Understand special issues in LP such as infeasibility, unboundedness, redundancy, and alternative optimal solutions.
4. Understand the role of sensitivity analysis.
5. Use Excel spreadsheets to solve LP problems.

CHAPTER OUTLINE

1 Introduction

Linear programming is a technique that helps in resource allocation decisions.

Many management decisions involve trying to make the most effective use of an organization's resources. Resources typically include machinery, labor, money, time, warehouse space, and raw materials. These resources may be used to make products (such as machinery, furniture, food, or clothing) or services (such as schedules for airlines or production, advertising policies, or investment decisions). **Linear programming (LP)** is a widely used mathematical modeling technique designed to help managers in planning and decision making relative to resource allocation. We devote this chapter to illustrating how and why linear programming works.

Despite its name, LP and the more general category of techniques called **"mathematical" programming** have very little to do with computer programming. In the world of management science, *programming* refers to modeling and solving a problem mathematically. Computer programming has, of course, played an important role in the advancement and use of LP. Real-life LP problems are too cumbersome to solve by hand or with a calculator. So throughout the text on LP we give examples of how valuable a computer program can be in solving an LP problem.

2 Requirements of a Linear Programming Problem

Problems seek to maximize or minimize an objective.

In the past 60 years, LP has been applied extensively to military, industrial, financial, marketing, accounting, and agricultural problems. Even though these applications are diverse, all LP problems have several properties and assumptions in common.

All problems seek to *maximize* or *minimize* some quantity, usually profit or cost. We refer to this property as the **objective function** of an LP problem. The major objective of a typical manufacturer is to maximize dollar profits. In the case of a trucking or railroad distribution system, the objective might be to minimize shipping costs. In any event, this objective must be stated clearly and defined mathematically. It does not matter, by the way, whether profits and costs are measured in cents, dollars, or millions of dollars.

Constraints limit the degree to which the objective can be obtained.

The second property that LP problems have in common is the presence of restrictions, or **constraints**, that limit the degree to which we can pursue our objective. For example, deciding how many units of each product in a firm's product line to manufacture is restricted by available personnel and machinery. Selection of an advertising policy or a financial portfolio is limited by the amount of money available to be spent or invested. We want, therefore, to maximize or minimize a quantity (the objective function) subject to limited resources (the constraints).

There must be alternatives available.

There must be alternative courses of action to choose from. For example, if a company produces three different products, management may use LP to decide how to allocate among them its limited production resources (of personnel, machinery, and so on). Should it devote all manufacturing capacity to make only the first product, should it produce equal amounts of each product, or should it allocate the resources in some other ratio? If there were no alternatives to select from, we would not need LP.

Mathematical relationships are linear.

The objective and constraints in LP problems must be expressed in terms of *linear* equations or inequalities. Linear mathematical relationships just mean that all terms used in the objective function and constraints are of the first degree (i.e., not squared, or to the third or higher power, or appearing more than once). Hence, the equation $2A + 5B = 10$ is an acceptable linear function, while the equation $2A^2 + 5B^3 + 3AB = 10$ is not linear because the variable A is squared, the variable B is cubed, and the two variables appear again as a product of each other.

The term *linear* implies both proportionality and additivity. Proportionality means that if production of 1 unit of a product uses 3 hours, production of 10 units would use 30 hours. Additivity means that the total of all activities equals the sum of the individual activities. If the production of one product generated \$3 profit and the production of another product generated \$8 profit, the total profit would be the sum of these two, which would be \$11.

We assume that conditions of *certainty* exist: that is, number in the objective and constraints are known with certainty and do not change during the period being studied.

We make the *divisibility* assumption that solutions need not be in whole numbers (integers). Instead, they are divisible and may take any fractional value. In production problems, we often

TABLE 1
LP Properties and Assumptions

PROPERTIES OF LINEAR PROGRAMS
1. One objective function
2. One or more constraints
3. Alternative courses of action
4. Objective function and constraints are linear—proportionality and divisibility
5. Certainty
6. Divisibility
7. Nonnegative variables

define variables as the number of units produced per week or per month, and a fractional value (e.g., 0.3 chairs) would simply mean that there is work in process. Something that was started in one week can be finished in the next. However, in other types of problems, fractional values do not make sense. If a fraction of a product cannot be purchased (for example, one-third of a submarine), an integer programming problem exists.

Finally, we assume that all answers or variables are *nonnegative*. Negative values of physical quantities are impossible; you simply cannot produce a negative number of chairs, shirts, lamps, or computers. Table 1 summarizes these properties and assumptions.

3 Formulating LP Problems

Formulating a linear program involves developing a mathematical model to represent the managerial problem. Thus, in order to formulate a linear program, it is necessary to completely understand the managerial problem being faced. Once this is understood, we can begin to develop the mathematical statement of the problem. The steps in formulating a linear program follow:

1. Completely understand the managerial problem being faced.
2. Identify the objective and the constraints.
3. Define the decision variables.
4. Use the decision variables to write mathematical expressions for the objective function and the constraints.

Product mix problems use LP to decide how much of each product to make, given a series of resource restrictions.

One of the most common LP applications is the **product mix problem**. Two or more products are usually produced using limited resources such as personnel, machines, raw materials, and so on. The profit that the firm seeks to maximize is based on the profit contribution per unit of each product. (Profit contribution, you may recall, is just the selling price per unit minus the

---

HISTORY   How Linear Programming Started

Linear programming was conceptually developed before World War II by the outstanding Soviet mathematician A. N. Kolmogorov. Another Russian, Leonid Kantorovich, won the Nobel Prize in Economics for advancing the concepts of optimal planning. An early application of LP, by Stigler in 1945, was in the area we today call "diet problems."

Major progress in the field, however, took place in 1947 and later when George D. Dantzig developed the solution procedure known as the *simplex algorithm*. Dantzig, then an Air Force mathematician, was assigned to work on logistics problems. He noticed that many problems involving limited resources and more than one demand could be set up in terms of a series of equations and inequalities. Although early LP applications were military in nature, industrial applications rapidly became apparent with the spread of business computers. In 1984, N. Karmarkar developed an algorithm that appears to be superior to the simplex method for many very large applications.

TABLE 2
**Flair Furniture
Company Data**

DEPARTMENT	HOURS REQUIRED TO PRODUCE 1 UNIT		AVAILABLE HOURS THIS WEEK
	(T) TABLES	(C) CHAIRS	
Carpentry	4	3	240
Painting and varnishing	2	1	100
Profit per unit	$70	$50	

variable cost per unit.*) The company would like to determine how many units of each product it should produce so as to maximize overall profit given its limited resources. A problem of this type is formulated in the following example.

Flair Furniture Company

The Flair Furniture Company produces inexpensive tables and chairs. The production process for each is similar in that both require a certain number of hours of carpentry work and a certain number of labor hours in the painting and varnishing department. Each table takes 4 hours of carpentry and 2 hours in the painting and varnishing shop. Each chair requires 3 hours in carpentry and 1 hour in painting and varnishing. During the current production period, 240 hours of carpentry time are available and 100 hours in painting and varnishing time are available. Each table sold yields a profit of $70; each chair produced is sold for a $50 profit.

Flair Furniture's problem is to determine the best possible combination of tables and chairs to manufacture in order to reach the maximum profit. The firm would like this production mix situation formulated as an LP problem.

We begin by summarizing the information needed to formulate and solve this problem (see Table 2). This helps us understand the problem being faced. Next we identify the objective and the constraints. The objective is

Maximize profit

The constraints are

1. The hours of carpentry time used cannot exceed 240 hours per week.
2. The hours of painting and varnishing time used cannot exceed 100 hours per week.

The decision variables that represent the actual decisions we will make are defined as

$$T = \text{number of tables to be produced per week}$$
$$C = \text{number of chairs to be produced per week}$$

Now we can create the LP objective function in terms of T and C. The objective function is Maximize profit $= \$70T + \$50C$.

Our next step is to develop mathematical relationships to describe the two constraints in this problem. One general relationship is that the amount of a resource used is to be less than or equal to ($\le$) the amount of resource *available*.

In the case of the carpentry department, the total time used is

$$(4 \text{ hours per table})(\text{Number of tables produced})$$
$$+ \ (3 \text{ hours per chair})(\text{Number of chairs produced})$$

The resource constraints put limits on the carpentry labor resource and the painting labor resource mathematically.

So the first constraint may be stated as follows:

$$\text{Carpentry time used} \le \text{Carpentry time available}$$
$$4T + 3C \le 240 \ (\text{hours of carpentry time})$$

---

*Technically, we maximize total contribution margin, which is the difference between unit selling price and costs that vary in proportion to the quantity of the item produced. Depreciation, fixed general expense, and advertising are excluded from calculations.

Similarly, the second constraint is as follows:

Painting and varnishing time used $\leq$ Painting and varnishing time available

$$②T + 1C \leq 100 \text{ (hours of painting and varnishing time)}$$

—(This means that each table produced takes two hours of the painting and varnishing resource.)

Both of these constraints represent production capacity restrictions and, of course, affect the total profit. For example, Flair Furniture cannot produce 80 tables during the production period because if $T = 80$, both constraints will be violated. It also cannot make $T = 50$ tables and $C = 10$ chairs. Why? Because this would violate the second constraint that no more than 100 hours of painting and varnishing time be allocated.

To obtain meaningful solutions, the values for T and C must be nonnegative numbers. That is, all potential solutions must represent real tables and real chairs. Mathematically, this means that

$$T \geq 0 \text{ (number of tables produced is greater than or equal to 0)}$$
$$C \geq 0 \text{ (number of chairs produced is greater than or euqal to 0)}$$

The complete problem may now be restated mathematically as

$$\text{Maximize profit} = \$70T + \$50C$$

subject to the constraints

Here is a complete mathematical statement of the LP problem.

$$
\begin{aligned}
4T + 3C &\leq 240 && \text{(carpentry constraint)} \\
2T + 1C &\leq 100 && \text{(painting and varnishing constraint)} \\
T &\geq 0 && \text{(first nonnegativity constraint)} \\
C &\geq 0 && \text{(second nonnegativity constraint)}
\end{aligned}
$$

While the nonnegativity constraints are technically separate constraints, they are often written on a single line with the variables separated by commas. In this example, this would be written as

$$T, C \geq 0$$

4   Graphical Solution to an LP Problem

The graphical method works only when there are two decision variables, but it provides valuable insight into how larger problems are structured.

The easiest way to solve a small LP problem such as that of the Flair Furniture Company is with the graphical solution approach. The graphical procedure is useful only when there are two decision variables (such as number of tables to produce, T, and number of chairs to produce, C) in the problem. When there are more than two variables, it is not possible to plot the solution on a two-dimensional graph and we must turn to more complex approaches. But the graphical method is invaluable in providing us with insights into how other approaches work. For that reason alone, it is worthwhile to spend the rest of this chapter exploring graphical solutions as an intuitive basis for the chapters on mathematical programming that follow.

Graphical Representation of Constraints

To find the optimal solution to an LP problem, we must first identify a set, or region, of feasible solutions. The first step in doing so is to plot each of the problem's constraints on a graph. The variable T (tables) is plotted as the horizontal axis of the graph and the variable C (chairs) is plotted as the vertical axis of the graph. The notation (T, C) is used to identify the points on the graph. The **nonnegativity constraints** mean that we are always working in the first (or northeast) quadrant of a graph (see Figure 1).

Nonnegativity constraints mean $T \geq 0$ and $C \geq 0$.

To represent the first constraint graphically, $4T + 3C \leq 240$, we must first graph the equality portion of this, which is

$$4T + 3C = 240$$

Plotting the first constraint involves finding points at which the line intersects the T and C axes.

As you may recall from elementary algebra, a linear equation in two variables is a straight line. The easiest way to plot the line is to find any two points that satisfy the equation, then draw a straight line through them.

The two easiest points to find are generally the points at which the line intersects the T and C axes.

FIGURE 1

Quadrant Containing All Positive Values

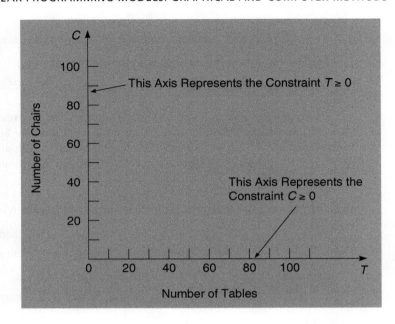

When Flair Furniture produces no tables, namely $T = 0$, it implies that

$$4(0) + 3C = 240$$

or

$$3C = 240$$

or

$$C = 80$$

In other words, if *all* of the carpentry time available is used to produce chairs, 80 chairs *could* be made. Thus, this constraint equation crosses the vertical axis at 80.

To find the point at which the line crosses the horizontal axis, we assume that the firm makes no chairs, that is, $C = 0$. Then

$$4T + 3(0) = 240$$

or

$$4T = 240$$

or

$$T = 60$$

Hence, when $C = 0$, we see that $4T = 240$ and that $T = 60$.

The carpentry constraint is illustrated in Figure 2. It is bounded by the line running from point $(T = 0, C = 80)$ to point $(T = 60, C = 0)$.

Recall, however, that the actual carpentry constraint was the **inequality** $4T + 3C \leq 240$. How can we identify all of the solution points that satisfy this constraint? It turns out that there are three possibilities. First, we know that any point that lies on the line $4T + 3C = 240$ satisfies the constraint. Any combination of tables and chairs on the line will use up all 240 hours of carpentry time.[*] Now we must find the set of solution points that would use less than the 240 hours. The points that satisfy the $<$ portion of the constraint (i.e., $4T + 3C < 240$) will be all the points on one side of the line, while all the points on the other side of the line will not satisfy this condition. To determine which side of the line this is, simply choose any point on either side

---

[*]Thus, what we have done is to plot the constraint equation in its most binding position, that is, using all of the carpentry resource.

FIGURE 2

Graph of Carpentry Constraint Equation $4T + 3C = 240$

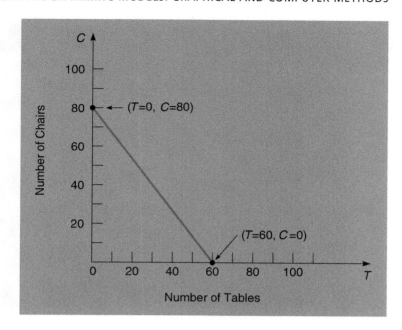

of the constraint line shown in Figure 2 and check to see if it satisfies this condition. For example, choose the point (30, 20), as illustrated in Figure 3:

$$4(30) + 3(20) = 180$$

Since $180 < 240$, this point satisfies the constraint, and all points on this side of the line will also satisfy the constraint. This set of points is indicated by the shaded region in Figure 3.

To see what would happen if the point did not satisfy the constraint, select a point on the other side of the line, such as (70, 40). This constraint would not be met at this point as

$$4(70) + 3(40) = 400$$

Since $400 > 240$, this point and every other point on that side of the line would not satisfy this constraint. Thus, the solution represented by the point (70, 40) would require more than the 240 hours that are available. There are not enough carpentry hours to produce 70 tables and 40 chairs.

FIGURE 3

Region that Satisfies the Carpentry Constraint

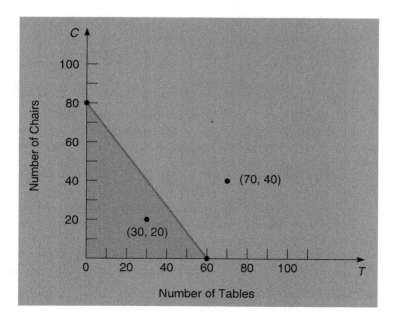

FIGURE 4

Region that Satisfies the Painting and Varnishing Constraint

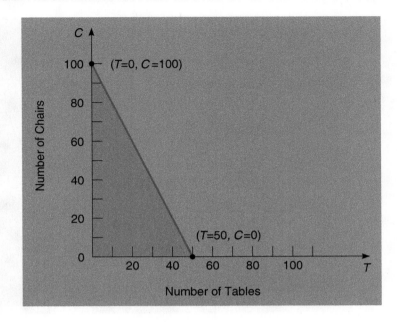

Next, let us identify the solution corresponding to the second constraint, which limits the time available in the painting and varnishing department. That constraint was given as $2T + 1C \leq 100$. As before, we start by graphing the equality portion of this constraint, which is

$$2T + 1C = 100$$

To find two points on the line, select $T = 0$ and solve for C:

$$2(0) + 1C = 100$$
$$C = 100$$

So, one point on the line is $(0, 100)$. To find the second point, select $C = 0$ and solve for T:

$$2T + 1(0) = 100$$
$$T = 50$$

The second point used to graph the line is $(50, 0)$. Plotting this point, $(50, 0)$, and the other point, $(0, 100)$, results in the line representing all the solutions in which exactly 100 hours of painting and varnishing time are used, as shown in Figure 4.

To find the points that require less than 100 hours, select a point on either side of this line to see if the inequality portion of the constraint is satisfied. Selecting $(0, 0)$ give us

$$2(0) + 1(0) = 0 < 100$$

This indicates that this and all the points below the line satisfy the constraint, and this region is shaded in Figure 4.

Now that each individual constraint has been plotted on a graph, it is time to move on to the next step. We recognize that to produce a chair or a table, both the carpentry and painting and *In LP problems we are interested* varnishing departments must be used. In an LP problem we need to find that set of solution *in satisfying all contraints at the* points that satisfies all of the constraints *simultaneously*. Hence, the constraints should be *same time.* redrawn on one graph (or superimposed one upon the other). This is shown in Figure 5.

The shaded region now represents the area of solutions that does not exceed either of the two Flair Furniture constraints. It is known by the term *area of feasible solutions* or, more *The feasible region is the set of* simply, the **feasible region**. The feasible region in an LP problem must satisfy *all* conditions *points that satisfy all the* specified by the problem's constraints, and is thus the region where all constraints overlap. *constraints.* Any point in the region would be a **feasible solution** to the Flair Furniture problem; any point outside the shaded area would represent an **infeasible solution**. Hence, it would be feasible to

FIGURE 5

Feasible Solution Region for the Flair Furniture Company Problem

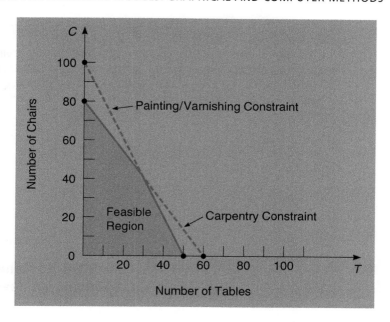

manufacture 30 tables and 20 chairs ($T = 30, C = 20$) during a production period because both constraints are observed:

Carpentry constraint	$4T + 3C \leq 240$ hours available
	$(4)(30) + (3)(20) = 180$ hours used ⊘
Painting constraint	$2T + 1C \leq 100$ hours available
	$(2)(30) + (1)(20) = 80$ hours used ⊘

But it would violate both of the constraints to produce 70 tables and 40 chairs, as we see here mathematically:

Carpentry constraint	$4T + 3C \leq 240$ hours available
	$(4)(70) + (3)(40) = 400$ hours used ⊗
Painting constraint	$2T + 1C \leq 100$ hours available
	$(2)(70) + (1)(40) = 180$ hours used ⊗

Furthermore, it would also be infeasible to manufacture 50 tables and 5 chairs ($T = 50$, $C = 5$). Can you see why?

Carpentry constraint	$4T + 3C \leq 240$ hours available
	$(4)(50) + (3)(5) = 215$ hours used ⊘
Painting constraint	$2T + 1C \leq 100$ hours available
	$(2)(50) + (1)(5) = 105$ hours used ⊗

This possible solution falls within the time available in carpentry but exceeds the time available in painting and varnishing and thus falls outside the feasible region.

Isoprofit Line Solution Method

Now that the feasible region has been graphed, we may proceed to find the optimal solution to the problem. The optimal solution is the point lying in the feasible region that produces the highest profit. Yet there are many, many possible solution points in the region. How do we go about selecting the best one, the one yielding the highest profit?

The isoprofit method is the first method we introduce for finding the optimal solution.

There are a few different approaches that can be taken in solving for the optimal solution when the feasible region has been established graphically. The speediest one to apply is called the *isoprofit line method.*

We start the technique by letting profits equal some arbitrary but small dollar amount. For the Flair Furniture problem we may choose a profit of $2,100. This is a profit level that can be obtained easily without violating either of the two constraints. The objective function can be written as $\$2,100 = 70T + 50C$.

This expression is just the equation of a line; we call it an **isoprofit line**. It represents all combinations of (T, C) that would yield a total profit of \$2,100. To plot the profit line, we proceed exactly as we did to plot a constraint line. First, let $T = 0$ and solve for the point at which the line crosses the C axis:

$$\$2,100 = \$70(0) = \$50C$$
$$C = 42 \text{ chairs}$$

Then, let $C = 0$ and solve for T:

$$\$2,100 = \$70T + 50(0)$$
$$T = 30 \text{ tables}$$

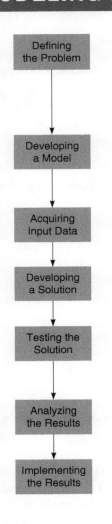

MODELING IN THE REAL WORLD

Setting Crew Schedules at American Airlines

Defining the Problem

American Airlines (AA) employs more than 8,300 pilots and 16,200 flight attendants to fly more than 5,000 aircraft. Total cost of American's crews exceed \$1.4 billion per year, second only to fuel cost. Scheduling crews is one of AA's biggest and most complex problems. The FAA sets work-time limitations designed to ensure that crew members can fulfill their duties safely. And union contracts specify that crews will be guaranteed pay for some number of hours each day or each trip.

Developing a Model

American Airlines Decision Technologies (AA's consulting group) spent 15 labor-years in developing an LP model called TRIP (trip reevaluation and improvement program). The TRIP model builds crew schedules that meet or exceed crews' pay guarantee to the maximum extent possible.

Acquiring Input Data

Data and constraints are derived from salary information and union and FAA rules that specify maximum duty lengths, overnight costs, airline schedules, and plane sizes.

Developing a Solution

It takes about 500 hours of mainframe computer time per month to develop crew schedules—these are prepared 40 days prior to the targeted month.

Testing the Solution

TRIP results were originally compared with crew assignments constructed manually. Since 1971, the model has been improved with new LP techniques, new constraints, and faster hardware and software. A series of what-if? studies have tested TRIP's ability to reach more accurate and optimal solutions.

Analyzing the Results

Each year the LP model improves AA's efficiency and allows the airline to operate with a proportionately smaller work crew. A faster TRIP system now allows sensitivity analysis of the schedule in its first week.

Implementing the Results

The model, fully implemented, generates annual savings of more than \$20 million. AA has also sold TRIP to 10 other airlines and one railroad.

Source: Based on R. Anbil, et al. "Recent Advances in Crew Pairing Optimization at American Airlines," *Interfaces* 21, 1 (January–February 1991): 62–74.

FIGURE 6

Profit Line of $2,100 Plotted for the Flair Furniture Company

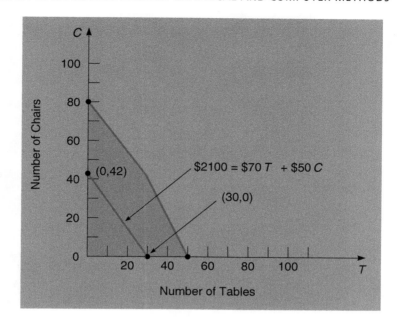

We can now connect these two points with a straight line. This profit line is illustrated in Figure 6. All points on the line represent feasible solutions that produce a profit of $2,100.*

Isoprofit involves graphing parallel profit lines.

Now, obviously, the isoprofit line for $2,100 does not produce the highest possible profit to the firm. In Figure 7 we try graphing two more lines, each yielding a higher profit. The middle equation, $2,800 = \$70T + \$50C$, was plotted in the same fashion as the lower line. When $T = 0$,

$$\$2,800 = \$70(0) + \$50C$$
$$C = 56$$

When $C = 0$,

$$\$2,800 = \$70T + \$50(C)$$
$$T = 40$$

FIGURE 7

Four Isoprofit Lines Plotted for the Flair Furniture Company

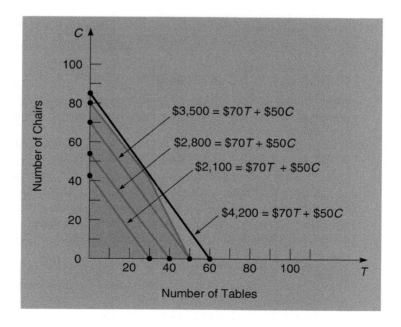

Iso means "equal" or "similar." Thus, an isoprofit line represents a line with all profits the same, in this case $2,100.

FIGURE 8

Optimal Solution to the
Flair Furniture Problem

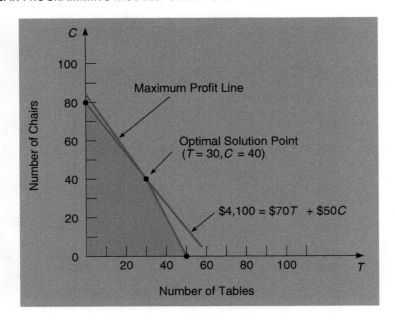

We draw a series of parallel isoprofit lines until we find the highest isoprofit line, that is, the one with the optimal solution.

Again, any combination of tables (*T*) and chairs (*C*) on this isoprofit line produces a total profit of $2,800. Note that the third line generates a profit of $3,500, even more of an improvement. The farther we move from the origin, the higher our profit will be. Another important point is that these isoprofit lines are parallel. We now have two clues as to how to find the optimal solution to the original problem. We can draw a series of parallel lines (by carefully moving our ruler in a plane parallel to the first profit line). The highest profit line that still touches some point of the feasible region pinpoints the optimal solution. Notice that the fourth line ($4,200) is too high to be considered.

The last point that an isoprofit line would touch in this feasible region is the corner point where the two constraint lines intersect, so this point will result in the maximum possible profit. To find the coordinates of this point, solve the two equations simultaneously (as detailed in the next section). This results in the point (30, 40) as shown in Figure 8. Calculating the profit at this point, we get

$$\text{Profit} = 70T + 50C = 70(30) + 50(40) = \$4,100$$

So producing 30 tables and 40 chairs yields the maximum profit of $4,100.

Corner Point Solution Method

A second approach to solving LP problems employs the **corner point method**. This technique is simpler conceptually than the isoprofit line approach, but it involves looking at the profit at every corner point of the feasible region.

The mathematical theory behind LP is that the optimal solution must lie at one of the corner points in the feasible region.

The mathematical theory behind LP states that an optimal solution to any problem (that is, the values of *T*, *C* that yield the maximum profit) will lie at a **corner point**, or **extreme point**, of the feasible region. Hence, it is only necessary to find the values of the variables at each corner; an optimal solution will lie at one (or more) of them.

The first step in the corner point method is to graph the constraints and find the feasible region. This was also the first step in the isoprofit method, and the feasible region is shown again in Figure 9. The second step is to find the corner points of the feasible region. For the Flair Furniture example, the coordinates of three of the corner points are obvious from observing the graph. These are (0, 0), (50, 0), and (0, 80). The fourth corner point is where the two constraint lines intersect, and the coordinates must be found algebraically by solving the two equations simultaneously for two variables.

There are a number of ways to solve equations simultaneously, and any of these may be used. We will illustrate the elimination method here. To begin the elimination method, select a variable to be eliminated. We will select *T* in this example. Then multiply or divide one equation

FIGURE 9

Four Corner Points of the Feasible Region

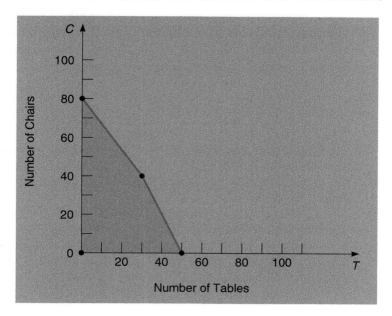

by a number so that the coefficient of that variable (T) in one equation will be the negative of the coefficient of that variable in the other equation. The two constraint equations are

$$4T + 3C = 240 \quad \text{(carpentry)}$$
$$2T + 1C = 100 \quad \text{(painting)}$$

To eliminate T, we multiply the second equation by -2:

$$-2(2T + 1C = 100) = -4T - 2C = -200$$

and then add it to the first equation:

$$\frac{+ 4T + 3C = 240}{+ 1C = 40}$$

or

$$C = 40$$

Doing this has enabled us to eliminate one variable, T, and to solve for C. We can now substitute 40 for C in either of the original equations and solve for T. Let's use the first equation. When $C = 40$, then

$$4T + (3)(40) = 240$$
$$4T + 120 = 240$$

or

$$4T = 120$$
$$T = 30$$

Thus, the last corner point is (30, 40).

The next step is to calculate the value of the objective function at each of the corner points. The final step is to select the corner with the best value, which would be the highest profit in this example. Table 3 lists these corners points with their profits. The highest profit is found to be $4,100, which is obtained when 30 tables and 40 chairs are produced. This is exactly what was obtained using the isoprofit method.

TABLE 3
Feasible Corner Points and Profits for Flair Furniture

NUMBER OF TABLES (T)	NUMBER OF CHAIRS (C)	Profit = $70T + $50C
0	0	$0
50	0	$3,500
0	80	$4,000
30	40	$4,100

Table 4 provides a summary of both the isoprofit method and the corner point method. Either of these can be used when there are two decision variables. If a problem has more than two decision variables, we must rely on the computer software or use the simplex algorithm discussed in Module 7.

Slack and Surplus

In addition to knowing the optimal solution to a linear program, it is helpful to know whether all of the available resources are being used. The term **slack** is used for the amount of a resource that is not used. For a less-than-or-equal to constraint,

$$\text{Slack} = (\text{Amount of resource available}) - (\text{Amount of resource used})$$

In the Flair Furniture example, there were 240 hours of carpentry time available. If the company decided to produce 20 tables and 25 chairs instead of the optimal solution, the amount of carpentry time used $(4T + 3C)$ would be $4(20) + 3(25) = 155$. So,

$$\text{Slack time in carpentry} = 240 - 155 = 85$$

For the optimal solution $(30, 40)$ to the Flair Furniture problem, the slack is 0 since all 240 hours are used.

The term **surplus** is used with greater-than-or-equal-to constraints to indicate the amount by which the right-hand-side of a constraint is exceeded. For a greater-than-or-equal-to constraint,

$$\text{Surplus} = (\text{Actual amount}) - (\text{Minimum amount})$$

Suppose there had been a constraint in the example that required the total number of tables and chairs combined to be at least 42 units (i.e., $T + C \geq 42$), and the company decided to produce 20 tables and 25 chairs. The total amount produced would be $20 + 25 = 45$, so the surplus would be

$$\text{Surplus} = 45 - 42 = 3$$

meaning that 3 units more than the minimum were produced. For the optimal solution $(30, 40)$ in the Flair Furniture problem, if this constraint had been in the problem, the surplus would be $70 - 42 = 28$.

TABLE 4
Summaries of Graphical Solution Methods

ISOPROFIT METHOD

1. Graph all constraints and find the feasible region.
2. Select a specific profit (or cost) line and graph it to find the slope.
3. Move the objective function line in the direction of increasing profit (or decreasing cost) while maintaining the slope. The last point it touches in the feasible region is the optimal solution.
4. Find the values of the decision variables at this last point and compute the profit (or cost).

CORNER POINT METHOD

1. Graph all constraints and find the feasible region.
2. Find the corner points of the feasible region.
3. Compute the profit (or cost) at each of the feasible corner points.
4. Select the corner point with the best value of the objective function found in step 3. This is the optimal solution.

So the slack and surplus represent the difference between the left-hand side (LHS) and the right-hand side (RHS) of a constraint. The term slack is used when referring to less-than-or-equal-to constraints, and the term *surplus* is used when referring to greater-than-or-equal-to constraints. Most computer software for linear programming will provide the amount of slack and surplus that exist for each constraint in the optimal solution.

A constraint that has zero slack or surplus for the optimal solution is called a **binding constraint**. A constraint with positive slack or surplus for the optimal solution is called a **nonbinding constraint**. Some computer output will specify whether a constraint is binding or nonbinding.

5   Solving Flair Furniture's LP Problem Using QM For Windows and Excel

Almost every organization has access to computer programs that are capable of solving enormous LP problems. Although each computer program is slightly different, the approach each takes toward handling LP problems is basically the same. The format of the input data and the level of detail provided in output results may differ from program to program and computer to computer, but once you are experienced in dealing with computerized LP algorithms, you can easily adjust to minor changes.

Using QM for Windows

Let us begin by demonstrating QM for Windows on the Flair Furniture Company problem. To use QM for Windows, select the Linear Programming module. Then specify the number of constraints (other than the nonnegativity constraints, as it is assumed that the variables must be nonnegative), the number of variables, and whether the objective is to be maximized or minimized. For the Flair Furniture Company problem, there are two constraints and two variables. Once these numbers are specified, the input window opens as shown in Program 1A. Then you can enter the coefficients for the objective function and the constraints. Placing the cursor over the $X1$ or $X2$ and typing a new name such as T and C will change the variable names. The constraint names can be similarly modified. Program 1B shows the QM for Windows screen after the data

PROGRAM 1A

QM for Windows Linear Programming Computer Screen for Input of Data

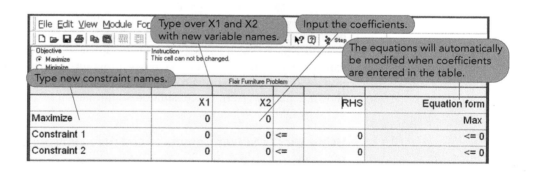

PROGRAM 1B

QM for Windows Data Input for Flair Furniture Problem

	T	C		RHS	Equation form
Maximize	70	50			Max 70T + 50C
Carpentry	4	3	<=	240	4T + 3C <= 240
Painting	2	1	<=	100	2T + C <= 100

PROGRAM 1C

QM for Windows Output for Flair Furniture Problem

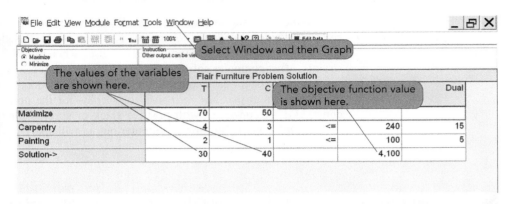

File Edit View Module Format Tools Window Help

Objective
○ Maximize
○ Minimize

Instruction
Other output can be vie...

Select Window and then Graph

The values of the variables are shown here.

Flair Furniture Problem Solution

The objective function value is shown here.

	T	C			Dual
Maximize	70	50			
Carpentry	4	3	<=	240	15
Painting	2	1	<=	100	5
Solution->	30	40		4,100	

PROGRAM 1D

QM for Windows Graphical Output for Flair Furniture Problem

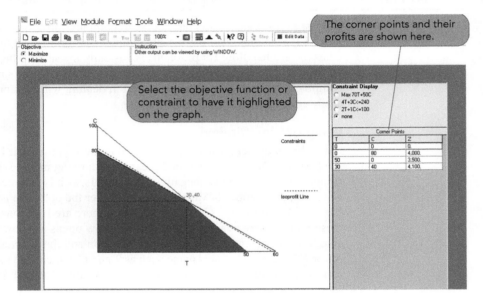

File Edit View Module Format Tools Window Help

Objective
○ Maximize
○ Minimize

Instruction
Other output can be viewed by using WINDOW.

The corner points and their profits are shown here.

Select the objective function or constraint to have it highlighted on the graph.

Constraint Display
○ Max 70T+50C
○ 4T+3C<=240
○ 2T+1C<=100
○ none

Constraints

Isoprofit Line

		Corner Points	
T	C	Z
0	0	0
0	80	4,000
50	0	3,500
30	40	4,100

has been input and before the problem is solved. When you click the Solve button, you get the output shown in Program 1C. Modify the problem by clicking the Edit button and returning to the input screen to make any desired changes.

Once the problem has been solved, a graph may be displayed by selecting Window—Graph from the menu bar in QM for Windows. Program 1D shows the output for the graphical solution. Notice that in addition to the graph, the corner points and the original problem are also shown. Later we return to see additional information related to sensitivity analysis that is provided by QM for Windows.

Using Excel's Solver Command to Solve LP Problems

Excel 2010 (as well as earlier versions) has an add-in called Solver that can be used to solve linear programs. If this add-in doesn't appear on the Data tab in Excel 2010, it has not been activated.

PREPARING THE SPREADSHEET FOR SOLVER The spreadsheet must be prepared with data and formulas for certain calculations before Solver can be used. Excel QM can be used to simplify this process (see Appendix 1). We will briefly describe the steps, and further discussion and suggestions will be provided when the Flair Furniture example is presented. Here is a summary of the steps to prepare the spreadsheet:

1. Enter the problem data. The problem data consist of the coefficients of the objective function and the constraints, plus the RHS values for each of the constraints. It is best to organize this in a logical and meaningful way. The coefficients will be used when writing formulas in steps 3 and 4, and the RHS will be entered into Solver.

PROGRAM 2A

Excel Data Input for the Flair Furniture Example

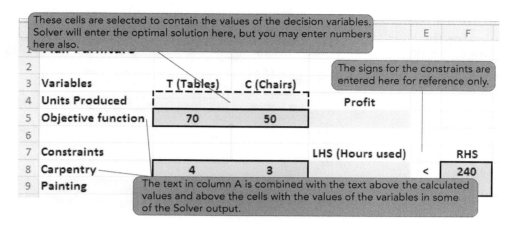

	These cells are selected to contain the values of the decision variables. Solver will enter the optimal solution here, but you may enter numbers here also.			E	F
2					
3	Variables	T (Tables)	C (Chairs)		The signs for the constraints are entered here for reference only.
4	Units Produced			Profit	
5	Objective function	70	50		
6					
7	Constraints			LHS (Hours used)	RHS
8	Carpentry	4	3	<	240
9	Painting	The text in column A is combined with the text above the calculated values and above the cells with the values of the variables in some of the Solver output.			

2. Designate specific cells for the values of the decision variables. Later, these cell addresses will be input into Solver.

3. Write a formula to calculate the value of the objective function, using the coefficients for the objective function (from step 1) that you have entered and the cells containing the values of the decision variables (from step 2). Later, this cell address will be input into Solver.

4. Write a formula to calculate the value of the left-hand-side (LHS) of each constraint, using the coefficients for the constraints (from step 1) that you have entered and the cells containing the values of the decision variables (from step 2). Later, these cell addresses and the cell addresses for the corresponding RHS value will be input into Solver.

These four steps must be completed in some way with all linear programs in Excel. Additional information may be put into the spreadsheet for clarification purposes. Let's illustrate these with an example. Helpful suggestions will be provided.

1. Enter the problem data. Program 2A contains input data for the Flair Furniture problem. It is usually best to use one column for each variable and one row for each constraint. Descriptive labels should be put in column A. Variable names or a description should be put just above the cells for the solution, and the coefficients in the objective function and constraints should be in the same columns as these names. For this example, T (Tables) and C (Chairs), have been entered in cells B3 and C3. Just the words Tables and Chairs or just the variables names T and C could have been used. The cells where the coefficients are to be entered have been given a different background color (shading) and outlined with a bold line to highlight them for this example.

Row 5 was chosen as the objective function row, and the words "Objective function" were entered into column A. Excel will use these words in the output. The profit (objective function coefficient) for each table is entered into B5, while the profit on each chair is entered into C5. Similarly, the words Carpentry and Painting were entered into column A for the carpentry and painting constraints. The coefficients for T and C in these constraints are in rows 8 and 9. The RHS values are entered in the appropriate rows; the test RHS is entered above the values, and this text will appear in the Solver output. Since both of these constraints are $\leq$ constraints, the symbol $<$ has been entered in column E, next to the RHS values. It is understood that the equality portion of $\leq$ is a part of the constraint. While it is not necessary to have the signs ($<$) for the constraints anywhere in the spreadsheet, having them explicitly shown acts as a reminder for the user of the spreadsheet when entering the problem into Solver.

PROGRAM 2B

Formulas for the Flair Furniture Example

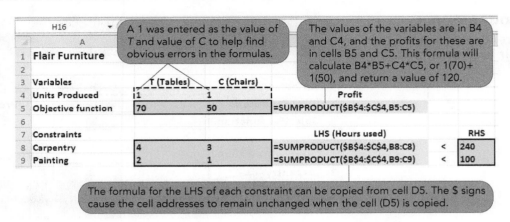

The words in column A and the words immediately above the input data are used in the Solver output unless the cells or cell ranges are explicitly named in Excel. In Excel 2010, names can be assigned by selecting *Name Manager* on the *Formula* tab.

2. Designate specific cells for the values of the decision variables. There must be one cell for the value of *T* (cell C4) and one cell for the value of *C* (cell D4). These should be in the row underneath the variable names, as the Solver output will associate the values to the text immediately above (cells C3 and D3) the values unless the cells with the values have been given other names using the Excel *Name Manager*.

3. Write a formula to calculate the value of the objective function. Before writing any formulas, it helps to enter a 1 as the value of each variable (cells B4 and C4). This will help to see if the formula has any obvious errors. Cell D5 is selected as the cell for the objective function value, although this cell could be anywhere. It is convenient to keep it in the objective row with the objective function coefficients. The formula in Excel could be written as =B4*B5+C4*C5. However, there is a function in Excel, SUMPRODUCT, that will make this easier. Since the values in cells B4:C4 (from B4 to C4) are to be multiplied by the values in cells B5:C5, the function would be written as =SUMPRODUCT(B4:C4, B5:C5). This will cause the numbers in the first range (B4:C4) to be multiplied by the numbers in the second range (B5:C5) on a term-by-term basis, and then these results will be summed. Since a similar formula will be used for the LHS of the two constraints, it helps to specify (using the $ symbol) that the addresses for the variables are absolute (as opposed to relative) and should not be changed when the formula is copied. This final function would be =SUMPRODUCT($B$4:$C$4,B5:C5), as shown in Program 2B. When this is entered into cell D5, the value in that cell becomes 120 since there is a 1 in cells B4 and D5, and the calculation from the SUMPRODUCT function would be $1(70) + 1(50) = 120$. Program 2C shows the values that resulted from the formulas, and a quick look at the profit per unit tells us we would expect the profit to be 120 if 1 unit of each were made. Had B4:C4 been empty, cell D5 would have a value of 0. There are many ways that a formula can be written incorrectly and result in a value of 0, and obvious errors are not readily seen.

4. Write a formula to calculate the value of the LHS of each constraint. While individual formulas may be written, it is easier to use the SUMPRODUCT function used in step 3. It is even easier to simply copy the formula in cell D5 and paste it into cells D8 and D9, as illustrated in Program 2B. The first cell range, $B$4:$C$4, does not change since it is an absolute address; the second range, B5:C5, does changes. Notice that the values in D8 and D9 are what would be expected since *T* and *C* both have a value of 1.

PROGRAM 2C

Excel Spreadsheet for the Flair Furniture Example

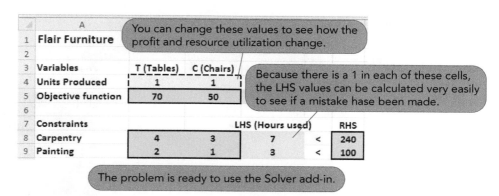

The problem is now ready for the use of Solver. However, even if the optimal solution is not found, this spreadsheet has benefits. You can enter different values for *T* and *C* into cells B4 and C4 just to see how the resource utilization (LHS) and profit change.

USING SOLVER To begin using Solver, go to the *Data* tab in Excel 2010 and click *Solver*, as shown in Program 2D. Once you click Solver, the Solver Parameters dialog box opens, as shown in Program 2E, and the following inputs should be entered, although the order is not important:

1. In the Set Objective box, enter the cell address for the total profit (D5).

2. In the By Changing Cells box, enter the cell addresses for the variable values (B4:C4). Solver will allow the values in these cells to change while searching for the best value in the Set Objective cell reference.

3. Click *Max* for a maximization problem and *Min* for a minimization problem.

4. Check the box for *Make Unconstrained Variables Non-Negative* since the variables *T* and *C* must be greater than or equal to zero.

5. Click the *Select Solving Method* button and select *Simplex LP* from the menu that appears.

6. Click *Add* to add the constraints. When you do this, the dialog box shown in Program 2F appears.

PROGRAM 2D

Starting Solver

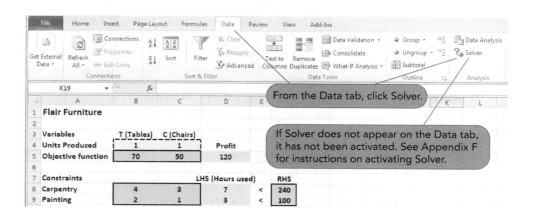

PROGRAM 2E   Solver Parameters Dialog Box

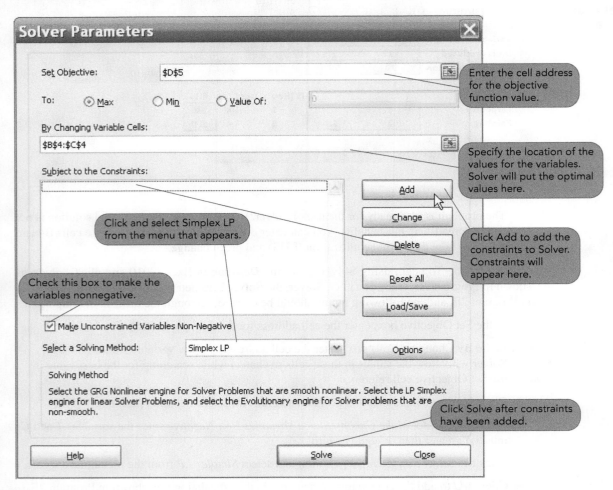

7. In the *Cell Reference* constraint, enter the cell references for the LHS values (D8:D9). Click the button to open the drop-down menu to select <=, which is for ≤ constraints. Then enter the cell references for the RHS values (F8:F9). Since these are all less-than-or-equal-to constraints, they can all be entered at one time by specifying the ranges. If there were other types of constraints, such as ≥ constraints, you could click *Add* after entering these first constraints, and the Add Constraint dialog box would allow you to enter additional constraints. When preparing the spreadsheet for Solver, it is easier if all the ≤ constraints are together and the ≥ constraints are together. When finished entering all the constraints, click *OK*. The Add Constraint dialog box closes, and the Solver Parameters dialog box reopens.

8. Click *Solve* on the Solver Parameters dialog box, and the solution is found. The Solver Results dialog box opens and indicates that a solution was found, as shown in Program 2G. In situations where there is no feasible solution, this box will indicate this. Additional information may be obtained from the Reports section of this as will be seen later. Program 2H shows the results of the spreadsheet with the optimal solution.

PROGRAM 2F

Solver Add Constraint Dialog Box

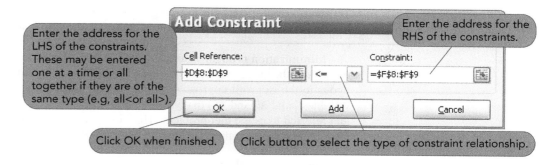

Enter the address for the LHS of the constraints. These may be entered one at a time or all together if they are of the same type (e.g, all< or all>).

Enter the address for the RHS of the constraints.

Add Constraint

Cell Reference: $D$8:$D$9   <=   =$F$8:$F$9

OK   Add   Cancel

Click OK when finished.   Click button to select the type of constraint relationship.

PROGRAM 2G

Solver Results Dialog Box

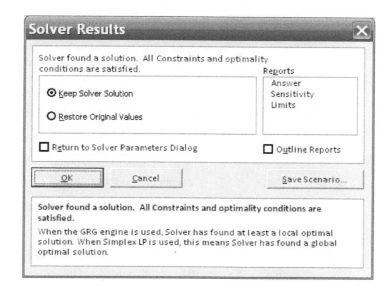

Solver Results

Solver found a solution. All Constraints and optimality conditions are satisfied.

Reports
Answer
Sensitivity
Limits

⦿ Keep Solver Solution

◯ Restore Original Values

☐ Return to Solver Parameters Dialog   ☐ Outline Reports

OK   Cancel   Save Scenario...

Solver found a solution. All Constraints and optimality conditions are satisfied.

When the GRG engine is used, Solver has found at least a local optimal solution. When Simplex LP is used, this means Solver has found a global optimal solution.

PROGRAM 2H

Solution Found by Solver

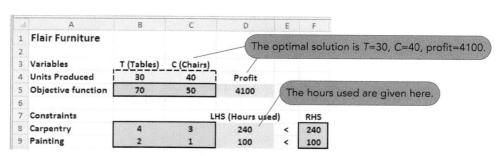

	A	B	C	D	E	F
1	Flair Furniture					
2						
3	Variables	T (Tables)	C (Chairs)			
4	Units Produced	30	40	Profit		
5	Objective function	70	50	4100		
6						
7	Constraints			LHS (Hours used)		RHS
8	Carpentry	4	3	240	<	240
9	Painting	2	1	100	<	100

The optimal solution is T=30, C=40, profit=4100.

The hours used are given here.

6 Solving Minimization Problems

Many LP problems involve minimizing an objective such as cost instead of maximizing a profit function. A restaurant, for example, may wish to develop a work schedule to meet staffing needs while minimizing the total number of employees. A manufacturer may seek to distribute its products from several factories to its many regional warehouses in such a way as to minimize total shipping costs. A hospital may want to provide a daily meal plan for its patients that meets certain nutritional standards while minimizing food purchase costs.

Minimization problems can be solved graphically by first setting up the feasible solution region and then using either the corner point method or an isocost line approach (which is analogous to the isoprofit approach in maximization problems) to find the values of the decision variables (e.g., X_1 and X_2) that yield the minimum cost. Let's take a look at a common LP problem referred to as the diet problem. This situation is similar to the one that the hospital faces in feeding its patients at the least cost.

Holiday Meal Turkey Ranch

The Holiday Meal Turkey Ranch is considering buying two different brands of turkey feed and blending them to provide a good, low-cost diet for its turkeys. Each feed contains, in varying proportions, some or all of the three nutritional ingredients essential for fattening turkeys. Each pound of brand 1 purchased, for example, contains 5 ounces of ingredient A, 4 ounces of ingredient B, and 0.5 ounce of ingredient C. Each pound of brand 2 contains 10 ounces of ingredient A, 3 ounces of ingredient B, but no ingredient C. The brand 1 feed costs the ranch 2 cents a pound, while the brand 2 feed costs 3 cents a pound. The owner of the ranch would like to use LP to determine the lowest-cost diet that meets the minimum monthly intake requirement for each nutritional ingredient.

Table 5 summarizes the relevant information. If we let

$$X_1 = \text{number of pounds of brand 1 feed purchased}$$
$$X_2 = \text{number of pounds of brand 2 feed purchased}$$

then we may proceed to formulate this linear programming problem as follows:

$$\text{Minimize cost (in cents)} = 2X_1 + 3X_2$$

subject to these constraints:

$$
\begin{aligned}
5X_1 + 10X_2 &\geq 90 \text{ ounces} && \text{(ingredient A constraint)}\\
4X_1 + 3X_2 &\geq 48 \text{ ounces} && \text{(ingredient B constraint)}\\
0.5\,X_1 &\geq 1.5 \text{ ounces} && \text{(ingredient C constraint)}\\
X_1 &\geq 0 && \text{(nonnegativity constraint)}\\
X_2 &\geq 0 && \text{(nonnegativity constraint)}
\end{aligned}
$$

Before solving this problem, we want to be sure to note three features that affect its solution. First, you should be aware that the third constraint implies that the farmer *must* purchase enough brand 1 feed to meet the minimum standards for the C nutritional ingredient. Buying only brand 2 would not be feasible because it lacks C. Second, as the problem is formulated, we

TABLE 5

Holiday Meal Turkey Ranch Data

INGREDIENT	COMPOSITION OF EACH POUND OF FEED (OZ.)		MINIMUM MONTHLY REQUIREMENT PER TURKEY (OZ.)
	BRAND 1 FEED	BRAND 2 FEED	
A	5	10	90
B	4	3	48
C	0.5	0	1.5
Cost per pound	2 cents	3 cents	

will be solving for the best blend of brands 1 and 2 to buy per turkey per month. If the ranch houses 5,000 turkeys in a given month, it need simply multiply the X_1 and X_2 quantities by 5,000 to decide how much feed to order overall. Third, we are now dealing with a series of greater-than-or-equal-to constraints. These cause the feasible solution area to be above the constraint lines in this example.

USING THE CORNER POINT METHOD ON A MINIMIZATION PROBLEM To solve the Holiday Meal Turkey Ranch problem, we first construct the feasible solution region. This is done by plotting each of the three constraint equations as in Figure 10. Note that the third constraint, $0.5\,X_1 \geq 1.5$, can be rewritten and plotted as $X_1 \geq 3$. (This involves multiplying both sides of the inequality by 2 but does not change the position of the constraint line in any way.) Minimization problems are often unbounded outward (i.e., on the right side and on top), but this causes no difficulty in solving them. As long as they are bounded inward (on the left side and the bottom), corner points may be established. The optimal solution will lie at one of the corners as it would in a maximization problem.

We plot the three constraints to develop a feasible solution region for the minimization problem.

Note that minimization problems often have unbounded feasible regions.

In this case, there are three corner points: *a*, *b*, and *c*. For point *a*, we find the coordinates at the intersection of the ingredient C and B constraints, that is, where the line $X_1 = 3$ crosses the line $4X_1 + 3X_2 = 48$. If we substitute $X_1 = 3$ into the B constraint equation, we get

$$4(3) + 3X_2 = 48$$

or

$$X_2 = 12$$

Thus, point *a* has the coordinates ($X_1 = 3, X_2 = 12$).

To find the coordinates of point *b* algebraically, we solve the equations $4X_1 + 3X_2 = 48$ and $5X_1 + 10X_2 = 90$ simultaneously. This yields ($X_1 = 8.4, X_2 = 4.8$).

IN ACTION | **NBC Uses Linear, Integer, and Goal Programming in Selling Advertising Slots**

The National Broadcasting Companay (NBC) sells over $4 billion in television advertising each year. About 60% to 80% of the air time for an upcoming season is sold in a 2- to 3-week period in late May. The advertising agencies approach the networks to purchase advertising time for their clients. Included in each request are the dollar amount, the demographic (e.g., age of the viewing audience) in which the client is interested, the program mix, weekly weighting, unit-length distribution, and a negotiated cost per 1,000 viewers. NBC must then develop detailed sales plans to meet these requirements. Traditionally, NBC developed these plans manually, and this required several hours per plan. These usually had to be reworked due to the complexity involved. With more than 300 such plans to be developed and reworked in a 2- to 3-week period, this was very time intensive and did not necessarily result in the maximum possible revenue.

In 1996, a project in the area of yield management was begun. Through this effort, NBC was able to create plans that more accurately meet customers' requirements, respond to customers more quickly, make the most profitable use of its limited inventory of advertising time slots, and reduce rework. The success of this system led to the development of a full-scale optimization system based on linear, integer, and goal programming. It is estimated that sales revenue between the years 1996 and 2000 increased by over $200 million due largely to this effort. Improvements in rework time, sales force productivity, and customer satisfaction were also benefits of this system.

Source: Based on Srinivas Bollapragada, et al. "NBC's Optimization Systems Increase Revenues and Productivity," *Interfaces* 32, 1 (January–February 2002): 47–60.

FIGURE 10

Feasible Region for the Holiday Meal Turkey Ranch Problem

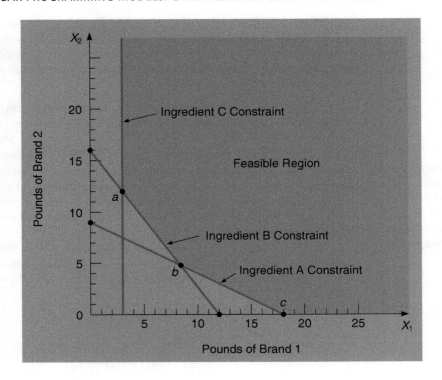

The coordinates at point c are seen by inspection to be $(X_1 = 18, X_2 = 0)$. We now evaluate the objective function at each corner point, and we get

$$\text{Cost} = 2X_1 + 3X_2$$
$$\text{Cost at point } a = 2(3) + 3(12) = 42$$
$$\text{Cost at point } b = 2(8.4) + 3(4.8) = 31.2$$
$$\text{Cost at point } c = 2(18) + 3(0) = 36$$

Hence, the minimum cost solution is to purchase 8.4 pounds of brand 1 feed and 4.8 pounds of brand 2 feed per turkey per month. This will yield a cost of 31.2 cents per turkey.

The isocost line method is analogous to the isoprofit line method we used on maximization problems.

ISOCOST LINE APPROACH As mentioned before, the **isocost line** approach may also be used to solve LP minimization problems such as that of the Holiday Meal Turkey Ranch. As with isoprofit lines, we need not compute the cost at each corner point, but instead draw a series of parallel cost lines. The lowest cost line (that is, the one closest in toward the origin) to touch the feasible region provides us with the optimal solution corner.

For example, we start in Figure 11 by drawing a 54-cent cost line, namely $54 = 2X_1 + 3X_2$. Obviously, there are many points in the feasible region that would yield a lower total cost. We proceed to move our isocost line toward the lower left, in a plane parallel to the 54-cent solution line. The last point we touch while still in contact with the feasible region is the same as corner point b of Figure 10. It has the coordinates $(X_1 = 8.4, X_2 = 4.8)$ and an associated cost of 31.2 cents.

COMPUTER APPROACH For the sake of completeness, we also solve the Holiday Meal Turkey Ranch problem using the QM for Windows software package (see Program 3) and with Excel's Solver function (see Programs 4A and 4B).

FIGURE 11

Graphical Solution to the Holiday Meal Turkey Ranch Problem Using the Isocost Line

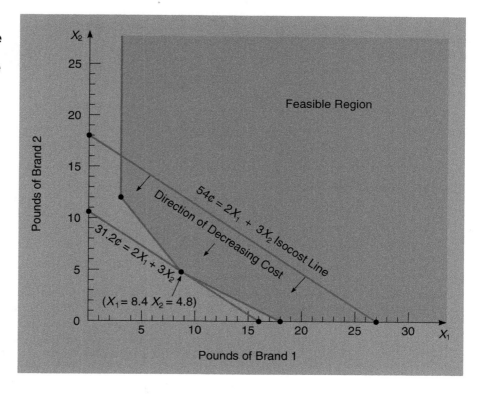

PROGRAM 3

Solving the Holiday Meal Turkey Ranch Problem Using QM for Windows Software

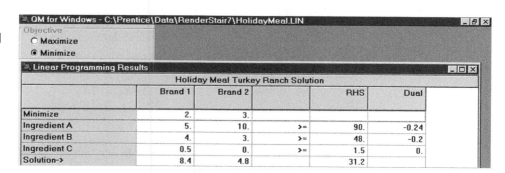

PROGRAM 4A

Excel 2010 Spreadsheet for the Holiday Meal Turkey Ranch Problem

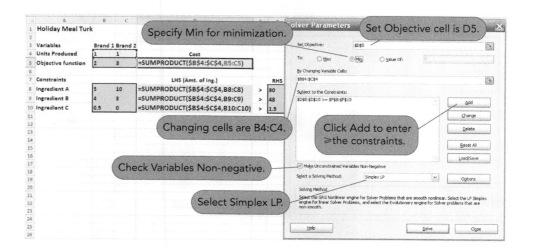

PROGRAM 4B

Excel 2010 Solution for the Holiday Meal Turkey Ranch Problem

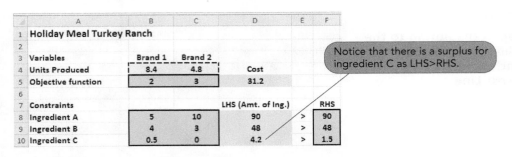

	A	B	C	D	E	F
1	Holiday Meal Turkey Ranch					
2						
3	Variables	Brand 1	Brand 2			
4	Units Produced	8.4	4.8	Cost		
5	Objective function	2	3	31.2		
6						
7	Constraints			LHS (Amt. of Ing.)		RHS
8	Ingredient A	5	10	90	>	90
9	Ingredient B	4	3	48	>	48
10	Ingredient C	0.5	0	4.2	>	1.5

Notice that there is a surplus for ingredient C as LHS>RHS.

7 Four Special Cases in LP

Four special cases and difficulties arise at times when using the graphical approach to solving LP problems: (1) infeasibility, (2) unboundedness, (3) redundancy, and (4) alternate optimal solutions.

No Feasible Solution

Lack of a feasible solution region can occur if constraints conflict with one another.

When there is no solution to an LP problem that satisfies all of the constraints given, then no feasible solution exists. Graphically, it means that no feasible solution region exists—a situation that might occur if the problem was formulated with conflicting constraints. This, by the way, is a frequent occurrence in real-life, large-scale LP problems that involve hundreds of constraints. For example, if one constraint is supplied by the marketing manager who states that at least 300 tables must be produced (namely, $X_1 \geq 300$) to meet sales demand, and a second restriction is supplied by the production manager, who insists that no more than 220 tables be produced (namely, $X_1 \leq 220$) because of a lumber shortage, no feasible solution region results. When the operations research analyst coordinating the LP problem points out this conflict, one manager or the other must revise his or her inputs. Perhaps more raw materials could be procured from a new source, or perhaps sales demand could be lowered by substituting a different model table to customers.

As a further graphic illustration of this, let us consider the following three constraints:

$$X_1 + 2X_2 \leq 6$$
$$2X_1 + X_2 \leq 8$$
$$X_1 \geq 7$$

As seen in Figure 12, there is no feasible solution region for this LP problem because of the presence of conflicting constraints.

FIGURE 12

A Problem with No Feasible Solution

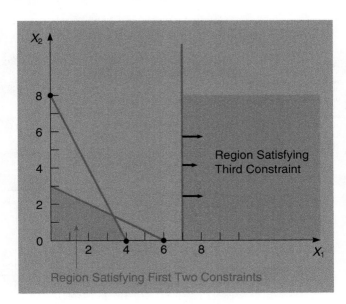

Unboundedness

When the profit in a maximization problem can be infinitely large, the problem is unbounded and is missing one or more constraints.

Sometimes a linear program will not have a finite solution. This means that in a maximization problem, for example, one or more solution variables, and the profit, can be made infinitely large without violating any constraints. If we try to solve such a problem graphically, we will note that the feasible region is open ended.

Let us consider a simple example to illustrate the situation. A firm has formulated the following LP problem:

$$\text{Maximize profit} = \$3X_1 + \$5X_2$$
$$\text{subject to} \quad X_1 \qquad\qquad \geq 5$$
$$X_2 \leq 10$$
$$X_1 + 2X_2 \geq 10$$
$$X_1, X_2 \geq 0$$

As you see in Figure 13, because this is a maximization problem and the feasible region extends infinitely to the right, there is **unboundedness**, or an unbounded solution. This implies that the problem has been formulated improperly. It would indeed be wonderful for the company to be able to produce an infinite number of units of X_1 (at a profit of $3 each!), but obviously no firm has infinite resources available or infinite product demand.

Redundancy

A redundant constraint is one that does not affect the feasible solution region.

The presence of redundant constraints is another common situation that occurs in large LP formulations. **Redundancy** causes no major difficulties in solving LP problems graphically, but you should be able to identify its occurrence. A redundant constraint is simply one that does not affect the feasible solution region. In other words, one constraint may be more binding or restrictive than another and thereby negate its need to be considered.

Let's look at the following example of an LP problem with three constraints:

$$\text{Maximize profit} = \$1X_1 + \$2X_2$$
$$\text{subject to} \quad X_1 + X_2 \leq 20$$
$$2X_1 + X_2 \leq 30$$
$$X_1 \leq 25$$
$$X_1, X_2 \geq 0$$

FIGURE 13

A Feasible Region that Is Unbounded to the Right

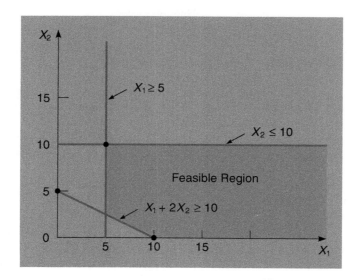

FIGURE 14

Problem with a Redundant Constraint

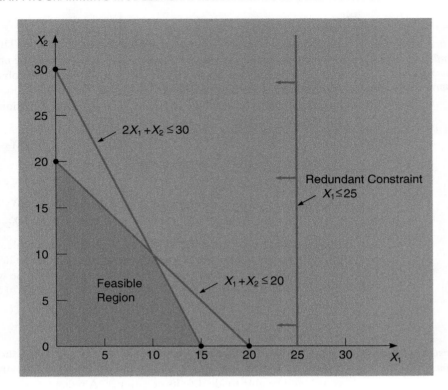

The third constraint, $X_1 \leq 25$, is redundant and unnecessary in the formulation and solution of the problem because it has no effect on the feasible region set from the first two more restrictive constraints (see Figure 14).

Alternate Optimal Solutions

Multiple optimal solutions are possible in LP problems.

An LP problem may, on occasion, have two or more **alternate optimal solutions**. Graphically, this is the case when the objective function's isoprofit or isocost line runs perfectly parallel to one of the problem's constraints—in other words, when they have the same slope.

Management of a firm noticed the presence of more than one optimal solution when they formulated this simple LP problem:

$$\text{Maximize profit} = \$3X_1 + \$2X_2$$
$$\text{subject to} \quad 6X_1 + 4X_2 \leq 24$$
$$X_1 \quad\quad \leq 3$$
$$X_1, X_2 \geq 0$$

As we see in Figure 15, our first isoprofit line of $8 runs parallel to the constraint equation. At a profit level of $12, the isoprofit line will rest directly on top of the segment of the first constraint line. This means that any point along the line between A and B provides an optimal X_1 and X_2 combination. Far from causing problems, the existence of more than one optimal solution allows management great flexibility in deciding which combination to select. The profit remains the same at each alternate solution.

8 Sensitivity Analysis

Optimal solutions to LP problems have thus far been found under what are called *deterministic assumptions*. This means that we assume complete certainty in the data and relationships of a problem—namely, prices are fixed, resources known, time needed to produce a unit exactly set. But in the real world, conditions are dynamic and changing. How can we handle this apparent discrepancy?

FIGURE 15

Example of Alternate Optimal Solutions

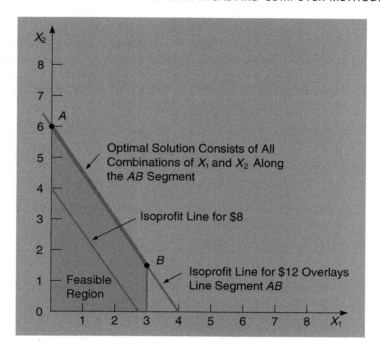

One way we can do so is by continuing to treat each particular LP problem as a deterministic situation. However, when an optimal solution is found, we recognize the importance of seeing just how *sensitive* that solution is to model assumptions and data. For example, if a firm realizes that profit per unit is not $5 as estimated but instead is closer to $5.50, how will the final solution mix and total profit change? If additional resources, such as 10 labor hours or 3 hours of machine time, should become available, will this change the problem's answer? Such analyses are used to examine the effects of changes in three areas: (1) contribution rates for each variable, (2) technological coefficients (the numbers in the constraint equations), and (3) available resources (the right-hand-side quantities in each constraint). This task is alternatively called **sensitivity analysis**, *postoptimality analysis*, *parametric programming*, or *optimality analysis*.

Sensitivity analysis also often involves a series of what-if? questions. What if the profit on product 1 increases by 10%? What if less money is available in the advertising budget constraint? What if workers each stay one hour longer every day at 1 ½-time pay to provide increased production capacity? What if new technology will allow a product to be wired in one-third the time it used to take? So we see that sensitivity analysis can be used to deal not only with errors in estimating input parameters to the LP model but also with management's experiments with possible future changes in the firm that may affect profits.

There are two approaches to determining just how sensitive an optimal solution is to changes. The first is simply a trial-and-error approach. This approach usually involves resolving the entire problem, preferably by computer, each time one input data item or parameter is changed. It can take a long time to test a series of possible changes in this way.

The approach we prefer is the analytic postoptimality method. After an LP problem has been solved, we attempt to determine a range of changes in problem parameters that will not affect the optimal solution or change the variables in the solution. This is done without resolving the whole problem.

Let's investigate sensitivity analysis by developing a small production mix problem. Our goal will be to demonstrate graphically and through the simplex tableau how sensitivity analysis can be used to make linear programming concepts more realistic and insightful.

How sensitive is the optimal solution to changes in profits, resources, or other input parameters?

An important function of sensitivity analysis is to allow managers to experiment with values of the input parameters.

Postoptimality analysis means examining changes after the optimal solution has been reached.

High Note Sound Company

The High Note Sound Company manufactures quality compact disc (CD) players and stereo receivers. Each of these products requires a certain amount of skilled artisanship, of which there is a limited weekly supply. The firm formulates the following LP problem in order to determine the best production mix of CD players (X_1) and receivers (X_2):

$$\text{Maximize profit} = \$50X_1 + \$120X_2$$

$$\begin{aligned}
\text{subject to} \quad 2X_1 + 4X_2 &\leq 80 &&\text{(hours of electricians' time available)} \\
3X_1 + 1X_2 &\leq 60 &&\text{(hours of audio technicians' time available)} \\
X_1, X_2 &\geq 0
\end{aligned}$$

The solution to this problem is illustrated graphically in Figure 16. Given this information and deterministic assumptions, the firm should produce only stereo receivers (20 of them), for a weekly profit of $2,400.

For the optimal solution, $(0, 20)$, the electrician hours used are

$$2X_1 + 4X_2 = 2(0) + 4(20) = 80$$

and this equals the amount available, so there is 0 slack for this constraint. Thus, it is a binding constraint. If a constraint is binding, obtaining additional units of that resource will usually result in higher profits. The audio technician hours used are for the optimal solution $(0, 20)$ are

$$3X_1 + 1X_2 = 3(0) + 1(20) = 20$$

but the hours available are 60. Thus, there is a slack of $60 - 20 = 40$ hours. Because there are extra hours available that are not being used, this is a nonbinding constraint. For a nonbinding constraint, obtaining additional units of that resource will not result in higher profits and will only increase the slack.

Changes in the Objective Function Coefficient

Changes in contribution rates are examined first.

In real-life problems, contribution rates (usually profit or cost) in the objective functions fluctuate periodically, as do most of a firm's expenses. Graphically, this means that although the feasible solution region remains exactly the same, the slope of the isoprofit or isocost line will

FIGURE 16

High Note Sound Company Graphical Solution

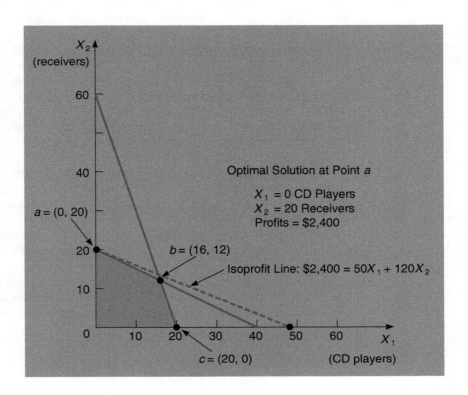

FIGURE 17
Changes in the Receiver Contribution Coefficients

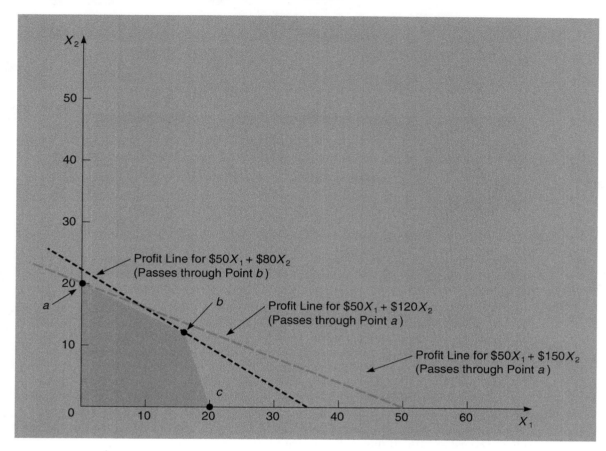

A new corner point becomes optimal if an objective function coefficient is decreased or increased too much.

change. It is easy to see in Figure 17 that the High Note Sound Company's profit line is optimal at point a. But what if a technical breakthrough just occurred that raised the profit per stereo receiver (X_2) from \$120 to \$150? Is the solution still optimal? The answer is definitely yes, for in this case the slope of the profit line accentuates the profitability at point a. The new profit is $\$3,000 = 0(\$50) + 20(\$150)$.

On the other hand, if X_2's profit coefficient was overestimated and should only have been \$80, the slope of the profit line changes enough to cause a new corner point (b) to become optimal. Here the profit is $\$1,760 = 16(\$50) + 12(\$80)$.

This example illustrates a very important concept about changes in objective function coefficients. We can increase or decrease the objective function coefficient (profit) of any variable, and the current corner point may remain optimal if the change is not too large. However, if we increase or decrease this coefficient by too much, then the optimal solution would be at a different corner point. How much can the objective function coefficient change before another corner point becomes optimal? Both QM for Windows and Excel provide the answer.

QM for Windows and Changes in Objective Function Coefficients

The QM for Windows input for the High Note Sound Company example is shown in Program 5A. When the solution has been found, selecting Window and Ranging allows us to see additional information on sensitivity analysis. Program 5B provides the output related to sensitivity analysis.

PROGRAM 5A

Input to QM for Windows for High Note Sound Company Data

Objective
⦿ Maximize
○ Minimize

High Note Sound					
	CD players	Receivers		RHS	
Maximize	50	120			
Electrician hrs	2	4	<=	80	
Audio tech hrs	3	1	<=	60	

PROGRAM 5B

High Note Sound Company's LP Sensitivity Analysis Output Using Input from Program 5A

◇ Ranging

High Note Sound Solution					
Variable	Value	Reduced Cost	Original Val	Lower Bound	Upper Bound
CD players	0.	10.	50.	-Infinity	60.
Receivers	20.	0.	120.	100.	Infinity
Constraint	Dual Value	Slack/Surplus	Original Val	Lower Bound	Upper Bound
Electrician hrs	30.	0.	80.	0.	240.
Audio tech hrs	0.	40.	60.	20.	Infinity

The current solution remains optimal unless an objective function coefficient is increased to a value above the upper bound or decreased to a value below the lower bound.

From Program 5B, we see the profit on CD players was $50, which is indicated as the original value in the output. This objective function coefficient has a lower bound of negative infinity and an upper bound of $60. This means that the current corner point solution remains optimal as long as the profit on CD players does not go above $60. If it equals $60, there would be two optimal solutions as the objective function would be parallel to the first constraint. The points (0, 20) and (16, 12) would both give a profit of $2,400. The profit on CD players may decrease any amount as indicated by the negative infinity, and the optimal corner point does not change. This negative infinity is logical because currently there are no CD players being produced because the profit is too low. Any decrease in the profit on CD players would make them less attractive relative to the receivers, and we certainly would not produce any CD players because of this.

The profit on receivers has an upper bound of infinity (it may increase by any amount) and a lower bound of $100. If this profit equaled $100, then the corner points (0, 20) and (16, 12) would both be optimal. The profit at each of these would be $2,000.

The upper and lower bounds relate to changing only one coefficient at a time.

In general, a change can be made to one (and only one) objective function coefficient, and the current optimal corner point remains optimal as long as the change is between the Upper and Lower Bounds. If two or more coefficients are changed simultaneously, then the problem should be solved with the new coefficients to determine whether or not this current solution remains optimal.

Excel Solver and Changes in Objective Function Coefficients

Program 6A illustrates how the Excel 2010 spreadsheet for this example is set up for Solver. When *Solver* is selected from the *Data* tab, the appropriate inputs are made, and *Solve* is clicked in the Solver dialog box, the solution and the Solver Results window will appear as in Program 6B. Selecting *Sensitivity* from the reports area of this window will provide a Sensitivity Report on a new worksheet, with results as shown in Program 6C. Note how the cells are named based on the text from Program 6A. Notice that Excel does not provide lower bounds and upper bounds for the objective function coefficients. Instead, it gives the allowable increases and decreases for these. By adding the allowable increase to the current value, we may obtain the upper bound. For example, the Allowable Increase on the profit (objective coefficient) for CD players is 10, which means that the upper bound on this profit is $50 + $10 = $60. Similarly, we may subtract the allowable decrease from the current value to obtain the lower bound.

Excel solver gives allowable increases and decreases rather than upper and lower bounds.

Changes in the Technological Coefficients

Changes in technological coefficients affect the shape of the feasible solution region.

Changes in what are called the **technological coefficients** often reflect changes in the state of technology. If fewer or more resources are needed to produce a product such as a CD player or stereo receiver, coefficients in the constraint equations will change. These changes

PROGRAM 6A

Excel 2010 Spreadsheet for High Note Sound Company

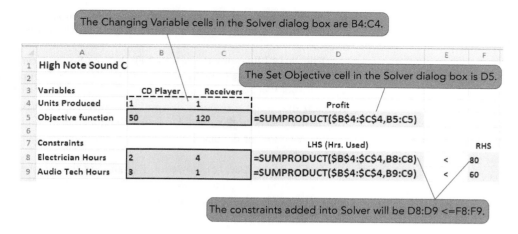

The Changing Variable cells in the Solver dialog box are B4:C4.

The Set Objective cell in the Solver dialog box is D5.

	A	B	C	D	E	F
1	High Note Sound C					
2						
3	Variables	CD Player	Receivers			
4	Units Produced	1	1	Profit		
5	Objective function	50	120	=SUMPRODUCT($B$4:$C$4,B5:C5)		
6						
7	Constraints			LHS (Hrs. Used)		RHS
8	Electrician Hours	2	4	=SUMPRODUCT($B$4:$C$4,B8:C8)	<	80
9	Audio Tech Hours	3	1	=SUMPRODUCT($B$4:$C$4,B9:C9)	<	60

The constraints added into Solver will be D8:D9 <=F8:F9.

PROGRAM 6B

Excel 2010 Solution and Solver Results Window for High Note Sound Company

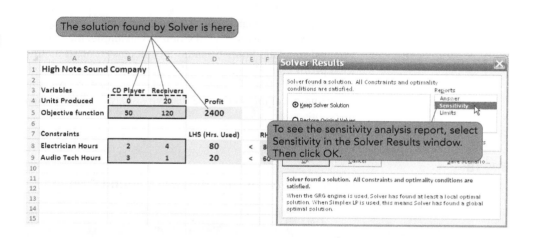

The solution found by Solver is here.

	A	B	C	D	E	F
1	High Note Sound Company					
2						
3	Variables	CD Player	Receivers			
4	Units Produced	0	20	Profit		
5	Objective function	50	120	2400		
6						
7	Constraints			LHS (Hrs. Used)		RH
8	Electrician Hours	2	4	80	<	8
9	Audio Tech Hours	3	1	20	<	60
10						

Solver Results

Solver found a solution. All Constraints and optimality conditions are satisfied.

Reports
Answer
Sensitivity
Limits

⊙ Keep Solver Solution
○ Restore Original Values

To see the sensitivity analysis report, select Sensitivity in the Solver Results window. Then click OK.

Solver found a solution. All Constraints and optimality conditions are satisfied.

When the GRG engine is used, Solver has found at least a local optimal solution. When Simplex LP is used, this means Solver has found a global optimal solution.

PROGRAM 6C

Excel 2010 Sensitivity Report for High Note Sound Company

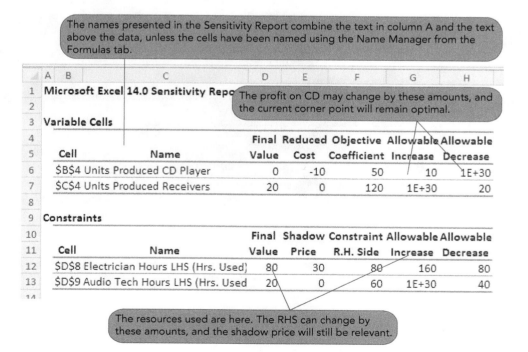

The names presented in the Sensitivity Report combine the text in column A and the text above the data, unless the cells have been named using the Name Manager from the Formulas tab.

The profit on CD may change by these amounts, and the current corner point will remain optimal.

	A	B	C	D	E	F	G	H
1	Microsoft Excel 14.0 Sensitivity Repo							
2								
3	Variable Cells							
4				Final	Reduced	Objective	Allowable	Allowable
5	Cell		Name	Value	Cost	Coefficient	Increase	Decrease
6	$B$4	Units Produced CD Player		0	-10	50	10	1E+30
7	$C$4	Units Produced Receivers		20	0	120	1E+30	20
8								
9	Constraints							
10				Final	Shadow	Constraint	Allowable	Allowable
11	Cell		Name	Value	Price	R.H. Side	Increase	Decrease
12	$D$8	Electrician Hours LHS (Hrs. Used)		80	30	80	160	80
13	$D$9	Audio Tech Hours LHS (Hrs. Used		20	0	60	1E+30	40
14								

The resources used are here. The RHS can change by these amounts, and the shadow price will still be relevant.

will have no effect on the objective function of an LP problem, but they can produce a significant change in the shape of the feasible solution region, and hence in the optimal profit or cost.

Figure 18 illustrates the original High Note Sound Company graphical solution as well as two separate changes in technological coefficients. In Figure 18, Part (a), we see that the optimal solution lies at point a, which represents $X_1 = 0$, $X_2 = 20$. You should be able to prove to yourself that point a remains optimal in Figure 18, Part (b) despite a constraint change from $3X_1 + 1X_2 \leq 60$ to $2X_1 + 1X_2 \leq 60$. Such a change might take place when the firm discovers that it no longer demands three hours of audio technicians' time to produce a CD player, but only two hours.

In Figure 18, Part (c), however, a change in the other constraint changes the shape of the feasible region enough to cause a new corner point (g) to become optimal. Before moving on, see if you reach an objective function value of $1,954 profit at point g (versus a profit of $1,920 at point f).*

Changes in the Resources or Right-Hand-Side Values

The right-hand-side values of the constraints often represent resources available to the firm. The resources could be labor hours or machine time or perhaps money or production materials available. In the High Note Sound Company example, the two resources are hours available of electricians' time and hours of audio technicians' time. If additional hours were available, a higher total profit could be realized. How much should the company be willing to pay for additional hours? Is it profitable to have some electricians work overtime? Should we be willing to pay for more audio technician time? Sensitivity analysis about these resources will help us answer these questions.

FIGURE 18
Change in the Technological Coefficients for the High Note Sound Company

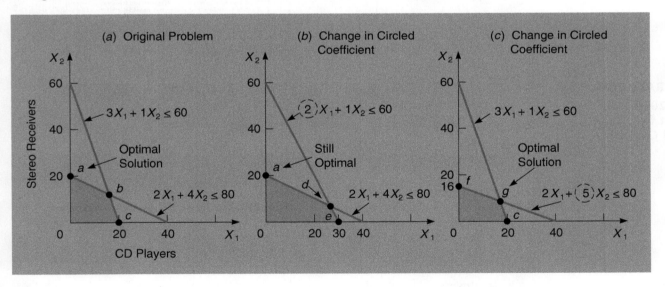

---

*Note that the values of X_1 and X_2 at point g are fractions. Although the High Note Sound Company cannot produce 0.67, 0.75, or 0.90 of a CD player or stereo, we can assume that the firm can *begin* a unit one week and complete it the next. As long as the production process is fairly stable from week to week, this raises no major problems.

IN ACTION — Swift & Company Uses LP to Schedule Production

Based in Greeley, Colorado, Swift & Company has annual sales over $8 billion, with beef and related products making up the vast majority of this. Swift has five processing plants, which handle over 6 billion pounds of beef each year. Each head of beef is cut into two sides, which yield the chuck, the brisket, the loins, the ribs, the round, the plate, and the flank. With some cuts in greater demand than others, the customer service representatives (CSRs) try to meet the demand for customers while providing discounts when necessary to clear out some cuts that might be in excess supply. It is important that the CSRs have accurate information on product availability in close to real time so they can react quickly to changing demand.

With the cost of raw material being as high as 85%, and with a very thin profit margin, it is essential that the company operate efficiently. Swift started a project in March 2001 to develop a mathematical programming model that would optimize the supply chain. Ten full-time employees worked with four operations research consultants from Aspen Technology on what was called Project Phoenix. At the heart of the final model are 45 integrated LP models that enable the company to dynamically schedule its operations in real time as orders are received.

With Project Phoenix, not only did profit margins increase, but the improvements in forecasting, cattle procurement, and manufacturing improved relations with customers and enhanced the reputation of Swift & Company in the marketplace. The company is better able to deliver products according to customer specification. While the model cost over $6 million to develop, in the first year of operation, it generated a benefit of $12.7 million.

Source: Based on Ann Bixby, Brian Downs, and Mike Self. "A Scheduling and Capable-to-Promise Application for Swift & Company," *Interfaces* 36, 1 (January–February 2006): 69–86.

If the right-hand side of a constraint is changed, the feasible region will change (unless the constraint is redundant), and often the optimal solution will change. In the High Note Sound Company example, there were 80 hours of electrician time available each week and the maximum possible profit was $2,400. There is no slack for this constraint, so it is a binding constraint. If the available electricians' hours are increased to 100 hours, the new optimal solution seen in Figure 19, part (a) is (0, 25) and the profit is $3,000. Thus, the extra 20 hours of time resulted in an increase in profit of $600 or $30 per hour. If the hours were decreased to 60 hours as shown in Figure 19, part (b), the new optimal solution is (0, 15) and the profit is $1,800. Thus, reducing the hours by 20 results in a decrease in profit of $600 or $30 per hour. This $30 per hour change in profit that resulted from a change in the hours available is called the dual price or dual value. The **dual price** for a constraint is the improvement in the objective function value that results from a one-unit increase in the right-hand side of the constraint.

The value of one additional unit of a scarce resource may be found from the dual price.

The dual price of $30 per hour of electrician time tells us we can increase profit if we have more electrician hours. However, there is a limit to this as there is limited audio technician time. If the total hours of electrician time were 240 hours, the optimal solution would be (0, 60) as shown in Figure 19, part (c) and the profit would be $7,200. Again, this is an increase of $30 profit per hour (the dual price) for each of the 160 hours that were added to the original amount. If the number of hours increased beyond 240, then profit would no longer increase and the optimal solution would still be (0, 60) as shown in Figure 19, part (c). There would simply be excess (slack) hours of electrician time and all of the audio technician time would be used. Thus, the dual price is relevant only within limits. Both QM for Windows and Excel Solver provide these limits.

QM for Windows and Changes in Right-Hand-Side Values

The QM for Windows sensitivity analysis output was shown in Program 5B. The dual value for the electrician hours constraint is given as 30, and the lower bound is zero while the upper bound is 240. This means that each additional hour of electrician time, up to a total of 240 hours, will

FIGURE 19

Changes in the Electricians' Time Resource for the High Note Sound Company

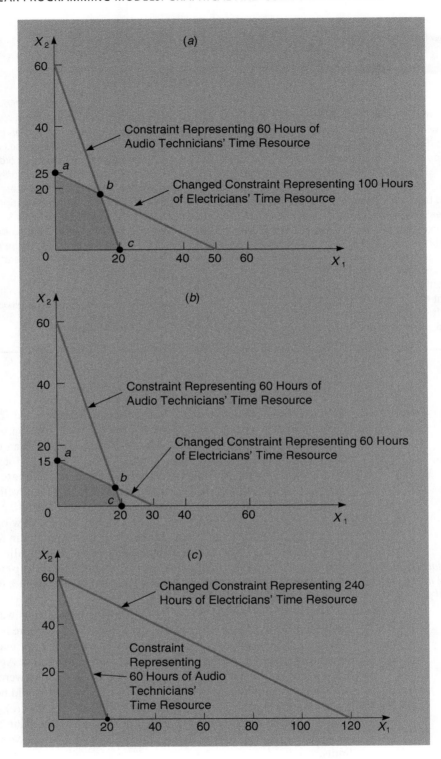

Dual prices will change if the amount of the resource (the right-hand side of the constraint) goes above the upper bound or below the lower bound given in the Ranging section of the QM for Windows output.

increase the maximum possible profit by $30. Similarly, if the available electrician time is decreased, the maximum possible profit will decrease by $30 per hour until the available time is decreased to the lower bound of 0. If the amount of electrician time (the right-hand-side value for this constraint) is outside this range (0 to 240), then the dual value is no longer relevant and the problem should be resolved with the new right-hand-side value.

In Program 5B, the dual value for audio technician hours is shown to be $0 and the slack is 40, so it is a nonbinding constraint. There are 40 hours of audio technician time that are not being used despite the fact that they are currently available. If additional hours were made available they would not increase profit but would simply increase the amount of slack. This dual value of zero is relevant as long as the right-hand side does not go below the lower bound of 20. The upper limit is infinity indicating that adding more hours would simply increase the amount of slack.

Excel Solver and Changes in Right-Hand-Side Values

The shadow price is the same as the dual price in maximization problems.

The Sensitivity report from Excel Solver was shown in Program 6C. Notice that Solver gives the shadow price instead of the dual price. A **shadow price** is the change in the objective function value (e.g., profit or cost) that results from a one-unit increase in the right-hand-side of a constraint.

Since an improvement in the objective function value in a maximization problem is the same as a positive change (increase), the dual price and the shadow price are exactly the same for maximization problems. For a minimization problem, an improvement in the objective function value is a decrease, which is a negative change. So for minimization problems, the shadow price will be the negative of the dual price.

The Allowable Increase and Allowable Decrease for the right-hand side of each constraint is provided, and the shadow price is relevant for changes within these limits. For the electrician hours, the right-hand-side value of 80 may be increased by 160 (for a total of 240) or decreased by 80 (for a total of 0) and the shadow price remains relevant. If a change is made that exceeds these limits, then the problem should be resolved to find the impact of the change.

Summary

In this chapter we introduce a mathematical modeling technique called linear programming (LP). It is used in reaching an optimum solution to problems that have a series of constraints binding the objective. We use both the corner point method and the isoprofit/isocost approaches for graphically solving problems with only two decision variables.

The graphical solution approaches of this chapter provide a conceptual basis for tackling larger, more complex problems. To solve real-life LP problems with numerous variables and constraints, we need a solution procedure such as the simplex algorithm, the subject of Module 7. The simplex algorithm is the method that QM for Windows and Excel use to tackle LP problems.

In this chapter we also present the important concept of sensitivity analysis. Sometimes referred to as postoptimality analysis, sensitivity analysis is used by management to answer a series of what-if? Questions about LP model parameters. It also tests just how sensitive the optimal solution is to changes in profit or cost coefficients, technological coefficients, and right-hand-side resources. We explored sensitivity analysis graphically (i.e., for problems with only two decision variables) and with computer output, but to see how to conduct sensitivity algebraically through the simplex algorithm, read Module 7 (located at **www.pearsonhighered.com/render**).

Glossary

Alternate Optimal Solution   A situation in which more than one optimal solution is possible. It arises when the slope of the objective function is the same as the slope of a constraint.

Binding Constraint   A constraint with zero slack or surplus for the optimal solution.

Constraint   A restriction on the resources available to a firm (stated in the form of an inequality or an equation).

Corner Point, or Extreme Point   A point that lies on one of the corners of the feasible region. This means that it falls at the intersection of two constraint lines.

Corner Point Method   The method of finding the optimal solution to an LP problem by testing the profit or cost level at each corner point of the feasible region. The theory of LP states that the optimal solution must lie at one of the corner points.

Decision Variable   A variable whose value may be chosen by the decision maker.

Dual Price (value)   The improvement in the objective function value that results from a one-unit increase in the right-hand side of that constraint.

Feasible Region   The area satisfying all of the problem's resource restrictions; that is, the region where all constraints overlap. All possible solutions to the problem lie in the feasible region.

Feasible Solution A point lying in the feasible region. Basically, it is any point that satisfies all of the problem's constraints.

Inequality A mathematical expression containing a greater-than-or-equal-to relation ($\geq$) or a less-than-or-equal-to relation ($\leq$) used to indicate that the total consumption of a resource must be $\geq$ or $\leq$ some limiting value.

Infeasible Solution Any point lying outside the feasible region. It violates one or more of the stated constraints.

Isocost Line A straight line representing all combinations of X_1 and X_2 for a particular cost level.

Isoprofit Line A straight line representing all nonnegative combinations of X_1 and X_2 for a particular profit level.

Linear Programming (LP) A mathematical technique used to help management decide how to make the most effective use of an organization's resources.

Mathematical Programming The general category of mathematical modeling and solution techniques used to allocate resources while optimizing a measurable goal. LP is one type of programming model.

Nonbinding Constraint A constraint with a positive amount of slack or surplus for the optimal solution.

Nonnegativity Constraints A set of constraints that requires each decision variable to be nonnegative; that is, each X_i must be greater than or equal to 0.

Objective Function A mathematical statement of the goal of an organization, stated as an intent to maximize or to minimize some important quantity such as profits or costs.

Product Mix Problem A common LP problem involving a decision as to which products a firm should produce given that it faces limited resources.

Redundancy The presence of one or more constraints that do not affect the feasible solution region.

Sensitivity Analysis The study of how sensitive an optimal solution is to model assumptions and to data changes. It is often referred to as postoptimality analysis.

Shadow Price The increase in the objective function value that results from a one-unit increase in the right-hand side of that constraint.

Simultaneous Equation Method The algebraic means of solving for the intersection point of two or more linear constraint equations.

Slack The difference between the left-hand side and the right-hand side of a less-than-or-equal-to constraint. Often this is the amount of a resource that is not being used.

Surplus The difference between the left-hand side and the right-hand side of a greater-than-or-equal-to constraint. Often this represents the amount by which a minimum quantity is exceeded.

Technological Coefficients Coefficients of the variables in the constraint equations. The coefficients represent the amount of resources needed to produce one unit of the variable.

Unboundedness A condition that exists when a solution variable and the profit can be made infinitely large without violating any of the problem's constraints in a maximization process.

Solved Problems

Solved Problem 1

Personal Mini Warehouses is planning to expand its successful Orlando business into Tampa. In doing so, the company must determine how many storage rooms of each size to build. Its objective and constraints follow:

$$\text{Maximize monthly earnings} = 50X_1 + 20X_2$$

$$\begin{aligned}
\text{subject to} \quad 2X_1 + 4X_2 &\leq 400 \quad \text{(advertising budget available)} \\
100X_1 + 50X_2 &\leq 8{,}000 \quad \text{(square footage required)} \\
X_1 &\leq 60 \quad \text{(rental limit expected)} \\
X_1, X_2 &\geq 0
\end{aligned}$$

where

X_1 = number of large spaces developed

X_2 = number of small spaces developed

Solution

An evaluation of the five corner points of the accompanying graph indicates that corner point C produces the greatest earnings. Refer to the graph and table.

CORNER POINT	VALUES OF X_1, X_2	OBJECTIVE FUNCTION VALUE ($)
A	(0, 0)	0
B	(60, 0)	3,000
C	(60, 40)	3,800
D	(40, 80)	3,600
E	(0, 100)	2,000

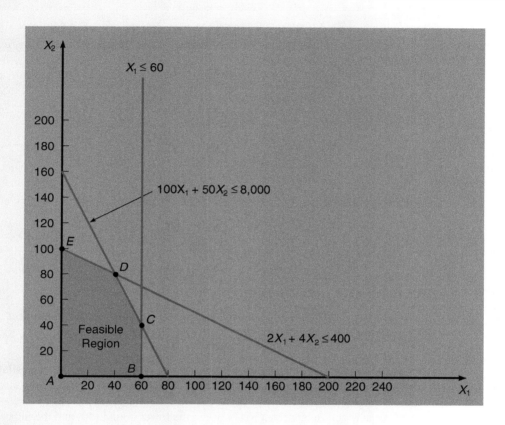

Solved Problem 2

The solution obtained with QM for Windows for Solved Problem 1 is given in the following program. Use this to answer the following questions.

a. For the optimal solution, how much of the advertising budget is spent?

b. For the optimal solution, how much square footage will be used?

c. Would the solution change if the budget were only $300 instead of $400?

d. What would the optimal solution be if the profit on the large spaces were reduced from $50 to $45?

e. How much would earnings increase if the square footage requirement were increased from 8,000 to 9,000?

Linear Programming Results						_ □ x
Solved Problem 7-2 Solution						
	X1	X2			RHS	Dual
Maximize	50.	20.				
Constraint 1	2.	4.	<=		400.	0.
Constraint 2	100.	50.	<=		8,000.	0.4
Constraint 3	1.	0.	<=		60.	10.
Solution->	60.	40.			3,800.	

Ranging						_ □ x
Solved Problem 7-2 Solution						
Variable	Value	Reduced Cost	Original Val	Lower Bound	Upper Bound	
X1	60.	0.	50.	40.	Infinity	
X2	40.	0.	20.	0.	25.	
Constraint	Dual Value	Slack/Surplus	Original Val	Lower Bound	Upper Bound	
Constraint 1	0.	120.	400.	280.	Infinity	
Constraint 2	0.4	0.	8,000.	6,000.	9,500.	
Constraint 3	10.	0.	60.	40.	80.	

Solution

a. In the optimal solution, $X_1 = 60$ and $X_2 = 40$. Using these values in the first constraint gives us

$$2X_1 + 4X_2 = 2(60) + 4(40) = 280$$

Another way to find this is by looking at the slack:

Slack for constraint 1 = 120 so the amount used is $400 - 120 = 280$

b. For the second constraint we have

$$100X_1 + 50X_2 = 100(60) + 50(40) = 8,000 \text{ square feet}$$

Instead of computing this, you may simply observe that the slack is 0, so all of the 8,000 square feet will be used.

c. No, the solution would not change. The dual price is 0 and there is slack available. The value 300 is between the lower bound of 280 and the upper bound of infinity. Only the slack for this constraint would change.

d. Since the new coefficient for X_1 is between the lower bound (40) and the upper bound (infinity), the current corner point remains optimal. So $X_1 = 60$ and $X_2 = 40$, and only the monthly earnings change.

$$\text{Earnings} = 45(60) + 20(40) = \$3,500$$

e. The dual price for this constraint is 0.4, and the upper bound is 9,500. The increase of 1,000 units will result in an increase in earnings of $1,000(0.4 \text{ per unit}) = \$400$.

Solved Problem 3

Solve the following LP formulation graphically, using the isocost line approach:

$$\text{Minimize costs} = 24X_1 + 28X_2$$
$$\text{subject to} \qquad 5X_1 + 4X_2 \le 2,000$$
$$X_1 \qquad \ge 80$$
$$X_1 + X_2 \ge 300$$
$$X_2 \ge 100$$
$$X_1, X_2 \ge 0$$

Solution

A graph of the four constraints follows. The arrows indicate the direction of feasibility for each constraint. The next graph illustrates the feasible solution region and plots of two possible objective function cost lines. The first, $10,000, was selected arbitrarily as a starting point. To find the optimal corner point, we need to move the cost line in the direction of lower cost, that is, down and to the left. The last point where a cost line touches the feasible region as it moves toward the origin is corner point D. Thus D, which represents $X_1 = 200$, $X_2 = 100$, and a cost of $7,600, is optimal.

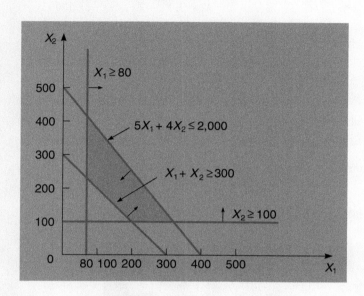

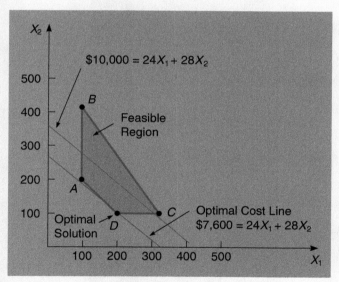

Solved Problem 4

Solve the following problem, using the corner point method. For the optimal solution, how much slack or surplus is there for each constraint?

$$\text{Maximize profit} = 30X_1 + 40X_2$$
$$\text{subject to} \qquad 4X_1 + 2X_2 \leq 16$$
$$2X_1 - X_2 \geq 2$$
$$X_2 \leq 2$$
$$X_1, X_2 \geq 0$$

Solution

The graph appears next with the feasible region shaded.

CORNER POINT	COORDINATES	PROFIT ($)
A	$X_1 = 1, X_2 = 0$	30
B	$X_1 = 4, X_2 = 0$	120
C	$X_1 = 3, X_2 = 2$	170
D	$X_1 = 2, X_2 = 2$	140

The optimal solution is (3, 2). For this point,

$$4X_1 + 2X_2 = 4(3) + 2(2) = 16$$

Therefore, slack = 0 for constraint 1. Also,

$$2X_1 - 1X_2 = 2(3) - 1(2) = 4 > 2$$

Therefore, surplus $= 4 - 2 = 2$ for constraint 2. Also,

$$X_2 = 2$$

Therefore, slack $= 0$ for constraint 3.

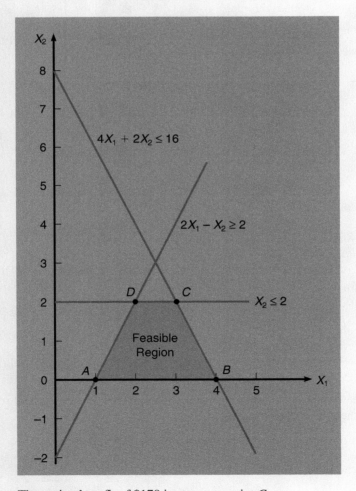

The optimal profit of $170 is at corner point C.

Self-Test

- Before taking the self-test, refer to the learning objectives at the beginning of the chapter, the notes in the margins, and the glossary at the end of the chapter.
- Use the key at the end of the chapter to correct your answers.
- Restudy pages that correspond to any questions that you answered incorrectly or material you feel uncertain about.

1. When using a graphical solution procedure, the region bounded by the set of constraints is called the
   a. solution.
   b. feasible region.
   c. infeasible region.
   d. maximum profit region.
   e. none of the above.

2. In an LP problem, at least one corner point must be an optimal solution if an optimal solution exists.
   a. True
   b. False

3. An LP problem has a bounded feasible region. If this problem has an equality ($=$) constraint, then
   a. this must be a minimization problem.
   b. the feasible region must consist of a line segment.
   c. the problem must be degenerate.
   d. the problem must have more than one optimal solution.

4. Which of the following would cause a change in the feasible region?
   a. increasing an objective function coefficient in a maximization problem
   b. adding a redundant constraint
   c. changing the right-hand side of a nonredundant constraint
   d. increasing an objective function coefficient in a minimization problem

5. If a nonredundant constraint is removed from an LP problem, then
   a. the feasible region will get larger.
   b. the feasible region will get smaller.
   c. the problem would become nonlinear.
   d. the problem would become infeasible.

6. In the optimal solution to a linear program, there are 20 units of slack for a constraint. From this we know that
   a. the dual price for this constraint is 20.
   b. the dual price for this constraint is 0.
   c. this constraint must be redundant.
   d. the problem must be a maximization problem.

7. A linear program has been solved and sensitivity analysis has been performed. The ranges for the objective function coefficients have been found. For the profit on X_1, the upper bound is 80, the lower bound is 60, and the current value is 75. Which of the following must be true if the profit on this variable is lowered to 70 and the optimal solution is found?
   a. a new corner point will become optimal
   b. the maximum possible total profit may increase
   c. the values for all the decision variables will remain the same
   d. all of the above are possible

8. A graphical method should only be used to solve an LP problem when
   a. there are only two constraints.
   b. there are more than two constraints.
   c. there are only two variables.
   d. there are more than two variables.

9. In LP, variables do not have to be integer valued and may take on any fractional value. This assumption is called
   a. proportionality.
   b. divisibility.
   c. additivity.
   d. certainty.

10. In solving a linear program, no feasible solution exists. To resolve this problem we might
    a. add another variable.
    b. add another constraint.
    c. remove or relax a constraint.
    d. try a different computer program.

11. If the feasible region gets larger due to a change in one of the constraints, the optimal value of the objective function
    a. must increase or remain the same for a maximization problem.
    b. must decrease or remain the same for a maximization problem.
    c. must increase or remain the same for a minimization problem.
    d. cannot change.

12. When alternate optimal solutions exist in an LP problem, then
    a. the objective function will be parallel to one of the constraints.
    b. one of the constraints will be redundant.
    c. two constraints will be parallel.
    d. the problem will also be unbounded.

13. If a linear program is unbounded, the problem probably has not been formulated correctly. Which of the following would most likely cause this?
    a. a constraint was inadvertently omitted
    b. an unnecessary constraint was added to the problem
    c. the objective function coefficients are too large
    d. the objective function coefficients are too small

14. A feasible solution to an LP problem
    a. must satisfy all of the problem's constraints simultaneously.
    b. need not satisfy all of the constraints, only some of them.
    c. must be a corner point of the feasible region.
    d. must give the maximum possible profit.

Discussion Questions and Problems

Discussion Questions

1 Discuss the similarities and differences between minimization and maximization problems using the graphical solution approaches of LP.

2 It is important to understand the assumptions underlying the use of any quantitative analysis model. What are the assumptions and requirements for an LP model to be formulated and used?

3 It has been said that each LP problem that has a feasible region has an infinite number of solutions. Explain.

4 You have just formulated a maximization LP problem and are preparing to solve it graphically. What criteria should you consider in deciding whether it would be easier to solve the problem by the corner point method or the isoprofit line approach?

5 Under what condition is it possible for an LP problem to have more than one optimal solution?

6 Develop your own set of constraint equations and inequalities and use them to illustrate graphically each of the following conditions:
    (a) an unbounded problem
    (b) an infeasible problem
    (c) a problem containing redundant constraints

7 The production manager of a large Cincinnati manufacturing firm once made the statement, "I would like to use LP, but it's a technique that operates under conditions of certainty. My plant doesn't have that certainty; it's a world of uncertainty. So LP can't be used here." Do you think this statement has any merit? Explain why the manager may have said it.

8 The mathematical relationships that follow were formulated by an operations research analyst at the Smith–Lawton Chemical Company. Which ones are invalid for use in an LP problem, and why?

$$\text{Maximize profit} = 4X_1 + 3X_1X_2 + 8X_2 + 5X_3$$

$$\text{subject to} \quad 2X_1 \qquad + X_2 + 2X_3 \le 50$$

$$X_1 \qquad - 4X_2 \qquad \ge 6$$

$$1.5X_1^2 + 6X_2 + 3X_3 \ge 21$$

$$19X_2 - 0.35X_3 = 17$$

$$5X_1 \qquad + 4X_2 + 32\ X_3 \le 80$$

$$-X_1 \qquad - X_2 + X_3 = 5$$

9 Discuss the role of sensitivity analysis in LP. Under what circumstances is it needed, and under what conditions do you think it is not necessary?

10 A linear program has the objective of maximizing profit $= 12X + 8Y$. The maximum profit is $8,000. Using a computer we find the upper bound for profit on X is 20 and the lower bound is 9. Discuss the changes to the optimal solution (the values of the variables and the profit) that would occur if the profit on X were increased to $15. How would the optimal solution change if the profit on X were increased to $25?

11 A linear program has a maximum profit of $600. One constraint in this problem is $4X + 2Y \le 80$. Using a computer we find the dual price for this constraint is 3, and there is a lower bound of 75 and an upper bound of 100. Explain what this means.

12 Develop your own original LP problem with two constraints and two real variables.
    (a) Explain the meaning of the numbers on the right-hand side of each of your constraints.
    (b) Explain the significance of the technological coefficients.
    (c) Solve your problem graphically to find the optimal solution.
    (d) Illustrate graphically the effect of increasing the contribution rate of your first variable (X_1) by 50% over the value you first assigned it. Does this change the optimal solution?

13 Explain how a change in a technological coefficient can affect a problem's optimal solution. How can a change in resource availability affect a solution?

Problems

●14 The Electrocomp Corporation manufactures two electrical products: air conditioners and large fans. The assembly process for each is similar in that both require a certain amount of wiring and drilling. Each air conditioner takes 3 hours of wiring and 2 hours of drilling. Each fan must go through 2 hours of wiring and 1 hour of drilling. During the next production period, 240 hours of wiring time are available and up to 140 hours of drilling time may be used. Each air conditioner sold yields a profit of $25. Each fan assembled may be sold for a $15 profit. Formulate and solve this LP production mix situation to find the best combination of air conditioners and fans that yields the highest profit. Use the corner point graphical approach.

●15 Electrocomp's management realizes that it forgot to include two critical constraints (see Problem 14). In particular, management decides that there should be a minimum number of air conditioners produced in order to fulfill a contract. Also, due to an oversupply

Note: ☺ means the problem may be solved with QM for Windows; ✗ means the problem may be solved with Excel; and ☺ means the problem may be solved with QM for Windows and/or Excel.

482

of fans in the preceding period, a limit should be placed on the total number of fans produced.

    (a) If Electrocomp decides that at least 20 air conditioners should be produced but no more than 80 fans should be produced, what would be the optimal solution? How much slack is there for each of the four constraints?

    (b) If Electrocomp decides that at least 30 air conditioners should be produced but no more than 50 fans should be produced, what would be the optimal solution? How much slack is there for each of the four constraints at the optimal solution?

: 16 A candidate for mayor in a small town has allocated $40,000 for last-minute advertising in the days preceding the election. Two types of ads will be used: radio and television. Each radio ad costs $200 and reaches an estimated 3,000 people. Each television ad costs $500 and reaches an estimated 7,000 people. In planning the advertising campaign, the campaign manager would like to reach as many people as possible, but she has stipulated that at least 10 ads of each type must be used. Also, the number of radio ads must be at least as great as the number of television ads. How many ads of each type should be used? How many people will this reach?

• 17 The Outdoor Furniture Corporation manufactures two products, benches and picnic tables, for use in yards and parks. The firm has two main resources: its carpenters (labor force) and a supply of redwood for use in the furniture. During the next production cycle, 1,200 hours of labor are available under a union agreement. The firm also has a stock of 3,500 feet of good-quality redwood. Each bench that Outdoor Furniture produces requires 4 labor hours and 10 feet of redwood; each picnic table takes 6 labor hours and 35 feet of redwood. Completed benches will yield a profit of $9 each, and tables will result in a profit of $20 each. How many benches and tables should Outdoor Furniture produce to obtain the largest possible profit? Use the graphical LP approach.

: 18 The dean of the Western College of Business must plan the school's course offerings for the fall semester. Student demands make it necessary to offer at least 30 undergraduate and 20 graduate courses in the term. Faculty contracts also dictate that at least 60 courses be offered in total. Each undergraduate course taught costs the college an average of $2,500 in faculty wages, and each graduate course costs $3,000. How many undergraduate and graduate courses should be taught in the fall so that total faculty salaries are kept to a minimum?

: 19 MSA Computer Corporation manufactures two models of minicomputers, the Alpha 4 and the Beta 5. The firm employs five technicians, working 160 hours each per month, on its assembly line. Management insists that full employment (i.e., *all* 160 hours of time) be maintained for each worker during next month's operations. It requires 20 labor hours to assemble each Alpha 4 computer and 25 labor hours to assemble each Beta 5 model. MSA wants to see at least 10 Alpha 4s and at least 15 Beta 5s produced during the production period. Alpha 4s generate $1,200 profit per unit, and Beta 5s yield $1,800 each. Determine the most profitable number of each model of minicomputer to produce during the coming month.

: 20 A winner of the Texas Lotto has decided to invest $50,000 per year in the stock market. Under consideration are stocks for a petrochemical firm and a public utility. Although a long-range goal is to get the highest possible return, some consideration is given to the risk involved with the stocks. A risk index on a scale of 1–10 (with 10 being the most risky) is assigned to each of the two stocks. The total risk of the portfolio is found by multiplying the risk of each stock by the dollars invested in that stock.

The following table provides a summary of the return and risk:

STOCK	ESTIMATED RETURN	RISK INDEX
Petrochemical	12%	9
Utility	6%	4

The investor would like to maximize the return on the investment, but the average risk index of the investment should not be higher than 6. How much should be invested in each stock? What is the average risk for this investment? What is the estimated return for this investment?

: 21 Referring to the Texas Lotto situation in Problem 20, suppose the investor has changed his attitude about the investment and wishes to give greater emphasis to the risk of the investment. Now the investor wishes to minimize the risk of the investment as long as a return of at least 8% is generated. Formulate this as an LP problem and find the optimal solution. How much should be invested in each stock? What is the average risk for this investment? What is the estimated return for this investment?

: 22 Solve the following LP problem using the corner point graphical method. At the optimal solution, calculate the slack for each constraint:

$$\text{Maximize profit} = 4X + 4Y$$
$$\text{subject to} \quad 3X + 5Y \leq 150$$
$$X - 2Y \leq 10$$
$$5X + 3Y \leq 150$$
$$X, Y \geq 0$$

: 23 Consider this LP formulation:

$$\text{Minimize cost} = \$X + 2Y$$
$$\text{subject to}$$
$$X + 3Y \geq 90$$
$$8X + 2Y \geq 160$$
$$3X + 2Y \geq 120$$
$$Y \leq 70$$
$$X, Y \geq 0$$

Graphically illustrate the feasible region and apply the isocost line procedure to indicate which corner point produces the optimal solution. What is the cost of this solution?

: 24 The stock brokerage firm of Blank, Leibowitz, and Weinberger has analyzed and recommended two stocks to an investors' club of college professors. The professors were interested in factors such as short-term growth, intermediate growth, and dividend rates. These data on each stock are as follows:

	STOCK ($)	
FACTOR	LOUISIANA GAS AND POWER	TRIMEX INSULATION COMPANY
Short-term growth potential, per dollar invested	.36	.24
Intermediate growth potential (over next three years), per dollar invested	1.67	1.50
Dividend rate potential	4%	8%

Each member of the club has an investment goal of (1) an appreciation of no less than $720 in the short term, (2) an appreciation of at least $5,000 in the next three years, and (3) a dividend income of at least $200 per year. What is the smallest investment that a professor can make to meet these three goals?

: 25 Woofer Pet Foods produces a low-calorie dog food for overweight dogs. This product is made from beef products and grain. Each pound of beef costs $0.90, and each pound of grain costs $0.60. A pound of the dog food must contain at least 9 units of Vitamin 1 and 10 units of Vitamin 2. A pound of beef contains 10 units of Vitamin 1 and 12 units of Vitamin 2. A pound of grain contains 6 units of Vitamin 1 and 9 units of Vitamin 2. Formulate this as an LP problem to minimize the cost of the dog food. How many pounds of beef and grain should be included in each pound of dog food? What is the cost and vitamin content of the final product?

: 26 The seasonal yield of olives in a Piraeus, Greece, vineyard is greatly influenced by a process of branch pruning. If olive trees are pruned every two weeks, output is increased. The pruning process, however, requires considerably more labor than permitting the olives to grow on their own and results in a smaller size olive. It also, though, permits olive trees to be spaced closer together. The yield of 1 barrel of olives by pruning requires 5 hours of labor and 1 acre of land. The production of a barrel of olives by the normal process requires only 2 labor hours but takes 2 acres of land. An olive grower has 250 hours of labor available and a total of 150 acres for growing. Because of the olive size difference, a barrel of olives produced on pruned trees sells for $20, whereas a barrel of regular olives has a market price of $30. The grower has determined that because of uncertain demand, no more than 40 barrels of pruned olives should be produced. Use graphical LP to find
(a) the maximum possible profit.
(b) the best combination of barrels of pruned and regular olives.
(c) the number of acres that the olive grower should devote to each growing process.

: 27 Consider the following four LP formulations. Using a graphical approach, determine
(a) which formulation has more than one optimal solution.
(b) which formulation is unbounded.
(c) which formulation has no feasible solution.
(d) which formulation is correct as is.

Formulation 1

$$\text{Maximize } 10X_1 + 10X_2$$
$$\text{subject to } 2X_1 \leq 10$$
$$2X_1 + 4X_2 \leq 16$$
$$4X_2 \leq 8$$
$$X_1 = 6$$

Formulation 2

$$\text{Maximize } X_1 + 2X_2$$
$$\text{subject to } X_1 \leq 1$$
$$2X_2 \leq 2$$
$$X_1 + 2X_2 \leq 2$$

Formulation 3

$$\text{Maximize } 3X_1 + 2X_2$$
$$\text{subject to } X_1 + X_2 \geq 5$$
$$X_1 \geq 2$$
$$2X_2 \geq 8$$

Formulation 4

$$\text{Maximize } 3X_1 + 3X_2$$
$$\text{subject to } 4X_1 + 6X_2 \leq 48$$
$$4X_1 + 2X_2 \leq 12$$
$$3X_2 \geq 3$$
$$2X_1 \geq 2$$

•28 Graph the following LP problem and indicate the optimal solution point:

$$\text{Maximize profit} = \$3X + \$2Y$$
$$\text{subject to}$$
$$2X + Y \leq 150$$
$$2X + 3Y \leq 300$$

(a) Does the optimal solution change if the profit per unit of X changes to $4.50?
(b) What happens if the profit function should have been $3X + $3Y?

•29 Graphically analyze the following problem:

$$\text{Maximize profit} = \$4X + \$6Y$$
$$\text{subject to}$$
$$X + 2Y \leq 8 \text{ hours}$$
$$6X + 4Y \leq 24 \text{ hours}$$

(a) What is the optimal solution?

(b) If the first constraint is altered to $X + 3Y \leq 8$, does the feasible region or optimal solution change?

: 30 Examine the LP formulation in Problem 29. The problem's second constraint reads

$$6X + 4Y \leq 24 \text{ hours} \quad (\text{time available on machine 2})$$

If the firm decides that 36 hours of time can be made available on machine 2 (namely, an additional 12 hours) at an additional cost of $10, should it add the hours?

: 31 Consider the following LP problem:

$$\text{Maximize profit} = 5X + 6Y$$

$$\text{subject to} \quad 2X + Y \leq 120$$
$$2X + 3Y \leq 240$$
$$X, Y \geq 0$$

(a) What is the optimal solution to this problem? Solve it graphically.

(b) If a technical breakthrough occurred that raised the profit per unit of X to $8, would this affect the optimal solution?

(c) Instead of an increase in the profit coefficient X to $8, suppose that profit was overestimated and should only have been $3. Does this change the optimal solution?

: 32 Consider the LP formulation given in Problem 31. If the second constraint is changed from $2X + 3Y \leq 240$ to $2X + 4Y \leq 240$, what effect will this have on the optimal solution?

: 33 The computer output given below is for Problem 31. Use this to answer the following questions.

(a) How much could the profit on X increase or decrease without changing the values of X and Y in the optimal solution?

(b) If the right-hand side of constraint 1 were increased by 1 unit, how much would the profit increase?

(c) If the right-hand side of constraint 1 were increased by 10 units, how much would the profit increase?

: 34 The computer output on the next page is for a product mix problem in which there are two products and three resource constraints. Use the output to help you answer the following questions. Assume that you wish to maximize profit in each case.

(a) How many units of product 1 and product 2 should be produced?

(b) How much of each of the three resources is being used? How much slack is there for each constraint? Which of the constraints are binding, and which are nonbinding?

(c) What are the dual prices for each resource?

(d) If you could obtain more of one of the resources, which one should you obtain? How much should you be willing to pay for this?

(e) What would happen to profit if, with the original output, management decided to produce one more unit of product 2?

: 35 Graphically solve the following problem:

$$\text{Maximize profit} = 8X_1 + 5X_2$$

$$\text{subject to} \quad X_1 + X_2 \leq 10$$
$$X_1 \leq 6$$
$$X_1, X_2 \geq 0$$

(a) What is the optimal solution?

(b) Change the right-hand side of constraint 1 to 11 (instead of 10) and resolve the problem. How much did the profit increase as a result of this?

(c) Change the right-hand side of constraint 1 to 6 (instead of 10) and resolve the problem. How much did the profit decrease as a result of this? Looking at the graph, what would happen if the right-hand-side value were to go below 6?

(d) Change the right-hand-side value of constraint 1 to 5 (instead of 10) and resolve the problem.

Output for Problem 33

Linear Programming Results

Problem 7-33 Solution

	X	Y		RHS	Dual
Maximize	5.	6.			
Constraint 1	2.	1.	<=	120.	0.75
Constraint 2	2.	3.	<=	240.	1.75
Solution->	30.	60.		510.	

Ranging

Problem 7-33 Solution

Variable	Value	Reduced Cost	Original Val	Lower Bound	Upper Bound
X	30.	0.	5.	4.	12.
Y	60.	0.	6.	2.5	7.5
Constraint	Dual Value	Slack/Surplus	Original Val	Lower Bound	Upper Bound
Constraint 1	0.75	0.	120.	80.	240.
Constraint 2	1.75	0.	240.	120.	360.

Output for Problem 34

Linear Programming Results ▪ _ □ ×

Problem 734 Solution					
	X1	X2		RHS	Dual
Maximize	50.	20.			
Constraint 1	1.	2.	<=	45.	0.
Constraint 2	3.	3.	<=	87.	0.
Constraint 3	2.	1.	<=	50.	25.
Solution->	25.	0.		1,250.	

Ranging _ □ ×

Problem 734 Solution					
Variable	Value	Reduced Cost	Original Val	Lower Bound	Upper Bound
X1	25.	0.	50.	40.	Infinity
X2	0.	5.	20.	-Infinity	25.
Constraint	Dual Value	Slack/Surplus	Original Val	Lower Bound	Upper Bound
Constraint 1	0.	20.	45.	25.	Infinity
Constraint 2	0.	12.	87.	75.	Infinity
Constraint 3	25.	0.	50.	0.	58.

Output for Problem 35

Linear Programming Results _ □ ×

Solved Problem 7-2 Solution					
	X1	X2		RHS	Dual
Maximize	50.	20.			
Constraint 1	2.	4.	<=	400.	0.
Constraint 2	100.	50.	<=	8,000.	0.4
Constraint 3	1.	0.	<=	60.	10.
Solution->	60.	40.		3,800.	

Ranging _ □ ×

Solved Problem 7-2 Solution					
Variable	Value	Reduced Cost	Original Val	Lower Bound	Upper Bound
X1	60.	0.	50.	40.	Infinity
X2	40.	0.	20.	0.	25.
Constraint	Dual Value	Slack/Surplus	Original Val	Lower Bound	Upper Bound
Constraint 1	0.	120.	400.	280.	Infinity
Constraint 2	0.4	0.	8,000.	6,000.	9,500.
Constraint 3	10.	0.	60.	40.	80.

How much did the profit decrease from the original profit as a result of this?

(e) Using the computer output on this page, what is the dual price of constraint 1? What is the lower bound on this?

(f) What conclusions can you draw from this regarding the bounds of the right-hand-side values and the dual price?

 36   Serendipity*

The three princes of Serendip
Went on a little trip.
They could not carry too much weight;
More than 300 pounds made them hesitate.
They planned to the ounce. When they returned to Ceylon

They discovered that their supplies were just about gone
When, what to their joy, Prince William found
A pile of coconuts on the ground.
"Each will bring 60 rupees," said Prince Richard with a grin
As he almost tripped over a lion skin.
"Look out!" cried Prince Robert with glee
As he spied some more lion skins under a tree.
"These are worth even more—300 rupees each
If we can just carry them all down to the beach."
Each skin weighed fifteen pounds and each coconut, five,
But they carried them all and made it alive.
The boat back to the island was very small

---

*The word _serendipity_ was coined by the English writer Horace Walpole after a fairy tale titled _The Three Princes of Serendip._ Source of problem is unknown.

15 cubic feet baggage capacity—that was all.
Each lion skin took up one cubic foot
While eight coconuts the same space took.
With everything stowed they headed to sea
And on the way calculated what their new wealth might be.
"Eureka!" cried Prince Robert, "Our worth is so great
That there's no other way we could return in this state.
Any other skins or nut that we might have brought
Would now have us poorer. And now I know what—
I'll write my friend Horace in England, for surely
Only he can appreciate our serendipity."
Formulate and solve **Serendipity** by graphical LP in order to calculate "what their new wealth might be."

:37 Bhavika Investments, a group of financial advisors and retirement planners, has been requested to provide advice on how to invest $200,000 for one of its clients. The client has stipulated that the money must be put into either a stock fund or a money market fund, and the annual return should be at least $14,000. Other conditions related to risk have also been specified, and the following linear program was developed to help with this investment decision:

Minimize risk $= 12S + 5M$
subject to

$S + M = 200,000$	total investment is $200,000
$0.10S + 0.05M \geq 14,000$	return must be at least $14,000
$M \geq 40,000$	at least $40,000 must be in money market fund
$S, M \geq 0$	

where
$S =$ dollars invested in stock fund
$M =$ dollars invested in money market fund

The QM for Windows output is shown below.
(a) How much money should be invested in the money market fund and the stock fund? What is the total risk?
(b) What is the total return? What rate of return is this?
(c) Would the solution change if risk measure for each dollar in the stock fund were 14 instead of 12?
(d) For each additional dollar that is available, how much does the risk change?
(e) Would the solution change if the amount that must be invested in the money market fund were changed from $40,000 to $50,000?

:38 Refer to the Bhavika Investments (Problem 37) situation once again. It has been decided that, rather than minimize risk, the objective should be to maximize return while placing restriction on the amount of risk. The average risk should be no more than 11 (with a total risk of 2,200,000 for the $200,000 invested). The linear program was reformulated, and the QM for Windows output is shown on the next page.
(a) How much money should be invested in the money market fund and the stock fund? What is the total return? What rate of return is this?
(b) What is the total risk? What is the average risk?
(c) Would the solution change if return for each dollar in the stock fund were 0.09 instead of 0.10?
(d) For each additional dollar that is available, what is the marginal rate of return?
(e) How much would the total return change if the amount that must be invested in the money market fund were changed from $40,000 to $50,000?

Problems 39 to 44 test your ability to formulate LP problems that have more than two variables. They cannot be solved graphically but will give you a chance to set up a larger problem.

:39 The Feed 'N Ship Ranch fattens cattle for local farmers and ships them to meat markets in Kansas

Output for Problem 37

Bhavika Investments Solution					
	S	M		RHS	Dual
Minimize	12	5			
Constraint 1	1	1	=	200000	2
Constraint 2	0.1	0.05	>=	14000	-140
Constraint 3	0	1	>=	40000	0
Solution->	80000	120000.0		1560000	

Bhavika Investments Solution					
Variable	Value	Reduced Cost	Original Val	Lower Bound	Upper Bound
S	80000	0	12	5	Infinity
M	120000.0	0	5	-Infinity	12
Constraint	Dual Value	Slack/Surplus	Original Val	Lower Bound	Upper Bound
Constraint 1	2	0	200000	160000	280000
Constraint 2	-140	0	14000	10000	18000
Constraint 3	0	80000.01	40000	-Infinity	120000.0

Output for Problem 38

Bhavika Investments Solution					
	S	M		RHS	Dual
Maximize	0.1	0.05			
Constraint 1	1	1	=	200000	0.1
Constraint 2	12	5	<=	2200000	0
Constraint 3	0	1	>=	40000	-0.05
Solution->	160000	40000		18000	

Bhavika Investments Solution					
Variable	Value	Reduced Cost	Original Val	Lower Bound	Upper Bound
S	160000	0	0.1	0.05	Infinity
M	40000	0	0.05	-Infinity	0.1
Constraint	Dual Value	Slack/Surplus	Original Val	Lower Bound	Upper Bound
Constraint 1	0.1	0	200000	40000	206666.7
Constraint 2	0	80000	2200000	2120000	Infinity
Constraint 3	-0.05	0	40000	28571.43	200000

City and Omaha. The owners of the ranch seek to determine the amounts of cattle feed to buy so that minimum nutritional standards are satisfied, and at the same time total feed costs are minimized. The feed mix can be made up of the three grains that contain the following ingredients per pound of feed:

	FEED (OZ.)		
INGREDIENT	STOCK X	STOCK Y	STOCK Z
A	3	2	4
B	2	3	1
C	1	0	2
D	6	8	4

The cost per pound of stocks X, Y, and Z are $2, $4, and $2.50, respectively. The minimum requirement per cow per month is 4 pounds of ingredient A, 5 pounds of ingredient B, 1 pound of ingredient C, and 8 pounds of ingredient D.

The ranch faces one additional restriction: it can only obtain 500 pounds of stock Z per month from the feed supplier regardless of its need. Because there are usually 100 cows at the Feed 'N Ship Ranch at any given time, this means that no more than 5 pounds of stock Z can be counted on for use in the feed of each cow per month.

(a) Formulate this as an LP problem.

(b) Solve using LP software.

(40) The Weinberger Electronics Corporation manufactures four highly technical products that it supplies to aerospace firms that hold NASA contracts. Each of the products must pass through the following departments before they are shipped: wiring, drilling, assembly, and inspection. The time requirement in hours for each unit produced and its corresponding profit value are summarized in the following table:

	DEPARTMENT				UNIT
PRODUCT	WIRING	DRILLING	ASSEMBLY	INSPECTION	PROFIT ($)
XJ201	0.5	0.3	0.2	0.5	9
XM897	1.5	1	4	1	12
TR29	1.5	2	1	0.5	15
BR788	1	3	2	0.5	11

The production available in each department each month, and the minimum monthly production requirement to fulfill contracts, are as follows:

DEPARTMENT	CAPACITY (HOURS)	PRODUCT	MINIMUM PRODUCTION LEVEL
Wiring	15,000	XJ201	150
Drilling	17,000	XM897	100
Assembly	26,000	TR29	300
Inspection	12,000	BR788	400

The production manager has the responsibility of specifying production levels for each product for the coming month. Help him by formulating (that is, setting up the constraints and objective function) Weinberger's problem using LP.

:41 Outdoor Inn, a camping equipment manufacturer in southern Utah, is developing a production schedule for a popular type of tent, the Double Inn. Orders have been received for 180 of these to be delivered at the end of this month, 220 to be delivered at the end of next month, and 240 to be delivered at the end of the month after that. This tent may be produced at a cost of $120, and the maximum number of tents that can be produced in a month is 230.

The company may produce some extra tents in one month and keep them in storage until the next month. The cost for keeping these in inventory for 1 month is estimated to be $6 per tent for each tent left at the end of the month. Formulate this as an LP problem to minimize cost while meeting demand and not exceeding the monthly production capacity. Solve it using any computer software. (*Hint:* Define variables to represent the number of tents left over at the end of each month.)

42 Outdoors Inn (see Problem 41) expanded its tent-making operations later in the year. While still making the Double Inn tent, it is also making a larger tent, the Family Rolls, which has four rooms. The company can produce up to a combined total of 280 tents per month. The following table provides the demand that must be met and the production costs for the next 3 months. Note that the costs will increase in month 2. The holding cost for keeping a tent in inventory at the end of the month for use in the next month is estimated to be $6 per tent for the Double Inn and $8 per tent for the Family Rolls. Develop a linear program to minimize the total cost. Solve it using any computer software.

MONTH	DEMAND FOR DOUBLE INN	COST TO PRODUCE DOUBLE INN	DEMAND FOR FAMILY ROLLS	COST TO PRODUCE FAMILY ROLLS
1	185	$120	60	$150
2	205	$130	70	$160
3	225	$130	65	$160

43 Modem Corporation of America (MCA) is the world's largest producer of modem communication devices for microcomputers. MCA sold 9,000 of the regular model and 10,400 of the smart ("intelligent") model this September. Its income statement for the month is shown in the table on this page. Costs presented are typical of prior months and are expected to remain at the same levels in the near future.

The firm is facing several constraints as it prepares its November production plan. First, it has experienced a tremendous demand and has been unable to keep any significant inventory in stock. This situation is not expected to change. Second, the firm is located in a small Iowa town from which additional labor is not readily available. Workers can be shifted from production of one modem to another, however. To produce the 9,000 regular modems in September required 5,000 direct labor hours. The 10,400 intelligent modems absorbed 10,400 direct labor hours.

TABLE FOR PROBLEM 43

MCA Income Statement Month Ended September 30

	REGULAR MODEMS	INTELLIGENT MODEMS
Sales	$450,000	$640,000
Less: Discounts	10,000	15,000
Returns	12,000	9,500
Warranty replacements	4,000	2,500
Net sales	$424,000	$613,000
Sales costs		
Direct labor	60,000	76,800
Indirect labor	9,000	11,520
Materials cost	90,000	128,000
Depreciation	40,000	50,800
Cost of sales	$199,000	$267,120
Gross profit	$225,000	$345,880
Selling and general expenses		
General expenses—variable	30,000	35,000
General expenses—fixed	36,000	40,000
Advertising	28,000	25,000
Sales commissions	31,000	60,000
Total operating cost	$125,000	$160,000
Pretax income	$100,000	$185,880
Income taxes (25%)	25,000	46,470
Net income	$ 75,000	$139,410

Third, MCA is experiencing a problem affecting the intelligent modems model. Its component supplier is able to guarantee only 8,000 microprocessors for November delivery. Each intelligent modem requires one of these specially made microprocessors. Alternative suppliers are not available on short notice.

MCA wants to plan the optimal mix of the two modem models to produce in November to maximize profits for MCA.

(a) Formulate, using September's data, MCA's problem as a linear program.

(b) Solve the problem graphically.

(c) Discuss the implications of your recommended solution.

44 Working with chemists at Virginia Tech and George Washington Universities, landscape contractor Kenneth Golding blended his own fertilizer, called "Golding-Grow." It consists of four chemical compounds, C-30, C-92, D-21, and E-11. The cost per pound for each compound is indicated as follows:

CHEMICAL COMPOUND	COST PER POUND ($)
C-30	0.12
C-92	0.09
D-21	0.11
E-11	0.04

The specifications for Golding-Grow are as follows:
(1) E-11 must constitute at least 15% of the blend;
(2) C-92 and C-30 must together constitute at least 45% of the blend; (3) D-21 and C-92 can together constitute no more than 30% of the blend; and (4) Golding-Grow is packaged and sold in 50-pound bags.

(a) Formulate an LP problem to determine what blend of the four chemicals will allow Golding to minimize the cost of a 50-pound bag of the fertilizer.

(b) Solve using a computer to find the best solution.

 :45 Raptor Fuels produces three grades of gasoline—Regular, Premium, and Super. All of these are produced by blending two types of crude oil—Crude A and Crude B. The two types of crude contain specific ingredients which help in determining the octane rating of gasoline. The important ingredients and the costs are contained in the following table:

	CRUDE A	CRUDE B
Cost per gallon	$0.42	$0.47
Ingredient 1	40%	52%
Other ingredients	60%	48%

In order to achieve the desired octane ratings, at least 41% of Regular gasoline should be Ingredient 1; at least 44% of Premium gasoline must be Ingredient 1, and at least 48% of Super gasoline must be Ingredient 1. Due to current contract commitments, Raptor Fuels must produce as least 20,000 gallons of Regular, at least 15,000 gallons of Premium, and at least 10,000 gallons of Super. Formulate a linear program that could be used to determine how much of Crude A and Crude B should be used in each of the gasolines to meet the demands at the minimum cost. What is the minimum cost? How much of Crude A and Crude B are used in each gallon of the different types of gasoline?

 Internet Homework Problems

See our Internet home page, at **www.pearsonhighered.com/render**, for additional homework problems, Problems 46 to 50.

Case Study

Mexicana Wire Works

Ron Garcia felt good about his first week as a management trainee at Mexicana Wire Winding, Inc. He had not yet developed any technical knowledge about the manufacturing process, but he had toured the entire facility, located in the suburbs of Mexico City, and had met many people in various areas of the operation.

Mexicana, a subsidiary of Westover Wire Works, a Texas firm, is a medium-sized producer of wire windings used in making electrical transformers. Carlos Alverez, the production control manager, described the windings to Garcia as being of standardized design. Garcia's tour of the plant, laid out by process type (see Figure 20), followed the manufacturing sequence for the windings: drawing, extrusion, winding, inspection, and packaging. After inspection, good product is packaged and sent to finished product storage; defective product is stored separately until it can be reworked.

On March 8, Vivian Espania, Mexicana's general manager, stopped by Garcia's office and asked him to attend a staff meeting at 1:00 P.M.

"Let's get started with the business at hand," Vivian said, opening the meeting. "You all have met Ron Garcia, our new management trainee. Ron studied operations management in his MBA program in southern California, so I think he is competent to help us with a problem we have been discussing for a long time without resolution. I'm sure that each of you on my staff will give Ron your full cooperation."

Vivian turned to José Arroyo, production control manager. "José, why don't you describe the problem we are facing?"

"Well," José said, "business is very good right now. We are booking more orders than we can fill. We will have some new equipment on line within the next several months, which will take care of our capacity problems, but that won't help us in April. I have located some retired employees who used to work in the drawing department, and I am planning to bring them in as temporary employees in April to increase capacity there. Because we are planning to refinance some of our long-term debt, Vivian wants our profits to look as good as possible in April. I'm having a hard time figuring out which orders to run and which to back order so that I can make the bottom line look as good as possible. Can you help me with this?"

Garcia was surprised and apprehensive to receive such an important, high-profile assignment so early in his career.

FIGURE 20

Mexicana Wire Winding, Inc.

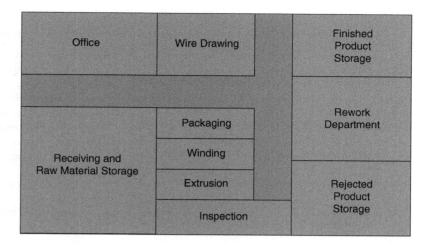

Recovering quickly, he said, "Give me your data and let me work with it for a day or two."

April Orders

Product W0075C	1,400 units
Product W0033C	250 units
Product W0005X	1,510 units
Product W0007X	1,116 units

Note: Vivian Espania has given her word to a key customer that we will manufacture 600 units of product W0007X and 150 units of product W0075C for him during April

Standard Cost

PRODUCT	MATERIAL	LABOR	OVERHEAD	SELLING PRICE
W0075C	$33.00	$ 9.90	$23.10	$100.00
W0033C	25.00	7.50	17.50	80.00
W0005X	35.00	10.50	24.50	130.00
W0007X	75.00	11.25	63.75	175.00

Selected Operating Data

Average output per month = 2,400 units

Average machine utilization = 63%

Average percentage of production set to rework department = 5% (mostly from Winding Department)

Average no. of rejected units awaiting rework = 850 (mostly from Winding Department)

Plant Capacity (Hours)

DRAWING	EXTRUSION	WINDING	PACKAGING
4,000	4,200	2,000	2,300

Note: Inspection capacity is not a problem; we can work overtime, as necessary, to accommodate any schedule.

Bill of Labor (Hours/Unit)

PRODUCT	DRAWING	EXTRUSION	WINDING	PACKAGING
W0075C	1.0	1.0	1.0	1.0
W0033C	2.0	1.0	3.0	0.0
W0005X	0.0	4.0	0.0	3.0
W0007X	1.0	1.0	0.0	2.0

Discussion Questions

1. What recommendations should Ron Garcia make, with what justification? Provide a detailed analysis with charts, graphs, and computer printouts included.
2. Discuss the need for temporary workers in the drawing department.
3. Discuss the plant layout.

Source: Professor Victor E. Sower, Sam Houston State University. This case material is based on an actual situation, with names and data altered for confidentiality.

 Internet Case Study

See our Internet home page, at **www.pearsonhighered.com/render**, for this additional case study: Agri Chem Corporation. This case involves a company's response to an energy shortage.

Bibliography

Bassamboo, Achal, J. Michael Harrison, and Assaf Zeevi. "Design and Control of a Large Call Center: Asymptotic Analysis of an LP-Based Method," *Operations Research* 54, 3 (May–June 2006): 419–435.

Behjat, Laleh, Anthony Vannelli, and William Rosehart. "Integer Linear Programming Model for Global Routing," *INFORMS Journal on Computing* 18, 2 (Spring 2006): 137–150.

Bixby, Robert E. "Solving Real-World Linear Programs: A Decade and More of Progress," *Operations Research* 50, 1 (January–February 2002): 3–15.

Bodington, C. E., and T. E. Baker. "A History of Mathematical Programming in the Petroleum Industry," *Interfaces* 20, 4 (July–August 1990): 117–132.

Boros, E., L. Fedzhora, P. B. Kantor, K. Saeger, and P. Stroud. "A Large-Scale Linear Programming Model For Finding Optimal Container Inspection Strategies," *Naval Research Logistics* 56, 5 (August 2009): 404–420.

Chakravarti, N. "Tea Company Steeped in OR," *OR/MS Today* 27, 2 (April 2000): 32–34.

Ching, Wai-Ki, Wai-On Yuen, Michael K. Ng, and Shu-Qin Zhang. "A Linear Programming Approach for Determining Optimal Advertising Policy," *IMA Journal of Management Mathematics* 17, 1 (2006): 83–96.

Dantzig, George B. "Linear Programming Under Uncertainty," *Management Science* 50, 12 (December 2004): 1764–1769.

Desroisers, Jacques. "Air Transat Uses ALTITUDE to Manage Its Aircraft Routing, Crew Pairing, and Work Assignment," *Interfaces* 30, 2 (March–April 2000): 41–53.

Dutta, Goutam, and Robert Fourer. "A Survey of Mathematical Programming Applications in Integrated Steel Plants," *Manufacturing & Service Operations Management* 3, 4 (Fall 2001): 387–400.

Farley, A. A. "Planning the Cutting of Photographic Color Paper Rolls for Kodak (Australasia) Pty. Ltd.," *Interfaces* 21, 1 (January–February 1991): 92–106.

Fourer, Robert. "Software Survey: Linear Programming," *OR/MS* Today 36, 3 (June 2009): 46–55.

Gass, Saul I. "The First Linear-Programming Shoppe," *Operations Research* 50, 1 (January–February 2002): 61–68.

Greenberg, H. J. "How to Analyze the Results of Linear Programs—Part 1: Preliminaries," *Interfaces* 23, 4 (July–August 1993): 56–68.

Greenberg, H. J. "How to Analyze the Results of Linear Programs—Part 3: Infeasibility Diagnosis," *Interfaces* 23, 6 (November–December 1993): 120–139.

Hafizoğlu, A. B., and M Azizoğlu. "Linear Programming Based Approaches for the Discrete Time/Cost Trade-off Problem in Project Networks," *Journal of the Operational Research Society* 61 (April 2010): 676–685.

Higle, Julia L., and Stein W. Wallace. "Sensitivity Analysis and Uncertainty in Linear Programming," *Interfaces* 33, 4(July–August 2003): 53–60.

Murphy, Frederic H. "ASP, the Art and Science of Practice: Elements of a Theory of the Practice of Operations Research: Expertise in Practice," Interfaces 35, 4 (July–August 2005): 313–322.

Orden, A. "LP from the '40s to the '90s," *Interfaces* 23, 5 (September–October 1993): 2–12.

Romeijn, H. Edwin, Ravindra K. Ahuja, James F. Dempsey, and Arvind Kumar. "A New Linear Programming Approach to Radiation Therapy Treatment Planning Problems," *Operations Research* 54, 2 (March–April 2006): 201–216.

Rubin, D. S., and H. M. Wagner. "Shadow Prices: Tips and Traps for Managers and Instructors," *Interfaces* 20, 4 (July–August 1990): 150–157.

Wendell, Richard E. "Tolerance Sensitivity and Optimality Bounds in Linear Programming," *Management Science* 50, 6 (June 2004) 797–803.

Appendix 1   Excel QM

Using the Excel QM add-in can help you easily solve linear programming problems. Excel QM automates the spreadsheet preparation for the use of the Solver add-in. We will illustrate this using the Flair Furniture example.

To begin, from the *Add-Ins* tab in Excel 2010, click *Excel QM* and then select *Linear, Integer & Mixed Integer Programming* from the drop-down menu, as shown in Program 7A. The Excel QM Spreadsheet Initialization window opens, and in it you enter the problem title, the number of variables, the number of constraints (do not count the nonnegativity constraints), and specify whether the problem is a maximization or minimization problem. This is illustrated in Program 7B. When finished, click *OK*.

When the initialization process is finished, a spreadsheet is prepared for data input, as shown in Program 7C. In this screen, enter the data in the section labeled Data. Specify the type of constraint (less-than, greater-than, or equal-to) and change the variable names and the constraint names, if desired.

Program 7D presents the same spreadsheet as Program 7C, with the data input and the variable names changed. Once the data have been entered, from the *Data* tab, select *Solver*. The Solver Parameters window opens, as shown in Program 7E. Excel QM will have made all the necessary inputs and selections, so simply click *OK* to find the solution.

The solution is displayed in Program 7F. In addition to the optimal values for the decision variables and the profit, the solution also includes slack or surplus for each constraint. You can obtain additional information from the Solver Results window that opens. Select a type of report (if any) and click *OK*. Any report that you selected will be placed on a separate worksheet.

PROGRAM 7A

Using Excel QM in Excel 2010 for the Flair Furniture Example

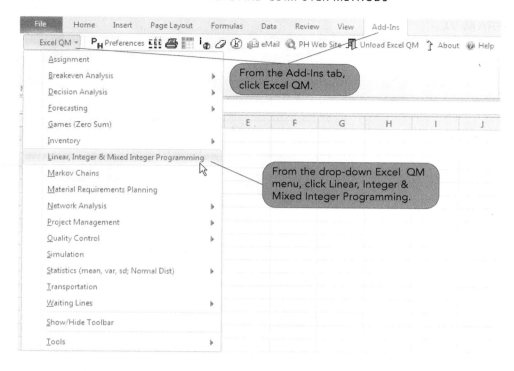

From the Add-Ins tab, click Excel QM.

From the drop-down Excel QM menu, click Linear, Integer & Mixed Integer Programming.

PROGRAM 7B

Using the Excel QM Spreadsheet Initialization Window

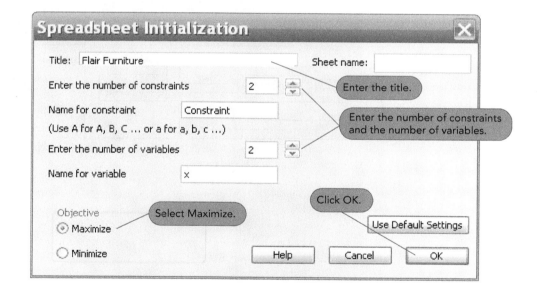

Enter the title.

Enter the number of constraints and the number of variables.

Select Maximize.

Click OK.

PROGRAM 7C

An Excel QM Initialized Spreadsheet

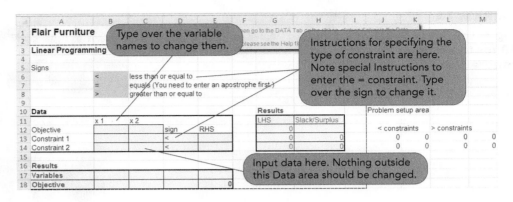

PROGRAM 7D

Excel QM Spreadsheet After Data Input for Flair Furniture

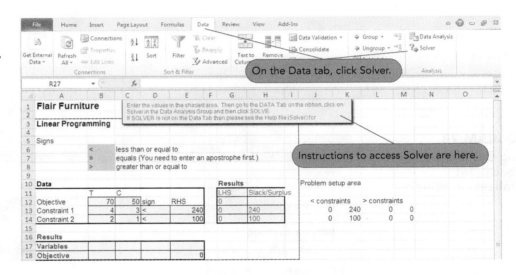

PROGRAM 7E

The Excel Solver Parameters Window

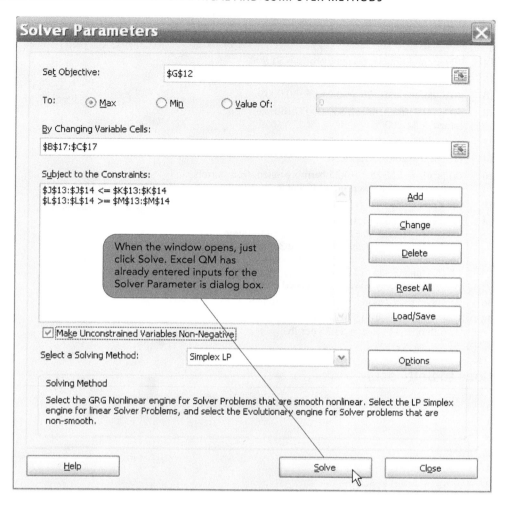

PROGRAM 7F

Excel QM output for Flair Furniture and the Solver Results Window

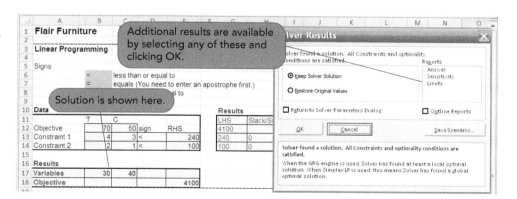

Solutions to Selected Problems

14	40 air conditioners, 60 fans, profit $= \$1,900$
16	175 radio ads, 10 TV ads
18	40 undergraduate, 20 graduate, $160,000
20	$20,000 Petrochemical; $30,000 Utilities; return $= \$4,200$; risk $= 6$
22	$X = 18.75$, $Y = 18.75$, profit $= \$150$
24	(1358.7, 1820.6), $3,179.30
26	(a) profit $= \$2,375$ (b) 25 barrels pruned, 62.5 barrels regular (c) 25 acres pruned, 125 acres regular
28	(a) Yes (b) Doesn't change
34	(a) 25 units product 1, 0 units product 2 (b) 25 units of resource 1 is used, slack $= 20$; 75 units of resource 2 is used, slack $= 12$; 50 units of resource 3 is used, slack $= 0$; constraint 3 is binding and others are not. (c) 0, 0, and 25 (d) Resource 3. Up to $25 (dual price) (e) Total profit would decrease by 5 (value of reduced cost).
36	24 coconuts, 12 skins; profit $= 5,040$ rupees
42	Use 7.5 lb of C-30, 15 lb of C-92, 0 lb of D-21, and 27.5 lb of E-11; cost $= \$3.35$ per lb

Solutions to Self-Tests

1.	b
2.	a
3.	b
4.	c
5.	a
6.	b
7.	c
8.	c
9.	b
10.	c
11.	a
12.	a
13.	a
14.	a

Transportation and Assignment Models

From Chapter 9 of *Quantitative Analysis for Management,* 11/e. Barry Render. Ralph M. Stair, Jr. Michael E. Hanna. Copyright © 2012 by Pearson Education. All rights reserved.

1 Introduction

In this chapter we explore three special types of linear programming problems—the transportation problem, the assignment problem, and the transshipment problem. All these may be modeled as *network flow problems*, with the use of nodes (points) and arcs (lines).

This first part of this chapter will explain these problems, provide network representations for them, and provide linear programming models for them. The solutions will be found using standard linear programming software. The transportation and assignment problems have a special structure that enables them to be solved with very efficient algorithms. The latter part of the chapter will present the special algorithms for solving them.

2 The Transportation Problem

The **transportation problem** deals with the distribution of goods from several points of supply (*origins* or **sources**) to a number of points of demand (**destinations**). Usually we are given a capacity (supply) of goods at each source, a requirement (demand) for goods at each destination, and the shipping cost per unit from each source to each destination. An example is shown in Figure 1. The objective of such a problem is to schedule shipments so that total transportation costs are minimized. At times, production costs are included also.

Transportation models can also be used when a firm is trying to decide where to locate a new facility. Before opening a new warehouse, factory, or sales office, it is good practice to consider a number of alternative sites. Good financial decisions concerning the facility location also attempt to minimize total transportation and production costs for the entire system.

Linear Program for the Transportation Example

The Executive Furniture Corporation is faced with the transportation problem shown in Figure 1. The company would like to minimize the transportation costs while meeting the demand at each destination and not exceeding the supply at each source. In formulating this as a linear

FIGURE 1

Network Representation of a Transportation problem, with Costs, Demands, and Supplies

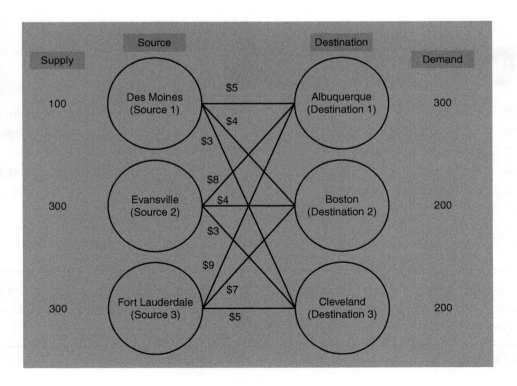

program, there are three supply constraints (one for each source) and three demand constraints (one for each destination). The decisions to be made are the number of units to ship on each route, so there is one decision variable for each arc (arrow) in the network. Let

$$X_{ij} = \text{number of units shipped from source } i \text{ to destination } j$$

where

$i = 1, 2, 3,$ with $1 =$ Des Moines, $2 =$ Evansville, and $3 =$ Fort Lauderdale

$j = 1, 2, 3,$ with $1 =$ Albuquerque, $2 =$ Boston, and $3 =$ Cleveland

The LP formulation is

$$\text{Minimize total cost} = 5X_{11} + 4X_{12} + 3X_{13} + 8X_{21} + 4X_{22}$$
$$+ 3X_{23} + 9X_{31} + 7X_{32} + 5X_{33}$$

subject to

$$X_{11} + X_{12} + X_{13} \leq 100 \quad \text{(Des Moines supply)}$$
$$X_{21} + X_{22} + X_{23} \leq 300 \quad \text{(Evansville supply)}$$
$$X_{31} + X_{32} + X_{33} \leq 300 \quad \text{(Fort Lauderdale supply)}$$
$$X_{11} + X_{21} + X_{31} = 300 \quad \text{(Albuquerque demand)}$$
$$X_{12} + X_{22} + X_{32} = 200 \quad \text{(Boston demand)}$$
$$X_{13} + X_{23} + X_{33} = 200 \quad \text{(Cleveland demand)}$$
$$X_{ij} \geq 0 \text{ for all } i \text{ and } j$$

The solution to this LP problem could be found using Solver in Excel 2010 by putting these constraints into a spreadsheet. However, the special structure of this problem allows for an easier and more intuitive format, as shown in Program 1. Solver is still used, but since all the constraint coefficients are 1 or 0, the left-hand side of each constraint is simply the sum of the variables from a particular source or to a particular destination. In Program 1 these are cells E10:E12 and B13:D13.

A General LP Model for Transportation Problems

In this example, there were 3 sources and 3 destinations. The LP had $3 \times 3 = 9$ variables and $3 + 3 = 6$ constraints. In general, for a transportation problem with m sources and n destination, the number of variables is mn, and the number of constraints is $m + n$. For example, if there are 5 (i.e., $m = 5$) constraints and 8 (i.e., $n = 8$) variables, the linear program would have $5(8) = 40$ variables and $5 + 8 = 13$ constraints.

The number of variables and constraints for a typical transportation problem can be found from the number of sources and destinations.

The use of the double subscripts on the variables makes the general form of the linear program for a transportation problem with m sources and n destinations easy to express. Let

$$x_{ij} = \text{number of units shipped from source } i \text{ to destination } j$$
$$c_{ij} = \text{cost one unit from source } i \text{ to destination } j$$
$$s_i = \text{supply at source } i$$
$$d_j = \text{demand at destination } j$$

The linear programming model is

$$\text{Minimize cost} = \sum_{j=1}^{n} \sum_{i=1}^{m} c_{ij} x_{ij}$$

subject to

$$\sum_{j=1}^{n} x_{ij} \leq s_i \qquad i = 1, 2, \ldots, m$$
$$\sum_{i=1}^{m} x_{ij} = d_j \qquad j = 1, 2, \ldots, n$$
$$x_{ij} \geq 0 \qquad \text{for all } i \text{ and } j$$

PROGRAM 1

Executive Furniture Corporation Solution in Excel 2010

▲	A	B	C	D	E	F
1			Shipping Cost Per Unit			
2	From\To	Albuquerque	Boston	Cleveland		
3	Des Moines	5	4	3		
4	Evansville	8	4	3		
5	Fort Lauderdale	9	7	5		
6						
7						
8			Solution - Number of units shipped			
9		Albuquerque	Boston	Cleveland	Total shipped	Supply
10	Des Moines	100	0	0	100	100
11	Evansville	0	200	100	300	300
12	Fort Lauderdale	200	0	100	300	300
13	Total received	300	200	200		
14	Demand	300	200	200		
15						
16	Total cost =	3900				

Solver Parameter Inputs and Selections

Set Objective: B16
By Changing cells: B10:D12
To: Min
Subject to the Constraints:
  E10:E12 <= F10:F12
  B13:D13 = B14:D14
Solving Method: Simplex LP
☑ **Make Variables Non-Negative**

Key Formulas

▲	E
9	**Total shipped**
10	=SUM(B10:D10)

Copy E10 to E11:E12

▲	B
13	=SUM(B10:B12)

Copy B13 to C13:D13

▲	B
16	=SUMPRODUCT(B3:D5,B10:D12)

3 The Assignment Problem

The assignment problem refers to the class of LP problem that involve determining the most efficient assignment of people to projects, sales people to territories, auditors to companies for audits, contracts to bidders, jobs to machines, heavy equipment (such as cranes) to construction jobs, and so on. The objective is most often to minimize total costs or total time of performing the tasks at hand. One important characteristic of assignment problems is that only one job or worker is assigned to one machine or project.

Figure 2 provides a network representation of an assignment problem. Notice that this network is very similar to the network for the transportation problem. In fact, an assignment problem may be viewed as a special type of transportation problem in which the supply at each source and the demand at each destination must equal one. Each person may only be assigned to one job or project, and each job only needs one person.

An assignment problem is equivalent to a transportation problem with each supply and demand equal to 1.

500

FIGURE 2

Example of an Assignment Problem in a Transportation Network Format

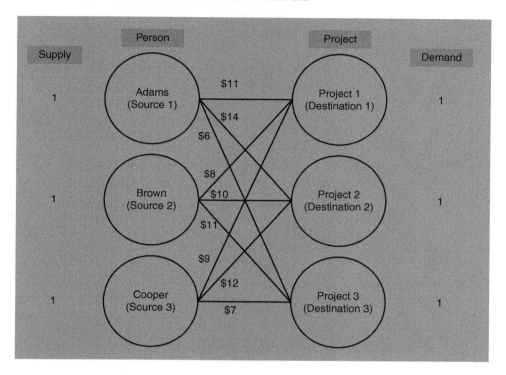

Linear Program for Assignment Example

The network in Figure 2 represents a problem faced by the Fix-It Shop, which has just received three new repair projects that must be completed quickly: (1) a radio, (2) a toaster oven, and (3) a coffee table. Three repair persons, each with different talents, are available to do the jobs. The shop owner estimates the cost in wages if the workers are assigned to each of the three projects. The costs differ due to the talents of each worker on each of the jobs. The owner wishes to assign the jobs so that total cost is minimized and each job must have one person assigned to it, and each person can only be assigned to one job.

In formulating this as a linear program, the general LP form of the transportation problem can be used. In defining the variables, let

Special variables 0-1 are used with the assignment model.

$$X_{ij} = \begin{cases} 1 \text{ if person } i \text{ is assigned to project } j \\ 0 \text{ otherwise} \end{cases}$$

where

$i = 1, 2, 3$, with $1 = $ Adams, $2 = $ Brown, and $3 = $ Cooper

$j = 1, 2, 3$, with $1 = $ Project 1, $2 = $ Project 2, and $3 = $ Project 3

The LP formulation is

$$\text{Minimize total cost} = 11X_{11} + 14X_{12} + 6X_{13} + 8X_{21} + 10X_{22}$$
$$+ 11X_{23} + 9X_{31} + 12X_{32} + 7X_{33}$$

subject to

$$X_{11} + X_{12} + X_{13} \leq 1$$
$$X_{21} + X_{22} + X_{23} \leq 1$$
$$X_{31} + X_{32} + X_{33} \leq 1$$
$$X_{11} + X_{21} + X_{31} = 1$$
$$X_{12} + X_{22} + X_{32} = 1$$
$$X_{13} + X_{23} + X_{33} = 1$$
$$x_{ij} = 0 \text{ or } 1 \text{ for all } i \text{ and } j$$

The solution is shown in Program 2. From this, $x_{13} = 1$, so Adams is assigned to project 3; $x_{22} = 1$, so Brown is assigned to project 2; and $x_{31} = 1$, so Cooper is assigned to project 1. All other variables are 0. The total cost is 25.

PROGRAM 2

Fix-It Shop Solution in Excel 2010

	A	B	C	D	E	F
1		**Cost for Assignments**				
2	Person\Project	Project 1	Project 2	Project 3		
3	Adams	11	14	6		
4	Brown	8	10	11		
5	Cooper	9	12	7		
6						
7						
8			**Made**			
9		Project 1	Project 2	Project 3	Total projects	Supply
10	Adams	0	0	1	1	1
11	Brown	0	1	0	1	1
12	Cooper	1	0	0	1	1
13	Total assigned	1	1	1		
14	Total workers	1	1	1		
15						
16	Total cost =	25				

Solver Parameter Inputs and Selections

Set Objective: B16
By Changing cells: B10:D12
To: Min
Subject to the Constraints:
    E10:E12 <= F10:F12
    B13:D13 = B14:D14
Solving Method: Simplex LP
☑ **Make Variables Non-Negative**

Key Formulas

	E
10	=SUM(B10:D10)

Copy E10 to E11:E12

	B
13	=SUM(B10:B12)

Copy B13 to C13:D13

	B
16	=SUMPRODUCT(B3:D5,B10:D12)

In the assignment problem, the variables are required to be either 0 or 1. Due to the special structure of this problem with the constraint coefficients as 0 or 1 and all the right-hand-side values equal to 1, the problem can be solved as a linear program. The solution to such a problem (if one exists) will always have the variables equal to 0 or 1. There are other types of problems where the use of such 0–1 variables is desired, but the solution to such problems using normal linear programming methods will not necessarily have only zeros and ones. In such cases, special methods must be used to force the variables to be either 0 or 1.

4 The Transshipment Problem

In a transportation problem, if the items being transported must go through an intermediate point (called a *transshipment point*) before reaching a final destination, the problem is called a *transshipment problem*. For example, a company might be manufacturing a product at several factories to be shipped to a set of regional distribution centers. From these centers, the items are

FIGURE 3

Network Representation of Transshipment Example

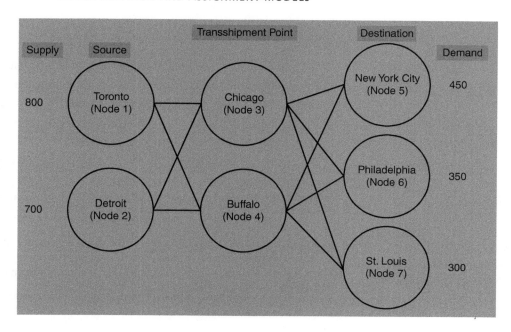

A transportation problem with intermediate points is a transshipment problem.

shipped to retail outlets that are the final destinations. Figure 3 provides a network representation of a transshipment problem. In this example, there are two sources, two transshipment points, and three final destinations.

Linear Program for Transshipment Example

Frosty Machines manufactures snow blowers in factories located in Toronto and Detroit. These are shipped to regional distribution centers in Chicago and Buffalo, where they are delivered to the supply houses in New York, Philadelphia, and St. Louis, as illustrated in Figure 3.

The available supplies at the factories, the demands at the final destination, and shipping costs are shown in the Table 1. Notice that snow blowers may not be shipped directly from Toronto or Detroit to any of the final destinations but must first go to either Chicago or Buffalo. This is why Chicago and Buffalo are listed not only as destinations but also as sources.

Frosty would like to minimize the transportation costs associated with shipping sufficient snow blowers to meet the demands at the three destinations while not exceeding the supply at each factory. Thus, we have supply and demand constraints similar to the transportation problem, but we also have one constraint for each transshipment point indicating that anything shipped from these to a final destination must have been shipped into that transshipment point from one of the sources. The verbal statement of this problem would be as follows:

TABLE 1 Frosty Machine Transshipment Data

FROM	CHICAGO	BUFFALO	NEW YORK CITY	PHILADELPHIA	ST. LOUIS	SUPPLY
Toronto	$4	$7	—	—	—	800
Detroit	$5	$7	—	—	—	700
Chicago	—	—	$6	$4	$5	—
Buffalo	—	—	$2	$3	$4	—
Demand	—	—	450	350	300	

Minimize cost

subject to

1. The number of units shipped from Toronto is not more than 800
2. The number of units shipped from Detroit is not more than 700
3. The number of units shipped to New York is 450
4. The number of units shipped to Philadelphia is 350
5. The number of units shipped to St. Louis is 300
6. The number of units shipped out of Chicago is equal to the number of units shipped into Chicago
7. The number of units shipped out of Buffalo is equal to the number of units shipped into Buffalo

Special transshipment constraints are used in the linear program.

The decision variables should represent the number of units shipped from each source to each transshipment point and the number of units shipped from each transshipment point to each final destination, as these are the decisions management must make. The decision variables are

$$x_{ij} = \text{number of units shipped from location (node) } i \text{ to location (node) } j$$

where

$$i = 1, 2, 3, 4$$
$$j = 3, 4, 5, 6, 7$$

The numbers are the nodes shown in Figure 3, and there is one variable for each arc (route) in the figure.

The LP model is

$$\text{Minimize total cost} = 4X_{13} + 7X_{14} + 5X_{23} + 7X_{24} + 6X_{35} + 4X_{36} \\ + 5X_{37} + 2X_{45} + 3X_{46} + 4X_{47}$$

subject to

$X_{13} + X_{14} \leq 800$	(Supply at Toronto [node 1])
$X_{23} + X_{24} \leq 700$	(Supply at Detroit [node 2])
$X_{35} + X_{45} = 450$	(Demand at New York City [node 5])
$X_{36} + X_{46} = 350$	(Demand at Philadelphia [node 6])
$X_{37} + X_{47} = 300$	(Demand at St. Louis [node 7])
$X_{13} + X_{23} = X_{35} + X_{36} + X_{37}$	(Shipping through Chicago [node 3])
$X_{14} + X_{24} = X_{45} + X_{46} + X_{47}$	(Shipping through Buffalo [node 4])

$$x_{ij} \geq 0 \text{ for all } i \text{ and } j$$

The solution found using Solver in Excel 2010 is shown in Program 3. The total cost is $9,550 by shipping 650 units from Toronto to Chicago, 150 unit from Toronto to Buffalo, 300 units from Detroit to Buffalo, 350 units from Chicago to Philadelphia, 300 from Chicago to St. Louis, and 450 units from Buffalo to New York City.

While all of these linear programs can be solved using computer software for linear programming, some very fast and easy-to-use special-purpose algorithms exist for the transportation and assignment problems. The rest of this chapter is devoted to these special-purpose algorithms.

5 The Transportation Algorithm

The transportation algorithm is an iterative procedure in which a solution to a transportation problem is found and evaluated using a special procedure to determine whether the solution is optimal. If it is optimal, the process stops. If it is not optimal, a new solution is generated. This new solution is at least as good as the previous one, and it is usually better. This new solution is then evaluated, and if it is not optimal, another solution is generated. The process continues until the optimal solution is found.

PROGRAM 3

Solution to Frosty Machines Transshipment Problem

	A	B	C	D	E	F	G	H
1	Frosty Machines Transshipment Problem							
2								
3				Shipping Cost Per Unit				
4	From\To	Chicago	Buffalo	NYC	Phil.	St.Louis		
5	Toronto	4	7					
6	Detroit	5	7					
7	Chicago			6	4	5		
8	Buffalo			2	3	4		
9								
10				Solution - Number of units shipped				
11		Chicago	Buffalo	NYC	Phil.	St.Louis	Total shipped	Supply
12	Toronto	650	150				800	800
13	Detroit	0	300				300	700
14	Chicago			0	350	300	650	
15	Buffalo			450	0	0	450	
16	Total received	650	450	450	350	300		
17	Demand			450	350	300		
18								
19	Total cost =	9550						

Solver Parameter Inputs and Selections

Set Objective: B19
By Changing cells: B12:C13, D14:F15
To: Min
Subject to the Constraints:

        G12:G13 <= H12:H13
        D16:F16 = D17:F17
        B16:C16 = G14:G15
Solving Method: Simplex LP
☑ **Make Variables Non-Negative**

Key Formulas

	G
11	Total shipped
12	=SUM(B12:C12)

Copy to G13

	G
14	=SUM(D14:F14)

Copy to G15

	B
16	=SUM(B12:B13)

Copy to C16

	D
16	=SUM(D14:D15)

Copy to E16:F16

	B
19	=SUMPRODUCT(B5:F8,B12:F15)

The use of transportation models to minimize the cost of shipping from a number of sources to a number of destinations was first proposed in 1941. This study, called "The Distribution of a Product from Several Sources to Numerous Localities," was written by F. L. Hitchcock. Six years later, T. C. Koopmans independently produced the second major contribution, a report titled "Optimum Utilization of the Transportation System." In 1953, A. Charnes and W. W. Cooper developed the stepping-stone method, an algorithm discussed in detail in this chapter. The modified-distribution (MODI) method, a quicker computational approach, came about in 1955.

We will illustrate this process using the Executive Furniture Corporation example shown in Figure 1. This is presented again in a special format in Table 2.

We see in Table 2 that the total factory supply available is exactly equal to the total warehouse demand. When this situation of equal demand and supply occurs (something that is rather unusual in real life), a *balanced problem* is said to exist. Later in this chapter we take a look at how to deal with unbalanced problems, namely, those in which destination requirements may be greater than or less than origin capacities.

Balanced supply and demand occurs when total demand equals total supply.

Developing an Initial Solution: Northwest Corner Rule

When the data have been arranged in tabular form, we must establish an initial feasible solution to the problem. One systematic procedure, known as the **northwest corner rule**, requires that we start in the upper-left-hand cell (or northwest corner) of the table and allocate units to shipping routes as follows:

1. Exhaust the supply (factory capacity) at each row before moving down to the next row.
2. Exhaust the (warehouse) requirements of each column before moving to the right to the next column.
3. Check that all supply and demands are met.

We can now use the northwest corner rule to find an initial feasible solution to the Executive Furniture Corporation problem shown in Table 2.

TABLE 2   Transportation Table for Executive Furniture Corporation

FROM \ TO	WAREHOUSE AT ALBUQUERQUE	WAREHOUSE AT BOSTON	WAREHOUSE AT CLEVELAND	FACTORY CAPACITY
DES MOINES FACTORY	$5	$4	$3	100
EVANSVILLE FACTORY	$8	$4	$3	300
FORT LAUDERDALE FACTORY	$9	$7	$5	300
WAREHOUSE REQUIREMENTS	300	200	200	700

Des Moines capacity constraint

Cell representing a source-to-destination (Evansville to Cleveland) shipping assignment that could be made

Cleveland warehouse demand

Total demand and total supply

Cost of shipping 1 unit from Fort Lauderdale factory to Boston warehouse

TABLE 3

Initial Solution to Executive Furniture Problem Using the Northwest Corner Method

FROM \ TO	ALBUQUERQUE (A)	BOSTON (B)	CLEVELAND (C)	FACTORY CAPACITY
DES MOINES (D)	100 — $5	— $4	— $3	100
EVANSVILLE (E)	200 — $8	100 — $4	— $3	300
FORT LAUDERDALE (F)	— $9	(100) — $7	200 — $5	300
WAREHOUSE REQUIREMENTS	300	200	200	700

Means that the firm is shipping 100 units along the Fort Lauderdale–Boston route

It takes five steps in this example to make the initial shipping assignments (see Table 3):

Here is an explanation of the five steps needed to make an initial shipping assignment for Executive Furniture.

1. Beginning the upper-left-hand corner, we assign 100 units from Des Moines to Albuquerque. This exhausts the capacity or supply at the Des Moines factory. But it still leaves the warehouse at Albuquerque 200 desks short. Move down to the second row in the same column.

2. Assign 200 units from Evansville to Albuquerque. This meets Albuquerque's demand for a total of 300 desks. The Evansville factory has 100 units remaining, so we move to the right to the next column of the second row.

3. Assign 100 units from Evansville to Boston. The Evansville supply has now been exhausted, but Boston's warehouse is still short by 100 desks. At this point, we move down vertically in the Boston column to the next row.

4. Assign 100 units from Fort Lauderdale to Boston. This shipment will fulfill Boston's demand for a total of 200 units. We note, though, that the Fort Lauderdale factory still has 200 units available that have not been shipped.

5. Assign 200 units from Fort Lauderdale to Cleveland. This final move exhausts Cleveland's demand *and* Fort Lauderdale's supply. This always happens with a balanced problem. The initial shipment schedule is now complete.

We can easily compute the cost of this shipping assignment:

ROUTE FROM	TO	UNITS SHIPPED	×	PER-UNIT COST ($)	=	TOTAL COST ($)
D	A	100		5		500
E	A	200		8		1,600
E	B	100		4		400
F	B	100		7		700
F	C	200		5		1,000
					Total	4,200

A feasible solution is reached when all demand and supply constraints are met.

This solution is feasible since demand and supply constraints are all satisfied. It was also very quick and easy to reach. However, we would be very lucky if this solution yielded the optimal transportation cost for the problem, because this route-loading method totally ignored the costs of shipping over each of the routes.

After the initial solution has been found, it must be evaluated to see if it is optimal. We compute an improvement index for each empty cell using the stepping-stone method. If this indicates a better solution is possible, we use the stepping-stone path to move from this solution to improved solutions until we find an optimal solution.

Stepping-Stone Method: Finding a Least-Cost Solution

The **stepping-stone method** is an iterative technique for moving from an initial feasible solution to an optimal feasible solution. This process has two distinct parts: The first involves testing the current solution to determine if improvement is possible, and the second part involves making changes to the current solution in order to obtain an improved solution. This process continues until the optimal solution is reached.

For the stepping-stone method to be applied to a transportation problem, one rule about the number of shipping routes being used must first be observed: *The number of occupied routes (or squares) must always be equal to one less than the sum of the number of rows plus the number of columns.* In the Executive Furniture problem, this means that the initial solution must have $3 + 3 - 1 = 5$ squares used. Thus

$$\text{Occupied shipping routes (squares)} = \text{Number of rows} + \text{Number of columns} - 1$$
$$5 = 3 + 3 - 1$$

When the number of occupied routes is less than this, the solution is called *degenerate*. Later in this chapter we talk about what to do if the number of used squares is less than the number of rows plus the number of columns minus 1.

The stepping-stone method involves testing each unused route to see if shipping one unit on that route would increase or decrease total costs.

TESTING THE SOLUTION FOR POSSIBLE IMPROVEMENT How does the stepping-stone method work? Its approach is to evaluate the cost-effectiveness of shipping goods via transportation routes not currently in the solution. Each unused shipping route (or square) in the **transportation table** is tested by asking the following question: "What would happen to total shipping costs if one unit of our product (in our example, one desk) were tentatively shipped on an unused route?"

This testing of each unused square is conducted using the following five steps:

Five Steps to Test Unused Squares with the Stepping-Stone Method

Note that every row and every column will have either two changes or no changes.

1. Select an unused square to be evaluated.
2. Beginning at this square, trace a closed path back to the original square via squares that are currently being used and moving with only horizontal and vertical moves.
3. Beginning with a plus (+) sign at the unused square, place alternate minus (−) signs and plus signs on each corner square of the closed path just traced.
4. Calculate an *improvement index* by adding together the unit cost figures found in each square containing a plus sign and then subtracting the unit costs in each square containing a minus sign.
5. Repeat steps 1 to 4 until an improvement index has been calculated for all unused squares. If all indices computed are greater than or equal to zero, an optimal solution has been reached. If not, it is possible to improve the current solution and decrease total shipping costs.

To see how the stepping-stone method works, let us apply these steps to the Executive Furniture Corporation data in Table 3 to evaluate unused shipping routes. The four currently unassigned routes are Des Moines to Boston, Des Moines to Cleveland, Evansville to Cleveland, and Fort Lauderdale to Albuquerque.

Closed paths are used to trace alternate plus and minus signs.

Steps 1 and 2. Beginning with the Des Moines–Boston route, we first trace a closed path using only currently occupied squares (see Table 4) and then place alternate plus signs and minus signs in the corners of this path. To indicate more clearly the meaning of a *closed path*, we see that only squares currently used for shipping can be used in turning the corners of the route being

MODELING IN THE REAL WORLD | Moving Sugar Cane in Cuba

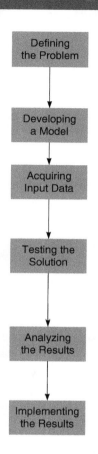

Defining the Problem

The sugar market has been in a crisis for over a decade. Low sugar prices and decreasing demand have added to an already unstable market. Sugar producers needed to minimize costs. They targeted the largest unit cost in the manufacturing of raw sugar contributor—namely, sugar cane transportation costs.

Developing a Model

To solve this problem, researchers developed a linear program with some integer decision variables (e.g., number of trucks) and some continuous (linear) variables and linear decision variables (e.g., tons of sugar cane).

Acquiring Input Data

In developing the model, the inputs gathered were the operating demands of the sugar mills involved, the capacities of the intermediary storage facilities, the per-unit transportation costs per route, and the production capacities of the various sugar cane fields.

Testing the Solution

The researchers involved first tested a small version of their mathematical formulation using a spreadsheet. After noting encouraging results, they implemented the full version of their model on large computer. Results were obtained for this very large and complex model (on the order of 40,000 decision variables and 10,000 constraints) in just a few milliseconds.

Analyzing the Results

The solution obtained contained information on the quantity of cane delivered to each sugar mill, the field where cane should be collected, and the means of transportation (by truck, by train, etc.), and several other vital operational attributes.

Implementing the Results

While solving such large problems with some integer variables might have been impossible only a decade ago, solving these problems now is certainly possible. To implement these results, the researchers worked to develop a more user-friendly interface so that managers would have no problem using this model to help make decisions.

Source: Based on E. L. Milan, S. M. Fernandez, and L. M. Pla Aragones. "Sugar Cane Transportation in Cuba: A Case Study," *European Journal of Operational Research*, 174, 1 (2006): 374–386.

traced. Hence the path Des Moines–Boston to Des Moines–Albuquerque to Fort Lauderdale–Albuquerque to Fort Lauderdale–Boston to Des Moines–Boston would not be acceptable since the Fort Lauderdale–Albuquerque square is currently empty. It turns out that *only one* closed route is possible for each square we wish to test.

How to assign + and − signs. **Step 3.** How do we decide which squares are given plus signs and which minus signs? The answer is simple. Since we are testing the cost-effectiveness of the Des Moines–Boston shipping route, we pretend we are shipping one desk from Des Moines to Boston. This is one more unit than we *were* sending between the two cities, so we place a plus sign in the box. But if we ship one *more* unit than before from Des Moines to Boston, we end up sending 101 desks out of the Des Moines factory.

That factory's capacity is only 100 units; hence we must ship one *fewer* desks from Des Moines–Albuquerque—this change is made to avoid violating the factory capacity constraint. To indicate that the Des Moines–Albuquerque shipment has been reduced, we place a minus sign in its box. Continuing along the closed path, we notice that we are no longer meeting the Albuquerque warehouse requirement for 300 units. In fact, if the Des Moines–Albuquerque shipment is reduced to 99 units, the Evansville–Albuquerque load has to be increased by 1 unit,

TABLE 4 Evaluating the Unused Des Moines–Boston Shipping Route

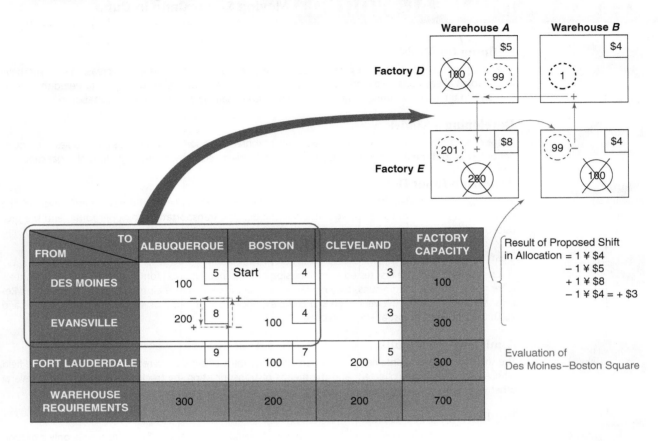

FROM \ TO	ALBUQUERQUE	BOSTON	CLEVELAND	FACTORY CAPACITY
DES MOINES	100 — 5	Start + 4	3	100
EVANSVILLE	200 + 8	100 — 4	3	300
FORT LAUDERDALE	9	100 7	200 5	300
WAREHOUSE REQUIREMENTS	300	200	200	700

Result of Proposed Shift
in Allocation = 1 ¥ $4
− 1 ¥ $5
+ 1 ¥ $8
− 1 ¥ $4 = + $3

Evaluation of
Des Moines–Boston Square

*Improvement index computation involves adding costs in squares with plus signs and subtracting costs in squares with minus signs. I_{ij} is the improvement index on the route from source **i** to destination **j**.*

to 201 desks. Therefore, we place a plus sign in that box to indicate the increase. Finally, we note that if the Evansville–Albuquerque route is assigned 201 desks, the Evansville–Boston route must be reduced by 1 unit, to 99 desks, to maintain the Evansville factory capacity constraint of 300 units. Thus, a minus sign is placed in the Evansville–Boston box. We observe in Table 4 that all four routes on the closed path are thereby balanced in terms of demand-and-supply limitations.

Step 4. An **improvement index** (I_{ij}) for the Des Moines–Boston route is now computed by adding unit costs in squares with plus signs and subtracting costs in squares with minus signs. Hence

$$\text{Does Moines–Boston index} = I_{DB} = +\$4 - \$5 + \$8 - \$4 = +\$3$$

This means that for every desk shipped via the Des Moines–Boston route, total transportation costs will *increase* by $3 over their current level.

A path can go through any box but can only turn at a box or cell that is occupied.

Step 5. Let us now examine the Des Moines–Cleveland unused route, which is slightly more difficult to trace with a closed path. Again, you will notice that we turn each corner along the path only at squares that represent existing routes. The path can go *through* the Evansville–Cleveland box but cannot turn a corner or place a + or − sign there. Only an occupied square may be used as a stepping stone (Table 5).

The closed path we use is $+DC - DA + EA - EB + FB - FC$:

$$\text{Des Moines—Cleveland improvement index} = I_{DC}$$
$$= +\$3 - \$5 + \$8 - \$4 + \$7 - \$5$$
$$= +\$4$$

Thus, opening this route will also not lower our total shipping costs.

TABLE 5

Evaluating the Des Moines–Cleveland (D–C) Shipping Route

FROM \ TO	(A) ALBUQUERQUE	(B) BOSTON	(C) CLEVELAND	FACTORY CAPACITY
(D) DES MOINES	$5 — 100	$4	$3 Start +	100
(E) EVANSVILLE	$8 + 200	$4 — 100	$3	300
(F) FORT LAUDERDALE	$9	$7 100	$5	300
	+ 100	200		300
WAREHOUSE REQUIREMENTS	300	200	200	700

The other two routes may be evaluated in a similar fashion:

$$\text{Evansville–Cleveland index} = I_{EC} = +\$3 - \$4 + \$7 - \$5$$
$$= +\$1$$

(closed path: $+EC - EB + FB - FC$)

$$\text{Fort Lauderdale–Albuquerque index} = I_{FA} = +\$9 - \$7 + \$4 - \$8$$
$$= -\$2$$

(closed path: $+FA - FB + EB - EA$)

Because this last improvement index (I_{FA}) is negative, a cost savings may be attained by making use of the (currently unused) Fort Lauderdale–Albuquerque route.

OBTAINING AN IMPROVED SOLUTION Each negative index computed by the stepping-stone method represents the amount by which total transportation costs could be decreased if 1 unit or product were shipped on that route. We found only one negative index in the Executive Furniture problem, that being −$2 on the Fort Lauderdale factory–Albuquerque warehouse route. If, however, there were more than one negative improvement index, our strategy would be to choose the route (unused square) with the negative index indicating the largest improvement.

To reduce our overall costs, we want to select the route with the negative index indicating the largest improvement.

The next step, then, is to ship the maximum allowable number of units (or desks, in our case) on the new route (Fort Lauderdale to Albuquerque). What is the maximum quantity that can be shipped on the money-saving route? That quantity is found by referring to the closed path of plus signs and minus signs drawn for the route and selecting the *smallest number* found in those squares containing *minus signs*. To obtain a new solution, that number is added to all squares on the closed path with plus signs and subtracted from all squares on the path assigned minus signs. All other squares are unchanged.

The maximum we can ship on the new route is found by looking at the closed path's minus signs. We select the smallest number found in the squares with minus signs.

Let us see how this process can help improve Executive Furniture's solution. We repeat the transportation table (Table 6) for the problem. Note that the stepping-stone route for Fort Lauderdale to Albuquerque (F–A) is drawn in. The maximum quantity that can be shipped on the newly opened route (F–A) is the smallest number found in squares containing minus signs—in this case, 100 units. Why 100 units? Since the total cost decreases by $2 per unit shipped, we know we would like to ship the maximum possible number of units. Table 6 indicates that each unit shipped over the F–A route results in an increase of 1 unit shipped from E to B and a decrease of 1 unit in both the amounts shipped from F to B (now 100 units) and from E to A (now 200 units). Hence, the maximum we can ship over the F–A route is 100. This results in 0 units being shipped from F to B.

Changing the shipping route involves adding to squares on the closed path with plus signs and subtracting from squares with minus signs.

TABLE 6
Stepping-Stone Path Used to Evaluate Route F–A

FROM \ TO	A	B	C	FACTORY CAPACITY
D	$5 100	$4	$3	100
E	$8 −200 ← − − − − − + 100	$4 +100	$3	300
F	$9 + − − − − − → −100	$7 −100	$5 200	300
WAREHOUSE REQUIREMENTS	300	200	200	700

We add 100 units to the 0 now being shipped on route F–A; then proceed to subtract 100 from route F–B, leaving 0 in that square (but still balancing the row total for F); then add 100 to route E–B, yielding 200; and finally, subtract 100 from route E–A, leaving 100 units shipped. Note that the new numbers still produce the correct row and column totals as required. The new solution is shown in Table 7.

Total shipping cost has been reduced by (100 units) × ($2 saved per unit) = $200, and is now $4,000. This cost figure can, of course, also be derived by multiplying each unit shipping cost times the number of units transported on its route, namely, (100 × $5) + (100 × $8) + (200 × $4) + (100 × $9) + (200 × $5) = $4,000.

The solution shown in Table 7 may or may not be optimal. To determine whether further improvement is possible, we return to the first five steps given earlier to test each square that is *now* unused. The four improvement indices—each representing an available shipping route—are as follows:

Improvement indices for each of the four unused shipping routes must now be tested to see if any are negative.

$$D \, to \, B = I_{DB} = +\$4 - \$5 + \$8 - \$4 = +\$3$$
$$(\text{closed path: } +DB - DA + EA - EB)$$

$$D \, to \, C = I_{DC} = +\$3 - \$5 + \$9 - \$5 = +\$2$$
$$(\text{closed path: } +DC - DA + FA - FC)$$

$$E \, to \, C = I_{EC} = +\$3 - \$8 + \$9 - \$5 = -\$1$$
$$(\text{closed path: } +EC - EA + FA - FC)$$

$$F \, to \, B = I_{FB} = +\$7 - \$4 + \$8 - \$9 = +\$2$$
$$(\text{closed path: } +FB - EB + EA - FA)$$

Hence, an improvement can be made by shipping the maximum allowable number of units from E to C (see Table 8). Only the squares E–A and F–C have minus signs in the closed path; because the smallest number in these two squares is 100, we add 100 units to E–C and F–A and

TABLE 7
Second Solution to the Executive Furniture Problem

FROM \ TO	A	B	C	FACTORY CAPACITY
D	$5 100	$4	$3	100
E	$8 100	$4 200	$3	300
F	$9 100	$7	$5 200	300
WAREHOUSE REQUIREMENTS	300	200	200	700

TABLE 8

Path to Evaluate the E–C Route

FROM \ TO	A	B	C	FACTORY CAPACITY
D	$5 — 100	$4	$3	100
E	$8 — 100 − ←----	$4 — 200	$3 — Start +	300
F	$9 — 100 + ----→	$7	$5 — 200 −	300
WAREHOUSE REQUIREMENTS	300	200	200	700

subtract 100 units from *E–A* and *F–C*. The new cost for this third solution, $3,900, is computed in the following table:

Total Cost of Third Solution

ROUTE FROM	TO	DESKS SHIPPED	×	PER-UNIT COST ($)	=	TOTAL COST ($)
D	A	100		5		500
E	B	200		4		800
E	C	100		3		300
F	A	200		9		1,800
F	C	100		5		500
						Total 3,900

Table 9 contains the optimal shipping assignments because each improvement index that can be computed at this point is greater than or equal to zero, as shown in the following equations. Improvement indices for the table are

$$D \text{ to } B = I_{DB} = +\$4 - \$5 + \$9 - \$5 + \$3 - \$4$$
$$= +\$2 \text{ (path: } +DB - DA + FA - FC + EC - EB)$$
$$D \text{ to } C = I_{DC} = +\$3 - \$5 + \$9 - \$5 = +\$2 \text{ (path: } +DC - DA + FA - FC)$$
$$E \text{ to } A = I_{EA} = +\$8 - \$9 + \$5 - \$3 = +\$1 \text{ (path: } +EA - FA + FC - EC)$$
$$F \text{ to } B = I_{FB} = +\$7 - \$5 + \$3 - \$4 = +\$1 \text{ (path: } +FB - FC + EC - EB)$$

Since all four of these improvement indices are greater than or equal to zero, we have reached an optimal solution.

TABLE 9

Third and Optimal Solution

FROM \ TO	A	B	C	FACTORY CAPACITY
D	$5 — 100	$4	$3	100
E	$8	$4 — 200	$3 — 100	300
F	$9 — 200	$7	$5 — 100	300
WAREHOUSE REQUIREMENTS	300	200	200	700

Let us summarize the steps in the transportation algorithm:

Summary of Steps in Transportation Algorithm (Minimization)

The transportation algorithm has four basic steps.

1. Set up a balanced transportation table.
2. Develop initial solution using the northwest corner method.
3. Calculate an improvement index for each empty cell using the stepping-stone method. If improvement indices are all nonnegative, stop; the optimal solution has been found. If any index is negative, continue to step 4.
4. Select the cell with the improvement index indicating the greatest decrease in cost. Fill this cell using a stepping-stone path and go to step 3.

Some special situations may occur when using this algorithm. They are presented in the next section.

6 Special Situations with the Transportation Algorithm

When using the transportation algorithm, some special situations may arise, including unbalanced problems, degenerate solutions, multiple optimal solutions, and unacceptable routes. This algorithm may be modified to maximize total profit rather than minimize total cost. All of these situations will be addressed, and other modifications of the transportation algorithm will be presented.

Unbalanced Transportation Problems

A situation occurring quite frequently in real-life problems is the case in which total demand is not equal to total supply. These *unbalanced problems* can be handled easily by the preceding solution procedures if we first introduce **dummy sources** or **dummy destinations**. In the event that total supply is greater than total demand, a dummy destination (warehouse), with demand exactly equal to the surplus, is created. If total demand is greater than total supply, we introduce a dummy source (factory) with a supply equal to the excess of demand over supply. In either case, shipping cost coefficients of zero are assigned to each dummy location or route because no shipments will actually be made from a dummy factory or to a dummy warehouse. Any units assigned to a dummy destination represent excess capacity, and units assigned to a dummy source represent unmet demand.

Dummy sources or destinations are used to balance problems in which demand is not equal to supply.

Ⓐ Ⓠ IN ACTION **Answering Warehousing Questions at San Miguel Corporation**

The San Miguel Corporation, based in the Philippines, faces unique distribution challenges. With more than 300 products, including beer, alcoholic drinks, juices, bottled water, feeds, poultry, and meats to be distributed to every corner of the Philippine archipelago, shipping and warehousing costs make up a large part of total product cost.

The company grappled with these questions:

- Which products should be produced in each plant and in which warehouse should they be stored?
- Which warehouses should be maintained and where should new ones be located?
- When should warehouses be closed or opened?
- Which demand centers should each warehouse serve?

Turning to the transportation model of LP, San Miguel is able to answer these questions. The firm uses these types of warehouses: company owned and staffed, rented but company staffed, and contracted out (i.e., not company owned or staffed).

San Miguel's Operations Research Department computed that the firm saves $7.5 million annually with optimal beer warehouse configurations over the existing national configurations. In addition, analysis of warehousing for ice cream and other frozen products indicated that the optimal configuration of warehouses, compared with existing setups, produced a $2.17 million savings.

Source: Based on Elise del Rosario. "Logistical Nightmare," *OR/MS Today* (April 1999): 44–46.

TABLE 10 Initial Solution to an Unbalanced Problem Where Demand is Less than Supply

TO FROM	ALBUQUERQUE (A)	BOSTON (B)	CLEVELAND (C)	DUMMY WAREHOUSE	FACTORY CAPACITY
DES MOINES (D)	5 250	4	3	0	250
EVANSVILLE (E)	8 50	4 200	3 50	0	300
FORT LAUDERDALE (F)	9	7	5 150	0 150	300
WAREHOUSE REQUIREMENTS	300	200	200	150	850

New Des Moines capacity

Total cost = 250($5) + 50($8) + 200($4) + 50($3) + 150($5) + 150($0) = $3,350

DEMAND LESS THAN SUPPLY Considering the original Executive Furniture Corporation problem, suppose that the Des Moines factory increases its rate of production to 250 desks. (That factory's capacity used to be 100 desks per production period.) The firm is now able to supply a total of 850 desks each period. Warehouse requirements, however, remain the same (at 700 desks), so the row and column totals do not balance.

To balance this type of problem, we simply add a dummy column that will represent a fake warehouse requiring 150 desks. This is somewhat analogous to adding a slack variable in solving an LP problem. Just as slack variables were assigned a value of zero dollars in the LP objective function, the shipping costs to this dummy warehouse are all set equal to zero.

The northwest corner rule is used once again, in Table 10, to find an initial solution to this modified Executive Furniture problem. To complete this task and find an optimal solution, you would employ the stepping-stone method.

Note that the 150 units from Fort Lauderdale to the dummy warehouse represent 150 units that are *not* shipped from Fort Lauderdale.

DEMAND GREATER THAN SUPPLY The second type of unbalanced condition occurs when total demand is greater than total supply. This means that customers or warehouses require more of a product than the firm's factories can provide. In this case we need to add a dummy row representing a fake factory.

The new factory will have a supply exactly equal to the difference between total demand and total real supply. The shipping costs from the dummy factory to each destination will be zero.

Let us set up such an unbalanced problem for the Happy Sound Stereo Company. Happy Sound assembles high-fidelity stereophonic systems at three plants and distributes through three regional warehouses. The production capacities at each plant, demand at each warehouse, and unit shipping costs are presented in Table 11.

As can be seen in Table 12, a dummy plant adds an extra row, balances the problem, and allows us to apply the northwest corner rule to find the initial solution shown. This initial solution shows 50 units being shipped from the dummy plant to warehouse *C*. This means that warehouse *C* will be 50 units short of its requirements. In general, any units shipped from a dummy source represent unmet demand at the respective destination.

Degeneracy in Transportation Problems

Degeneracy arises when the number of occupied squares is less than the number of rows + columns −1.

We briefly mentioned the subject of **degeneracy** earlier in this chapter. Degeneracy occurs when the number of occupied squares or routes in a transportation table solution is less than the number of rows plus the number of columns minus 1. Such a situation may arise in the initial solution or in any subsequent solution. Degeneracy requires a special procedure to correct the

TABLE 11

Unbalanced Transportation Table for Happy Sound Stereo Company

FROM \ TO	WAREHOUSE A	WAREHOUSE B	WAREHOUSE C	PLANT SUPPLY
PLANT W	$6	$4	$9	200
PLANT X	$10	$5	$8	175
PLANT Y	$12	$7	$6	75
WAREHOUSE DEMAND	250	100	150	500 / 450 *Totals do not balance*

TABLE 12

Initial Solution to an Unbalanced Problem in which Demand Is Greater Than Supply

FROM \ TO	WAREHOUSE A	WAREHOUSE B	WAREHOUSE C	PLANT SUPPLY
PLANT W	6 / 200	4	9	200
PLANT X	10 / 50	5 / 100	8 / 25	175
PLANT Y	12	7	6 / 75	75
DUMMY PLANT	0	0	0 / 50	50
WAREHOUSE DEMAND	250	100	150	500

Total cost of initial solution = 200($6) + 50($10) + 100($5) + 25($8) + 75($6) + 50($0) = $2,850

problem. Without enough occupied squares to trace a closed path for each unused route, it would be impossible to apply the stepping-stone method. You might recall that no problem discussed in the chapter thus far has been degenerate.

To handle degenerate problems, we create an artificially occupied cell—that is, we place a zero (representing a fake shipment) in one of the unused squares and then treat that square as if it were occupied. The square chosen must be in such a position as to allow *all* stepping-stone paths to be closed, although there is usually a good deal of flexibility in selecting the unused square that will receive the zero.

DEGENERACY IN AN INITIAL SOLUTION Degeneracy can occur in our application of the northwest corner rule to find an initial solution, as we see in the case of the Martin Shipping Company. Martin has three warehouses from which to supply its three major retail customers in San Jose. Martin's hipping costs, warehouse supplies, and customer demands are presented in Table 13. Note that origins in this problem are warehouses and destinations are retail stores. Initial shipping assignments are made in the table by application of the northwest corner rule.

This initial solution is degenerate because it violates the rule that the number of used squares must be equal to the number of rows plus the number of columns minus 1 (i.e., 3 + 3 − 1 = 5 is greater than the number of occupied boxes). In this particular problem, degeneracy arose because both a column and a row requirement (that being column 1 and row 1) were satisfied simultaneously. This broke the stair-step pattern that we usually see with northwest corner solutions.

To correct the problem, we can place a zero in an unused square. With the northwest corner method, this zero should be placed in one of the cells that is adjacent to the last filled cell so the

TABLE 13

Initial Solution of a Degenerate Problem

TO FROM	CUSTOMER 1	CUSTOMER 2	CUSTOMER 3	WAREHOUSE SUPPLY
WAREHOUSE 1	8 100	2	6	100
WAREHOUSE 2	10	9 100	9 20	120
WAREHOUSE 3	7	10	7 80	80
CUSTOMER DEMAND	100	100	100	300

stair-step pattern continues. In this case, those squares representing either the shipping route from warehouse 1 to customer 2 or from warehouse 2 to customer 1 will do. If you treat the new zero square just like any other occupied square, the regular solution method can be used.

DEGENERACY DURING LATER SOLUTION STAGES A transportation problem can become degenerate after the initial solution stage if the filling of an empty square results in two (or more) filled cells becoming empty simultaneously instead of just one cell becoming empty. Such a problem occurs when two or more squares assigned minus signs on a closed path tie for the lowest quantity. To correct this problem, a zero should be put in one (or more) of the previously filled squares so that only one previously filled square becomes empty.

Bagwell Paint Example. After one iteration of the stepping-stone method, cost analysts at Bagwell Paint produced the transportation table shown as Table 14. We observe that the solution in Table 14 is not degenerate, but it is also not optimal. The improvement indices for the four currently unused squares are

factory A – warehouse 2 index $= +2$

factory A – warehouse 3 index $= +1$

factory B – warehouse 3 index $= -15$ ◄——— *Only route with a negative index*

factory C – warehouse 2 index $= +11$

Hence, an improved solution can be obtained by opening the route from factory B to warehouse 3. Let us go through the stepping-stone procedure for finding the next solution to Bagwell Paint's problem. We begin by drawing a closed path for the unused square representing factory B–warehouse 3. This is shown in Table 15, which is an abbreviated version of Table 14 and contains only the factories and warehouses necessary to close the path.

TABLE 14

Bagwell Paint Transportation Table

TO FROM	WAREHOUSE 1	WAREHOUSE 2	WAREHOUSE 3	FACTORY CAPACITY
FACTORY A	8 70	5	16	70
FACTORY B	15 50	10 80	7	130
FACTORY C	3 30	9	10 50	80
WAREHOUSE REQUIREMENT	150	80	50	280

Total shipping cost = $2,700

TABLE 15

Tracing a Closed Path for the Factory B–Warehouse 3 Route

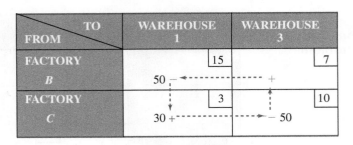

The smallest quantity in a square containing a minus sign is 50, so we add 50 units to the factory B–warehouse 3 and factory C–warehouse 1 routes, and subtract 50 units from the two squares containing minus signs. However, this act causes two formerly occupied squares to drop to 0. It also means that there are not enough occupied squares in the new solution and that it will be degenerate. We will have to place an artificial zero in one of the previously filled squares (generally, the one with the lowest shipping cost) to handle the degeneracy problem.

More Than One Optimal Solution

Multiple solutions are possible when one or more improvement indices in the optimal solution stages are equal to zero.

Just as with LP problems, it is possible for a transportation problem to have multiple optimal solutions. Such a situation is indicated when one or more of the improvement indices that we calculate for each unused square is zero in the optimal solution. This means that it is possible to design alternative shipping routes with the same total shipping cost. The alternate optimal solution can be found by shipping the most to this unused square using a stepping-stone path. Practically speaking, multiple optimal solutions provide management with greater flexibility in selecting and using resources.

Maximization Transportation Problems

The optimal solution to a maximization problem has been found when all improvement indices are negative or zero.

If the objective in a transportation problem is to maximize profit, a minor change is required in the transportation algorithm. Since the improvement index for an empty cell indicates how the objective function value will change if one unit is placed in that empty cell, the optimal solution is reached when all the improvement indices are negative or zero. If any index is positive, the cell with the largest positive improvement index is selected to be filled using a stepping-stone path. This new solution is evaluated and the process continues until there are no positive improvement indices.

Unacceptable or Prohibited Routes

A prohibited route is assigned a very high cost to prevent it from being used.

At times there are *transportation problems* in which one of the sources is unable to ship to one or more of the destinations. When this occurs, the problem is said to have an *unacceptable* or *prohibited route*. In a minimization problem, such a prohibited route is assigned a very high cost to prevent this route from ever being used in the optimal solution. After this high cost is placed in the transportation table, the problem is solved using the techniques previously discussed. In a maximization problem, the very high cost used in minimization problems is given a negative sign, turning it into a very bad profit.

Other Transportation Methods

While the northwest corner method is very easy to use, there are other methods for finding an initial solution to a transportation problem. Two of these are the least-cost method and Vogel's approximation method. Similarly, the stepping-stone method is used to evaluate empty cells, and there is another technique called the modified distribution (MODI) method that can evaluate empty cells. For very large problems, the MODI method is usually much faster than the stepping-stone method.

7 Facility Location Analysis

Locating a new facility within one overall distribution system is aided by the transportation method.

The transportation method has proved to be especially useful in helping a firm decide where to locate a new factory or warehouse. Since a new location is an issue of major financial importance to a company, several alternative locations must ordinarily be considered and evaluated. Even though a wide variety of subjective factors are considered, including quality of labor supply, presence of labor unions, community attitude and appearance, utilities, and recreational and educational facilities for employees, a final decision also involves minimizing total shipping and production costs. This means that each alternative facility location should be analyzed within the framework of one *overall* distribution system. The new location that will yield the minimum cost for the *entire system* will be the one recommended. Let us consider the case of the Hardgrave Machine Company.

Locating a New Factory for Hardgrave Machine Company

The Hardgrave Machine Company produces computer components at its plants in Cincinnati, Salt Lake City, and Pittsburgh. These plants have not been able to keep up with demand for orders at Hardgrave's four warehouses in Detroit, Dallas, New York, and Los Angeles. As a result, the firm has decided to build a new plant to expand its productive capacity. The two sites being considered are Seattle and Birmingham; both cities are attractive in terms of labor supply, municipal services, and ease of factory financing.

Table 16 presents the production costs and output requirements for each of the three existing plants, demand at each of the four warehouses, and estimated production costs of the new proposed plants. Transportation costs from each plant to each warehouse are summarized in Table 17.

TABLE 16
Hardgrave's Demand and Supply Data

WAREHOUSE	MONTHLY DEMAND (UNITS)	PRODUCTION PLANT	MONTHLY SUPPLY	COST TO PRODUCE ONE UNIT ($)
Detroit	10,000	Cincinnati	15,000	48
Dallas	12,000	Salt Lake City	6,000	50
New York	15,000	Pittsburgh	14,000	52
Los Angeles	9,000		35,000	
	46,000			

Supply needed from new plant = 46,000 − 35,000 = 11,000 units per month

ESTIMATED PRODUCTION COST PER UNIT AT PROPOSED PLANTS	
Seattle	$53
Birmingham	$49

TABLE 17
Hardgrave's Shipping Costs

TO FROM	DETROIT	DALLAS	NEW YORK	LOS ANGELES
CINCINNATI	$25	$55	$40	$60
SALT LAKE CITY	35	30	50	40
PITTSBURGH	36	45	26	66
SEATTLE	60	38	65	27
BIRMINGHAM	35	30	41	50

TABLE 18

Birmingham Plant Optimal Solution: Total Hardgrave Cost Is $3,741,000

FROM \ TO	DETROIT	DALLAS	NEW YORK	LOS ANGELES	MONTHLY SUPPLY
CINCINNATI	73	103	88	108	
	10,000		1,000	4,000	15,000
SALT LAKE CITY	85	80	100	90	
		1,000		5,000	6,000
PITTSBURGH	88	97	78	118	
			14,000		14,000
BIRMINGHAM	84	79	90	99	
		11,000			11,000
MONTHLY DEMAND	10,000	12,000	15,000	9,000	46,000

The important question that Hardgrave now faces is this: Which of the new locations will yield the lowest cost for the firm in combination with the existing plants and warehouses? Note that the cost of each individual plant-to-warehouse route is found by adding the shipping costs (in the body of Table 17) to the respective unit production costs (from Table 16). Thus, the total production plus shipping cost of one computer component from Cincinnati to Detroit is $73 ($25 for shipping plus $48 for production).

To determine which new plant (Seattle or Birmingham) shows the lowest total systemwide cost of distribution and production, we solve two transportation problems—one for each of the two possible combinations. Tables 18 and 19 show the resulting two optimum solutions with the total cost for each. It appears that Seattle should be selected as the new plant site: Its total cost of $3,704,000 is less than the $3,741,000 cost at Birmingham.

We solve two transportation problems to find the new plant with lowest system cost.

USING EXCEL QM AS A SOLUTION TOOL We can use Excel QM to solve each of the two Hardgrave Machine Company problems. To do this, select *Excel QM* from the *Add-Ins* tab in Excel 2010 and scroll down to select *Transportation*. When the window opens, enter the number of Origins (sources) and Destinations, specify Minimize, give this a title if desired, and click *OK*. Then simply enter the costs, supplies, and demands in the table labeled Data, as shown in Problem 4. Then select *Solver* from the *Data* tab and click *Solve*. No further input is needed as Excel QM automatically specifies the necessary parameters and selections. Excel also prepares the formulas for the constraints used by Solver. The solution will appear in the table labeled Shipments, and the cost will be specified below this table.

TABLE 19

Seattle Plant Optimal Solution: Total Hardgrave Cost Is $3,704,000

FROM \ TO	DETROIT	DALLAS	NEW YORK	LOS ANGELES	MONTHLY SUPPLY
CINCINNATI	73	103	88	108	
	10,000	4,000	1,000		15,000
SALT LAKE CITY	85	80	100	90	
	6,000				6,000
PITTSBURGH	88	97	78	118	
			14,000		14,000
SEATTLE	113	91	118	80	
		2,000		9,000	11,000
MONTHLY DEMAND	10,000	12,000	15,000	9,000	46,000

PROGRAM 4

Excel QM Solution for Facility Location Example

	A	B	C	D	E	F	G	H
1	Birmingham							
2			From the Data tab, select Solver and click Solve.					
3	Transportation							
4								
5		Enter the transportation data in the shaded area. Then go to the DATA Tab on the ribbon, click on Solver in the Data Analysis Group and then click SOLVE.						
6		If SOLVER is not on the Data Tab then please see the Help file (Solver) for instructions.						
7				Enter the costs, supplies, and demands in this table.				
8	Data							
9	COSTS	Dest 1	Dest 2	Dest 3	Dest 4	Supply		
10	Origin 1	73	103	88	108	15000		
11	Origin 2	85	80	100	90	6000		
12	Origin 3	88	97	78	118	14000		
13	Origin 4	84	79	90	99	11000		
14	Demand	10000	12000	15000	9000	46000 \ 46000		
15					Solver puts the solution here.			
16	Shipments							
17	Shipments	Dest 1	Dest 2	Dest 3	Dest 4	Row Total		
18	Origin 1	10000		1000	4000	15000		
19	Origin 2		1000		5000	6000		
20	Origin 3			14000		14000		
21	Origin 4		11000			11000		
22	Column Total	10000	12000	15000	9000	46000 \ 46000		
23								
24	Total Cost	3741000						

8   The Assignment Algorithm

The second special-purpose LP algorithm discussed in this chapter is the assignment method. Each assignment problem has associated with it a table, or matrix. Generally, the rows contain the objects or people we wish to assign, and the columns comprise the tasks or things we want them assigned to. The numbers in the table are the costs associated with each particular assignment.

An assignment problem can be viewed as a transportation problem in which the capacity from each source (or person to be assigned) is 1 and the demand at each destination (or job to be done) is 1. Such a formulation could be solved using the transportation algorithm, but it would have a severe degeneracy problem. However, this type of problem is very easy to solve using the assignment method.

As an illustration of the assignment method, let us consider the case of the Fix-It Shop, which has just received three new rush projects to repair: (1) a radio, (2) a toaster oven, and (3) a broken coffee table. Three repair persons, each with different talents and abilities, are available to do the jobs. The Fix-It Shop owner estimates what it will cost in wages to assign each of the workers to each of the three projects. The costs, which are shown in Table 20, differ because the owner believes that each worker will differ in speed and skill on these quite varied jobs.

The goal is to assign projects to people (one project to one person) so that the total costs are minimized.

The owner's objective is to assign the three projects to the workers in a way that will result in the lowest total cost to the shop. Note that the assignment of people to projects must be on a one-to-one basis; each project will be assigned exclusively to one worker only. Hence the number of rows must always equal the number of columns in an assignment problem's cost table.

TABLE 20

Estimated Project Repair Costs for the Fix-It Shop Assignment Problem

	PROJECT		
PERSON	**1**	**2**	**3**
Adams	$11	$14	$6
Brown	8	10	11
Cooper	9	12	7

TABLE 21

Summary of Fix-It Shop Assignment Alternatives and Costs

PROJECT ASSIGNMENT			LABOR COSTS ($)	TOTAL COSTS ($)
1	2	3		
Adams	Brown	Cooper	11 + 10 + 7	28
Adams	Cooper	Brown	11 + 12 + 11	34
Brown	Adams	Cooper	8 + 14 + 7	29
Brown	Cooper	Adams	8 + 12 + 6	26
Cooper	Adams	Brown	9 + 14 + 11	34
Cooper	Brown	Adams	9 + 10 + 6	25

One way to solve (small) problems is to enumerate all possible outcomes.

Because the Fix-It Shop problem only consists of three workers and three projects, one easy way to find the best solution is to list all possible assignments and their respective costs. For example, if Adams is assigned to project 1, Brown to project 2, and Cooper to project 3, the total cost will be $11 + $10 + $7 = $28. Table 21 summarizes all six assignment options. The table also shows that the least-cost solution would be to assign Cooper to project 1, Brown to project 2, and Adams to project 3, at a total cost of $25.

Obtaining solutions by enumeration works well for small problems but quickly becomes inefficient as assignment problems become larger. For example, a problem involving the assignment of four workers to four projects requires that we consider 4! (= 4 × 3 × 2 × 1), or 24 alternatives. A problem with eight workers and eight tasks, which actually is not that large in a realistic situation, yields 8! (= 8 × 7 × 6 × 5 × 4 × 3 × 2 × 1), or 40,320 possible solutions! Since it would clearly be impractical to compare so many alternatives, a more efficient solution method is needed.

The Hungarian Method (Flood's Technique)

The **Hungarian method** of assignment provides us with an efficient means of finding the optimal solution without having to make a direct comparison of every option. It operates on a principle of **matrix reduction**, which means that by subtracting and adding appropriate numbers in the cost table or matrix, we can reduce the problem to a matrix of **opportunity costs**. Opportunity costs show the relative penalties associated with assigning *any* person to a project as opposed to making the *best*, or least-cost, assignment. We would like to make assignments such that the opportunity cost for each assignment is zero. The Hungarian method will indicate when it is possible to make such assignments.

Matrix reduction reduces the table to a set of opportunity costs. These show the penalty of not making the least-cost (or best) assignment.

There are basically three steps in the assignment method[*]:

Three Steps of the Assignment Method

Here are the three steps of the assignment method.

1. *Find the opportunity cost table by*
   (a) Subtracting the smallest number in each row of the original cost table or matrix from every number in that row.
   (b) Then subtracting the smallest number in each column of the table obtained in part (a) from every number in that column.

2. *Test the table resulting from step 1 to see whether an optimal assignment can be made.* The procedure is to draw the minimum number of vertical and horizontal straight lines necessary to cover all zeros in the table. If the number of lines equals either the number of rows or columns in the table, an optimal assignment can be made. If the number of lines is less than the number of rows or columns, we proceed to step 3.

3. *Revise the present opportunity cost table.* This is done by subtracting the smallest number not covered by a line from every uncovered number. This same smallest number is also added to any number(s) lying at the intersection of horizontal and vertical lines. We then return to step 2 and continue the cycle until an optimal assignment is possible.

---

[*]The steps apply if we can assume that the matrix is balanced, that is, the number of rows in the matrix equals the number of columns. In Section 9 we discuss how to handle unbalanced problems.

FIGURE 4   Steps in the Assignment Method

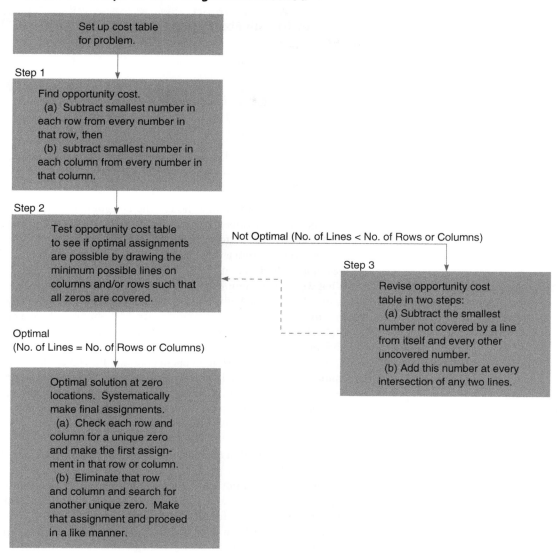

These steps are charted in Figure 4. Let us now apply them.

Step 1: Find the Opportunity Cost Table. As mentioned earlier, the opportunity cost of any decision we make in life consists of the opportunities that are sacrificed in making that decision. For example, the opportunity cost of the unpaid time a person spends starting a new business is the salary that person would earn for those hours that he or she could have worked on another job. This important concept in the assignment method is best illustrated by applying it to a problem. For your convenience, the original cost table for the Fix-It Shop problem is repeated in Table 22.

Row and column opportunity costs reflect the cost we are sacrificing by not making the least-cost selection.

Suppose that we decide to assign Cooper to project 2. The table shows that the cost of this assignment is $12. Based on the concept of opportunity costs, this is not the best decision, since Cooper could perform project 3 for only $7. The assignment of Cooper to project 2 then involves an opportunity cost of $5 (= $12 − $7), the amount we are sacrificing by making this assignment instead of the least-cost one. Similarly, an assignment of Cooper to project 1 represents an opportunity cost of $9 − $7 = $2. Finally, because the assignment of Cooper to project 3 is the best assignment, we can say that the opportunity cost of this assignment is zero ($7 − $7). The results of this operation for each of the rows in Table 22 are called the row opportunity costs and are shown in Table 23.

TABLE 22

Cost of Each Person–Project Assignment for the Fix-It Shop Problem

	PROJECT		
PERSON	**1**	**2**	**3**
Adams	$11	$14	$6
Brown	8	10	11
Cooper	9	12	7

TABLE 23

Row Opportunity Cost Table for the Fix-It Shop Step 1, Part (a)

	PROJECT		
PERSON	**1**	**2**	**3**
Adams	$5	$8	$0
Brown	0	2	3
Cooper	2	5	0

Total opportunity costs reflect the row and column opportunity cost analyses.

We note at this point that although the assignment of Cooper to project 3 is the cheapest way to make use of Cooper, it is not necessarily the least-expensive approach to completing project 3. Adams can perform the same task for only $6. In other words, if we look at this assignment problem from a project angle instead of a people angle, the *column* opportunity costs may be completely different.

What we need to complete step 1 of the assignment method is a *total* opportunity cost table, that is, one that reflects both row and column opportunity costs. This involves following part (b) of step 1 to derive column opportunity costs.* We simply take the costs in Table 23 and subtract the smallest number in each column from each number in that column. The resulting total opportunity costs are given in Table 24.

You might note that the numbers in columns 1 and 3 are the same as those in Table 23, since the smallest column entry in each case was zero. Thus, it may turn out that the assignment of Cooper to project 3 is part of the optimal solution because of the relative nature of opportunity costs. What we are trying to measure are the relative efficiencies for the entire cost table and to find what assignments are best for the overall solution.

Step 2: Test for an Optimal Assignment. The objective of the Fix-It Shop owner is to assign the three workers to the repair projects in such a way that total labor costs are kept at a minimum. When translated to making assignments using our total opportunity cost table, this means that we would like to have a total assigned opportunity cost of 0. In other words, an optimal solution has zero opportunity costs for all of the assignments.

When a zero opportunity cost is found for all of the assignments, an optimal assignment can be made.

Looking at Table 24, we see that there are four possible zero opportunity cost assignments. We could assign Adams to project 3 and Brown to either project 1 or project 2. But this leaves Cooper without a zero opportunity cost assignment. Recall that two workers cannot be given the same task; each must do one and only one repair project, and each project must be assigned to only one person. Hence, even though four zeros appear in this cost table, it is not yet possible to make an assignment yielding a total opportunity cost of zero.

This line test is used to see if a solution is optimal.

A simple test has been designed to help us determine whether an optimal assignment can be made. The method consists of finding the *minimum* number of straight lines (vertical and horizontal) necessary to cover all zeros in the cost table. (Each line is drawn so that it covers as many zeros as possible at one time.) If the number of lines equals the number of rows or columns in the table, then an optimal assignment can be made. If, on the other hand, the number of lines is less than the number of rows or columns, an optimal assignment cannot be made. In the latter case, we must proceed to step 3 and develop a new total opportunity cost table.

Table 25 illustrates that it is possible to cover all four zero entries in Table 24 with only two lines. Because there are three rows, an optimal assignment may not yet be made.

Step 3: Revise the Opportunity-Cost Table. An optimal solution is seldom obtained from the initial opportunity cost table. Often, we need to revise the table in order to shift one (or more) of the zero costs from its present location (covered by lines) to a new uncovered location in the table. Intuitively, we would want this uncovered location to emerge with a new zero opportunity cost.

---

*Can you think of a situation in which part (b) of step 1 would not be required? See if you can design a cost table in which an optimal solution is possible after part (a) of step 1 is completed.

TABLE 24

Total Opportunity Cost Table for the Fix-It Shop Step 1, Part (b)

PERSON	PROJECT		
	1	2	3
Adams	$5	$6	$0
Brown	0	0	3
Cooper	2	3	0

TABLE 25

Test for Optimal Solution to Fix-It Shop Problem

PERSON	PROJECT		
	1	2	3
Adams	$5	$6	$0
Brown	0	0	3 — Covering line 1
Cooper	2	3	0

Covering line 2

TABLE 26

Revised Opportunity Cost Table for the Fix-It Shop Problem

PERSON	PROJECT		
	1	2	3
Adams	$3	$4	$0
Brown	0	0	5
Cooper	0	1	0

TABLE 27

Optimality Test on the Revised Fix-It Shop Opportunity Cost Table

PERSON	PROJECT		
	1	2	3
Adams	$3	$4	$0
Brown	0	0	5 — Covering line 2
Cooper	0	1	0

Covering line 1   Covering line 3

This is accomplished by *subtracting* the smallest number not covered by a line from all numbers not covered by a straight line. This same smallest number is then added to every number (including zeros) lying at the intersection of any two lines.

The smallest uncovered number in Table 25 is 2, so this value is subtracted from each of the four uncovered numbers. A 2 is also added to the number that is covered by the intersecting horizontal and vertical lines. The results of step 3 are shown in Table 26.

To test now for an optimal assignment, we return to step 2 and find the minimum number of lines necessary to cover all zeros in the revised opportunity cost table. Because it requires three lines to cover the zeros (see Table 27), an optimal assignment can be made.

Making the Final Assignment

Making an optimal assignment involves first checking the rows and columns where there is only one zero cell.

It is apparent that the Fix-It Shop problem's optimal assignment is Adams to project 3, Brown to project 2, and Cooper to project 1. In solving larger problems, however, it is best to rely on a more systematic approach to making valid assignments. One such way is first to select a row or column that contains only one zero cell. Such a situation is found in the first row, Adams's row, in which the only zero is in the project 3 column. An assignment can be made to that cell, and then lines drawn through its row and column (see Table 28). From the uncovered rows and columns, we again choose a row or column in which there is only one zero cell. We make that assignment and continue the procedure until each person is assigned to one task.

The total labor costs of this assignment are computed from the original cost table (see Table 22). They are as follows:

ASSIGNMENT	COST ($)
Adams to project 3	6
Brown to project 2	10
Cooper to project 1	9
Total cost	25

TABLE 28 Making the Final Fix-It Shop Assignments

(A) FIRST ASSIGNMENT				(B) SECOND ASSIGNMENT				(C) THIRD ASSIGNMENT		
	1	2	3		1	2	3		1	2	3
Adams	3	4	0	Adams	3	4	0	Adams	3	4	0
Brown	0	0	5	Brown	0	0	5	Brown	0	0	5
Cooper	0	1	0	Cooper	0	1	0	Cooper	0	1	0

USING EXCEL QM FOR THE FIX-IT SHOP ASSIGNMENT PROBLEM Excel QM's Assignment module can be used to solve the Fix-It problem. Simply select *Excel QM* from the *Add-Ins* tab in Excel 2010 and then select *Assignment*. When the window opens, give the problem a title, enter the number of assignments (row or columns), and specify Minimize. Excel QM will initialize the spreadsheet, and the costs are then entered, as shown in Program 5. Then select *Solver* from the *Data* tab and click *Solve*. The solution will be placed in the Assignments area of the spreadsheet, as shown in Program 5. Adams will be assigned job 3, Brown will be assigned job 2, and Cooper will be assigned job 1. The total cost is $25.

PROGRAM 5

Excel QM Solution for Fix-It Shop Assignment Problem

	A	B	C	D	E	F
1	**Fix-It Shop Assignment**					
2				From the Data tab, select Solver and click Solve.		
3	**Assignment**					
4		Enter the assignment costs in the shaded area. Then go to the DATA Tab on the ribbon,				
5		click on Solver in the Data Analysis Group and then click SOLVE.				
6		If SOLVER is not on the Data Tab then please see the Help file (Solver) for instructions.				
7		Enter the costs.				
8	**Data**					
9	COSTS	Project 1	Project 2	Project 3		
10	Adams	11	14	6		
11	Brown	8	10	11		
12	Cooper	9	12	7		
13				Solver puts the optimal assignments here.		
14	**Assignments**					
15	**Shipments**	Project 1	Project 2	Project 3	Row Total	
16	**Adams**			1	1	
17	**Brown**		1		1	
18	**Cooper**	1			1	
19	**Column Tota**	1	1	1	3	
20						
21	**Total Cost**	25				

9 Special Situations with the Assignment Algorithm

There are two special situations that require special procedures when using the Hungarian algorithm for assignment problems. The first involves problems that are not balanced, and the second involves solving a maximization problem instead of a minimization problem.

Unbalanced Assignment Problems

The solution procedure to assignment problems just discussed requires that the number of rows in the table equal the number of columns. Such a problem is called a **balanced assignment problem**. Often, however, the number of people or objects to be assigned does not equal the number of tasks or clients or machines listed in the columns, and the problem is *unbalanced*. When this occurs, and we have more rows than columns, we simply add a **dummy column** or task (similar to how we handled unbalanced transportation problems earlier in this chapter). If the number of tasks that need to be done exceeds the number of people available, we add a **dummy row**. This creates a table of equal dimensions and allows us to solve the problem as before. Since the dummy task or person is really nonexistent, it is reasonable to enter zeros in its row or column as the cost or time estimate.

A balanced assignment problem is one in which the number of rows equals the number of columns.

Suppose the owner of the Fix-It Shop realizes that a fourth worker, Davis, is also available to work on one of the three rush jobs that just came in. Davis can do the first project for $10, the second for $13, and the third project for $8. The shop's owner still faces the same basic problem, that is, which worker to assign to which project to minimize total labor costs. We do not have a fourth project, however, so we simply add a dummy column or dummy project. The initial cost table is shown in Table 29. One of the four workers, you should realize, will be assigned to the dummy project; in other words, the worker will not really be assigned any of the tasks.

Maximization Assignment Problems

Some assignment problems are phrased in terms of maximizing the payoff, profit, or effectiveness of an assignment instead of minimizing costs. It is easy to obtain an equivalent minimization problem by converting all numbers in the table to opportunity costs. This is brought about by subtracting every number in the original payoff table from the largest single number in that table. The transformed entries represent opportunity costs; it turns out that minimizing opportunity costs produces the same assignment as the original maximization problem. Once the optimal assignment for this transformed problem has been computed, the total payoff or profit is found by adding the original payoffs of those cells that are in the optimal assignment.

Maximization problems can easily be converted to minimization problems. This is done by subtracting each rating from the largest rating in the table.

Let us consider the following example. The British navy wishes to assign four ships to patrol four sectors of the North Sea. In some areas ships are to be on the outlook for illegal fishing boats, and in other sectors to watch for enemy submarines, so the commander rates each ship in terms of its probable efficiency in each sector. These relative efficiencies are illustrated in Table 30. On the basis of the ratings shown, the commander wants to determine the patrol assignments producing the greatest overall efficiencies.

TABLE 29

Estimated Project Repair Costs for Fix-It Shop with Davis Included

| PERSON | PROJECT | | | |
	1	2	3	DUMMY
Adams	$11	$14	$6	$0
Brown	8	10	11	0
Cooper	9	12	7	0
Davis	10	13	8	0

TABLE 30
Efficiencies of British Ships in Patrol Sectors

	SECTOR			
SHIP	A	B	C	D
1	20	60	50	55
2	60	30	80	75
3	80	100	90	80
4	65	80	75	70

TABLE 31
Opportunity Costs of British Ships

	SECTOR			
SHIP	A	B	C	D
1	80	40	50	45
2	40	70	20	25
3	20	0	10	20
4	35	20	25	30

Row subtractions: the smallest number in each row is subtracted from every number in that row.

Column subtractions: the smallest number in each column is subtracted from every number in that column.

Step by step, the solution procedure is as follows. We first convert the maximizing efficiency table into a minimizing opportunity cost table. This is done by subtracting each rating from 100, the largest rating in the whole table. The resulting opportunity costs are given in Table 31.

We now follow steps 1 and 2 of the assignment algorithm. The smallest number in each row is subtracted from every number in that row (see Table 32); and then the smallest number in each column is subtracted from every number in that column (as shown in Table 33).

The minimum number of straight lines needed to cover all zeros in this total opportunity cost table is four. Hence an optimal assignment can be made already. You should be able by now to spot the best solution, namely, ship 1 to sector D, ship 2 to sector C, ship 3 to sector B, and ship 4 to sector A.

The overall efficiency, computed from the original efficiency data in Table 30, can now be shown:

ASSIGNMENT	EFFICIENCY
Ship 1 to sector D	55
Ship 2 to sector C	80
Ship 3 to sector B	100
Ship 4 to sector A	65
Total efficiency	300

TABLE 32
Row Opportunity Costs for the British Navy Problem

	SECTOR			
SHIP	A	B	C	D
1	40	0	10	5
2	20	50	0	5
3	20	0	10	20
4	15	0	5	10

TABLE 33
Total Opportunity Costs for the British Navy Problem

	SECTOR			
SHIP	A	B	C	D
1	25	0	10	0
2	5	50	0	0
3	5	0	10	15
4	0	0	5	5

IN ACTION   Facility Location Leads to Improved Supply-Chain Reliability

Supply chains are, at their physical level, an interconnected network of delivery routes (roads, bridges, shipping lanes, etc.) that lead from multiple sources (warehouse, factories, refineries, etc.) to multiple destinations (stores, outlets, other warehouses, etc.) along which products and commodities travel. In most cases, the allocation of particular destinations to particular sources is known and fairly constant.

Researchers, in trying to help companies plan for emergencies, have investigated the problem of supply-chain disruption. What would happen if one of the sources were to catastrophically fail due to an earthquake, a tornado, or worse? The answer lies in the area of the facility location problem: Which warehouses should deliver to which stores addresses this issue. Analyzing the transportation problem with current sources eliminated one by one, the analysts were able to measure the impact of such disruption. The researchers concluded that "backup assignments" of warehouses to stores should be planned ahead of time to help mitigate the impact of possible catastrophes. It always pays to plan ahead!

Source: Based on L. Snyder and M. Daskin, "Reliability Models for Facility Location: The Expected Failure Cost Case," *Transportation Science* 39, 3 (2005): 400–416.

Summary

In this chapter we explored the transportation model and the assignment model. We saw how to develop an initial solution to the transportation problem with the northwest corner method. The stepping-stone path method was used to calculate improvement indices for the empty cells. Improved solutions were developed using a stepping-stone path. The special cases of the transportation problem included degeneracy, unbalanced problems, and multiple optimal solutions. We demonstrated how to use the transportation model for facility location analysis.

We saw how the assignment problem may be viewed as a special case of the transportation problem. The Hungarian method for solving assignment problems was presented. When assignment problems are unbalanced, dummy rows or columns are used to balance the problem. Assignment problems with maximization objectives were also presented.

Glossary

Balanced Assignment Problem.   An assignment problem in which the number of rows is equal to the number of columns.

Balanced Transportation Problem.   The condition under which total demand (at all destinations) is equal to total supply (at all sources).

Degeneracy.   A condition that occurs when the number of occupied squares in any solution is less than the number of rows plus the number of columns minus 1 in a transportation table.

Destination.   A demand location in a transportation problem.

Dummy Destination.   An artificial destination added to a transportation table when total supply is greater than total demand. The demand at the dummy destination is set so that total supply and demand are equal. The transportation cost for dummy destination cells is zero.

Dummy Rows or Columns.   Extra rows or columns added in order to "balance" an assignment problem so that the number of rows equals the number of columns.

Dummy Source.   An artificial source added to a transportation table when total demand is greater than total supply. The supply at the dummy source is set so that total demand and supply are equal. The transportation cost for dummy source cells is zero.

Facility Location Analysis.   An application of the transportation method to help a firm decide where to locate a new factory, warehouse, or other facility.

Flood's Technique.   Another name for the Hungarian method.

Hungarian Method.   A matrix reduction approach to solving the assignment problem.

Improvement Index.   The net cost of shipping one unit on a route not used in the current transportation problem solution.

Matrix Reduction.   The approach of the assignment method that reduces the original assignment costs to a table of opportunity costs.

Northwest Corner Rule.   A systematic procedure for establishing an initial feasible solution to the transportation problem.

Opportunity Costs. In an assignment problem, this is the additional cost incurred when the assignment with the lowest possible cost in a row or column is not selected.

Source. An origin or supply location in a transportation problem.

Stepping-Stone Method. An iterative technique for moving from an initial feasible solution to an optimal solution in transportation problems.

Transportation Problems. A specific case of LP concerned with scheduling shipments from sources to destinations so that total transportation costs are minimized.

Transportation Table. A table summarizing all transportation data to help keep track of all algorithm computations. It stores information on demands, supplies, shipping costs, units shipped, origins, and destinations.

Solved Problems

Solved Problem 1

Don Yale, president of Hardrock Concrete Company, has plants in three locations and is currently working on three major construction projects, located at different sites. The shipping cost per truckload of concrete, plant capacities, and project requirements are provided in the accompanying table.

a. Formulate an initial feasible solution to Hardrock's transportation problem using the northwest corner rule.

b. Then evaluate each unused shipping route (each empty cell) by applying the stepping-stone method and computing all improvement indices. Remember to do the following:

1. Check that supply and demand are equal.

2. Load the table via the northwest corner method.

3. Check that there are the proper number of occupied cells for a "normal" solution, namely, Number of rows + Number of columns − 1 = Number of occupied cells.

4. Find a closed path to each empty cell.

5. Determine the improvement index for each unused cell.

6. Move as many units as possible to the cell that provides the most improvement (if there is one).

7. Repeat steps 3 through 6 until no further improvement can be found.

TO FROM	PROJECT A	PROJECT B	PROJECT C	PLANT CAPACITIES
PLANT 1	$10	$4	$11	70
PLANT 2	$12	$5	$8	50
PLANT 3	$9	$7	$6	30
PROJECT REQUIREMENTS	40	50	60	150

Solution

a. Northwest corner solution:

$$\text{Initial cost} = 40(\$10) + 30(\$4) + 20(\$5) + 30(\$8) + 30(\$6) = \$1,040$$

TO〈br〉FROM	PROJECT A	PROJECT B	PROJECT C	PLANT CAPACITIES
PLANT 1	$10〈br〉40	$4〈br〉30	$11	70
PLANT 2	$12	$5〈br〉20	$8〈br〉30	50
PLANT 3	$9	$7	$6〈br〉30	30
PROJECT REQUIREMENTS	40	50	60	150

b. Using the stepping-stone method, the following improvement indices are computed:

Path: plant 1 to project $C = \$11 - \$4 + \$5 - \$8 = +\$4$

(closed path: $1C$ to $1B$ to $2B$ to $2C$)

TO〈br〉FROM	PROJECT A	PROJECT B	PROJECT C	PLANT CAPACITIES	
PLANT 1	10〈br〉40	4〈br〉30	11	70	Path: plant 1 to project C
PLANT 2	12	5〈br〉20	8〈br〉30	50	
PLANT 3	9	7	6〈br〉30	30	
PROJECT REQUIREMENTS	40	50	60	150	

Path: plant 2 to project $A = \$12 - \$5 + \$4 - \$10 = +\$1$

(closed path: 2A to 2B to 1B to 1A)

FROM \ TO	PROJECT A	PROJECT B	PROJECT C	PLANT CAPACITIES
PLANT 1	40 10	30 4	11	70
PLANT 2	12	20 5	30 8	50
PLANT 3	9	7	30 6	30
PROJECT REQUIREMENTS	40	50	60	150

Path: plant 2 to project A

Path: plant 3 to project $A = \$9 - \$6 + \$8 - \$5 + \$4 - \$10 = \$0$

(closed path: 3A to 3C to 2C to 2B to 1B to 1A)

FROM \ TO	PROJECT A	PROJECT B	PROJECT C	PLANT CAPACITIES
PLANT 1	40 10	30 4	11	70
PLANT 2	12	20 5	30 8	50
PLANT 3	9	7	30 6	30
PROJECT REQUIREMENTS	40	50	60	150

Path: plant 3 to project A

Path: plant 3 to project $B = \$7 - \$6 + \$8 - \$5 = +\$4$
(closed path: $3B$ to $3C$ to $2C$ to $2B$)

FROM \ TO	PROJECT A	PROJECT B	PROJECT C	PLANT CAPACITIES
PLANT 1	10 / 40	4 / 30	11 /	70
PLANT 2	12 /	5 / 20	8 / 30	50
PLANT 3	9 /	7 /	6 / 30	30
PROJECT REQUIREMENTS	40	50	60	150

Path: plant 3 to project B

Since all indices are greater than or equal to zero (all are positive or zero), this initial solution provides the optimal transportation schedule, namely, 40 units from 1 to *A*, 30 units from 1 to *B*, 20 units from 2 to *B*, 30 units from 2 to *C*, and 30 units from 3 to *C*.

Had we found a path that allowed improvement, we would move all units possible to that cell and then check every empty cell again. Because the plant 3 to project A improvement index was equal to zero, we note that multiple optimal solutions exist.

Solved Problem 2

The initial solution found in Solved Problem 1 was optimal, but the improvement index for one of the empty cells was zero, indicating another optimal solution. Use a stepping-stone path to develop this other optimal solution.

Solution

Using the stepping-stone path, we see that the lowest number of units in a cell where a subtraction is to be made is 20 units from plant 2 to project *B*. Therefore, 20 units will be subtracted from each cell with a minus sign and added to each cell with a plus sign. The result is shown here:

FROM \ TO	PROJECT A	PROJECT B	PROJECT C	PLANT CAPACITIES
PLANT 1	10 / 20	4 / 50	11 /	70
PLANT 2	12 /	5 /	8 / 50	50
PLANT 3	9 / 20	7 /	6 / 10	30
PROJECT REQUIREMENTS	40	50	60	150

533

Solved Problem 3

Solve the Hardgrave Machine Company facility location problem shown in Table 19 on page 366 with an LP formulation.

Solution

First we shall formulate this transportation problem as an LP model by introducing double-subscripted decision variables. We let X_{11} denote the number of units shipped from origin 1 (Cincinnati) to destination 1 (Detroit), X_{12} denote shipments from origin 1 (Cincinnati) to destination 2 (Dallas), and so on. In general, the decision variables for a transportation problem having m origins and n destinations are written as

$$X_{ij} = \text{Number of units shipped from origin } i \text{ to destination } j$$

where

$$i = 1, 2, \ldots, m$$
$$j = 1, 2, \ldots, n$$

Because the objective of the transportation model is to minimize total transportation costs, we develop the following cost expression:

$$\begin{aligned}
\text{Minimize} = \; & 73X_{11} + 103X_{12} + 88X_{13} + 108X_{14} \\
& + 85X_{21} + 80X_{22} + 100X_{23} + 90X_{24} \\
& + 88X_{31} + 97X_{32} + 78X_{33} + 118X_{34} \\
& + 113X_{41} + 91X_{42} + 118X_{43} + 80X_{44}
\end{aligned}$$

Now we establish supply constraints for each of the four plants:

$$X_{11} + X_{12} + X_{13} + X_{14} \leq 15,000 \text{ (Cincinnati supply)}$$
$$X_{21} + X_{22} + X_{23} + X_{24} \leq 6,000 \quad \text{(Salt Lake supply)}$$
$$X_{31} + X_{32} + X_{33} + X_{34} \leq 14,000 \text{ (Pittsburgh supply)}$$
$$X_{41} + X_{42} + X_{43} + X_{44} \leq 11,000 \text{ (Seattle supply)}$$

With four warehouses as the destinations, we need the following four demand constraints:

$$X_{11} + X_{21} + X_{31} + X_{41} = 10,000 \text{ (Detroit demand)}$$
$$X_{12} + X_{22} + X_{32} + X_{42} = 12,000 \text{ (Dallas demand)}$$
$$X_{13} + X_{23} + X_{33} + X_{43} = 15,000 \text{ (New York demand)}$$
$$X_{14} + X_{24} + X_{34} + X_{44} = 9,000 \quad \text{(Los Angeles demand)}$$

A computer solution will confirm that total shipping costs will be $3,704,000. Although LP codes can indeed be used on transportation problems, the special transportation module for Excel QM (shown earlier) and QM for Windows (shown in Appendix 1) tend to be easier to input, run, and interpret.

Solved Problem 4

Prentice Hall, Inc., a publisher headquartered in New Jersey, wants to assign three recently hired college graduates, Jones, Smith, and Wilson to regional sales districts in Omaha, Dallas, and Miami. But the firm also has an opening in New York and would send one of the three there if it were more economical than a move to Omaha, Dallas, or Miami. It will cost $1,000 to relocate Jones to New York, $800 to relocate Smith there, and $1,500 to move Wilson. What is the optimal assignment of personnel to offices?

OFFICE HIREE	OMAHA	MIAMI	DALLAS
JONES	$800	$1,100	$1,200
SMITH	$500	$1,600	$1,300
WILSON	$500	$1,000	$2,300

Solution

a. The cost table has a fourth column to represent New York. To balance the problem, we add a dummy row (person) with a zero relocation cost to each city.

HIREE \ OFFICE	OMAHA	MIAMI	DALLAS	NEW YORK
JONES	$800	$1,100	$1,200	$1,000
SMITH	$500	$1,600	$1,300	$800
WILSON	$500	$1,000	$2,300	$1,500
DUMMY	0	0	0	0

b. Subtract smallest number in each row and cover zeros (column subtraction will give the same numbers and therefore is not necessary).

HIREE \ OFFICE	OMAHA	MIAMI	DALLAS	NEW YORK
JONES	0	300	400	200
SMITH	0	1,100	800	300
WILSON	0	500	1,800	1,000
DUMMY	0	0	0	0

c. Subtract smallest uncovered number (200), add it to each square where two lines intersect, and cover all zeros.

HIREE \ OFFICE	OMAHA	MIAMI	DALLAS	NEW YORK
JONES	0	100	200	0
SMITH	0	900	600	100
WILSON	0	300	1,600	800
DUMMY	200	0	0	0

d. Subtract smallest uncovered number (100), add it to each square where two lines intersect, and cover all zeros.

HIREE \ OFFICE	OMAHA	MIAMI	DALLAS	NEW YORK
JONES	0	0	100	0
SMITH	0	800	500	100
WILSON	0	200	1,500	800
DUMMY	300	0	0	100

e. Subtract smallest uncovered number (100), add it to squares where two lines intersect, and cover all zeros.

OFFICE HIREE	OMAHA	MIAMI	DALLAS	NEW YORK
JONES	100	0	100	0
SMITH	0	700	400	0
WILSON	0	100	1,400	700
DUMMY	400	0	0	100

f. Since it takes four lines to cover all zeros, an optimal assignment can be made at zero squares. We assign

Dummy (no one) to Dallas

Wilson to Omaha

Smith to New York

Jones to Miami

Cost = $0 + $500 + $800 + $1,100 = $2,400

Self-Test

- Before taking the self-test, refer to the learning objectives at the beginning of the chapter, the notes in the margins, and the glossary at the end of the chapter.
- Use the key at the end of the chapter to correct your answers.
- Restudy pages that correspond to any questions that you answered incorrectly or material you feel uncertain about.

1. If the total demand equals the total supply in a transportation problem, the problem is
   a. degenerate.
   b. balanced.
   c. unbalanced.
   d. infeasible.
2. If a transportation problem has 4 sources and 5 destinations, the linear program for this will have
   a. 4 variables and 5 constraints.
   b. 5 variable and 4 constraints.
   c. 9 variables and 20 constraints.
   d. 20 variables and 9 constraints.
3. In a transportation problem, what indicates that the minimum cost solution has been found?
   a. all improvement indices are negative or zero
   b. all improvement indices are positive or zero
   c. all improvement indices are equal to zero
   d. all cells in the dummy row are empty
4. An assignment problem may be viewed as a transportation problem with
   a. a cost of $1 for all shipping routes.
   b. all supplies and demands equal to 1.

   c. only demand constraints.
   d. only supply constraints.
5. If the number of filled cells in a transportation table does not equal the number of rows plus the number of columns minus 1, then the problem is said to be
   a. unbalanced.
   b. degenerate.
   c. optimal.
   d. maximization problem.
6. If a solution to a transportation problem is degenerate, then
   a. it will be impossible to evaluate all empty cells without removing the degeneracy.
   b. a dummy row or column must be added.
   c. there will be more than one optimal solution.
   d. the problem has no feasible solution.
7. If the total demand is greater than the total capacity in a transportation problem, then
   a. the optimal solution will be degenerate.
   b. a dummy source must be added.
   c. a dummy destination must be added.
   d. both a dummy source and a dummy destination must be added.

8. In solving a facility location problem in which there are two possible locations being considered, the transportation algorithm may be used. In doing this,
   a. two rows (sources) would be added to the existing rows and the enlarged problem would be solved.
   b. two separate transportation problems would be solved.
   c. costs of zero would be used for each of the new facilities.
   d. the problem would be a transshipment problem.

9. The Hungarian method is
   a. a way to develop an initial solution to a transportation problem.
   b. used to solve assignment problems.
   c. also called Vogel's approximation method.
   d. only used for problems in which the objective is to maximize profit.

10. In an assignment problem, it may be necessary to add more than one row to the table.
    a. True
    b. False

11. When using the Hungarian method, an optimal assignment can always be made when every row and every column has at least one zero.
    a. True
    b. False

12. An assignment problem can be viewed as a special type of transportation problem with which of the following features?
    a. the capacity for each source and the demand for each destination is equal to one
    b. the number of rows is equal to the number of columns
    c. the cost for each shipping route is equal to one
    d. all of the above

Discussion Questions and Problems

Discussion Questions

1 Is the transportation model an example of decision making under certainty or decision making under uncertainty? Why?

2 Explain how to determine the number of variables and constraints that would be in a transportation problem simply by knowing the number of sources and the number of destinations.

3 What is a *balanced* transportation problem? Describe the approach you would use to solve an *unbalanced* problem.

4 The stepping-stone method is being used to solve a transportation problem. The smallest quantity in a cell with a minus sign is 35, but two different cells with minus signs have 35 units in them. What problem will this cause, and how should this difficulty be resolved?

5 The stepping-stone method is being used to solve a transportation problem. There is only one empty cell having a negative improvement index, and this index is -2. The stepping-stone path for this cell indicates that the smallest quantity for the cells with minus signs is 80 units. If the total cost for the current solution is $900, what will the total cost be for the improved solution? What can you conclude about how much the total cost will decrease when developing each new solution for any transportation problem?

6 Explain what happens when the solution to a transportation problem does not have $m + n - 1$ occupied squares (where m = number of rows in the table and n = number of columns in the table).

7 What is the enumeration approach to solving assignment problems? Is it a practical way to solve a 5 row × 5 column problem? a 7 × 7 problem? Why?

8 How could an assignment problem be solved using the transportation approach? What condition will make the solution of this problem difficult?

9 You are the plant supervisor and are responsible for scheduling workers to jobs on hand. After estimating the cost of assigning each of five available workers in your plant to five projects that must be completed immediately, you solve the problem using the Hungarian method. The following solution is reached and you post these job assignments:

Jones to project A

Smith to project B

Thomas to project C

Gibbs to project D

Heldman to project E

The optimal cost was found to be $492 for these assignments. The plant general manager inspects your original cost estimates and informs you that increased employee benefits mean that each of the 25 numbers in your cost table is too low by $5. He suggests that you immediately rework the problem and post the new assignments.
Is this necessary? Why? What will the new optimal cost be?

10 Sue Simmons's marketing research firm has local representatives in all but five states. She decides to expand to cover the whole United States by transferring five experienced volunteers from their current locations to new offices in each of the five states. Simmons's goal is to relocate the five representatives at the least total cost. Consequently, she sets up a 5 × 5 relocation cost table and prepares to solve it for the best assignments by use of the Hungarian

method. At the last moment, Simmons recalls that although the first four volunteers did not pose any objections to being placed in any of the five new cities, the fifth volunteer *did* make one restriction. That person absolutely refused to be assigned to the new office in Tallahassee, Florida—fear of southern roaches, the representative claimed! How should Sue alter the cost matrix to ensure that this assignment is not included in the optimal solution?

Problems*

11 The management of the Executive Furniture Corporation decided to expand the production capacity at its Des Moines factory and to cut back production at its other factories. It also recognizes a shifting market for its desks and revises the requirements at its three warehouses.

  (a) Use the northwest corner rule to establish an initial feasible shipping schedule and calculate its cost.

  (b) Use the stepping-stone method to test whether an improved solution is possible.

(c) Explain the meaning and implications of an improvement index that is equal to 0. What decisions might management make with this information? Exactly how is the final solution affected?

12 Formulate the transportation problem in Problem 11 as a linear program and solve using computer software.

13 The Hardrock Concrete Company has plants in three locations and is currently working on three major construction projects, each located at a different site. The shipping cost per truckload of concrete, daily plant capacities, and daily project requirements are provided in the table below.

  (a) Formulate an initial feasible solution to Hardrock's transportation problem using the northwest corner rule. Then evaluate each unused shipping route by computing all improvement indices. Is this solution optimal? Why?

  (b) Is there more than one optimal solution to this problem? Why?

Data for Problem 11

NEW WAREHOUSE REQUIREMENTS		NEW FACTORY CAPACITIES	
Albuquerque (A)	200 desks	Des Moines (D)	300 desks
Boston (B)	200 desks	Evansville (E)	150 desks
Cleveland (C)	300 desks	Fort Lauderdale (F)	250 desks

Table for Problem 11

FROM \ TO	ALBUQUERQUE	BOSTON	CLEVELAND
DES MOINES	5	4	3
EVANSVILLE	8	4	3
FORT LAUDERDALE	9	7	5

Data for Problem 13

FROM \ TO	PROJECT A	PROJECT B	PROJECT C	PLANT CAPACITIES
PLANT 1	$10	$4	$11	70
PLANT 2	12	5	8	50
PLANT 3	9	7	6	30
PROJECT REQUIREMENTS	40	50	60	150

Note: 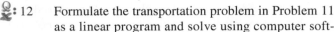 means the problem may be solved with QM for Windows; means the problem may be solved with Excel QM; and means the problem may be solved with QM for Windows and/or Excel QM.

Table for Problem 16

FROM \ TO	SUPPLY HOUSE 1	SUPPLY HOUSE 2	SUPPLY HOUSE 3	MILL CAPACITY (TONS)
PINEVILLE	$3	$3	$2	25
OAK RIDGE	4	2	3	40
MAPLETOWN	3	2	3	30
SUPPLY HOUSE DEMAND (TONS)	30	30	35	95

14 Hardrock Concrete's owner has decided to increase the capacity at his smallest plant (see Problem 13). Instead of producing 30 loads of concrete per day at plant 3, that plant's capacity is doubled to 60 loads. Find the new optimal solution using the northwest corner rule and stepping-stone method. How has changing the third plant's capacity altered the optimal shipping assignment? Discuss the concepts of degeneracy and multiple optimal solutions with regard to this problem.

15 Formulate the Hardrock Concrete Company transportation problem in Problem 13 as a linear program and solve using computer software. What would change in the linear program if the change in Problem 14 were implemented?

16 The Saussy Lumber Company ships pine flooring to three building supply houses from its mills in Pineville, Oak Ridge, and Mapletown. Determine the best transportation schedule for the data given in the table. Use the northwest corner rule and the stepping-stone method.

17 The Krampf Lines Railway Company specializes in coal handling. On Friday, April 13, Krampf had empty cars at the following towns in the quantities indicated:

TOWN	SUPPLY OF CARS
Morgantown	35
Youngstown	60
Pittsburgh	25

By Monday, April 16, the following towns will need coal cars as follows:

TOWN	DEMAND FOR CARS
Coal Valley	30
Coaltown	45
Coal Junction	25
Coalsburg	20

Using a railway city-to-city distance chart, the dispatcher constructs a mileage table for the preceding towns. The result is shown in the table below. Minimizing total miles over which cars are moved to new locations, compute the best shipment of coal cars.

18 Formulate the Krampf Lines Railway Company situation (Problem 17) as a linear program and solve using computer software.

19 An air conditioning manufacturer produces room air conditioners at plants in Houston, Phoenix, and Memphis. These are sent to regional distributors in Dallas, Atlanta, and Denver. The shipping costs vary, and the company would like to find the least-cost way to meet the demands at each of the distribution centers. Dallas needs to receive 800 air conditioners per month, Atlanta needs 600, and Denver needs 200. Houston has 850 air conditioners available each month, Phoenix has 650, and Memphis has 300. The shipping cost per unit from Houston to Dallas is $8,

Table for Problem 17

FROM \ TO	COAL VALLEY	COALTOWN	COAL JUNCTION	COALSBURG
MORGANTOWN	50	30	60	70
YOUNGSTOWN	20	80	10	90
PITTSBURGH	100	40	80	30

to Atlanta is $12, and to Denver is $10. The cost per unit from Phoenix to Dallas is $10, to Atlanta is $14, and to Denver is $9. The cost per unit from Memphis to Dallas is $11, to Atlanta is $8, and to Denver is $12. How many units should be shipped from each plant to each regional distribution center? What is the total cost for this?

: 20 Formulate the air conditioning situation present in Problem 18 as a linear program and solve using computer software.

: 21 Finnish Furniture manufactures tables in facilities located in three cities—Reno, Denver, and Pittsburgh. The tables are then shipped to three retail stores located in Phoenix, Cleveland, and Chicago. Management wishes to develop a distribution schedule that will meet the demands at the lowest possible cost. The shipping cost per unit from each of the sources to each of the destinations is shown in the following table:

TO FROM	PHOENIX	CLEVELAND	CHICAGO
RENO	10	16	19
DENVER	12	14	13
PITTSBURGH	18	12	12

The available supplies are 120 units from Reno, 200 from Denver, and 160 from Pittsburgh. Phoenix has a demand of 140 units, Cleveland has a demand of 160 units, and Chicago has a demand of 180 units. How many units should be shipped from each manufacturing facility to each of the retail stores if cost is to be minimized? What is the total cost?

22 Finnish Furniture has experienced a decrease in the demand for tables in Chicago; the demand has fallen

to 150 units (see Problem 21). What special condition would exist? What is the minimum-cost solution? Will there be any units remaining at any of the manufacturing facilities?

:23 Formulate the Finnish Furniture situation (Problem 21) as a linear program and solve using computer software.

: 24 The state of Missouri has three major power-generating companies (A, B, and C). During the months of peak demand, the Missouri Power Authority authorizes these companies to pool their excess supply and to distribute it to smaller independent power companies that do not have generators large enough to handle the demand. Excess supply is distributed on the basis of cost per kilowatt hour transmitted. The following table shows the demand and supply in millions of kilowatt hours and the cost per kilowatt hour of transmitting electric power to four small companies in cities W, X, Y, and Z:

TO FROM	W	X	Y	Z	EXCESS SUPPLY
A	12¢	4¢	9¢	5¢	55
B	8¢	1¢	6¢	6¢	45
C	1¢	12¢	4¢	7¢	30
UNFILLED POWER DEMAND	40	20	50	20	

Find an initial transmission assignment of the excess power supply. Then find the least-cost distribution system.

: 25 Consider the transportation table given below. Find an initial solution using the northwest corner rule. What special condition exists? Explain how you will proceed to solve the problem.

Table for Problem 25

TO FROM	DESTINATION A	DESTINATION B	DESTINATION C	SUPPLY
SOURCE 1	$8	$9	$4	72
SOURCE 2	5	6	8	38
SOURCE 3	7	9	6	46
SOURCE 4	5	3	7	19
DEMAND	110	34	31	175

:26 The three blood banks in Franklin County are coordinated through a central office that facilitates blood delivery to four hospitals in the region. The cost to ship a standard container of blood from each bank to each hospital is shown in the table below. Also given are the biweekly number of containers available at each bank and the biweekly number of containers of blood needed at each hospital. How many shipments should be made biweekly from each blood bank to each hospital so that total shipment costs are minimized?

:27 Formulate the Franklin County Blood Bank situation (Problem 26) as a linear program and solve using computer software.

:28 The B. Hall Real Estate Investment Corporation has identified four small apartment buildings in which it would like to invest. Mrs. Hall has approached three savings and loan companies regarding financing. Because Hall has been a good client in the past and has maintained a high credit rating in the community, each savings and loan company is willing to consider providing all or part of the mortgage loan needed on each property. Each loan officer has set differing interest rates on each property (rates are affected by the neighborhood of the apartment building, condition of the property, and desire by the individual savings and loan to finance various-size buildings), *and* each loan company has placed a

maximum credit ceiling on how much it will lend Hall in total. This information is summarized in the table on this page.

Each apartment building is equally attractive as an investment to Hall, so she has decided to purchase all buildings possible at the lowest total payment of interest. From which savings and loan companies should she borrow to purchase which buildings? More than one savings and loan can finance the same property.

:29 Formulate the B. Hall Real Estate Investment Corporation problem (Problem 28) as a linear program and solve using computer software.

:30 The J. Mehta Company's production manager is planning for a series of 1-month production periods for stainless steel sinks. The demand for the next 4 months is as follows:

MONTH	DEMAND FOR STAINLESS STEEL SINKS
1	120
2	160
3	240
4	100

Table for Problem 26

FROM \ TO	HOSPITAL 1	HOSPITAL 2	HOSPITAL 3	HOSPITAL 4	SUPPLY
BANK 1	$8	$9	$11	$16	50
BANK 2	12	7	5	8	80
BANK 3	14	10	6	7	120
DEMAND	90	70	40	50	250

Table for Problem 28

SAVINGS AND LOAN COMPANY	PROPERTY (INTEREST RATES) (%)				
	HILL ST.	BANKS ST.	PARK AVE.	DRURY LANE	MAXIMUM CREDIT LINE ($)
FIRST HOMESTEAD	8	8	10	11	80,000
COMMONWEALTH	9	10	12	10	100,000
WASHINGTON FEDERAL	9	11	10	9	120,000
LOAN REQUIRED TO PURCHASE BUILDING	$60,000	$40,000	$130,000	$70,000	

The Mehta firm can normally produce 100 stainless steel sinks in a month. This is done during regular production hours at a cost of $100 per sink. If demand in any 1 month cannot be satisfied by regular production, the production manager has three other choices: (1) He can produce up to 50 more sinks per month in overtime but at a cost of $130 per sink; (2) he can purchase a limited number of sinks from a friendly competitor for resale (the maximum number of outside purchases over the 4-month period is 450 sinks, at a cost of $150 each); or (3) he can fill the demand from his on-hand inventory. The inventory carrying cost is $10 per sink per month. Back orders are not permitted. Inventory on hand at the beginning of month 1 is 40 sinks. Set up this "production smoothing" problem as a transportation problem to minimize cost. Use the northwest corner rule to find an initial level for production and outside purchases over the 4-month period.

31 Formulate the J. Mehta production problem (See Problem 30) as a linear program and solve using computer software.

32 Ashley's Auto Top Carriers currently maintains plants in Atlanta and Tulsa that supply major distribution centers in Los Angeles and New York. Because of an expanding demand, Ashley has decided to open a third plant and has narrowed the choice to one of two cities—New Orleans or Houston. The pertinent production and distribution costs, as well as the plant capacities and distribution demands, are shown in the table below.

Which of the new possible plants should be opened?

33 Formulate and solve linear programs to help Ashley's Auto Top Carriers (See Problem 32) determine

where to open the new plant. How much difference in the costs for the two locations?

34 Marc Smith, vice president for operations of HHN, Inc., a manufacturer of cabinets for telephone switches, is constrained from meeting the 5-year forecast by limited capacity at the existing three plants. These three plants are Waterloo, Pusan, and Bogota. You, as his able assistant, have been told that because of existing capacity constraints and the expanding world market for HHN cabinets, a new plant is to be added to the existing three plants. The real estate department has advised Marc that two sites seem particularly good because of a stable political situation and tolerable exchange rate: Dublin, Ireland, and Fontainebleau, France. Marc suggests that you should be able to take the data on the next page and determine where the fourth plant should be located on the basis of production costs and transportation costs. Which location is better?

35 Don Levine Corporation is considering adding an additional plant to its three existing facilities in Decatur, Minneapolis, and Carbondale. Both St. Louis and East St. Louis are being considered. Evaluating only the transportation costs per unit as shown in the tables below and on the next page, which site is best?

	FROM EXISTING PLANTS			
TO	DECATUR	MINNEAPOLIS	CARBONDALE	DEMAND
Blue Earth	$20	$17	$21	250
Ciro	25	27	20	200
Des Moines	22	25	22	350
Capacity	300	200	150	

Data for Problem 32

TO DISTRIBUTION CENTERS / FROM PLANTS	LOS ANGELES	NEW YORK	NORMAL PRODUCTION	UNIT PRODUCTION COST ($)
ATLANTA	$8	$5	600	6
TULSA	$4	$7	900	5
NEW ORLEANS	$5	$6	500	4 (anticipated)
HOUSTON	$4	$6	500	3 (anticipated)
FORECAST DEMAND	800	1,200	2,000	

Existing plants → ATLANTA, TULSA

Proposed locations → NEW ORLEANS, HOUSTON

Indicates distribution cost (shipping, handling, storage) will be $6 per carrier if sent from Houston to New York

Data for Problem 34

MARKET AREA	PLANT LOCATION				
	WATERLOO	PUSAN	BOGOTA	FONTAINEBLEAU	DUBLIN
Canada					
Demand 4,000					
Production cost	$50	$30	$40	$50	$45
Transportation cost	10	25	20	25	25
South America					
Demand 5,000					
Production cost	50	30	40	50	45
Transportation cost	20	25	10	30	30
Pacific Rim					
Demand 10,000					
Production cost	50	30	40	50	45
Transportation cost	25	10	25	40	40
Europe					
Demand 5,000					
Production cost	50	30	40	50	45
Transportation cost	25	40	30	10	20
Capacity	8,000	2,000	5,000	9,000	9,000

TO	FROM PROPOSED PLANTS	
	EAST ST. LOUIS	ST. LOUIS
Blue Earth	$29	$27
Ciro	30	28
Des Moines	30	31
Capacity	150	150

JOB	MACHINE			
	W	X	Y	Z
A12	10	14	16	13
A15	12	13	15	12
B2	9	12	12	11
B9	14	16	18	16

 36 Using the data from Problem 35 plus the unit production costs shown in the following table, which locations yield the lowest cost?

LOCATION	PRODUCTION COSTS
Decatur	$50
Minneapolis	60
Carbondale	70
East St. Louis	40
St. Louis	50

  37 In a job shop operation, four jobs may be performed on any of four machines. The hours required for each job on each machine are presented in the following table. The plant supervisor would like to assign jobs so that total time is minimized. Find the best solution.

 38 Four automobiles have entered Bubba's Repair Shop for various types of work, ranging from a transmission overhaul to a brake job. The experience level of the mechanics is quite varied, and Bubba would like to minimize the time required to complete all of the jobs. He has estimated the time in minutes for each mechanic to complete each job. Billy can complete job 1 in 400 minutes, job 2 in 90 minutes, job 3 in 60 minutes, and job 4 in 120 minutes. Taylor will finish job 1 in 650 minutes, job 2 in 120 minutes, job 3 in 90 minutes, and job 4 in 180 minutes. Mark will finish job 1 in 480 minutes, job 2 in 120 minutes, job 3 in 80 minutes, and job 4 in 180 minutes. John will complete job 1 in 500 minutes, job 2 in 110 minutes, job 3 in 90 minutes, and job 4 in 150 minutes. Each mechanic should be assigned to just one of these jobs. What is the minimum total time required to finish the four jobs? Who should be assigned to each job?

: 39 Baseball umpiring crews are currently in four cities where three-game series are beginning. When these are finished, the crews are needed to work games in four different cities. The distances (miles) from each of the cities where the crews are currently working to the cities where the new games will begin are shown in the following table:

	TO			
FROM	KANSAS CITY	CHICAGO	DETROIT	TORONTO
Seattle	1,500	1,730	1,940	2,070
Arlington	460	810	1,020	1,270
Oakland	1,500	1,850	2,080	X
Baltimore	960	610	400	330

The X indicates that the crew in Oakland cannot be sent to Toronto. Determine which crew should be sent to each city to minimize the total distance traveled. How many miles will be traveled if these assignments are made?

: 40 In Problem 39, the minimum travel distance was found. To see how much better this solution is than the assignments that might have been made, find the assignments that would give the maximum distance traveled. Compare this total distance with the distance found in Problem 39.

: 41 Roscoe Davis, chairman of a college's business department, has decided to apply a new method in assigning professors to courses next semester. As a criterion for judging who should teach each course, Professor Davis reviews the past two years' teaching evaluations (which were filled out by students). Since each of the four professors taught each of the four courses at one time or another during the two-year period, Davis is able to record a course rating for each instructor. These ratings are shown in the table. Find the best assignment of professors to courses to maximize the overall teaching rating.

	COURSE			
PROFESSOR	STATISTICS	MANAGEMENT	FINANCE	ECONOMICS
Anderson	90	65	95	40
Sweeney	70	60	80	75
Williams	85	40	80	60
McKinney	55	80	65	55

: 42 The hospital administrator at St. Charles General must appoint head nurses to four newly established departments: urology, cardiology, orthopedics, and obstetrics. In anticipation of this staffing problem, she had hired four nurses: Hawkins, Condriac, Bardot, and Hoolihan. Believing in the quantitative analysis approach to problem solving, the administrator has interviewed each nurse, considered his or her background, personality, and talents, and developed a cost scale ranging from 0 to 100 to be used in the assignment. A 0 for Nurse Bardot being assigned to the cardiology unit implies that she would be perfectly suited to that task. A value close to 100, on the other hand, would imply that she is not at all suited to head that unit. The accompanying table gives the complete set of cost figures that the hospital administrator felt represented all possible assignments. Which nurse should be assigned to which unit?

	DEPARTMENT			
NURSE	UROLOGY	CARDIOLOGY	ORTHOPEDICS	OBSTETRICS
Hawkins	28	18	15	75
Condriac	32	48	23	38
Bardot	51	36	24	36
Hoolihan	25	38	55	12

: 43 The Gleaming Company has just developed a new dishwashing liquid and is preparing for a national television promotional campaign. The firm has decided to schedule a series of 1-minute commercials during the peak homemaker audience viewing hours of 1 to 5 p.m. To reach the widest possible audience, Gleaming wants to schedule one commercial on each of four networks and to have one commercial appear during each of the four 1-hour time blocks. The exposure ratings for each hour, which represent the number of viewers per $1,000 spent, are presented in the following table. Which network should be scheduled each hour to provide the maximum audience exposure?

	NETWORK			
VIEWING HOURS	A	B	C	INDEPENDENT
1–2 P.M.	27.1	18.1	11.3	9.5
2–3 P.M.	18.9	15.5	17.1	10.6
3–4 P.M.	19.2	18.5	9.9	7.7
4–5 P.M.	11.5	21.4	16.8	12.8

: 44 The Fix-It Shop (see Section 8) has added a fourth repairman, Davis. Solve the accompanying cost table for the new optimal assignment of workers to projects. Why did this solution occur?

	PROJECT		
WORKER	1	2	3
Adams	$11	$14	$6
Brown	8	10	11
Cooper	9	12	7
Davis	10	13	8

Data for Problem 45

ELECTRONIC COMPONENT	PLANT							
	1	2	3	4	5	6	7	8
C53	$0.10	$0.12	$0.13	$0.11	$0.10	$0.06	$0.16	$0.12
C81	0.05	0.06	0.04	0.08	0.04	0.09	0.06	0.06
D5	0.32	0.40	0.31	0.30	0.42	0.35	0.36	0.49
D44	0.17	0.14	0.19	0.15	0.10	0.16	0.19	0.12
E2	0.06	0.07	0.10	0.05	0.08	0.10	0.11	0.05
E35	0.08	0.10	0.12	0.08	0.09	0.10	0.09	0.06
G99	0.55	0.62	0.61	0.70	0.62	0.63	0.65	0.59

: 45 The Patricia Garcia Company is producing seven new medical products. Each of Garcia's eight plants can add one more product to its current line of medical devices. The unit manufacturing costs for producing the different parts at the eight plants are shown in the table above. How should Garcia assign the new products to the plants to minimize manufacturing costs?

: 46 Haifa Instruments, an Israeli producer of portable kidney dialysis units and other medical products, develops an 8-month aggregate plan. Demand and capacity (in units) are forecast as shown in the table below.

The cost of producing each dialysis unit is $1,000 on regular time, $1,300 on overtime, and $1,500 on a subcontract. Inventory carrying cost is $100 per unit per month. There is no beginning or ending inventory in stock.

(a) Set up a production plan, using the transportation model, that minimizes cost. What is this plan's cost?

(b) Through better planning, regular time production can be set at exactly the same value, 275 per month. Does this alter the solution?

(c) If overtime costs rise from $1,300 to $1,400, does this change your answer to part (a)? What if they fall to $1,200?

: 47 NASA's astronaut crew currently includes 10 mission specialists who hold a doctoral degree in either astrophysics or astromedicine. One of these specialists will be assigned to each of the 10 flights scheduled for the upcoming nine months. Mission specialists are responsible for carrying out scientific and medical experiments in space or for launching, retrieving, or repairing satellites. The chief of astronaut personnel, himself a former crew member with three missions under his belt, must decide who should be assigned and trained for each of the very different missions. Clearly, astronauts with medical educations are more suited to missions involving biological or medical experiments, whereas those with engineering- or physics-oriented degrees are best suited to other types of missions. The chief assigns each astronaut a rating on a scale of 1 to 10 for each possible mission, with a 10 being a perfect match for the task at hand and a 1 being a mismatch. Only one specialist is assigned to each flight, and none is reassigned until all others have flown at least once.

(a) Who should be assigned to which flight?

(b) NASA has just been notified that Anderson is getting married in February and has been granted a highly sought publicity tour in Europe that month. (He intends to take his wife and let

Data for Problem 46

CAPACITY SOURCE	JAN.	FEB.	MAR.	APR.	MAY	JUNE	JULY	AUG.
Labor								
Regular time	235	255	290	300	300	290	300	290
Overtime	20	24	26	24	30	28	30	30
Subcontract	12	15	15	17	17	19	19	20
Demand	255	294	321	301	330	320	345	340

Data for Problem 47

ASTRONAUT	MISSION JAN. 12	JAN. 27	FEB. 5	FEB. 26	MAR. 26	APR. 12	MAY 1	JUN. 9	AUG. 20	SEP. 19
Vincze	9	7	2	1	10	9	8	9	2	6
Veit	8	8	3	4	7	9	7	7	4	4
Anderson	2	1	10	10	1	4	7	6	6	7
Herbert	4	4	10	9	9	9	1	2	3	4
Schatz	10	10	9	9	8	9	1	1	1	1
Plane	1	3	5	7	9	7	10	10	9	2
Certo	9	9	8	8	9	1	1	2	2	9
Moses	3	2	7	6	4	3	9	7	7	9
Brandon	5	4	5	9	10	10	5	4	9	8
Drtina	10	10	9	7	6	7	5	4	8	8

the trip double as a honeymoon.) How does this change the final schedule?

(c) Certo has complained that he was misrated on his January missions. Both ratings should be 10s, he claims to the chief, who agrees and recomputes the schedule. Do any changes occur over the schedule set in part (b)?

(d) What are the strengths and weaknesses of this approach to scheduling?

 48 The XYZ Corporation is expanding its market to include Texas. Each salesperson is assigned to potential distributors in one of five different areas. It is anticipated that the salesperson will spend about three to four weeks in each area. A statewide marketing campaign will begin once the product has been delivered to the distributors. The five sales people who will be assigned to these areas (one person for each area) have rated the areas on the desirability of the assignment as shown in the following table. The scale is 1 (least desirable) to 5 (most desirable). Which assignments should be made if the total of the ratings is to be maximized?

	AUSTIN/SAN ANTONIO	DALLAS/FT. WORTH	EL PASO/WEST TEXAS	HOUSTON/ GALVESTON	CORPUS CHRISTI/RIO GRANDE VALLEY
Erica	5	3	2	3	4
Louis	3	4	4	2	2
Maria	4	5	4	3	3
Paul	2	4	3	4	3
Orlando	4	5	3	5	4

Internet Homework Problems

See our Internet home page, at **www.pearsonhighered.com/render**, for additional problems, Problems 49 through 55.

Case Study

Andrew–Carter, Inc.

Andrew–Carter, Inc. (A–C), is a major Canadian producer and distributor of outdoor lighting fixtures. Its fixture is distributed throughout North America and has been in high demand for several years. The company operates three plants that manufacture the fixture and distribute it to five distribution centers (warehouses).

During the present recession, A–C has seen a major drop in demand for its fixture as the housing market has declined. Based on the forecast of interest rates, the head of operations feels that demand for housing and thus for its product will remain depressed for the foreseeable future. A–C is considering closing one of its plants, as it is now operating with a forecasted excess capacity of 34,000 units per week. The forecasted weekly demands for the coming year are

Warehouse 1	9,000 units
Warehouse 2	13,000 units
Warehouse 3	11,000 units
Warehouse 4	15,000 units
Warehouse 5	8,000 units

The plant capacities in units per week are

Plant 1, regular time	27,000 units
Plant 1, on overtime	7,000 units
Plant 2, regular time	20,000 units
Plant 2, on overtime	5,000 units
Plant 3, regular time	25,000 units
Plant 3, on overtime	6,000 units

If A–C shuts down any plants, its weekly costs will change, as fixed costs are lower for a nonoperating plant. Table 34 shows production costs at each plant, both variable at regular time and overtime, and fixed when operating and shut down. Table 35 shows distribution costs from each plant to each warehouse (distribution center).

Discussion Questions

1. Evaluate the various configurations of operating and closed plants that will meet weekly demand. Determine which configuration minimizes total costs.
2. Discuss the implications of closing a plant.

Source: Professor Michael Ballot, University of the Pacific.

TABLE 34
Andrew–Carter, Inc., Variable Costs and Fixed Production Costs per Week

PLANT	VARIABLE COST	FIXED COST PER WEEK OPERATING	FIXED COST PER WEEK NOT OPERATING
No. 1, regular time	$2.80/unit	$14,000	$6,000
No. 1, overtime	3.52		
No. 2, regular time	2.78	12,000	5,000
No. 2, overtime	3.48		
No. 3, regular time	2.72	15,000	7,500
No. 3, overtime	3.42		

TABLE 35
Andrew–Carter, Inc., Distribution Costs per Unit

FROM PLANT	TO DISTRIBUTION CENTER W1	W2	W3	W4	W5
No. 1	$0.50	$0.44	$0.49	$0.46	$0.56
No. 2	0.40	0.52	0.50	0.56	0.57
No. 3	0.56	0.53	0.51	0.54	0.35

Case Study

Old Oregon Wood Store

In 1992, George Brown started the Old Oregon Wood Store to manufacture Old Oregon tables. Each table is carefully constructed by hand using the highest-quality oak. Old Oregon tables can support more than 500 pounds, and since the start of the Old Oregon Wood Store, not one table has been returned because of faulty workmanship or structural problems. In addition to being rugged, each table is beautifully finished using a urethane varnish that George developed over 20 years of working with wood-finishing materials.

The manufacturing process consists of four steps: preparation, assembly, finishing, and packaging. Each step is performed by one person. In addition to overseeing the entire operation, George does all of the finishing. Tom Surowski performs the preparation step, which involves cutting and forming the basic components of the tables. Leon Davis is in charge of the assembly, and Cathy Stark performs the packaging.

Although each person is responsible for only one step in the manufacturing process, everyone can perform any one of the steps. It is George's policy that occasionally everyone should complete several tables on his or her own without any help or assistance. A small competition is used to see who can complete an entire table in the least amount of time. George maintains average total and intermediate completion times. The data are shown in Figure 5.

It takes Cathy longer than the other employees to construct an Old Oregon table. In addition to being slower than the other employees, Cathy is also unhappy about her current responsibility of packaging, which leaves her idle most of the day. Her first preference is finishing, and her second preference is preparation.

In addition to quality, George is concerned with costs and efficiency. When one of the employees misses a day, it causes major scheduling problems. In some cases, George assigns another employee overtime to complete the necessary work. At other times, George simply waits until the employee returns to work to complete his or her step in the manufacturing process. Both solutions cause problems. Overtime is expensive, and waiting causes delays and sometimes stops the entire manufacturing process.

To overcome some of these problems, Randy Lane was hired. Randy's major duties are to perform miscellaneous jobs and to help out if one of the employees is absent. George has given Randy training in all phases of the manufacturing process, and he is pleased with the speed at which Randy has been able to learn how to completely assemble Old Oregon tables. Total and intermediate completion times are given in Figure 6.

FIGURE 5
Manufacturing Time in Minutes

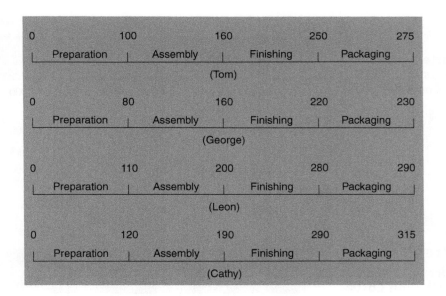

FIGURE 6
Randy's Completion Times in Minutes

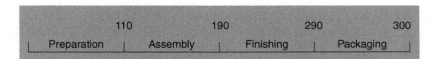

Discussion Questions

1. What is the fastest way to manufacture Old Oregon tables using the original crew? How many could be made per day?
2. Would production rates and quantities change significantly if George would allow Randy to perform one of the four functions and make one of the original crew the backup person?
3. What is the fastest time to manufacture a table with the original crew if Cathy is moved to either preparation or finishing?
4. Whoever performs the packaging function is severely underutilized. Can you find a better way of utilizing the four- or five-person crew than either giving each a single job or allowing each to manufacture an entire table? How many tables could be manufactured per day with this scheme?

Internet Case Studies

See our Internet home page, at **www.pearsonhighered.com/render**, for these additional case studies:

(1) **Northwest General Hospital:** This case involves improving the food distribution system in a hospital to reduce the chances of food getting cold before it is delivered to the patients.

(2) **Custom Vans, Inc:** This case involves finding the best location for a plant that will manufacture showers used in customized vans.

Bibliography

Adlakha, V., and K. Kowalski. "Simple Algorithm for the Source-Induced Fixed-Charge Transportation Problem," *Journal of the Operational Research Society* 55, 12 (2004): 1275–1280.

Awad, Rania M., and John W. Chinneck. "Proctor Assignment at Carleton University," *Interfaces* 28, 2 (March–April 1998): 58–71.

Bowman, E. "Production Scheduling by the Transportation Method of Linear Programming," *Operations Research* 4 (1956).

Dawid, Herbert, Johannes Konig, and Christine Strauss. "An Enhanced Rostering Model for Airline Crews," *Computers and Operations Research* 28, 7 (June 2001): 671–688.

Domich, P. D., K. L. Hoffman, R. H. F. Jackson, and M. A. McClain. "Locating Tax Facilities: A Graphics-Based Microcomputer Optimization Model," *Management Science* 37 (August 1991): 960–979.

Hezarkhani, Behzad, and Wieslaw Kubiak. "A Coordinating Contract for Transshipment In a Two-Company Supply Chain," *European Journal of Operational Research* 207, 1 (2010): 232–237.

Koksalan, Murat, and Haldun Sural. "Efes Beverage Group Makes Location and Distribution Decisions for Its Malt Plants," *Interfaces* 29, 2 (March–April, 1999): 89–103.

Liu, Shiang-Tai. "The Total Cost Bounds of the Transportation Problem with Varying Demand and Supply," *Omega* 31, 4 (2003): 247–251.

Martello, Silvano. "Jeno Egervary: From the Origins of the Hungarian Algorithm to Satellite Communication," *Central European Journal of Operations Research* 18, 1 (2010): 47–58.

McKeown, P., and B. Workman. "A Study in Using Linear Programming to Assign Students to Schools," *Interfaces* 6, 4 (August 1976).

Pooley, J. "Integrated Production and Distribution Facility Planning at Ault Foods," *Interfaces* 24, 4 (July–August 1994): 113–121.

Render, B., and R. M. Stair. *Introduction to Management Science.* Boston: Allyn & Bacon, Inc., 1992.

Appendix 1: Using QM for Windows

QM for Windows has both a transportation module and an assignment module in its menu. Both are easy to use in terms of data entry and easy to interpret in terms of output. Program 6A shows the input screen for the Executive Furniture transportation example. The starting solution technique may be specified. The results are shown in Figure 6B. By clicking *Window*, you have the option of seeing the iterations that are performed to reach the final solution. Program 7A provides the input screen for the Fix-It Shop assignment example. Simply enter the costs and then click *Solve*. Program 7B gives the solution to this.

PROGRAM 6A

QM for Windows Input
for Executive Furniture
Transportation Example

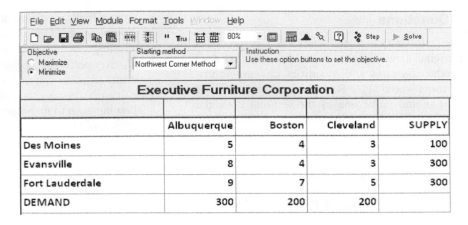

PROGRAM 6B

QM for Windows
Solution for Executive
Furniture Transportation
Example

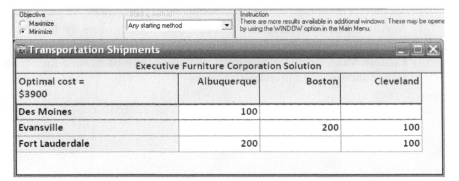

PROGRAM 7A

QM for Windows Input
for the Fix-It Shop
Assignment Example

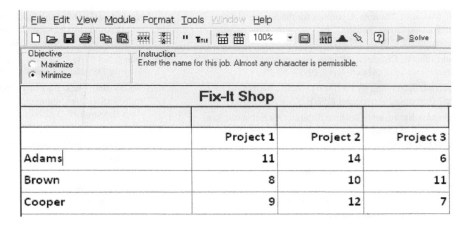

PROGRAM 7B

QM for Windows Solution
for the Fix-It Shop
Assignment Example

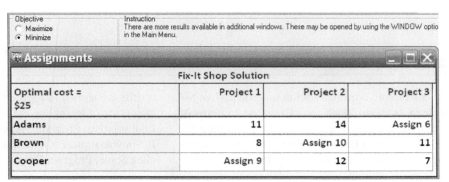

Solutions to Selected Problems

12   Des Moines to Albuquerque 200, Des Moines to Boston 50, Des Moines to Cleveland 50, Evansville to Boston 150, Ft. Lauderdale to Cleveland 250. Cost = $3,200.

16   25 units from Pineville to 3; 30 units from Oak Ridge to 2; 10 units from Oakville to 3; 30 units from Mapletown to 1. Cost = $230. Multiple optimal solutions.

18   Total cost = $3,100.

22   Unbalanced, $5,310

24   Total cost = $635.

32   New Orleans' systems cost = $20,000; Houston's is $19,500, so Houston should be selected.

34   Fontainebleau, $1,530,000; Dublin, $1,535,000

36   East St. Louis cost = 60,900; St. Louis cost = 62,250

38   Total time = 750 minutes

40   Total distance = 6,040

42   Total rating = 86

44   No change; Cost = $45

46   (a) $2,591,200   (b) $2,640,500   (c) $2,610,100 and $2,572,100

Solutions to Self-Tests

1.   b
2.   d
3.   b
4.   b
5.   b
6.   a
7.   b
8.   b
9.   b
10.   a
11.   b
12.   a

Statistical Quality Control

Summary • Glossary • Key Equations • Solved Problems • Self-Test • Discussion Questions and Problems • Internet Homework Problems • Internet Case Study • Bibliography

Appendix 1: Using QM for Windows for SPC

1 Introduction

For almost every product or service, there is more than one organization trying to make a sale. Price may be a major issue in whether a sale is made or lost, but another factor is *quality*. In fact, quality is often the major issue; and poor quality can be very expensive for both the producing firm and the customer.

Consequently, firms employ quality management tactics. Quality management, or as it is more commonly called, *quality control* (QC), is critical throughout the organization. One of the manager's major roles is to ensure that his or her firm can deliver a quality product at the right place, at the right time, and at the right price. Quality is not just of concern for manufactured products either; it is also important in services, from banking to hospital care to education.

Statistical process control uses statistical and probability tools to help control processes and produce consistent goods and services.

We begin this chapter with an attempt to define just what quality really is. Then we deal with the most important statistical methodology for quality management: *statistical process control* (SPC). SPC is the application of the statistical tools to the control of processes that result in products or services.

2 Defining Quality and TQM

The quality of a product or service is the degree to which the product or service meets specifications.

To some people, a high-quality product is one that is stronger, will last longer, is built heavier, and is, in general, more durable than other products. In some cases this is a good definition of a quality product, but not always. A good circuit breaker, for example, is *not* one that lasts longer during periods of high current or voltage. So the **quality** *of a product* or *service* is the degree to which the product or service meets specifications. Increasingly, definitions of *quality* include an added emphasis on meeting the customer's needs. As you can see in Table 1, the first and second ones are similar to our definition.

Total quality management encompasses the whole organization.

Total quality management (TQM) refers to a quality emphasis that encompasses the entire organization, from supplier to customer. TQM emphasizes a commitment by management to have a companywide drive toward excellence in all aspects of the products and services that are important to the customer. Meeting the customer's expectations requires an emphasis on TQM if the firm is to compete as a leader in world markets.

This emphasis on quality means that the company will seek continuous improvement in every aspect of the delivery of products and services.

TABLE 1
Several Definitions of Quality

"Quality is the degree to which a specific product conforms to a design or specification."

H. L. Gilmore. "Product Conformance Cost," *Quality Progress* (June 1974): 16.

"Quality is the totality of features and characteristics of a product or service that bears on its ability to satisfy stated or implied needs."

Ross Johnson and William O. Winchell. *Production and Quality.* Milwaukee, WI: American Society of Quality Control, 1989, p. 2.

"Quality is fitness for use."

J. M. Juran, ed. *Quality Control Handbook*, 3rd ed. New York: McGraw-Hill, 1974, p. 2.

"Quality is defined by the customer; customers want products and services that, throughout their lives, meet customers' needs and expectations at a cost that represents value."

Ford's definition, as presented in William W. Scherkenbach. *Deming's Road to Continual Improvement.* Knoxville, TN: SPC Press, 1991, p. 161.

"Even though quality cannot be defined, you know what it is."

R. M. Pirsig. *Zen and the Art of Motorcycle Maintenance.* New York: Bantam Books, 1974, p. 213.

In the early nineteenth century an individual skilled artisan started and finished a whole product. With the Industrial Revolution and the factory system, semiskilled workers, each making a small portion of the final product, became common. With this, responsibility for the quality of the final product tended to shift to supervisors, and pride of workmanship declined.

As organizations became larger in the twentieth century, inspection became more technical and organized. Inspectors were often grouped together; their job was to make sure that bad lots were not shipped to customers. Starting in the 1920s, major statistical QC tools were developed. W. Shewhart introduced control charts in 1924, and in 1930, H. F. Dodge and H. G. Romig designed acceptance sampling tables. Also at that time the important role of QC in all areas of the company's performance became recognized.

During and after World War II, the importance of quality grew, often with the encouragement of the U.S. government. Companies recognized that more than just inspection was needed to make a quality product. Quality needed to be built into the production process.

After World War II, an American, W. Edwards Deming, went to Japan to teach statistical QC concepts to the devastated Japanese manufacturing sector. A second pioneer, J. M. Juran, followed

Deming to Japan, stressing top management support and involvement in the quality battle. In 1961 A. V. Feigenbaum wrote his classic book *Total Quality Control*, which delivered a fundamental message: Make it right the first time! In 1979, Philip Crosby published *Quality Is Free*, stressing the need for management and employee commitment to the battle against poor quality. In 1988, the U.S. government presented its first awards for quality achievement. These are known as the Malcolm Baldrige National Quality Awards.

A method of quality management called Six Sigma was developed in the electronics industry. The goal of Six Sigma is continuous improvement in performance to reduce and eliminate defects. Technically, to achieve Six Sigma quality, there would have to be fewer than 3.4 defects per million opportunities. This approach to quality has been credited with achieving significant cost savings for a number of companies. General Electric estimated savings of $12 billion over a 5-year period, and other firms have reported savings in the hundreds of millions of dollars.

Today, companies strive to be ISO 9000 certified as this is an international quality standard that is recognized worldwide. ISO 9000 was developed by the International Organization for Standardization (ISO), the world's largest developer and publisher of international standards.

3 Statiscal Process Control

Statistical process control helps set standards. It can also monitor, measure, and correct quality problems.

Statistical process control involves establishing standards, monitoring standards, making measurements, and taking corrective action as a product or service is being produced. Samples of process outputs are examined; if they are within acceptable limits, the process is permitted to continue. If they fall outside certain specific ranges, the process is stopped and, typically, the assignable cause is located and removed.

A control chart is a graphic way of presenting data over time.

Control charts are graphs that show upper and lower limits for the process we want to control. A **control chart** is a graphic presentation of data over time. Control charts are constructed in such a way that new data can quickly be compared with past performance. Upper and lower limits in a control chart can be in units of temperature, pressure, weight, length, and so on. We take samples of the process output and plot the averages of these samples on a chart that has the limits on it.

Figure 1 graphically reveals the useful information that can be portrayed in control charts. When the averages of the samples fall within the upper and lower control limits and no discernible pattern is present, the process is said to be in control; otherwise, the process is out of control or out of adjustment.

Variability in the Process

All processes are subject to a certain degree of variability. Walter Shewhart of Bell Laboratories, while studying process data in the 1920s, made the distinction between the common and special causes of variation. The key is keeping variations under control. So we now look at how to build control charts that help managers and workers develop a process that is capable of producing within established limits.

BUILDING CONTROL CHARTS When building control charts, averages of small samples (often of five items or parts) are used, as opposed to data on individual parts. Individual pieces tend to be too erratic to make trends quickly visible. The purpose of control charts is to help distinguish between **natural variations** and *variations due to assignable causes*.

FIGURE 1
Patterns to Look for in Control Charts

(**Source:** Bertrand L. Hansen, *Quality Control: Theory and Applications,* © 1963, renewed 1991, p. 65. Reprinted by permission of Prentice Hall, Upper Saddle River, NJ.)

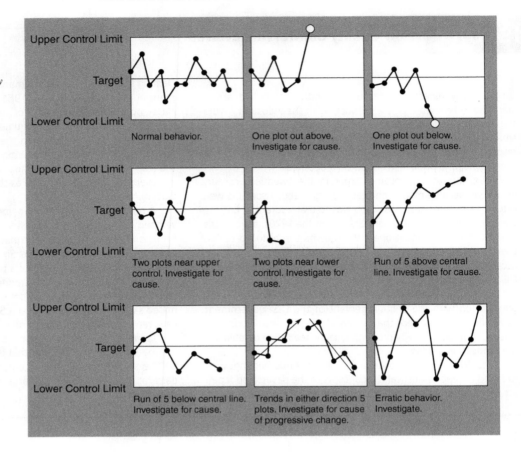

IN ACTION
Bank of America Uses Statistics to Combat Pecuniary Corruption

Banks and similar financial institutions have good reason to help law enforcement fight fiscal improprieties. Debit card fraud alone costs the banking industry over $2.75 billion annually! In their fight against fraud, analysts at Bank of America use statistical *outlier analysis* to help detect suspicious fiscal activities. Bank of America specifically targets money laundering and retail banking fraud in its analysis. The company tracks characteristics such as where, when, and how much money is involved in each transaction for every customer. Then it performs statistical analyses to see if the activity falls within usual activity boundaries for that particular customer. For you as a customer, that means nothing more than that the bank knows how much money you typically withdraw from an ATM and which ATM you normally use.

The bank analysts are on the lookout for *outliers*, which are unusual events that have a very small probability of occurring. For example, if you normally use one particular ATM and then use a different ATM, the transaction at the unusual location may raise a small flag, but the transaction would likely proceed without interference. However, if you try to cash a very large third-party check at an out-of-state location, several flags will be raised, as this is very unusual behavior for you. The teller may require several forms of identification and then get approval from the branch manager before completing the transaction.

Source: Based on A. Sudjianto, S. Nair, M. Yuan, A. Zhang, D. Ker, and F. Cela-Díaz. "Statistical Methods for Fighting Financial Crimes," *Technometrics,* 52, 1 (2010): 5–19.

Natural variations are sources of variation in a process that is statistically in control.

NATURAL VARIATIONS Natural variations affect almost every production process and are to be expected. These variations are random and uncontrollable. *Natural variations* are the many sources of variation within a process that is in statistical control. They behave like a constant system of chance causes. Although individual measured values are all different, as a group they form a pattern that can be described as a distribution. When these distributions are *normal*, they are characterized by two parameters:

1. Mean, μ (the measure of central tendency, in this case, the average value)
2. Standard deviation, σ (variation, the amount by which the smaller values differ from the larger ones)

As long as the distribution (output precision) remains within specified limits, the process is said to be "in control," and the modest variations are tolerated.

Assignable variations in a process can be traced to a specific problem.

ASSIGNABLE VARIATIONS When a process is not in control, we must detect and eliminate special (*assignable*) causes of *variation*. These variations are not random and can be controlled when the cause of the variation is determined. Factors such as machine wear, misadjusted equipment, fatigued or untrained workers, or new batches of raw material are all potential sources of **assignable variations**. Control charts such as those illustrated in Figure 1 help the manager pinpoint where a problem may lie.

The ability of a process to operate within statistical control is determined by the total variation that comes from natural causes—the minimum variation that can be achieved after all assignable causes have been eliminated. The objective of a process control system, then, is *to provide a statistical signal when assignable causes of variation are present*. Such a signal can quicken appropriate action to eliminate assignable causes.

4 Control Charts for Variables

x̄-charts measure central tendency of a process.

Control charts for the mean, $\overline{x}$, and the range, R, are used to monitor processes that are measured in continuous units. Examples of these would be weight, height, and volume. The **x̄-chart** (x-bar chart) tells us whether changes have occurred in the central tendency of a process. This might be due to such factors as tool wear, a gradual increase in temperature, a different method used on the second shift, or new and stronger materials. The **R-chart** values indicate that a gain or loss in uniformity has occurred. Such a change might be due to worn bearings, a loose tool part, an erratic flow of lubricants to a machine, or sloppiness on the part of a machine operator. The two types of charts go hand in hand when monitoring variables.

R-charts measure the range between the biggest (or heaviest) and smallest (or lightest) items in a random sample.

The Central Limit Theorem

The central limit theorem says that the distribution of sample means will be approximately normally distributed.

The statistical foundation for $\overline{x}$-charts is the **central limit theorem**. In general terms, this theorem states that regardless of the distribution of the population of all parts or services, the distribution of $\overline{x}$'s (each of which is a mean of a sample drawn from the population) will tend to follow a normal curve as the sample size grows large. Fortunately, even if n is fairly small (say 4 or 5), the distributions of the averages will still roughly follow a normal curve. The theorem also states that (1) the mean of the distribution of the $\overline{x}$'s (called $\mu_{\overline{x}}$) will equal the mean of the overall population (called μ); and (2) the standard deviation of the sampling distribution, $\sigma_{\overline{x}}$, will be the population deviation, σ_x, divided by the square root of the sample size, n. In other words,

$$\mu_{\overline{x}} = \mu \quad \text{and} \quad \sigma_{\overline{x}} = \frac{\sigma_x}{\sqrt{n}}$$

Although there may be times when we may know $\mu_{\overline{x}}$ (and μ), often we must estimate this with the average of all the sample means (written as $\overline{\overline{x}}$).

Figure 2 shows three possible population distributions, each with its own mean, μ, and standard deviation, σ_x. If a series of random samples ($\overline{x}_1, \overline{x}_2, \overline{x}_3, \overline{x}_4$, and so on) each of size n is drawn from any one of these, the resulting distribution of $\overline{x}_i$s will appear as in the bottom graph of that figure. Because this is a normal distribution, we can state that

1. 99.7% of the time, the sample averages will fall within $\pm 3\sigma_{\overline{x}}$ of the population mean if the process has only random variations.
2. 95.5% of the time, the sample averages will fall within $\pm 2\sigma_{\overline{x}}$ of the population mean if the process has only random variations.

If a point on the control chart falls outside the $\pm 3\sigma_{\overline{x}}$ control limits, we are 99.7% sure that the process has changed. This is the theory behind control charts.

FIGURE 2
Population and Sampling Distributions

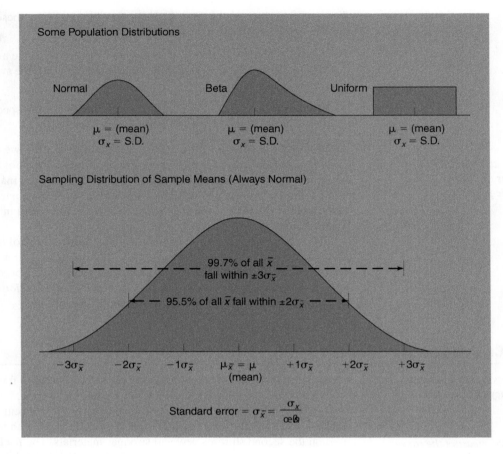

Setting $\bar{x}$-Chart Limits

If we know through historical data the standard deviation of the process population, $\sigma_{\bar{x}}$, we can set upper and lower control limits by these formulas:

$$\text{Upper control limit (UCL)} = \bar{\bar{x}} + z\sigma_{\bar{x}} \tag{1}$$

$$\text{Lower control limit (LCL)} = \bar{\bar{x}} - z\sigma_{\bar{x}} \tag{2}$$

where

$\bar{\bar{x}}$ = mean of the sample means

z = number of normal standard deviations (2 for 95.5% confidence, 3 for 99.7%)

$\sigma_{\bar{x}}$ = standard deviation of the sampling distribution of the sample means $= \dfrac{\sigma_x}{\sqrt{n}}$

BOX-FILLING EXAMPLE Let us say that a large production lot of boxes of cornflakes is sampled every hour. To set control limits that include 99.7% of the sample means, 36 boxes are randomly selected and weighed. The standard deviation of the overall population of boxes is estimated, through analysis of old records, to be 2 ounces. The average mean of all samples taken is 16 ounces. We therefore have $\bar{\bar{x}}$ = 16 ounces, $\sigma_{\bar{x}}$ = 2 ounces, n = 36, and z = 3. The control limits are

$$\text{UCL}_{\bar{x}} = \bar{\bar{x}} + z\sigma_{\bar{x}} = 16 + 3\left(\frac{2}{\sqrt{36}}\right) = 16 + 1 = 17 \text{ ounces}$$

$$\text{LCL}_{\bar{x}} = \bar{\bar{x}} - z\sigma_{\bar{x}} = 16 - 3\left(\frac{2}{\sqrt{36}}\right) = 16 - 1 = 15 \text{ ounces}$$

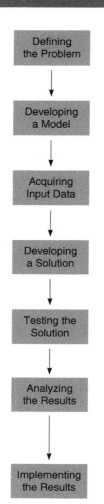

MODELING IN THE REAL WORLD

Statistical Process Control at AVX-Kyocera

Defining the Problem

AVX-Kyocera, a Japanese-owned maker of electronic chip components located in Raleigh, North Carolina, needed to improve the quality of its products and services to achieve total customer satisfaction.

Developing a Model

Statistical process control models such as $\bar{x}$- and R-charts were chosen as appropriate tools.

Acquiring Input Data

Employees are empowered to collect their own data. For example, a casting machine operator measures the thickness of periodic samples that he takes from his process.

Developing a Solution

Employees plot data observations to generate SPC charts that track trends, comparing results with process limits and final customer specifications.

Testing the Solution

Samples at each machine are evaluated to ensure that the processes are indeed capable of achieving the desired results. Quality control inspectors are transferred to manufacturing duties as all plant personnel become trained in statistical methodology.

Analyzing the Results

Results of SPC are analyzed by individual operators to see if trends are present in their processes. Quality trend boards are posted in the building to display not only SPC charts, but also procedures, process document change approvals, and the names of all certified operators. Work teams are in charge of analysis of clusters of machines.

Implementing the Results

The firm has implemented a policy of zero defectives at a very low tolerance for variable data and nearly zero defects for parts per million for attribute data.

Source: Based on Basile A. Denisson. "War with Defects and Peace with Quality," *Quality Progress* (September 1993): 97–101.

If the process standard deviation is not available or is difficult to compute, which is usually the case, these equations become impractical. In practice, the calculation of control limits is based on the average *range* rather than on standard deviations. We can use the equations

Control chart limits can be found using the range rather than the standard deviation.

$$\text{UCL}_{\bar{x}} = \bar{\bar{x}} + A_2\overline{R} \tag{3}$$
$$\text{LCL}_{\bar{x}} = \bar{\bar{x}} - A_2\overline{R} \tag{4}$$

where

$\overline{R}$ = average of the samples

A_2 = value found in Table 2 (which assumes that $z = 3$)

$\bar{\bar{x}}$ = mean of the sample means

USING EXCEL QM FOR BOX FILLING EXAMPLE The upper and lower limits for this example can be found using Excel QM, as shown in Program 1. From the Excel QM menu, select *Quality Control* and specify the *X-Bar* and *R Charts* option. Enter the number of samples (1) and select *Standard Deviation* in the initialization window. When the spreadsheet is initialized, enter the sample size (36), the standard deviation (2), and the mean of the sample (16). The upper and lower limits are immediately displayed.

TABLE 2

Factors for Computing Control Chart Limits

SAMPLE SIZE, n	MEAN FACTOR, A_2	UPPER RANGE, D_4	LOWER RANGE, D_3
2	1.880	3.268	0
3	1.023	2.574	0
4	0.729	2.282	0
5	0.577	2.114	0
6	0.483	2.004	0
7	0.419	1.924	0.076
8	0.373	1.864	0.136
9	0.337	1.816	0.184
10	0.308	1.777	0.223
12	0.266	1.716	0.284
14	0.235	1.671	0.329
16	0.212	1.636	0.364
18	0.194	1.608	0.392
20	0.180	1.586	0.414
25	0.153	1.541	0.459

Source: Reprinted by permission of the American Society for Testing and Materials, copyright 1951. Taken from Special Technical Publication 15-C, "Quality Control of Materials," pp. 63 and 72.

PROGRAM 1

Excel QM Solution for Box-Filling Example

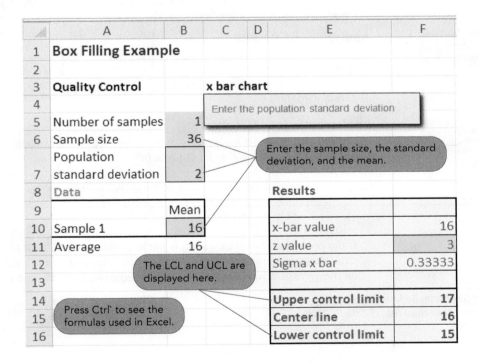

SUPER COLA EXAMPLE Super Cola bottles soft drinks labeled "net weight 16 ounces." An overall process average of 16.01 ounces has been found by taking several batches of samples, in which each sample contained five bottles. The average range of the process is 0.25 ounce. We want to determine the upper and lower control limits for averages for this process.

Looking in Table 2 for a sample size of 5 in the mean factor A_2 column, we find the number 0.577. Thus, the upper and lower control chart limits are

$$UCL_{\bar{x}} = \bar{\bar{x}} + A_2\bar{R}$$
$$= 16.01 + (0.577)(0.25)$$
$$= 16.01 + 0.144$$
$$= 16.154$$
$$LCL_{\bar{x}} = \bar{\bar{x}} - A_2\bar{R}$$
$$= 16.01 - 0.144$$
$$= 15.866$$

The upper control limit is 16.154, and the lower control limit is 15.866.

USING EXCEL QM FOR SUPER COLA EXAMPLE The upper and lower limits for this example can be found using Excel QM, as shown in Program 2. From the Excel QM menu, select *Quality Control* and specify the *X-Bar* and *R Charts* option. Enter the number of samples (1) and select *Range* in the initialization window. The sample size (5) can be entered in this initialization window or in the spreadsheet. When the spreadsheet is initialized, enter the range (0.25) and the mean of the sample (16.01). The upper and lower limits are immediately displayed.

Setting Range Chart Limits

We just determined the upper and lower control limits for the process *average*. In addition to being concerned with the process average, managers are interested in the *dispersion* or *variability*. Even though the process average is under control, the variability of the process may not be. For example, something may have worked itself loose in a piece of equipment. As a result, the average of the samples may remain the same, but the variation within the samples could be entirely too large. For this reason it is very common to find a control chart for *ranges* in order to monitor the process variability. The theory behind the control charts for ranges is the same for the process average. Limits are established that contain ±3 standard deviations of the distribution for the average range $\bar{R}$. With a few simplifying assumptions, we can set the upper and lower control limits for ranges:

$$UCL_R = D_4\bar{R} \tag{5}$$
$$LCL_R = D_3\bar{R} \tag{6}$$

where

$$UCL_R = \text{upper control chart limit for the range}$$
$$LCL_R = \text{lower control chart limit for the range}$$
$$D_4 \text{ and } D_3 = \text{values from Table 2}$$

Dispersion or variability is also important. The central tendency can be under control, but ranges can be out of control.

PROGRAM 2

Excel QM Solution for Super Cola Example

	A	B	C	D	E	F	G
1	**Super Cola Example**						
2							
3	**Quality Control**		x bar chart				
4				Enter the mean and range from each			
5	Number of samples	1					
6	Sample size	5					
7							
8	Data				Results		
9		Mean	Range			Xbar	Range
10	Sample 1	16.01	0.25		x-bar value	16.01	
11	Average	16.01	0.25				
12					R bar		0.25
13							
14					Upper control limit	16.1543	0.52875
15					Center line	16.01	0.25
16					Lower control limit	15.8658	0

RANGE EXAMPLE As an example, consider a process in which the average *range* is 53 pounds. If the sample size is 5, we want to determine the upper and lower control chart limits.

Looking in Table 2 for a sample size of 5, we find that $D_4 = 2.114$ and $D_3 = 0$. The range control chart limits are

$$\text{UCL}_R = D_4 \overline{R}$$
$$= (2.114)(53 \text{ pounds})$$
$$= 112.042 \text{ pounds}$$

$$\text{LCL}_R = D_3 \overline{R}$$
$$= (0)(53 \text{ pounds})$$
$$= 0$$

A summary of the steps used for creating and using control charts for the mean and the range.

Five Steps to Follow in using $\overline{x}$ and *R*-Charts

1. Collect 20 to 25 samples of $n = 4$ or $n = 5$ each from a stable process and compute the mean and range of each.
2. Compute the overall means ($\overline{\overline{x}}$ and $\overline{R}$), set appropriate control limits, usually at the 99.7% level, and calculate the preliminary upper and lower control limits. If the process is not currently stable, use the desired mean, μ, instead of $\overline{\overline{x}}$ to calculate limits.
3. Graph the sample means and ranges on their respective control charts and determine whether they fall outside the acceptable limits.
4. Investigate points or patterns that indicate the process is out of control. Try to assign causes for the variation and then resume the process.
5. Collect additional samples and, if necessary, revalidate the control limits using the new data.

---

5 Control Charts for Attributes

Sampling attributes differ from sampling variables.

Control charts for $\overline{x}$ and R do not apply when we are sampling *attributes*, which are typically classified as defective or nondefective. Measuring defectives involves counting them (e.g., number of bad lightbulbs in a given lot, or number of letters or data entry records typed with errors). There are two kinds of attribute control charts: (1) those that measure the percent defective in a sample, called *p-charts* and (2) those that count the number of defects, called *c-charts*.

p-Charts

p-chart limits are based on the binomial distribution and are easy to compute.

p-charts are the principal means of controlling attributes. Although attributes that are either good or bad follow the binomial distribution, the normal distribution can be used to calculate *p*-chart limits when sample sizes are large. The procedure resembles the $\overline{x}$-chart approach, which is also based on the central limit theorem.

The formulas for *p*-chart upper and lower control limits follow:

$$\text{UCL}_p = \overline{p} + z\sigma_p \tag{7}$$
$$\text{LCL}_p = \overline{p} - z\sigma_p \tag{8}$$

where

$\overline{p}$ = mean proportion or fraction defective in the sample

z = number of standard deviations ($z = 2$ for 95.5% limits; $z = 3$ for 99.7% limits)

σ_p = standard deviation of the sampling distribution

σ_p is estimated by $\hat{\sigma}_p$, which is

$$\hat{\sigma}_p = \sqrt{\frac{\overline{p}(1 - \overline{p})}{n}} \tag{9}$$

where n is the size of each sample.

IN ACTION — Unisys Corp.'s Costly Experiment in Health Care Services

In January 1996 things looked rosy for Unisys Corp.'s expansion into the computerized health care service business. It had just beat out Blue Cross/Blue Shield of Florida for an $86 million contract to serve Florida's state employee health insurance services. Its job was to handle the 215,000 Florida employees' claims processing—a seemingly simple and lucrative growth area for an old-line computer company like Unisys.

But one year later the contract was not only torn up, Unisys was fined over $500,000 for not meeting quality standards. Here are two of the measures of quality, both attributes (that is, either "defective" or "not defective") on which the firm was out of control:

1. **Percentage of claims processed with errors.** An audit over a 3 month period, by Coopers and Lybrand, found that Unysis made errors in 8.5% of claims processed. The industry standard is 3.5% "defectives."

2. **Percentage of claims processed within 30 days.** For this attribute measure, a "defect" is a processing time longer than the contract's time allowance. In one month's sample, 13% of the claims exceed the 30-day limit, far above the 5% allowed by the state of Florida.

The Florida contract was a migraine for Unisys, which underestimated the labor-intensiveness of health claims. Chief executive officer James Unruh pulled the plug on future ambitions in health care. Meanwhile, the state of Florida's Ron Poppel says, "We really need somebody that's in the insurance business."

Sources: *Business Week* (June 16, 1997): 6 and (July 15, 1996): 32; and *Information Week* (June 16, 1997): 144.

ARCO *p*-CHART EXAMPLE Using a popular database software package, data-entry clerks at ARCO key in thousands of insurance records each day. Samples of the work of 20 clerks are shown in the following table. One hundred records entered by each clerk were carefully examined to determine if they contained any errors; the fraction defective in each sample was then computed.

SAMPLE NUMBER	NUMBER OF ERRORS	FRACTION DEFECTIVE	SAMPLE NUMBER	NUMBER OF ERRORS	FRACTION DEFECTIVE
1	6	0.06	11	6	0.06
2	5	0.05	12	1	0.01
3	0	0.00	13	8	0.08
4	1	0.01	14	7	0.07
5	4	0.04	15	5	0.05
6	2	0.02	16	4	0.04
7	5	0.05	17	11	0.11
8	3	0.03	18	3	0.03
9	3	0.03	19	0	0.00
10	2	0.02	20	4	0.04
				80	

We want to set control limits that include 99.7% of the random variation in the entry process when it is in control. Thus, $z = 3$.

$$\overline{p} = \frac{\text{Total number of errors}}{\text{Total number of records examined}} = \frac{80}{(100)(20)} = 0.04$$

$$\hat{\sigma}_p = \sqrt{\frac{(0.04)(1 - 0.04)}{100}} = 0.02$$

(*Note:* 100 *is the size of each sample* = n)

$$\text{UCL}_p = \overline{p} + z\hat{\sigma}_p = 0.04 + 3(0.02) = 0.10$$

$$\text{LCL}_p = \overline{p} - z\hat{\sigma}_p = 0.04 - 3(0.02) = 0$$

(since we cannot have a negative percentage defective)

FIGURE 3

_p_-Chart for Data Entry for ARCO

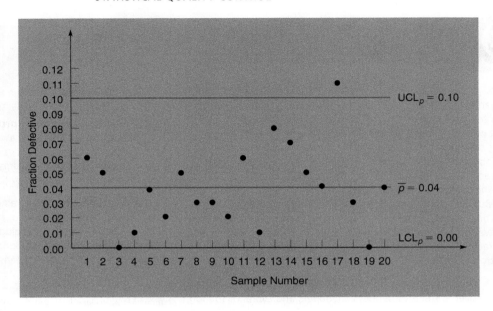

When we plot the control limits and the sample fraction defectives, we find that only one data-entry clerk (number 17) is out of control. The firm may wish to examine that person's work a bit more closely to see whether a serious problem exists (see Figure 3).

USING EXCEL QM FOR _p_-CHARTS Excel QM can be used to develop the limits for a _p_-chart, determine which samples exceed the limits, and develop the graph. Program 3 provides the output for the ARCO example, with the graph. To use Excel QM, from the Add-Ins tab select Excel QM. From the drop-down menu, select Quality Control and specify the _p_ Charts option. Enter the number of samples (20), input a title if desired, and select Graph if you wish to view the _p_-chart. When the spreadsheet is initialized, enter the size of each sample (100) and the number of defects in each of the 20 samples. One of the 20 samples (sample number 17) is identified as a sample that exceeds the limits.

PROGRAM 3

Excel QM Solution for ARCO _p_-Chart Example

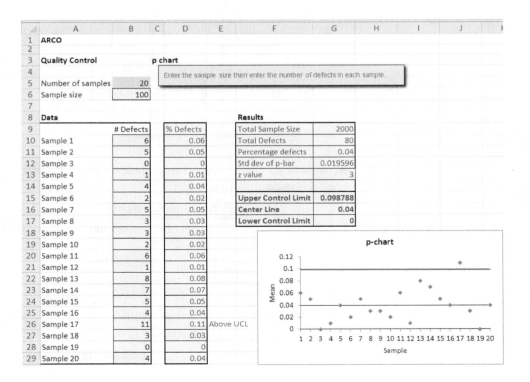

c-Charts

c-charts count the number of defects, whereas p-charts track the percentage defective.

In the ARCO example discussed previously, we counted the number of defective database records entered. A defective record is one that was not exactly correct. A bad record may contain more than one defect, however. We use **c-charts** to control the *number* of defects per unit of output (or per insurance record in this case).

Control charts for defects are helpful for monitoring processes in which a large number of potential errors can occur but the actual number that do occur is relatively small. Defects may be mistyped words in a newspaper, blemishes on a table, or missing pickles on a fast-food hamburger.

The Poisson probability distribution, which has a variance equal to its mean, is the basis for c-charts. Since $\bar{c}$ is the mean number of defects per unit, the standard deviation is equal to $\sqrt{c}$. To compute 99.7% control limits for c, we use the formula

$$\bar{c} \pm 3\sqrt{\bar{c}} \qquad (10)$$

Here is an example.

RED TOP CAB COMPANY c-CHART EXAMPLE Red Top Cab Company receives several complaints per day about the behavior of its drivers. Over a nine-day period (in which days are the units of measure), the owner received the following number of calls from irate passengers: 3, 0, 8, 9, 6, 7, 4, 9, 8, for a total of 54 complaints.

To compute 99.7% control limits, we take

$$\bar{c} = \frac{54}{9} = 6 \text{ complaints per day}$$

Thus,

$$\text{UCL}_c = \bar{c} + 3\sqrt{\bar{c}} = 6 + 3\sqrt{6} = 6 + 3(2.45) = 13.35$$
$$\text{LCL}_c = \bar{c} - 3\sqrt{\bar{c}} = 6 - 3\sqrt{6} = 6 - 3(2.45) = 0 \quad \longleftarrow$$

(because we cannot have a negative control limit)

After the owner plotted a control chart summarizing these data and posted it prominently in the drivers' locker room, the number of calls received dropped to an average of 3 per day. Can you explain why this may have occurred?

USING EXCEL QM FOR c-CHARTS Excel QM can be used to develop the limits for a c-chart, determine which samples exceed the limits, and develop the graph. Program 4 provides the output for the Red Top Cab Company example, with the graph. To use Excel QM, from the Add-Ins tab select *Excel QM*. From the drop-down menu, select *Quality Control* and specify the *c Charts* option. Enter the number of samples (9 days, in this example), input a title if desired, and select *Graph* if you wish to view the c-chart. When the spreadsheet is initialized, enter the number of complaints (i.e., defects) in each of the 9 samples.

PROGRAM 4

Excel QM Solution for Red Top Cab Company c-Chart Example

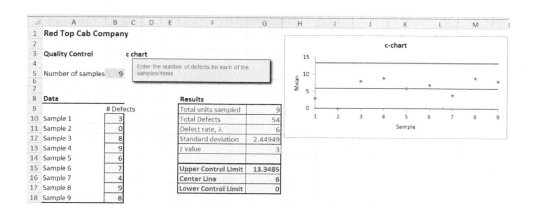

Summary

To the manager of a firm producing goods or services, quality is the degree to which the product meets specifications. Quality control has become one of the most important precepts of business.

The expression "quality cannot be inspected into a product" is a central theme of organizations today. More and more world-class companies are following the ideas of total quality management (TQM), which emphasizes the entire organization, from supplier to customer.

Statistical aspects of quality control date to the 1920s but are of special interest in our global marketplaces of this new century. Statistical process control tools described in this chapter include the $\bar{x}$- and R-charts for variable sampling and the p- and c-charts for attribute sampling.

Glossary

Assignable Variation Variation in the production process that can be traced to specific causes.

c-Chart A quality control chart that is used to control the number of defects per unit of output.

Central Limit Theorem The theoretical foundation for $\bar{x}$-charts. It states that regardless of the distribution of the population of all parts or services, the distribution of $\bar{x}$s will tend to follow a normal curve as the sample size grows.

Control Chart A graphic presentation of process data over time.

Natural Variations Variabilities that affect almost every production process to some degree and are to be expected; also known as common causes.

p-Chart A quality control chart that is used to control attributes.

Quality The degree to which a product or service meets the specifications set for it.

R-Chart A process control chart that tracks the "range" within a sample; indicates that a gain or loss of uniformity has occurred in a production process.

Total Quality Management (TQM) An emphasis on quality that encompasses the entire organization.

$\bar{x}$-Chart A quality control chart for variables that indicates when changes occur in the central tendency of a production process.

Key Equations

(1) Upper control limit (UCL) $= \bar{\bar{x}} + z\sigma_{\bar{x}}$
Upper limit for an $\bar{x}$-chart using standard deviations.

(2) Lower control limit (UCL) $= \bar{\bar{x}} - z\sigma_{\bar{x}}$
Lower control limit for an $\bar{x}$-chart using standard deviations.

(3) $\text{UCL}_{\bar{x}} = \bar{\bar{x}} + A_2\bar{R}$
Upper control limit for an $\bar{x}$-chart using tabled values and ranges.

(4) $\text{LCL}_{\bar{x}} = \bar{\bar{x}} - A_2\bar{R}$
Lower control limit for an $\bar{x}$-chart using tabled values and ranges.

(5) $\text{UCL}_R = D_4\bar{R}$
Upper control limit for a range chart.

(6) $\text{LCL}_R = D_3\bar{R}$
Lower control limit for a range chart.

(7) $\text{UCL}_p = \bar{p} + z\sigma_p$
Upper control unit for a p-chart.

(8) $\text{LCL}_p = \bar{p} - z\sigma_p$
Lower control limit for a p-chart.

(9) $\hat{\sigma}_p = \sqrt{\dfrac{\bar{p}(1 - \bar{p})}{n}}$

Estimated standard deviation of a binomial distribution.

(10) $\bar{c} \pm 3\sqrt{\bar{c}}$
Upper and lower limits for a c-chart.

Solved Problems

Solved Problem 1

The manufacturer of precision parts for drill presses produces round shafts for use in the construction of drill presses. The average diameter of a shaft is 0.56 inch. The inspection samples contain six shafts each. The average range of these samples is 0.006 inch. Determine the upper and lower control chart limits.

Solution

The mean factor A_2 from Table 2, where the sample size is 6, is seen to be 0.483. With this factor, you can obtain the upper and lower control limits:

$$UCL_{\bar{x}} = 0.56 + (0.483)(0.006)$$
$$= 0.56 + 0.0029 = 0.5629$$
$$LCL_{\bar{x}} = 0.56 - 0.0029$$
$$= 0.5571$$

Solved Problem 2

Nocaf Drinks, Inc., a producer of decaffeinated coffee, bottles Nocaf. Each bottle should have a net weight of 4 ounces. The machine that fills the bottles with coffee is new, and the operations manager wants to make sure that it is properly adjusted. The operations manager takes a sample of $n = 8$ bottles and records the average and range in ounces for each sample. The data for several samples are given in the following table. Note that every sample consists of 8 bottles.

SAMPLE	SAMPLE RANGE	SAMPLE AVERAGE	SAMPLE	SAMPLE RANGE	SAMPLE AVERAGE
A	0.41	4.00	E	0.56	4.17
B	0.55	4.16	F	0.62	3.93
C	0.44	3.99	G	0.54	3.98
D	0.48	4.00	H	0.44	4.01

Is the machine properly adjusted and in control?

Solution

We first find that $\bar{\bar{x}} = 4.03$ and $\bar{R} = 0.51$. Then, using Table 2, we find

$$UCL_{\bar{x}} = \bar{\bar{x}} + A_2\bar{R} = 4.03 + (0.373)(0.51) = 4.22$$
$$LCL_{\bar{x}} = \bar{\bar{x}} - A_2\bar{R} = 4.03 - (0.373)(0.51) = 3.84$$
$$UCL_R = D_4\bar{R} = (1.864)(0.51) = 0.95$$
$$LCL_R = D_3\bar{R} = (0.136)(0.51) = 0.07$$

It appears that the process average and range are both in control.

Solved Problem 3

Crabill Electronics, Inc., makes resistors, and among the last 100 resistors inspected, the percentage defective has been 0.05. Determine the upper and lower limits for this process for 99.7% confidence.

Solution

$$\text{UCL}_p = \bar{p} + 3\sqrt{\frac{\bar{p}(1 - \bar{p})}{n}} = 0.05 + 3\sqrt{\frac{(0.05)(1 - 0.05)}{100}}$$

$$= 0.05 + 3(0.0218) = 0.1154$$

$$\text{LCL}_p = \bar{p} - 3\sqrt{\frac{\bar{p}(1 - \bar{p})}{n}} = 0.05 - 3(0.0218)$$

$$= 0.05 - 0.0654 = 0 \text{ (since percent defective cannot be negative)}$$

Self-Test

- Before taking the self-test, refer to the learning objectives at the beginning of the chapter, the notes in the margins, and the glossary at the end of the chapter.
- Use the key at the end of the chapter to correct your answers.
- Restudy pages that correspond to any questions that you answered incorrectly or material you feel uncertain about.

1. The degree to which the product or service meets specifications is one definition of
   a. sigma.
   b. quality.
   c. range.
   d. process variability.

2. A control chart for monitoring processes in which values are measured in continuous units such as weight or volume is called a control chart for
   a. attributes.
   b. measurements.
   c. variables.
   d. quality.

3. The type of chart used to control the number of defects per unit of output is the
   a. $\bar{x}$-chart.
   b. R-chart.
   c. p-chart.
   d. c-chart.

4. Control charts for attributes are
   a. p-charts.
   b. m-charts.
   c. R-charts.
   d. $\bar{x}$-charts.

5. The Poisson distribution is often used with
   a. R-charts.
   b. p-charts.
   c. c-charts.
   d. x-charts.

6. A type of variability that indicates that a process is out of control is called
   a. natural variation.
   b. assignable variation.

   c. random variation.
   d. average variation.

7. A company is implementing a new quality control program. Items are sampled and classified as being defective or nondefective. The type of control chart that should be used is
   a. an R-chart.
   b. a control chart for variables.
   c. a control chart for attributes.
   d. a control limit chart.

8. After a control chart (for means) has been developed, samples are taken and the average is computed for each sample. The process could be considered out of control if
   a. one of the sample means is above the upper control limit.
   b. one of the sample means is below the lower control limit.
   c. five consecutive sample means show a consistent trend (either increasing or decreasing).
   d. all of the above were true.

9. A machine is supposed to fill soft drink cans to 12 ounces. It appears that although the average amount in the cans is about 12 ounces (based on sample means), there is a great deal of variability in each of the individual cans. The type of chart that would best detect this problem would be
   a. a p-chart.
   b. an R-chart.
   c. a c-chart.
   d. an attribute chart.

10. If a process only has random variations (it is in control), then 95.5% of the time the sample averages will fall within
    a. 1 standard deviation of the population mean.
    b. 2 standard deviations of the population mean.
    c. 3 standard deviations of the population mean.
    d. 4 standard deviations of the population mean.

Discussion Questions and Problems

Discussion Questions

1. Why is the central limit theorem so important in quality control?
2. Why are $\bar{x}$- and R-charts usually used hand in hand?
3. Explain the difference between control charts for variables and control charts for attributes.
4. Explain the difference between c-charts and p-charts.
5. When using a control chart, what are some patterns that would indicate that the process is out of control?
6. What might cause a process to be out of control?
7. Explain why a process can be out of control even though all the samples fall within the upper and lower control limits.

Problems*

8. Shader Storage Technologies produces refrigeration units for food producers and retail food establishments. The overall average temperature that these units maintain is 46° Fahrenheit. The average range is 2° Fahrenheit. Samples of 6 are taken to monitor the process. Determine the upper and lower control chart limits for averages and ranges for these refrigeration units.

9. When set at the standard position, Autopitch can throw hard balls toward a batter at an average speed of 60 mph. Autopitch devices are made for both major- and minor-league teams to help them improve their batting averages. Autopitch executives take samples of 10 Autopitch devices at a time to monitor these devices and to maintain the highest quality. The average range is 3 mph. Using control-chart techniques, determine control-chart limits for averages and ranges for Autopitch.

10. Zipper Products, Inc., produces granola cereal, granola bars, and other natural food products. Its natural granola cereal is sampled to ensure proper weight. Each sample contains eight boxes of cereal. The overall average for the samples is 17 ounces. The range is only 0.5 ounce. Determine the upper and lower control-chart limits for averages for the boxes of cereal.

11. Small boxes of NutraFlakes cereal are labeled "net weight 10 ounces." Each hour, random samples of size $n = 4$ boxes are weighed to check process control. Five hours of observations yielded the following:

	WEIGHT			
TIME	BOX 1	BOX 2	BOX 3	BOX 4
9 A.M.	9.8	10.4	9.9	10.3
10 A.M.	10.1	10.2	9.9	9.8
11 A.M.	9.9	10.5	10.3	10.1
Noon	9.7	9.8	10.3	10.2
1 P.M.	9.7	10.1	9.9	9.9

Using these data, construct limits for $\bar{x}$- and R-Charts. Is the process in control? What other steps should the QC department follow at this point?

12. Sampling four pieces of precision-cut wire (to be used in computer assembly) every hour for the past 24 hours has produced the following results:

HOUR	$\bar{x}$	R	HOUR	$\bar{x}$	R
1	3.25"	0.71"	13	3.11"	0.85"
2	3.10	1.18	14	2.83	1.31
3	3.22	1.43	15	3.12	1.06
4	3.39	1.26	16	2.84	0.50
5	3.07	1.17	17	2.86	1.43
6	2.86	0.32	18	2.74	1.29
7	3.05	0.53	19	3.41	1.61
8	2.65	1.13	20	2.89	1.09
9	3.02	0.71	21	2.65	1.08
10	2.85	1.33	22	3.28	0.46
11	2.83	1.17	23	2.94	1.58
12	2.97	0.40	24	2.64	0.97

Develop appropriate control limits and determine whether there is any cause for concern in the cutting process.

13. Due to the poor quality of various semiconductor products used in their manufacturing process, Microlaboratories has decided to develop a QC program. Because the semiconductor parts they get from suppliers are either good or defective, Milton Fisher has decided to develop control charts for attributes. The total number of semiconductors in every sample is 200. Furthermore, Milton would like

---

*Note: Ⓠ means the problem may be solved with QM for Windows; ✖ means the problem may be solved with Excel QM; and ▓ means the problem may be solved with QM for Windows and/or Excel QM.

to determine the upper control chart limit and the lower control chart limit for various values of the fraction defective (p) in the sample taken. To allow more flexibility, he has decided to develop a table that lists values for p, UCL, and LCL. The values for p should range from 0.01 to 0.10, incrementing by 0.01 each time. What are the UCLs and the LCLs for 99.7% confidence?

♨: 14   For the past two months, Suzan Shader has been concerned about machine number 5 at the West Factory. To make sure that the machine is operating correctly, samples are taken, and the average and range for each sample is computed. Each sample consists of 12 items produced from the machine. Recently, 12 samples were taken, and for each, the sample range and average were computed. The sample range and sample average were 1.1 and 46 for the first sample, 1.31 and 45 for the second sample, 0.91 and 46 for the third sample, and 1.1 and 47 for the fourth sample. After the fourth sample, the sample averages increased. For the fifth sample, the range was 1.21, and the average was 48; for sample number 6, it was 0.82 and 47; for sample number 7, it was 0.86 and 50; and for the eighth sample, it was 1.11 and 49. After the eighth sample, the sample average continued to increase, never getting below 50. For sample number 9, the range and average were 1.12 and 51; for sample number 10, they were 0.99 and 52; for sample number 11, they were 0.86 and 50; and for sample number 12, they were 1.2 and 52.

Although Suzan's boss wasn't overly concerned about the process, Suzan was. During installation, the supplier set a value of 47 for the process average with an average range of 1.0. It was Suzan's feeling that something was definitely wrong with machine number 5. Do you agree?

♨: 15   Kitty Products caters to the growing market for cat supplies, with a full line of products, ranging from litter to toys to flea powder. One of its newer products, a tube of fluid that prevents hair balls in long-haired cats, is produced by an automated machine that is set to fill each tube with 63.5 grams of paste.

To keep this filling process under control, four tubes are pulled randomly from the assembly line every 4 hours. After several days, the data shown in the following table resulted. Set control limits for this process and graph the sample data for both the $\bar{x}$- and R-charts.

♨: 16   Colonel Electric is a large company that produces lightbulbs and other electrical products. One particular lightbulb is supposed to have an average life of about 1,000 hours before it burns out. Periodically the company will test 5 of these and measure the average time before these burn out. The following table gives the results of 10 such samples:

SAMPLE NO.	$\bar{x}$	R	SAMPLE NO.	$\bar{x}$	R	SAMPLE NO.	$\bar{x}$	R
1	63.5	2.0	10	63.5	1.3	18	63.6	1.8
2	63.6	1.0	11	63.3	1.8	19	63.8	1.3
3	63.7	1.7	12	63.2	1.0	20	63.5	1.6
4	63.9	0.9	13	63.6	1.8	21	63.9	1.0
5	63.4	1.2	14	63.3	1.5	22	63.2	1.8
6	63.0	1.6	15	63.4	1.7	23	63.3	1.7
7	63.2	1.8	16	63.4	1.4	24	64.0	2.0
8	63.3	1.3	17	63.5	1.1	25	63.4	1.5
9	63.7	1.6						

SAMPLE	1	2	3	4	5	6	7	8	9	10
Mean	979	1087	1080	934	1072	1007	952	986	1063	958
Range	50	94	57	65	135	134	101	98	145	84

(a) What is the overall average of these means? What is the average range?

(b) What are the upper and lower control limits for a 99.7% control chart for the mean?

(c) Does this process appear to be in control? Explain.

♨: 17   For Problem 16, develop upper and lower control limits for the range. Do these samples indicate that the process is in control?

♨: 18   Kate Drew has been hand-painting wooden Christmas ornaments for several years. Recently, she has hired some friends to help her increase the volume of her business. In checking the quality of the work, she notices that some slight blemishes occasionally are apparent. A sample of 20 pieces of work resulted in the following number of blemishes on each piece: 0, 2, 1, 0, 0, 3, 2, 0, 4, 1, 2, 0, 0, 1, 2, 1, 0, 0, 0, 1. Develop upper and lower control limits for the number of blemishes on each piece.

♨: 19   A new president at Big State University has made student satisfaction with the enrollment and registration process one of her highest priorities. Students must see an advisor, sign up for classes, obtain a parking permit, pay tuition and fees, and buy textbooks and other supplies. During one registration period, 10 students every hour are sampled and asked about satisfaction with each of these areas. Twelve different groups of students were sampled, and the number in each group who had at least one complaint are as follows: 0, 2, 1, 0, 0, 1, 3, 0, 1, 2, 2, 0.

Develop upper and lower control limits (99.7%) for the proportion of students with complaints.

Internet Homework Problems

See our Internet home page, at **www.pearsonhighered.com/render**, for additional homework problems, Problems 20 to 23.

Internet Case Study

See our Internet home page, at **www.pearsonhighered.com/render** for this additional case study: Bayfield Mud Company. This case involes bags of mud-treating agents used in drilling for oil and natural gas.

Bibliography

Crosby, P. B. *Quality Is Free. New* York: McGraw-Hill, 1979.

Deming, W. E. *Out of the Crisis.* Cambridge, MA: MIT Center for Advanced Engineering Study, 1986.

Foster, S. Thomas. *Managing Quality*, 2nd ed. Upper Saddle River, NJ: Prentice Hall, 2004.

Foster, S. Thomas. *Managing Quality: Integrating the Supply Chain* , 3rd ed. Upper Saddle River, NJ: Prentice Hall, 2007.

Goetsch, David, and Stanley Davis. *Quality Management*, 5th ed. Upper Saddle River, NJ: Prentice Hall, 2006.

Juran, Joseph M., and A. Blanton Godfrey. *Juran's Quality Handbook*, 5th ed. New York: McGraw-Hill, 1999.

Naveh, Eitan, and Miriam Erez. "Innovation and Attention to Detail in the Quality Improvement Paradigm," *Management Science* 50, 11 (November 2004): 1576–1586.

Ravichandran, T. "Swiftness and Intensity of Administrative Innovation Adoption: An Empirical Study of TQM in Information Systems," *Decision Sciences* 31, 3 (Summer 2000): 691–724.

Smith, Gerald. *Statistical Process Control and Quality Improvement*, 5th ed. Upper Saddle River, NJ: Prentice Hall, 2004.

Summers, Donna. *Quality*, 4th ed. Upper Saddle River, NJ: Prentice Hall, 2006.

Tarí, Juan José, José Francisco Molina, and Juan Luis Castejón. "The Relationship between Quality Management Practices and Their Effects on Quality Outcomes," *European Journal of Operational Research* 183, 2 (December 2007): 483–501.

Wilson, Darryl D., and David A. Collier. "An Empirical Investigation of the Malcolm Baldrige National Quality Award Casual Model," *Decision Sciences* 31, 2 (Spring 2000): 361–390.

Witte, Robert D. "Quality Control Defined," *Contract Management* 47, 5 (May 2007): 51–53.

Zhu, Kaijie, Rachel Q. Zhang, and Fugee Tsung. "Pushing Quality Improvement Along Supply Chains," *Management Science* 53, 3 (March 2007): 421–436.

Appendix 1   Using QM for Windows for SPC

The QM for Windows Quality Control module can compute most of the SPC control charts and limits introduced in this chapter. Once the module is selected, we select *New* and indicate which type of chart (*p*-chart, *x*-bar chart, or *c*-chart). Program 5A displays the different possible choices in QM for Windows. When the *p*-chart is selected for the ARCO example, the initialization window opens, as displayed in Program 5B. We enter a title and the number of samples (20 in this example), and then click *OK*. An input window opens, and we enter the 20 sample values (number of errors or defects in the sample) and specify the sample size (100). We click *Solve*, and the output window opens, as illustrated in Program 5C. The original input data and the sample size are displayed, as are the results. While this problem has been set to use the 3 standard deviation (sigma) limits, other values are possible, also. QM for Windows computes the average proportion ($\overline{p}$), standard deviation, and upper and lower control limits. From this screen, we can select *Window* and select *Control Chart* to actually view the chart and look for patterns which might indicate that the process is out of control.

PROGRAM 5A

Using *p*-Charts from the Quality Control Module in QM for Windows

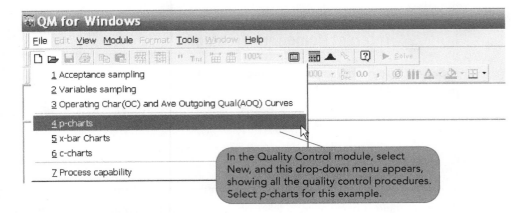

In the Quality Control module, select New, and this drop-down menu appears, showing all the quality control procedures. Select *p*-charts for this example.

PROGRAM 5B

QM for Windows Initialization Window for *p*-Charts with ARCO Insurance

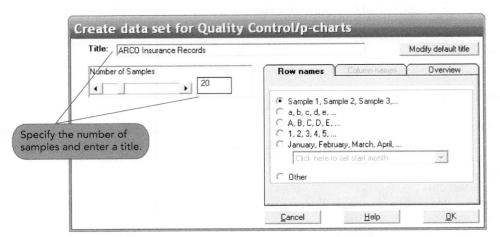

Specify the number of samples and enter a title.

PROGRAM 5C

QM for Windows Solution for ARCO Insurance Records Example

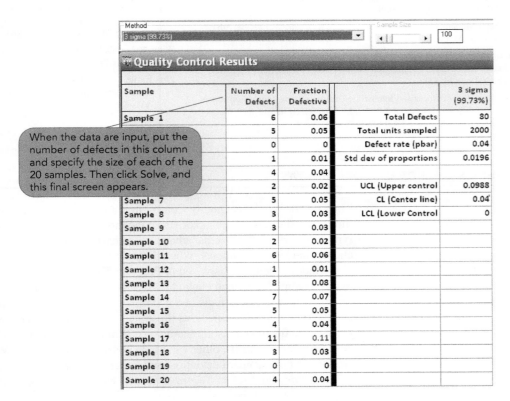

When the data are input, put the number of defects in this column and specify the size of each of the 20 samples. Then click Solve, and this final screen appears.

Solutions to Selected Problems

8 45.034 to 46.966 for $\bar{x}$
0 to 4.008 for R

10 16.814 to 17.187 for $\bar{x}$.
0.068 to 0.932 for R

12 2.236 to 3.728 for $\bar{x}$
0 to 2.336 for R
In control

16 (a) 1011.8 for $\bar{x}$ and 96.3 for R (b) 956.23 to 1067.37
(c) Process is out of control.

18 LCL $= 0$, UCL $= 4$

Solutions to Self-Tests

1. b
2. c
3. d
4. a
5. c
6. b
7. c
8. d
9. b
10. b

Index